New Riders

New Riders Publishing, Indianapolis, Indiana

This directory is published by:
New Riders Publishing
201 West 103rd Street
Indianapolis, IN 46290 USA

Copyright © 1995 by New Riders Publishing

Printed in the United States of America 1 2 3 4 5 6 7 8 9 0

CIP data available upon request

Warning and Disclaimer

This book is designed to provide information about the World Wide Web.
Every effort has been made to make this book as complete and as accurate
as possible, but no warranty or fitness is implied.

The information is provided on an "as is" basis. The author and New Riders
Publishing shall have neither liability nor responsibility to any person or
entity with respect to any loss or damages arising from the information
contained in this book or from the use of the disks or programs that may
accompany it.

Publisher	Don Fowley
Marketing Manager	Ray Robinson
Acquisitions Manager	Jim LeValley
Managing Editor	Tad Ringo

Product Development Specialist
Julie Fairweather

Acquisitions Editor
Alan Harris

Software Specialist
Steve Weiss

Development Editor
Suzanne Snyder

Production Editor
Phil Worthington

Copy Editors
Laura Frey
Stacia Mellinger

Associate Marketing Manager
Tamara Apple

Acquisitions Coordinator
Tracy Turgeson

Publisher's Assistant
Karen Opal

Cover Designer
Karen Ruggles

Cover Illustrator
Tracey Rae

Cover Production
Aren Howell

Book Designer
Sandra Schroeder

Manufacturing Coordinator
Paul Gilchrist

Production Manager
Kelly Dobbs

Production Team Supervisor
Laurie Casey

Graphics Image Specialists

Jason Hand, Clint Lahnan,
Laurie Robbins, Craig Small,
Todd Wente

Production Analysts
Angela D. Bannan
Bobbi Satterfield

Production Team
Gary Adair, Heather Butler,
Dan Caparo, Kim Cofer,
Jennifer Eberhardt, Erika Millen,
Beth Rago, Gina Rexrode,
Erich J. Richter, Christine Tyner,
Karen Walsh, Robert Wolf

Indexers
Bront Davis, Brad Herriman,
Chris Cleveland

About the Editor

Barbara Bouton is a computer consultant and author with a rich background in operating systems and authoring tools. Her latest book for New Riders was *Inside Adobe Photoshop 3*, which she coauthored with her husband, Gary. She also has contributed to New Riders' *Inside WordPerfect 6 for Windows*, and has compiled online references for *NetWare: The Professional Reference*, and *Inside Adobe Photoshop*. Barbara's personal commitments to education and communication are only equaled by her desire to learn about cutting-edge technology.

Trademark Acknowledgments

All terms mentioned in this book that are known to be trademarks or service marks have been appropriately capitalized. New Riders Publishing cannot attest to the accuracy of this information. Use of a term in this book should not be regarded as affecting the validity of any trademark or service mark.

Acknowledgments

New Riders Publishing would like to thank all of the following "surfers" who helped make this book possible:

Bryan Decker
Jay Tomlin
Jeremy Fischer
Sean Benham
Laurence Cooke
Scott Dooley
Barbara Dunn
Phil Foster
Susan Funke
Melanie Harper
Jamie Kirkley
Sonny Kirkley
Lara J. Ray
Todd Rosenthal
Chris Rowland
Torrin Sanders
Kaushik Sengupta
Paul Yachnes
Amy Yan
Holly Kulikowski
Jennifer Campbell
Thomas Porter
Jay Weinshenker

Special thanks goes to Larry Hughes, Jr., who aided in the recruitment process. We also wish to thank Eric Garrison, whose assistance was greatly appreciated.

Suzanne Snyder deserves special recognition for her efforts in organizing the Introduction of this book, as well as coordinating the project so that none of us missed a beat! Special thanks also goes out to Alan Harris, who truly went the extra mile to make sure this project happened successfully and on time.

CONTENTS AT A GLANCE

TABLE OF CONTENTS

Architecture 23

Art   31

TABLE OF CONTENTS

Business   69

TABLE OF CONTENTS

TABLE OF CONTENTS

Cooking   181

Education   193

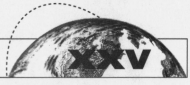

Entertainment   235

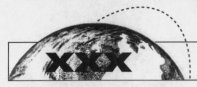

Games   285

Health 293

History   309

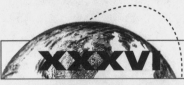

TABLE OF CONTENTS

Media 357

Music 393

New Age 425

Philosophy 429

Recreation 435

Religion   447

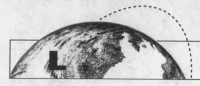

TABLE OF CONTENTS

Science 463

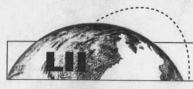

Travel   533

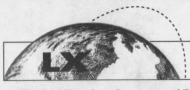

TABLE OF CONTENTS

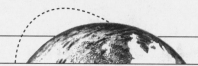

Introduction

This section introduces you to the World Wide Web and the basic concepts and terminology associated with it. Much more information is available about the Web and the Internet, of which the Web is a part, than what is presented here. At the end of this Introduction is a list of recommended publications that you might find of interest for further reading.

Scope of the World Wide Web

The Internet is a collection of interconnected computer networks from around the world that provides a wealth of information on nearly any topic you can imagine. The World Wide Web, or often simply called the Web, is a subsystem of the Internet. The Web has become the definitive "hot spot" for Internet users primarily because it allows for anyone to graphically and visually "advertise" themselves or a specific cause, and have this representation 24 hours a day. Many individuals do not have the need to create their own Web page, as this type of representation is called, but they do want to have access to and be able to view the Web sites of others. Whatever your situation, you will be utterly amazed by the tremendous variety and amount of information that is available on the World Wide Web and captured in this book.

Features and Uses of the World Wide Web

The Web can link together information from anywhere in the world and make it available to anyone. A grade-school student can jump from Dun & Bradstreet's financial information to a pictorial tour of Croatia's capital, Zagreb, to the state of the Internet in southern Africa, without ever leaving his desk.

There's far more to the Web than just information. You can learn static facts from any encyclopedia. The information stored in the Web is constantly updated. With the Web, you'll always have the freshest information at your fingertips.

The Web also dynamically links information into a seamless whole. You may start your information hunt next door and finally track down your quarry somewhere in Singapore. From where you sit, however, the distance between the two online data sources makes no difference. The Web enables you to move around the world as easily as to the local library—with a click of a mouse.

Although the Web has existed for only a short time, it is already being used in numerous areas by both public and private institutions. Businesses have discovered how beneficial advertising and performing transactions on the Web can be. Educational institutions also are making more information available on the Web, and students are discovering that they can get increasingly more research done by searching Web pages rather than library books. You can make travel plans, buy houses, read about your favorite hobby and make new friends via the Web.

Business

Individual companies have set up advertisements on the Web. Before long, it will be almost unprofitable for any major company—especially one that deals in new technologies—to exist without its own site to show advertisements and product information. Buyers, moreover, are rapidly finding out that it is far easier to take a look at a new product by going to a business' Web page than by physically going to the store to look for a product or searching advertisements in the newspaper. In addition to finding advertisements on the Web, consumers can do their shopping on the Web as well.

Do you want to actually purchase an item that you've been viewing? Step into a shopping mall! These malls allow users to place orders for items that can then be shipped to their homes or businesses. Holiday shopping couldn't be easier! No longer will you have to stand in lines at stores or wait on hold for the attendant at the mail-order company to take your order. Instead, you can find the item you want and enter your credit information in order to have it shipped right away.

Users can order almost anything from the Web: chocolate, books, games, clothing, music, or anything else they might desire. This directory contains listings for numerous stores and shopping centers.

Education

Many educational resources already are available through the Web. Libraries are adding their catalogs and universities are posting information about degree programs. You can also find research documents containing information about almost any subject. Before long, travelling to a library to find this information will become a near obsolete venture. Instead, students will be able to find any information sources they need without leaving their desks.

The possibilities for education on the Web are amazing. Many college and university classes presently create Web pages for semester class projects. Research papers on many different topics are also available. Even elementary school students are using the Web to access information and pass along news to other students. Exchange students can communicate with their classmates-to-be long before they actually arrive at their new school. It won't be long before

students will be able to take language classes that are actually taught in the country where the language is spoken.

Many elementary and secondary schools have created and are maintaining Web pages. Students and teachers work together to decide what information should be included on the site, and to prepare it for publication. By doing this, not only do they make more information available to the community, but students gain useful knowledge of new technologies and their use.

Travel

Planning a vacation? There are many sites on the Web that can help you solidify your travel plans, or give you ideas of places you might want to visit. These sites offer information about tours and hotel accommodations, as well as car rentals, airfare, and other forms of transportation. Cruise lines have Web pages that outline various types of cruise packages and describe destinations. Many cities sponsor Web pages as well, where you can learn about restaurants, sightseeing and shopping opportunities, and local points of interest.

The Web, Controversial Content, and Freedom of Expression

This book will show you many thousands of places to visit on the Web. There are, however, countless thousands more that aren't listed, with new sites springing up every day. The World Wide Web is a growing, dynamic, virtual world, and just like in the real world—at least in the places where unfettered freedom of expression exists—the points of view represented are myriad to the extreme. It's almost a certainty that something out there on the Web will strike you as offensive in some way.

The *Time* magazine cyberporn scare of July 1995 brought Web-content issues and freedom of expression into the national spotlight. Even though the evidence used in the report that *Time* based its story on was largely discredited, some people (few of whom seemed to be users of the Internet) began to call for government regulation of the Internet and the World Wide Web.

Everyone *Can* Use the Web

The response from actual users of the Web to this call for censorship was quick and adamant, and can be summed up as "Who do you want to decide what your kids can read, you or the government?"

In fact, before the cyberporn scare made it into the news, lots of users, content providers, and software developers were working to create means to make the Web a place for all sensibilities—without censorship.

What follows are just a couple of examples that illustrate how you can make the Web "safe" for your kids. The exclusion of other software companies or user organizations is by no means a reflection of their quality or utility.

SurfWatch Software

One of the first and most high-profile companies to address the Web "family security" issue was SurfWatch Software. The SurfWatch software you load on your computer is designed to block sexually explicit and otherwise obscene material on the Internet from being accessed by your computer (which doesn't mean it's not out there—just that your kids can't get to it).

The company has demonstrated their software before Congress in an effort to show that real alternatives to Internet censorship exist, "giving parents and educators the opportunity to limit unwanted material locally without restricting the access rights of other Internet users."

So how do they do it? Basically, the software screens your computer (while you're online) for material likely to contain sexually explicit material. Access to unwanted sites is automatically denied. You pay $49.95 for a copy of the software, and can then purchase a subscription for $5.95 a month, which provides you with updates to the exisiting SurfWatch software (remember, several thousand new Web sites come online *each month*).

SurfWatch comes configured for Mac or Windows. You can try out the software and find out more about the company by accessing http://www.surfwatch.com/.

SafeSurf

SafeSurf (http://www.safesurf.com/wave) is a great example of Internet users working together to make the Web "safe" for kids while avoiding censorship. The folks at SafeSurf are working toward implementaion of an Internet Rating Standard using the input of "parents, providers, publishers, developers, and all the resources available on the Internet."

Ultimately, SafeSurf would like to see all "child Safe" Web sites marked with the SafeSurf Wave symbol. SafeSurf's home page explains how providers can mark their own pages with the Wave code; you can also check out SafeSurf's newsletter, lists of SafeSurf approved sites, and The Declaration of an Independent Internet:

The Declaration of an Independent Internet, July 4, 1995

We hold these truths to be self-evident, that all information is created equal, that information is endowed by its creator with certain inalienable rights, that among these is the right to be distributed via the Internet without governmental censorship. That whenever any legislation becomes destructive of these ends, it is the duty of the members of the Internet to oppose it, and to institute self-regulation with parental control, laying its foundation on such principles and organizing its powers in such form, as to them shall seem most likely to effect the safety of children and the sanctity of distribution.

Prudence, indeed, will dictate that regulations long established should not be changed for light and transient causes; and accordingly all experience hath shewn, that mankind are more disposed to accept censorship where none is required, than to right things by opposing such censorship. But when an unnecessary attempt at censorship, pursuing central-ized control, evinces a design to place information under absolute Despotism, it is the right of the members of the Internet, it is their duty, to oppose such legislation, and to promote self-regulation with parental control.

We therefore, Parents and Representatives of the Online World, in cooperation, appealing to concerned parents everywhere for the rectitude of our intentions, do, in the Name, and by the authority of the Internet Community, solemnly publish and declare, that the Internet is and of Right ought to be self-regulated with parental control and free from govermental censorship. And for the support of this Declaration, with a firm reliance on the protection of Divine Providence, We mutually pledge to each other and to our children, our Lives, our Fortunes, and our sacred Honor.

What's especially encouraging is that companies and organizations like SurfWatch and SafeSurf are developing software that enables you to set up a computer to access a limited list of Web resources: Parents can decide not only what their kids shouldn't access; they can decide which particular Web sites their kids can visit.

Basic World Wide Web Terminology

This section briefly explains certain terms and concepts, such as hypertext, hypermedia, URLs, HTTP, HTML, and so forth, that are commonly associated with the Web. If you want or need more indepth knowledge of these or other terms, please refer to the additional reading list provided near the end of this Introduction.

Hypertext and Hypermedia

Before there was the World Wide Web, before there was an Internet, there was the dream of Xanadu. Named after the "pleasure dome" envisioned by the nineteenth-century English poet Samuel Taylor Coleridge, Xanadu encom-passed all of human knowledge, and all documents, images, sounds, and videos that it contained would be instantly accessible to anyone who had a computer, anywhere, anytime.

Xanadu was the dream of Ted Nelson, a computer visionary. He foresaw a world where all information could be linked together in a world-wide web of hypertext and hypermedia. In short, he saw a world where the constant Babel of incompatible data formats and protocols would be replaced by a universal library of information. It would be a world transformed, one that would have as little in common with our world as ours does with the one before Gutenberg invented the printing press.

In hypertext, related information is linked together. Instead of being forced to move linearly from page 1 to page 2 and so on, a hypertext document lets you leap from word to word using *links*.

In a hypertext encyclopedia, for example, you could be reading about Michael Jordan and find a reference to the Chicago Bulls winning the NBA championship in 1992, and that makes you wonder which team won the champi-onship the year before. In an ordinary book, you're stuck; you must either go to the index or continue reading through the book searching for the information you seek. In hypertext, however, a simple click on the phrase 'NBA championship' can take you to the next occurrence of the phrase or to a fuller description of the NBA championship's history.

Now, take this concept one step further. With hypermedia, you can link pictures, sounds, and movies to form multime-dia documents—not only words are linked together, but images and sounds are bound together as well.

For example, in *The New Grolier MultiMedia Encyclopedia*, a well-known CD-ROM encyclopedia, you can click your way from an article on the Apollo 11 moon landing to a video of the moon landing. From there, you can click on a caption about the launch and from there continue your study of space exploration.

Hypermedia tries to make computers work the way people think: that is, in jumps rather than always moving straight forward or backward. It is not perfect, of course. A hyperdocument link may lead you far astray from the destination you have in mind. Still, hypermedia can be a great help in chasing down elusive information.

Uniform Resource Locators (URLs)

A *Uniform Resource Locator* (or URL—pronounced like the name *Earl*) is the address of a Web document. This address consists of the way the target document can be accessed (the protocol), the name of the computer, the directory on which the document resides, and the file name of the document. Here is an example of an URL that will take you to New Riders' online *World Wide Web Yellow Pages*:

```
http://www.mcp.com/newriders/wwwyp/index.html
```

The first section (http:) tells you how the target document can be accessed. In this case, it's by means of the HTTP protocol. The double slashes (//) indicate that you're talking to a server. If you were accessing a file on your local machine, you would see triple slashes.

Next, you have the Internet domain name and address of the Web server (`www.mcp.com`). When you have a complete address such as this, it's called a *fully qualified* domain name. The letters at the end of the address, depending on the naming style used by the site, either tell you something about who owns the server or where the server is located. Common abbreviations used to describe who owns the server are *edu, com, gov,* or *org* (meaning educational, commercial, governmental, and organizational servers, respectively).

If the site you are accessing is a non-U.S. site, you will probably see a two-letter country identifier. For example, '.uk' is the United Kingdom, '.ja' is Japan, and so on. In some countries, notably the UK, the order in the domain name fields are reversed from typical U.S. practice. That is, instead of the following:

```
fred@thisplace.somwhere.uk,
```

the address in the UK would read:

```
fred@uk.somewhere.thisplace
```

Both styles are equally valid. In the States, most, but not all, sites use organizational type designators. Some sites do use geographical identifiers, in which case they usually correspond to the site's home state. A few sites mix organizational and geographical domain names.

Continuing on, (newriders/wwwyp/index), you see the path to your destination. Windows and DOS users in particular should note two things.

- ⊕ On the Web, like almost all of the Unix-based Internet, directories use forward slashes instead of backslashes for directory names.
- ⊕ Both upper- and lowercase letters are used and are significant, which means that 'a.txt' is not the same file as 'A.txt'.

At the end of the URL is the actual resource or resource name. This time around, it's a file, and its file extension (.html) tells us that it's an HTML document. Systems that can't deal with extensions longer than three letters, such as MS-DOS or Windows, use exactly three letters instead. For example, a Windows server would list the same file with an extension of '.htm.'

Most of the time, you won't have to get down and dirty with typing URLs because you can usually just click on the link. Most browsers also let you cut and paste URLs so you can grab one from a document and drop it into the URL area. Nevertheless, being able to read URLs can tell you more about the file you're bringing in, which can help you if you run into trouble with it.

HTTP, Web Servers, Browsers, and HTML

HyperText Transfer Protocol (HTTP) is a simple data transfer protocol that binds the Web together. Essentially, the protocol consists of a set of messages and replies for both servers and browsers. HTTP makes sure that hypermedia files get from Web servers to your computer.

HTTP runs on Web servers. A *Web server* is software that, upon receiving a browser request, sends the document you requested back to your browser. If for some reason it can't send the file—maybe the machine that document is on is down for the count with a power failure—the server sends your browser a simple error message. That's it. The server doesn't worry about what the document looks like or how a menu is presented to your computer—that's the browser's job.

A *browser* is a program that enables your computer to access the World Wide Web. If you like to think of the Web as being a subsection of the information superhighway, you

can think of the browser as being a car that lets you drive from one Web site to another. Netscape is currently the most widely used Web browser, a position formerly held by NCSA Mosaic. Other browsers include America Online, Pipeline, Prodigy, Lynx, and Slipknot, to name just a few. For an overview of browser types, as well as features to look for in a browser, you might want to refer to New Riders Publishing's *Inside the World Wide Web*.

HyperText Markup Language (HTML) is a set of codes or tags that determine the way components of a document are displayed on the World Wide Web. If you want to see what HTML tags look like, choose "View Source" from your browser menu (most browsers have this option or something similar to it) while your screen is displaying a Web page. You will see angle brackets surrounding text <like this>. The command <I> will make a word appear in italics, the <B> command makes a word appear in boldface, and so forth. HTML is an open standard. Anyone can use it without paying a penny for it; moreover, the rules for using HTML commands are publicly available on the Web. There are also many good books, such as New Riders Publishing's *Inside the World Wide Web*, on how to create HTML documents.

How Your Browser Works

When you put all the components together, the Web works in the following manner. The whole network is held together by links. Your browser sends an HTTP request to an URL. At the other end of the URL sits an HTTP server that sends the requested information back, using HTTP.

Let's look at the process in more detail. The first thing you see after starting up your browser is the loading of your default home page. This home page is the document that's been set for you to visit whenever you start the browser. Your browser is actually checking for a network connection between itself and the Internet.

Next, it takes your home page's URL and tries to find the IP (Internet Protocol) address for its Internet site. A browser, like almost all client-server Internet applications, does this by checking with the URL's known DNS (Domain Name Server). If it can't find the DNS, the program returns an error message, but this usually won't be a problem. Now, armed with the IP address of the destination site, your browser sends out an HTTP request.

If all goes well, this request is received by the server's HTTP program. Normally, HTTP programs run as daemons—programs that are always running in the background and are constantly checking to see if they need to perform their job. After the HTTP daemon receives your request, it relays it to the appropriate service.

If the service you required is to fetch an HTML document, the HTTP daemon fetches the document and sends it to you using HTTP. If it's some other resource that HTTP can access directly, it still follows this routine.

HTTP works differently, however, when you call upon other Internet services such as FTP or Gopher. In these cases, HTTP acts as your go-between. For instance, when you transfer a file with HTTP, the HTTP server logs you in with a login id of 'anonymous' and uses your Internet address as a password.

This might all sound terribly complicated, but you really don't need to be concerned. When all you want to do is use the Web, you never see the layers of complexity underlying your browser. This, after all, is the idea of the Web—to make information access easy.

What You Need to Access the World Wide Web

Internet service providers exist worldwide and provide access to the Internet. Recently, telephone companies have also begun to offer this service. Your Internet service provider will tell you exactly what you need to access the Internet. However, in general, all you need is a computer system, a modem with an analog telephone line (or some other form of communication hook-up such as a T-1 line), and telecommunications software to access the Internet. Once you have connected to the Internet, you can tap into the wealth of resources there, including the World Wide Web, by installing the appropriate application software that is available. For example, you will need Web browser software, such as Netscape or Mosaic, to be able to access the Web.

About This Directory

This directory lists more than 4,800 selected World Wide Web sites. Each listing presents the site's title and URL, as well as a brief description of the site. Many listings also contain icons that provide extra information about a site, such as whether the site is graphics-intensive or contains sound files.

The sites have been placed in category groupings, such as Children, Health, Music, Religion, and Travel, and are then presented alphabetically within those categories. Because New Riders Publishing wanted to present as many sites as possible in this directory, maximum effort has been made to avoid site duplication from category to category, even if the site's contents qualify it for more than one category (for example, a site about church music could

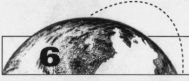

conceivably fall under either the Music or Religion category). For the widest range of listings under a given subject, therefore, please check our comprehensive index that lists Web site titles under an extensive number of subject headings.

Parts of the Directory Listings

- **Title**—The name of the site.
- **Uniform Resource Locator (URL)**—This is the "address" of the Web site. In some cases, the URL is followed by a screen shot of a graphically interesting portion of the site.
- **Description**—This section gives you an idea of the site's contents and some of the site's outstanding features.
- **Attribute Icons**—This directory contains the following attribute icons that provide extra information about a site.

 Forms—This site contains some type of form that you can fill out if you want. Your browser may or may not have the capability to display forms. If your browser falls in the latter category, take heart. In many cases the site supplies an e-mail address so that you can contact the site's webmaster and provide him or her with the required information in lieu of filling out a form.

 Graphics—A site bearing this icon is graphics-intensive and may take a long time for your screen to display.

 Netscape-enhanced—This icon means that a particular site has been created and designed in such a way that it should be viewed with the latest version of Netscape. You may still view the site with an older version of Netscape or any other browser, but the site may not properly display on your screen.

 Parental Guidance—This site may contain "adult" material. If you are a parent or guardian, you may wish to preview the site before allowing your child to view its contents.

 Search engine—A site with this icon offers the capability to search for specific topics throughout the Web or at that particular site.

 Shopping—This site offers goods or services for you to purchase if you want.

 Sound—This icon alerts you that a site contains links to sound files. Because sound files take up large amounts of disk space, they may be tedious to load. Moreover, unless your hardware is configured for sound, you may not be able to listen to sound files.

 Video—This site contains links to video files. Unless your hardware is configured for video, you may not be able to run these video files.

Further Reading

There are many books and articles about the World Wide Web; moreover, any relatively recent book about the Internet will contain some material on the subject of the Web. Here are some possible sources for further information:

Books

Inside the World Wide Web, New Riders Publishing, 1995.

Riding the Internet Highway, IntenetWorks Edition, New Riders Publishing, 1995.

New Riders' Official Internet Yellow Pages, Second Edition, New Riders Publishing, 1994.

New Riders Publishing

The staff of New Riders is committed to bringing you the very best in computer reference material. Each New Riders book is the result of months of work by authors and staff who research and refine the information contained within its covers.

As part of this commitment to you, the reader, New Riders invites your input. Please let us know if you enjoy this book, if you have trouble with the information and examples presented, or if you have a suggestion for the next edition.

Please note, though: New Riders staff cannot serve as a technical resource for the World Wide Web or for related questions about software- or hardware-related problems. Moreover, the World Wide Web is a dynamic environment that changes daily. Because changes will inevitably have taken place between the time of this book's compilation

and its publication date, New Riders welcomes and solicits your feedback regarding inaccuracies or possible improvements and additions for subsequent editions of this directory. We, therefore, invite you to fill out the form provided for this purpose in the back of this book.

If you have a question or comment about any New Riders book, there are several ways to contact New Riders. We will respond to as many readers as we can. Your name, address, or phone number will never become part of a mailing list or be used for any purpose other than to help us continue to bring you the best books possible. You can write us at the following address:

> New Riders
> Attn: Publisher
> 201 W. 103rd Street
> Indianapolis, IN 46290

If you prefer, you can fax New Riders at (317) 581-4670.

You can send electronic mail to New Riders at the following Internet address:

`jfairweather@newriders.mcp.com`

Or you may visit the New Riders Web site at the following location:

`http://www.mcp.com/newriders`

NRP is an imprint of Macmillan Computer Publishing. To obtain a catalog or information, or to purchase any Macmillan Computer Publishing book, call (800)428-5331.

Thank you for selecting this directory!

 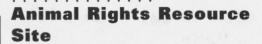
A.S.M.N.—Cover and Contents Page

http://www.und.ac.za/und/cogen/asmn/asmncovr.html

Online newsletter. Focuses primarily on zoological explorations in various parts of the African continent.

Aberdeen University Riding Club World Equestrian Information Source

http://www.abdn.ac.uk/~src011/aurc.equine.resource.html

Offers resources including software, newsletters, books, clubs, and events for horse lovers.

Akbash Dog Home Page

http://www.upei.ca/akbash/akbash.htm

Offers two-column layout on the Akbash dog. Some links allow direct e-mail contact with the publishers of the site.

Amphibian and Reptile Collection

http://www.mip.berkeley.edu/mvz/mvzherpe.html

Describes reptilian/amphibian collection. Includes a few pictures. Also contains a link to information about their animal tissue collection, which can be used for DNA research.

Animal Rights Resource Site

http://envirolink.org/arrs/index.html

Supports issues of animal rights. Provides an icon-based menu to take you to FAQs, journals, the latest news, and extra resources.

Animals

http://rs306.ccs.bbk.ac.uk/flora/animals.htm#inverts

Contains an abundance of information about all kinds of mammals, birds, amphibians, reptiles, and butterflies. Offers many links to other animal specific sites.

Antarctica and Its Environment

http://icair.iac.org.nz/reports/nz/visitor.html

Examines the ecosystems and wildlife on the Antarctic continent.

AutPut—Home Page

http://www.luga.or.at/~hackeha/zooneu/html/zoo1.html

Presents a zoo in Austria (offers English and German language versions).

Bat Information Resource Area

http://www.batcon.org/batinfo.html

Provides information on bats.

Belgian Sheepdogs

http://snapple.cs.washington.edu/canine/belgians/

Provides text and links about Belgian sheepdogs. Includes a photo album of Belgian sheepdog pictures submitted by various owners, as well as links to those owners' Web sites.

Bernese Mountain Dog Home Page

http://www.prairienet.org/~mkleiman/berner.html

Focuses on the Bernese Mountain dog. Incorporates links to mailing lists, FAQs, and owner sites.

Birds, United States National Park Service (NPS) (Information Center for the Environment)

http://ice.ucdavis.edu/US_National_Park_Service/NPS_birds.html

Provides a searchable index of birds in the United States National Parks system.

The Birmingham Zoo

http://www.bhm.tis.net/zoo/

Features the zoo in Birmingham, Alabama.

Border Collies

http://mendel.berkeley.edu/dogs/bcs.html

Picture-filled site that provides special information on Border Collie e-mail lists and an FTP site dedicated to Border Collie information.

Borzoi Info Online

http://www.clark.net/pub/bdalzell/borzoiinfo.html

Provides information on the Borzoi breed. Offers articles and links to additional general dog-related information.

Brazilian Zoos Directory

http://www.ftpt.br/cgi-bin/bdtnet/zoocadastro

Serves as a resource for zoos located in Brazil (*note*: most of the site is in Portugese).

Canada Whale Watching

http://www.csi.nb.ca/tourism/page1.html

Provides information about the lesser-known whale species in the Canadian seas.

Canine Web

http://snapple.cs.washington.edu/canine/canine.html

Provides general and specific knowledge about dogs. Contains listing of numerous well-known and lesser-known breeds.

Cat Fanciers' Home Page

http://www.ai.mit.edu/fanciers/fanciers.html

Provides cat-related information. Offers numerous FAQs on different cat breeds, feline health, and care issues. Offers links to show schedules, cat organizations, ftp and gopher sites, as well as links to commercial sites, picture sites, and cat owners' home pages.

Cat House (EFBC/FCC) Home Page

http://www.cathouse-fcc.org/

Contains pictures and some audio clips straight from the cat's mouth.

Caucasian Ovcharka Info

http://pasture.ecn.purdue.edu/~laird/Dogs/Ovcharka/

Focuses on the Caucasian Mountain dog. Includes special information on the national club for this breed.

Chaffee Zoological Gardens—Fresno, California

http://www.cybergate.com/~compugrf/zoo/index.html

Contains great realistic and surrealistic pictures of the animals on exhibit. Also lets you visit the gift shop where you can order items online.

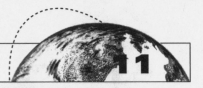

Chase Tavern Farm Alpacas

http://www.maine.com/ctalpacas/

Focuses on the art of breeding alpacas.

The Chihuahua FAQ

http://www.cathouse.org/CathousePeople/MelindaCasino/
Chihuahua/

Provides information on the Chihuahua. Includes not only frequently asked questions but also pictures, special information on the demeanor and physical qualities of these animals, and health information.

Cochrane Wildlife Reserve

http://www.cuug.ab.ca:8001/~scholefp/swiftfox.html

Focuses on reintroducing the swift fox species back into the wild. Stylish, colorful, and contains good reading.

Collection: Orcinus Orca (Killer Whales)

http://hmu1.hmu.auckland.ac.nz:80/3A05ECA2/Corca

Provides general information on killer whale sightings and photos. Offers a link to pictures of penguins, elephants, seals, and albatrosses.

Complete List of Dog-Related Email Lists

http://www.io.com/~tittle/dogs-faq/lists/email-list.html

Provides list of mail and newsgroups focusing on all types of dog and animal welfare issues. Offers links to a multiplicity of dog breeds.

Deer Net

http://cervid.forsci.ualberta.ca/

Focuses on the impact of humans on Canadian wildlife and their habitats. Provides interesting facts on the grizzly and livestock diversification.

Dismal Swamp Shrew

http://bluegoose.arw.r9.fws.gov:80/NWRSFiles/
WildlifeMgmt/SpeciesAccounts/DismalSwampShrew.html

Provides information on what is being done to manage the Dismal Swamp Shrew.

Division of Mammals

http://ukanaix.cc.ukans.edu/~mammals/start.html

Describes the services and collection of the Division of Mammals of The Natural History Museum of The University of Kansas. Offers links to other related sites and includes a picture of a bat.

Dog Breeding

http://www.clark.net/pub/bdalzell/21stcent.html

Covers how to properly care for and raise a dog. Includes tips. Discusses aspects of several different breeds.

Dog Term Glossary

http://pasture.ecn.purdue.edu/~laird/Dogs/glossary.html

Presents terminology both common and uncommon to the canine field. Provides many links to additional sites, as well as pointers to other parts of the glossary.

Dogs (Malamute, Siberian, Samoyed, Greenlander) and Dog Sledding

http://www.umdc.umu.se/umdac/employees/mmn/northern.html

Focuses on several northern breeds, including the Greenlander and Siberian Husky. Provides information on special events and projects that focus on showcasing these breeds. Includes a Lots of Mal pictures page that offers a colorful page where most links point to Malamute pictures, although a few point to other Malamute and northern breed sites. Provides English and Swedish versions.

The Dolphin Alliance

http://envirolink.org/arrs/ahimsa/tda/

Focuses on dolphins, earth, and wildlife conservation.

Dolphin Information Server—Home Page

http://info.lut.ac.uk/departments/el/research/
bioacoustics/dolphins/index.html

Serves as a simple resource for pictures and information on dolphins, killer whales, and other marine mammals.

The Dolphin Page

http://wjh-www.harvard.edu/~furmansk/dolphin.html

Provides information on the dolphin, including protection issues, research, and sound and graphics.

Donald Firsching's Chicken Page

http://ccwf.cc.utexas.edu/~ifza664/index.html

Focuses on the chicken. Contains many valuable links to information on the history of chickens, the poultry industry, and how to raise and care for chickens. Also offers hen and rooster .WAV sound files.

The Eagle Page from Rocky Mountain High

http://www.sky.net/~emily/eagle.html

Pays homage to birds of prey and provides a resource list of other related sites.

Eastern Slope Grizzly

http://www.rr.ualberta.ca/~lmorgant/grizzly.html

Describes the activity of a project aimed at protecting the eastern slopes grizzly bear.

Endangered Species

http://www.nceet.snre.umich.edu/EndSpp/Endangered.html

Provides information on endangered species. Contains a large list of extinct species and clickable image maps that identify at-risk species by region.

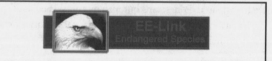

Exotic Pets

http://dca.net:80/exoticpets/

Online exotic pet shop. Specializes in birds, reptiles, frogs, ferrets, iguanas, snakes, hedgehogs, chinchillas, emus, fish, turtles, chameleons, sugar gliders, wolf dogs, rabbits, and more. Lets you place classified ads for buying or selling (for a $10.00 fee).

The Fabulous Kakapo (Strigops Habroptilus)

http://www.resort.com/~ruhue/kakapo.html

Focuses on the Kakapo, a rare nocturnal, flightless parrot. Provides information about this endangered bird.

Friends of Grassmere Wildlife Park Home Page

http://www.infi.net:80/~savegwp/

Online zoo, complete with video clips from the park and great animal shots.

GORP—Nature & Wildlife

http://www.gorp.com/gorp/activity/wildlife.htm

Provides information about almost any conceivable animal-related topic—from bird watching to protection/preservation societies. Offers a wealth of knowledge as well as links to animal-related sites and resources on the Web.

Greyhound Starting Gate

http://pasture.ecn.purdue.edu/~laird/Dogs/Greyhound/

Focuses on getting retired racing Greyhounds adopted. Provides information on the Greyhound and its history in the United States.

Hedgehogs

http://fohnix.metronet.com/~mcgary/hedgehogs.html

Contains a great FAQ about hedgehogs and a special hedgehog game.

Honolulu Community College Dinosaur Exhibit

http://www.hcc.hawaii.edu/dinos/dinos.1.html

Features skeletal and sculpted dinosaur exhibits.

Hyenas

http://www.csulb.edu/~persepha/hyena.html

Focuses on the much maligned and misunderstood spotted hyena.

Hyrax

http://www.med.nyu.edu/~akavia/hyrax.html

Presents pictures of the curious little creature known as the hyrax.

Index of /animal_gifs/

http://aazk.ind.net/animal_gifs/

Contains an archive of stock photos of animals. Indexes animals by species.

Introduced Wild Animals in Australia

http://kaos.erin.gov.au/life/end_vuln/Threats/wildanim.html

Provides detailed information on Australian wildlife evolution. Takes an intriguing look at the impact of animals introduced into the Australian ecosystem.

Introduction to the Mammoth Saga

http://www.nrm.se/mammweb/mamintro.htm

Presents a virtual exhibit that highlights the woolly mammoth and other prehistoric beasts who roamed the frigid parts of this earth. Accompanies graphics with text to help you better understand the subject.

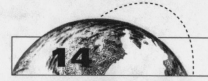

Kaehler's Mill Farm

http://www.execpc.com/~slc/k-m.html

Interesting site for those curious about cattle and sheep farming.

Kids' Action: Rainforest Animals

http://www.ran.org/ran/kids_action/animals.html#pagetop

Provides information on the animals from the tropical rainforests of the world.

LAL Cat Archive

http://lal.cs.byu.edu/cats/cats.html

Offers pictures of cats—many cat pictues in GIF format, many of them quite large. Also contains links to more cat pictures as well as other cat-related sites. Lets you send your cat's picture for display.

LAL Cat Archive

Les Oiseaux de l'Autoroute Èlectronique:

http://www.jrv.qc.ca/~meigs/

Offers a combination of France and birdwatching, and provides French and American birding resources.

Lion Pictures of the Month

http://www.frontiertech.com/gall.htm

Exhibits a monthly gallery of fine feline photography.

LlamaWeb

http://www.webcom.com/~degraham/

Focuses on llamas and llama breeding. Contains pictures of llamas, the lineage of specific llamas, how to have fun with llamas, and all about llama shows, products, literature, and llama associations.

Manatees

http://www.bev.net/education/SeaWorld/manatee/
manatees.html

Provides information on the habits, habitat, diet, and just about anything else you would want to know about the manatee.

Maria's Cat Page (Oriental, Sacred Birman, British)

http://www.umdc.umu.se/umdac/employees/mmn/cats.html

Focuses on Oriental, British Shorthair, and the Sacred Birman house cats. Offers a FAQ on Orientals, along with some pictures and links to other cat sites. Presents English and Swedish versions of the site.

Marine World Africa USA

http://www.freerun.com/napavalley/outdoor/marinewo/
marinewo.html

Discusses the Marine World exhibits and other information on additional wildlife in this wild animal park in California.

Mexican Wolf Management

http://bluegoose.arw.r9.fws.gov:80/NWRSFiles/
WildlifeMgmt/SpeciesAccounts/MexicanWolf.html

Serves as a source of data on the steps being taken to preserve and protect the Mexican wolf in the wild.

Michael's Photo Gallery

http://www.netaxs.com/~mhmyers/image.html#birdtel

Caters to the virtual birdwatcher. Offers a straightforward presentation and displays some pictures.

Moose Page

http://www.halcyon.com/moose/welcome.html

Provides a great painting of a family of moose. Lets you sign up for the Mickey Moose club.

National Zoological Park Home Page

http://www.si.edu/organiza/museums/zoo/homepage/nzphome.htm

Includes a user questionnaire, news, and information, as well as a photo library.

© 1993 Smithsonian Institution

Nature Subject Page

http://secondnature.com/nature.htm

Features photographic artwork of animals in their natural habitats.

Nebraska Hunting Information

http://ngp.ngpc.state.ne.us/hunting/hunting.html

Provides information on hunting in Nebraska. Emphasizes how to hunt safely and legally.

Nebraska Wildlife Descriptions

http://ngp.ngpc.State.ne.us/wildlife/critters.html

Provides information on rabbits, prairie dogs, and the unusual species like cranes and minks that live on the plains of Nebraska.

Neopolis Zoo

http://www.neosoft.com/neopolis/zoo/default.html

Presents a picture of a panda couple and offers links to other animal sites on the Web.

Welcome to the Neopolis Zoo

Have a Great Day at the Zoo, but remember, "Take only Pictures and Leave only Footprints".

New Orleans Zoo

http://www-swiss.ai.mit.edu/philg/summer94/new-orleans-zoo.html

Displays pictures of some of the more unique exhibits at the New Orleans Zoo.

North Carolina Zoo Home Page

http://ils.unc.edu/nczoo/zoohome.html

Provides a look at some of the animals in their collection. Lets you tour each continent.

The Oakland Zoo Web Page

http://www.fwl.org/seaba/members/oz/
oak.zoo.web.page.html

Provides data pages on specific animal species in the Oakland Zoo.

OSU's Breeds of Livestock

http://www.okstate.edu/~animsci/breeds/

Showcases a comprehensive list of the various breeds of livestock.

The Penguin Page

http://www.sas.upenn.edu/~kwelch/penguin.html

Focuses on these comical sea birds. Provides information on the various species of penguin, their behavior, predators of penguins, and even information about fossil penguins. Includes sections on penguin literature, humor, and photos of penguins.

Period.Com Virtual Safari!

http://www.period.com/safari/safari.htm

Offers a colorful virtual safari.

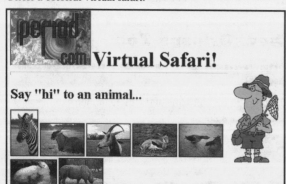

The Pet Bird Page

http://aloha.net/~granty/

Serves as a guide to pet birding or more information about bird breeds. Includes FAQs and newsgroup connections in addition to specific information on most of the major breeds of commonly domesticated birds.

The Phoenix Zoo Home Page

http://aztec.asu.edu/phxzoo/homepage.html

Focuses on the Phoenix Zoo and many of its species. Provides text and animal facts but not many pictures.

The Polar Regions

http://www.stud.unit.no:80/~sveinw/arctic/wild.html

Offers links to arctic wildlife and resources.

Pomeranian Dog Home Page

http://www.u-net.com/~galley/

Provides information on the Pomeranian. Includes links to pictures, history, and breed standards, as well as information on other links related to the Pomeranian.

Portuguese Water Dog Index

http://pasture.ecn.purdue.edu/~laird/Dogs/PWD/index.html

Offers links to other related sites, including the Pacific NW Portugese Water Dog Club site, which incorporates HTML 3.0 background imaging techniques.

Private Zoo

http://www.io.tudelft.nl/~veldkamp/
private_zoo_felidae.html

Lets you visit an international zoo in the Netherlands, as well as mail and link to other international zoos.

The Pug Dog Home Page

http://www.camme.ac.be/~cammess/www-pug/home.html

Provides a guestbook to record comments for passersby, as well as a considerable scope of information.

rec.pets.cats FAQ Homepage

http://www.io.com/~tittle/cats-faq/homepage.html

Contains up-to-date FAQs on all kinds of cats and cat-related issues. Also offers jumps to feline WWW sites, breed FAQs, and other resources.

rec.pets.dogs FAQ Homepage

http://www.io.com/~tittle/dogs-faq/

Provides answers to frequently asked questions about many breeds of dogs, from Airedales to Malamutes to Yorkies. Also provides information on dog care, behavior, and services, including links to other Internet resources.

Rhodesian Ridgebacks

http://warthog.cns.udel.edu/richard/RhoRidge/rrfaq.html

Offers information on e-mail lists of owners of the Ridgeback dog, as well as links to other sites.

Rottweiler Home Page

http://www.in.net/~katl/rottpage/rottie.html

Contains smaller images designed to identify links that provide more information. Includes a shopping guide for Rottweilers and their owners.

San Diego Wild Animal Park

http://www.infopost.com/sandiego/points/sdzoo.html

Lets you visit the San Diego Wild Animal Park online. Offers a montage of the animals that live in the park.

Savage Studios Homepage

http://www.awod.com/gallery/wgd/savage/

Features stuff on cats of all shapes and sizes. Offers links to big cat organizations and the Zoe Foundation.

Schipperke Page

http://www.eskimo.com/~baubo/schip.html

Includes information and pictures of Schipperkes. Features a list of additional canine sites that offer information on canines including medical projects and veterinary studies.

Sea World/Busch Gardens

http://www.bev.net/education/SeaWorld/homepage.html

Contains an animal information database maintained by the Sea World/Busch Gardens theme parks. Also includes images on numerous zoo species.

Seneca Park Zoo

http://www.eznet.net/rochester/todo/sights/zoo/zoo.html

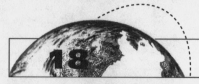
Presents the Seneca Park Zoo in western New York, a fact sheet, and pictures of the California sea lion, the Siberian tiger, and the South African bush elephant. Provides information about the zoo and events at the zoo.

Singapore Zoological Gardens

http://www.ncb.gov.sg/sog/att/abal/zoo.html

Features information on its orangutans and tigers and offers a short video clip of the zoo animals.

Singapore Zoological Gardens

Swiss Canine Breeds

http://www-nmbe.unibe.ch/abtwt/swiss_dogs.html

Focuses on Swiss canine breeds. Lets you jump to pages that contain the history and physiological traits of the following breeds: Saint Bernard, Great Swiss Mountain dog, Bernese Mountain dog, Appenzell Cattle dog, Entlebuch Cattle dog, Swiss hounds, and Smaller Swiss hounds. Includes many pictures of the dogs.

The Tarheel Mall

http://netmar.com/mall/shops/atlantis/

Lets you order supplies, clothing, and companions for your pets over the Net.

Tennessee Aquarium Home Page

http://www.tennis.org/

Presents a colorful aquarium site and has an audio welcome message. Also contains video clips and a visitor registry.

Terry Polk's Zoological E-mail Directory

http://www.wcmc.org.uk/infoserv/zoodir.html

Archives e-mail addresses of professionals in the zoological fields, which also helps locate particular aquariums or zoos.

Thylacine (*Thylacinus Cynocephalus*)—A Species Presumed Extinct

http://kaos.erin.gov.au/life/end_vuln/animals/thylacine.html

Provides information on the Australian marsupial, the Thylacine, presumed to be extinct. Explains what happened to this wolf-like creature.

Tibetan Mastiff Home Page

http://www.primenet.com/~khyri/tm.html

Focuses on the Tibetan Mastiff breed of dog. Includes Tibetan Mastiff-related links to clubs, pictures, purchasing, and information on relevant health matters.

Turtle Trax—A Marine Turtle Page

http://www.io.org/~bunrab/

Provides information on marine turtles, which are larger and more interesting than the ones from the store. Also points out that marine turtles are endangered and explains the issue, including how you can help.

UAS Home Page

http://www.upatsix.com/upatsix/

Introduces aviary practices. Provides software on aviculture and birding.

United States Fish and Wildlife Service Home Page

http://www.fws.gov/

Offers information on numerous species (both endangered and non-endangered), including migratory habits and habitats.

Virtual Birding in Tokyo

http://www.st.rim.or.jp/~koike/

Provides exquisite pictures of wild and domestic birds in Tokyo, Japan.

The Visual Rhodesian Ridgeback

http://wintermute.sr.unh.edu/ridgeback/ridgeback.html

Focuses on the Rhodesian Ridgeback breed. Contains some links to adorable pictures of the young Ridgeback and the owners who love them.

Weimaraner Index

http://www.eskimo.com/~chipper/weim.html

Contains information on the history of the Weimaraner pointer and provides additional links to other canine sites.

Welcome to the Oklahoma City Zoo

http://www.cpb.uokhsc.edu/okc/okczoo/zoomap.html

Presents small exhibits and an image map that features specific zoo sites.

Welcome to the Tirpitz Whaling Web Page

http://tirpitz.ibg.uit.no/wwww/ss.html

Focuses on whales and the whaling industry. Provides links to the latest news, FAQs, organizations, Internet whale information, and literature on whaling.

Westies Home Page

http://www.stpt.usf.edu/~greek/westies.html

Displays pictures of small terriers and doggie cartoon images. Also provides information to other terrier-oriented sites.

Whale Songs

http://kingfish.ssp.nmfs.gov/songs.html

Presents the sounds of whales. Includes a small archive of audio files.

The Whale Watching Web

http://www.physics.helsinki.fi/whale/

Serves as the whale watchers network on the Internet. Offers pictures, information about whales, information about countries around which whales are active.

Wolf Resource Page

http://www.greywolf.com/wolf.html

Lists wolf resources and provides special reports on wolf-related news throughout the country.

The Wolf Studies Project

http://informns.k12.mn.us/wolf.html

Includes a chance to listen to the howl of the wolf, pictures of wolves, and links to newsgroups that cover wolves.

The Wolf's Den: Home Page of Wolf McSherry

http://www.widomaker.com/~wolf/

Provides wolf information. Also sports a welcome message and encourages you to send in comments.

WolfPark Info

http://www.clark.net/pub/bdalzell/wolf/wolfpark.html

Focuses on the wolf.

Wolves on the Internet

http://www.cyber.net/~grinch/wolves.html

Provides Internet wolf resources. Includes information and links to magazine and newsgroup connections.

Wombats, Marsupials, and Other Animals

http://www.batnet.com/wombat/animals.html

Serves as a resource site for marsupials as well as other kinds of existing and extinct species in the animal kingdom.

The Wonderful Skunk and Opossum Page

http://elvis.neep.wisc.edu/~firmiss/mephitis-didelphis.html

Focuses on the skunk and opossum. Contains drawings and newsgroup information.

Wonderful Wombats

http://py2.genetics.uga.edu/PFfolder/wombats.html

Explains why wombats are wonderful. Also offers links to other marsupial-related sites

Wonderful Wombats!

 This page is dedicated to that most noble of all animals, the Wombat .

More detailed information will be added to this page soon!

The World Wide Raccoon Web

http://deja-vu.oldiron.cornell.edu/~sjm1/raccoons/

Features pictures, stories about raccoons, raccoon wildlife management, and links to a raccoon lovers' mailing list.

Zoo

http://sensemedia.net/sprawl/38047

Provides online tour of a zoo. Uses an image map to guide you from exhibit to exhibit.

Zoo Atlanta Home Page

http://www.gatech.edu/3020/zoo/home-page.html

Offers a virtual trip to the Atlanta Zoo. Includes video and sound clips, information about zoo animals, and links to other zoo sites.

ZooNet

http://www.mindspring.com/~zoonet/

Attempts to provide information about every zoo in the world. Includes the ZooLinks page, which offers jumps to hundreds of zoos and zoo-related information. Offers the ZooNet Image Archives, which features numerous jumps to online zoos and animal pictures.

ACADIA—The Association for Computer-Aided Design in Architecture

http://www.clr.toronto.edu/ORG/ACADIA/home.html

Focuses on integrating computer technology into architectural education and practice. Provides a searchable database of conference papers, journals, newsletters, and other contributions. Also provides members a chat space and access to the CAD resource BBS.

AEC Access

http://www.interlog.com/~bhewlitt/index.html

Serves the architectural, engineering, and construction communities; and is more than just a simple pointer to other AEC-related sites on the net. Provides information, directories, databases, and online services. Primarily serves the AEC industry service, but provides resources to the public free of charge. Lets you access directories of shareware/freeware files, public forums, and discussion groups.

Anderson and Associates: Geographic Information Systems

http://www.bnt.com:80/anderson/technlgy.html

Specializes in technology-based solutions for architectural problems. Offers remarkable digital simulations that use CAD tools to digitally view what a finished project would look like before it was even started. Also offers a *geographic information system (GIS)*, an automated mapping system linked with a spatial database. Also provides information regarding a *global positioning system (GPS)* that lets you survey land by satellite.

ARCHIGOPHER

gopher://libra.arch.umich.edu/

Attempts to offer unique resources for architectural researchers not readily available anywhere else. Includes image collections of the architectual works of Andrea Palladio, Lunar architecture, Greek architecture, Tunisian architecture, Hellenic and Byzantine architecture and monuments, and 3-D CAD models done by students. Provides links to other gophers, such as Architecture Job Openings, ICARIS, ICOMOS, Architronic, and IRM-tica '93.

The Architectonics Studio

http://darkwing.uoregon.edu/~struct/

Provides online courseware, historical case studies, structural typologies, correspondence, and essays on teaching technology in Schools of Architecture. Also provides information and samples of MultiFrame, a three-dimensional structural analysis program for the Macintosh. Also features a link to Connector, an independent forum for those interested in the teaching of technology in schools of Architecture around the world.

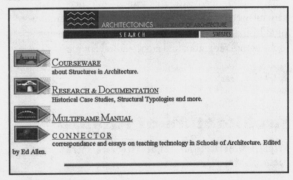

Architectural Computing Bibliography

http://www.arch.unsw.edu.au/faculty/arch/research/archcomp.htm

Offers detailed bibliography of references compiled by students studying architectural computing in Sydney,

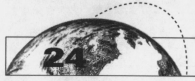
Australia. Provides information about CAD renderings, 3D design, and other information related to computers and architecture.

Architecture and Architectural Sculpture

http://www.ncsa.uiuc.edu/SDG/Experimental/anu-art-history/architecture.html

Serves primarily as a catalog of a large collection of research images of architecture and architectural sculpture in the Mediterranean Basin. Emphasizes classical and Hellenistic architecture in Italy, Greece, and Turkey, and Renaissance architecture in Italy, but also offers a National Gallery Overview link, as well as a link that examines Hong Kong architecture.

Architecture and Building Net Resources

http://www.uky.edu/Artsource/bibliographies/brown.html

Offers links to many sites that provide information in general architecture, architecture and building, architectural history, architecture libraries, images, university architecture programs, and architectural computing.

Architecture of Atlanta

http://www.gatech.edu/3020/architecture/intro/homepage.html

Showcases some well-known and architecturally significant buildings in the city of Atlanta. Contains the many architectural styles represented in Atlanta, ranging from neoclassicism to streamline modern. Lists and briefly describes buildings and gives dates of construction (and renovation), in alphabetical order by area and period.

Arcosanti

http://www.getnet.com/~nkoren/arcosanti/arcosant.html

Arcosanti, a project of the nonprofit Cosanti Foundation, is a prototype arcology ("the concept of architecture and ecology working as an integral process to produce new urban habitats") for 5,000 people, combining compact urban structure with large-scale, solar greenhouses on 20 acres of a 4,000 acre preserve. Provides information relating to the project, such as images and hypermedia, forums, workshops, and lists of events.

The Barcelona Pavilion

http://archpropplan.auckland.ac.nz/People/Mat/barcelona/barcelona.html

Designed as the German Pavilion for the 1929 World Exposition at Barcelona, which was dismantled for shipping back to Germany but vanished in transit. Even with no physical presence it became renowned as a masterpiece of modern architecture, and at this site you can take an incredible virtual tour of this definitive architectural work, as well as examine a varied bibliography of related resources.

Building, Construction, and Engineering

http://www.bf.rmit.edu.au/~s9410536/build.html

Provides construction and engineering information. Offers links to the Division of the State Architect of California and an organization called CSIRO (under construction). Features link to the Construction Sites link, which provides an index to many other sites, some of which aren't present elsewhere. Serves as a useful index site.

Building Industry Exchange (BIX)

http://www.building.com/bix/aboutbix.html

Serves as an interactive exchange center of building industry resources and communications on the Internet.

Features include an education and training center, a government and legislation center, a health and safety center, an environmental protection center, and an advertising and marketing center.

Christus Rex

http://www.christusrex.org/www1/icons/index.html

Features virtual tours of Vatican City, the Sistine Chapel, the Raphael Stanzas, and the Vatican Museum, a wonderous collection of images sure to delight anyone interested in classical architecture and the Italian Renaissance.

The Crosby Group's Architectural/Structural Resource Home Page

http://www.webcom.com:80/~archeng/welcome.html

Contains online architecture and engineering resources and provides links to libraries, FAQs, e-zines and other industry-related Web sites. Provides links to the Structural Engineers Association of California (SEAOC), the Shock and Vibration Information Analysis Center, and the WWW Virtual Library of Civil Engineering. Also presents a disturbing image exhibit of the structural damage produced by the Kobe earthquake.

Design Architecture

http://www.netaxis.com/design/Design_Architecture.Html

Showcases the work of various contemporary architects building around the country today, using still photographs, audio, video, and animation. Currently focuses on a fascinating residential home in Miami. Coming attractions include an architectural exhibition from the Museum of Modern Art. Offers high-quality graphics and content, as well as some unusual links to other design firms, resource collections, newsgroups, and schools.

Digital Design Lab, Columbia University

http://www.arch.columbia.edu/

Explores the uses of computer technology in the field of architecture. Focuses on developing 3-D interfaces for multimedia and online learning environments. Uses state-of-the-art animation technology to construct and test these graphics and worlds, which can be based on real-world examples or completely virtual. Offers pedagogical possibilities for anyone who has a computer terminal, but the real gem here is the online tour of Amiens Cathedral in France.

Ellipsis

http://www.gold.net/ellipsis/ellipsis.html#top

Avant-garde site relating to contemporary architecture and technology. Features "The Interactivator," an interactive computer model that creates an evolving virtual architecture in response to a changing environment, "architecture," an edited listing of architectural sites and events on the net, and "Tokyo—a guide to recent architecture," which contains buildings and images.

Energy Efficient Housing in Canada

http://web.cs.ualberta.ca/~art/house/

Provides information about and pointers to information about energy-efficient and environmentally responsible housing in Canada (new home construction, renovation, and related topics). Culls most resources from government offices and public libraries, but also includes technical information about R-2000 homes, which claims to be the most energy-efficient and environmentally responsible houses commercially available.

Equinox Design Group

http://magicnet.net/~toddmac/equinox.html

Provides information on landscape architecture and computer consulting. Equinox is a registered trainer for MiniCad, Blueprint, and the forthcoming Graphsoft CAD for Wind.

Frank Lloyd Wright in Wisconsin

`http://www.gnn.com/gnn/wic/arch.03.html`

Offers a virtual tour of all eight of Wright's works in Wisconsin and a multimedia gallery of images, including video images of Wright explaining aspects of his design philosophy and theory of architecture. Provides not only images of Wright's works, but also a map and other information regarding real tours of these buildings.

Gamsau's Home Page

`http://www-gams.cnrs-mrs.fr/SOM_ENG.HTM`

Serves as a research group on topics linking architecture and urban design to computer science. Lets you peruse their current scientific program, examine their research activities, and look at images of their projects.

Graduate School of Architecture, Planning, and Preservation (COLUMBIA)

`http://www.cc.columbia.edu/~archpub/`

Offers links to the Digital Design Lab at Columbia, the Gateway Learning Laboratory, Building Technologies highlights, and the "City on the Bias: Contouring Istanbul with Indirection." Includes animations, interactive maps, videos, and models.

ICARIS—CIC Research Network

`http://audrey.fagg.uni-lj.si:80/ICARIS/index.html`

Serves as a research network related to integrated CAD in civil engineering and architecture. Provides access to EDITECH, an education program for civil engineers, NICE, a very useful network of information servers for civil engineering, a searchable library, a mailing list and subscription service, and a gopher.

ICOMOS

`http://hpb1.hwc.ca:10002/`

Focuses on conserving the world's historic monuments and sites. Seeks to establish international standards for the preservation, restoration, and management of the cultural environment. Aims to make available to the larger global community the standards and documentation that the international organization has been developing over the past thirty years via the ICOMOS Documents Page, which includes hypertext versions of many of the charters and agreements that have been established by the organization over the last three decades.

LAVA Home Page

`http://www.tue.nl:80/lava/indexx.html`

Provides information and resources. Features the Gallery, which contains multiple views of the architecture of the most famous museums in America and Europe. Also features the Modelshop, which contains some amazing architectural computer models. Lastly, features the Lab and Studio section, which houses experimental designs and projects.

Leininger Home Page

`http://www.mit.edu:8001/afs/athena.mit.edu/user/m/j/mjl/www/pageone.html`

Provides bibliographic resources. Doesn't provide links to other pages, but offers a guide to architectural periodicals, design and construction sources, a "People, Places, and Things" index, construction diaries, building codes, cost estimation, and design drawing guides with industry standards and specifications. Also includes a bibliography relating to Boston and its architecture.

Lighting Research Center

http://www.rpi.edu/dept/lrc/LRC.html

Studies how light, architecture, and people interrelate. Aims "to change architecture, through lighting that is energy efficient and responsive to human needs." Offers links to many other sites that deal specifically with lighting and its applications, but the real highlights involve the student research projects and the "Demonstration and Evaluation of Lighting Technologies and Applications" program, designed to showcase energy-saving lighting techniques in residential, commercial, and industrial applications.

Matiu Carr

http://archpropplan.auckland.ac.nz:80/People/Mat/Mat.html

Involves architecture property and planning. Features the Gallery, an eclectic collection of architectural sketches, exercises, images, virtual tours, models, and exhibits, CAD designs, and drawings. Also offers links to Radiance, a lighting design, graphic design, rendering, and analysis tool available freely for use anywhere in the world, and the Virtual Studio, an environment for architects "as space and concept engineers, where theory, form, texture and space interweave."

MBT

http://www.dnai.com:80/~mbt/

Showcases MBT's many works around the San Francisco area. Presents an online gallery and a brochure that contains a collection of images that demonstrate both the architectural and interior design aesthetic of the firm, and provides artist renderings of the entire external structure. Contains a comprehensive list of clients, project summaries, and other resources.

Metropolis

http://virtumall.com/newsstand/metropolis/main.html

Metropolis, the magazine of architecture and design, explores the ways design (architecture, industrial design, urban planning, graphic design) shapes the world. Provides the current copy, as well as an archive of previous issues.

MIT School of Architecture and Planning

http://alberti.mit.edu/ap/

Focuses on the study and design of the human environment—architectural, urban, and electronic. Provides all the requisite university information, such as available programs, student and faculty searches, articles, events, and projects. Focuses on urban studies and planning, but offers a fascinating media laboratory of online exhibits, a center for real estate information, a center for advanced visual studies, and a computer resource laboratory that includes a collection of student drawings and works, as well as works by other reknowned architects.

Moscow Kremlin Online Excursion

http://www.kiae.su/www/wtr/kremlin/begin.html

Provides information for anyone searching on landscape architecture and planning. Brings the city of Moscow alive online, including detailed maps, images, videos, sounds, and historical texts.

Planning and Architecture Internet Resource Center

http://arch.buffalo.edu:8001/internet/
h_pa_resources.html

Provides information such as architecture and planning firms and services, architecture exhibits and images, building and construction technology resources, CAD and GIS resources, census information and demographic resources, conferences and design competitions, economic development agencies, environmental resources, government agencies and services, historic preservation, and more. Compiles the newest resources available on the Web.

Renaissance and Baroque Architecture: Architectural History 102

http://www.lib.virginia.edu:80/dic/colls/arh102/
index.html

Provides collection of images dealing primarily with France in the baroque period and Italy during the renaissance, for students, scholars, and the public.

Rice Design Alliance

http://riceinfo.rice.edu:80/ES/Architecture/RDA/RDA/

Specializes in contemporary architecture and urban design. Lists the many lectures, seminars, symposia, exhibits, and tours that the RDA has sponsored since 1994. Features "Cinemarchitecture V: The Virtual City," a look at how the cinema creates environments and "structures" for characters to live and dwell within.

A Roman Palace in Ex-Yugoslavia

http://sunsite.unc.edu/expo/palace.exhibit/intro.html

Presents a virtual tour of the Palace of Diocletian at Split. Provides an online history lesson, architectural images, and everything from art history to CAD.

S.P.Q.R.

http://www.pathfinder.com/@@VV1ENgAAAAAgOsQ/twep/rome/

Offers a beautifully illustrated online computer adventure game from CyberSites. Lets you explore the architecture of ancient Rome while searching for the journals of five Roman characters. Provides excellent playability and phenomenal graphics.

Sabo & Zahn Construction Law Attorneys

http://www.webcom.com/~sabozahn/

A firm of architect/attorneys concentrating in construction law. Provides information about the firm, news of interest to architects, and information about the Chicago Chapter Construction Specifications Institute. Provides many links to other law- and construction-related Web sites.

School of Architecture Home Page (University of Miami)

http://rossi.arc.miami.edu/home.htm

Houses the School of Architecture in Miami, replete with course offerings, online courses, lectures, events, and student home pages. Features the Galleria, a forum for student and faculty work, the AthenÆum, a library of

slides, research publications, maps, and drawings, and the Arquitectura Tropicana, which features images of local architecture in the city of Miami.

School of Architecture Property and Planning

http://archpropplan.auckland.ac.nz/ArchPropPlan.html

Offers a collection of resources, especially the Virtual Study Tour, an index of links to a number of new architectural creations, as well as reconstructed historic works. Provides access to research projects being carried out by staff and students at the Department of Architecture, as well as images, movies, and discussion in and around the field of architectural visualization.

Southeastern Architectural Archive

http://www.tulane.edu/~lmiller/SEAAHome.html

Contains one of the country's most important architectural research collections. Focuses on the architectural and urban history of New Orleans and the Gulf South, from the 1830s through the 1980s. Presents a "Mini-Tour" of the SEAA, which provides tantalizing glimpses of the types of items in the collection.

Space Ink

http://www.echonyc.com/~danb/spaceint.html

Presents a multidisciplinary and multimedia laboratory, primarily concerned with investigations of the transformation of architecture and its integration with media. Provides a range of services, such as educational projects, designs for science museum installations, audiovisuals, and virtual reality applications. Offers publications in the form of books, articles, as well as electronic media.

Structural Engineers Association of California (SEAOC)

http://www.power.net/users/seaoc-ad/

Lets you access the many documents it maintains relating to structural engineering and safety. Also allows you to receive SEAOSC publications via e-mail and provides a healthy set of links relating to everything from wood to seismology.

The World Wide Web Virtual Library: Architecture

http://www.clr.toronto.edu:1080//VIRTUALLIB/arch.html

Presents a clearinghouse of links to many Internet-based architectual resources. Provides information on conferences, jobs, schools, publications, competitions, government agencies, organizations, firms, history, models, engineering, software, newsgroups, and mailing lists.

Virtual Gallery

http://rossi.arc.miami.edu/cmputing/gallery.htm

Offers the School of Architecture's virtual gallery at the University of Miami. Presents examples of the student work produced in the school's computing in design courses. Includes areas for modeling and rendering, graphics, student folios, and animations.

Worldwide Architectural Services

http://www.architect.com/

Provides an alternative to the "instant Mediterranean architecture so prevalent in Southern California today." Includes examples of several contemporary revivalist architects' work, excerpts from books and articles, art by

architects, and a bookstore/source list. Features a collection of the world's best architects. Offers a resource for individuals looking for an architect or merely interested in architecture.

@art gallery

`http://gertrude.art.uiuc.edu/@art/gallery.html`

Provides links to talented and mature artists and archives past exhibitions; UIUC faculty members curate the exhibitions.

@rtweb Art Gallery

`http://www.bitech.com/gallery`

Eugene, Oregon's first online gallery, specializes in digital photography, but features new work in all two-dimensional media. Current exhibit changes each month.

1002situations

`http://fgidec1.tuwien.ac.at/1002situations/`

Place the text, photos, and sounds that define your *heimat* (homeland) into this virtual museum. Not only do you visit, you can participate and interact.

2D Productions

`http://www.ip.net/2d/`

Wit and sarcasm abound in this humorous look at all things "techno." Includes a *Star Trek: The Next Generation* plot generator and a random Haiku generator.

5-D Stereograms Home Page

`http://www.ais.net:80/netmall/bma/`

Offers 5-D™ *stereograms* (hidden multidimensional images incorporated into five-dimensional pictures). Although the images look at first like no more than a colorful collection of dots, the actual picture comes into focus after you "find" the right perspective. Three different images are available for viewing; if you like what you see, you can order from a large selection of other 5-D images.

911 Gallery Home Page

`http://www.iquest.net/911/iq_911.html`

A frequently updated virtual gallery. You can purchase art shown here offline. *Note:* Does not provide links to other art-related resources.

A8

`http://www.leonardo.net/a8/index.html`

Fast new utilization of html; Netscape 1.1N required.

Able Cain

`http://www.netads.com/netads/arts/music/marathon/ac`

Progressive modern rock band.

Abulafia Gallery

`http://www.cgrg.ohio-state.edu/~mlewis/Gallery/gallery.html`

Highlights the work of artists who work in any medium, including computers. Offers choice for large or small monitor viewing. Hint: Choose the small option for faster results. Includes a VRML section: you can obtain the best results if you have the WebSpace viewer and an SGI computer, although a PC and a VRML viewer do work, the results are just of low resolution and without texture.

Access Art

`http://www.mgainc.com/Art/HomePage.html`

Helps connect collectors with artists. You can view the work of many contemporary artists, and you can purchase works of art by filling out an online order form on-screen.

ADG Graphix Home Page

http://www.earthlink.net/~anthony/index.html

Offers links to African-American sites on the Web, as well as other sites, including to the design and graphics arts community.

Adriana's Artwork

http://www.webcom.com/~geomanda/adrianaart.html

Offers one child's drawings and connections to other topics of interest, as well as several links to other children's pages.

African Art

http://www.lib.virginia.edu/dic/exhib/93.ray.aa/African.html

The University of Virginia's Bayly Art Museum presents an exhibit of African art, including an overview of African aesthetics, pictures and descriptions of masks, headdresses, statuettes, and other artifacts.

AFRICAN ART: AESTHETICS AND MEANING

The Age of Enlightenment

http://dmf.culture.fr/files/imaginary_exhibition.html

Highlights the paintings of France's national museums during the age of enlightenment. Presents the information from a historical and artistic perspective.

The Akron Art Museum

http://www.winc.com/~aam/

Showcases artists of our time and the recent past and offers links to modern art for visitors of all ages. Provides links to other museums around the world as well.

Akteo Watch Boutique

http://www.tiac.net/users/uwc

Affords opportunity to view and/or purchase AKTEO watches designed by J. C. Mareschal.

Alamkara: 5000 Years of Indian Art

http://www.ncb.gov.sg/nhb/alam/

Displays the art of East India.

Alaskan Dance Theater

http://www.alaska.net/~ethan/adt.html

Covers primarily ballet, but offers a variety of links both to other dance sites and Alaska. Mostly text.

Alder Yarrow's Photography

http://www-leland.stanford.edu/~alder/photography.html

Contains five portfolios of Alder Yarrow's latest photographic work, as well as links to photography-related resources on the Web. He works in the 4-x-5-inch format, primarily in black and white. The majority of his work would be considered landscape photography, although he would not classify the majority of his photographs as pure landscapes.

The Allen Memorial Art Museum

http://www.oberlin.edu/wwwmap/allen_art.html

Displays art objects, including paintings, ivories, and bronzes received. The Allen Memorial Art Museum is a museum on the campus of Oberlin College.

Allen Toney's Home Page

http://marshall.edu/~jtoney/

Displays the art work of Allen Toney, the 1st place winner of the 1995 Fractal Designs "Painter" International Computer Art Contest. His work "weds liquid, sensual, neoclassical forms with mystical, mathematical, and surreal sensibilities."

Alternative Virtual Biennial

http://www.interport.net/avb/

Presents an alternative view of art, providing comprehensive explanations of the art and artists. Doesn't link to other art-related sites.

Amsterdam Valley

http://valley.interact.nl/av/int/home.html

Contains an eclectic mix of off-beat publications, forums for musicians, and high-tech businesses. Amsterdam Valley provides a wide range of activities, from touring a virtual art gallery known for its mood enhancing paintings and artistic sounds to sampling Dutch culture by viewing the online windmill collection.

Anderson Photo Galleries

http://www.spectra.net/mall/anderson/

Exhibits the professional work of Richard Anderson, a professional photographer who specializes in portraits.

Andy Warhol Museum

http://www.warhol.org/warhol

Features extensive permanent collections of art and archives by Warhol, and regularly presents temporary exhibitions that may include the work of other artists.

The Andy Warhol Museum Home Page

http://www.warhol.org/warhol/

Displays information regarding the Andy Warhol Museum, offers a virtual tour through the museum, and provides links to other museums and art collection sites.

ANIMA

http://www.anima.wis.net//ANIMAhome.html

ANIMA is the Arts Network for Integrated Media Applications, a global cultural information source for the media arts. Links an array of categories: art work, spectrum, atlas, nexus, techne, persona, and connections.

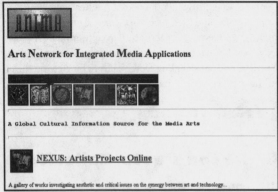

Arts Network for Integrated Media Applications

A Global Cultural Information Source for the Media Arts

NEXUS: Artists Projects Online

A gallery of works investigating aesthetic and critical issues on the synergy between art and technology...

Anonima Fumetti—Italian Comics, Cartoons, and Cartoonists

http://www.alpcom.it/fumetti/

Nonprofit Italian cartoonists society. You can find (and send messages to) more than 500 Italian authors. Offers courses, news, shows, conventions, bibliographies on comics, and links to other comics sites.

Ansel Adams

http://bookweb.cwis.uci.edu:8042/AdamsHome.html

Exhibits "Fiat Lux," the book of photographs Ansel Adams produced to commemorate the University of California's centennial celebration. You can place electronic orders here for these and other works by Adams and others.

Anti-Art Productions

http://www.nauticom.net/www/dada/index.html

Claims to be an independent artistic endeavor whose purported goal is to expose "that which lies underneath the complacent mediocre facade of the contemporary human condition."

Arizona Museum for Youth

http://www.primenet.com/art-rom/museumweb/azmusyou/azmusyou.html

Displays exhibits with intent of introducing children to the fine arts world to generate interest in nonvirtual visits to the museum.

Art by Belinda Di Leo

http://gort.ucsd.edu/mw/bdl.html

Appalachian artist Belinda Di Leo demonstrates the relationships between culture, religion, and death in her art. The paintings depict these interrelationships with a sense of place, character, and spiritual conviction, all of which are reinforced by a repetition of visual imagery.

Art by Tim Pascoe

http://www.hub.co.uk/intercafe/tpascoe/Cat.Art.T.Pascoe.P1.Home.HTML

Tim Pascoe presents an online exhibition of his sculptures, accompanied by essays.

Art Crimes Index

http://www.gatech.edu/desoto/graf/Index.Art_Crimes.html

Displays graffiti art from around the world, providing explanations and examples of "art crime." Also provides links to other art-related sites.

The Art Kelderie

http://www.xs4all.nl/~mad/kelderie/kelderie.htm

Shows the work of Theo Kelderman over the last 20 years: acrylic, air-brush, and oil paintings, as well as some black and white photos from his early years.

Art Knife Collector's Association

http://artknife.com

Consists of collectors and makers of handmade custom knives and publishes *Blade Trader* monthly.

Art Links on the World Wide Web

http://amanda.physics.wisc.edu/outside.html

Contains links to most of the major and minor galleries on the Web featuring new and innovative art, music, video, photography, and 3D renderings. You can contact other artists; view paintings, sketches, and renderings in virtual art galleries; check out current events in the art field; or submit your own art-related Web site for others to view.

Art Net—The Art Place

http://telescope.com/telescope/artnet/

Offers original art, prints, crafts, pottery, and so on.

The Art of Barbara Weigel

http://198.66.88.2/blw/blwhome.html

Presents the art of Barbara Weigel, a New Orleans artist who specializes in a brightly colored, hard-edged style that has evolved into dramatic figures and portraits on canvas and wood cutouts.

Art on the Net

http://www.art.net

Serves as a site to which artists can come to curate their own studios and gallery rooms, share their works, and help each other learn how to use the Web. Includes links to art-related topics other than visual art and to other art-related sites.

Art on the Net

The Voice of Reason in a World of Chaos...

Art To Live with Original Prints

http://www.10e-design.com/ArtTLW

Includes original prints by internationally recognized artists such as Appel, Chamberlain, Hamaguchi, Tooker, Wesselmann, and more, and offers the opportunity to purchase art.

Art.Online

http://bighorn.terra.net/artonline/

Highlights African-American, Native American, wildlife, nautical, and rock art. Enables you to view and/or purchase limited edition art. Doesn't provide links to other art-related sites.

Art?

http://www.directnet.com/Crash/Art/index.html

Contains nontraditonal perspective on art.

Now that art has died, and the audience has withered away, we find ourselves free of two dead weights. Now, everyone is some kind of artist, and the audience has regained it's innocence, we now have the ability to become the art we experience. Among the offerings here, is the anti-elitist art of Robert Williams, the clown apocalypse of R.K. Sloane, the poetic terrorism of the new underground poster art of T/AZ, Derek Hess, and Pablo. Along with the millnium ending rehash of the Art Sabotage of previous generations.

Arthole

http://www.mcs.net/~wallach/arthole.html

Contains a plentitude of art and photography for display.

Arthur Hall and Black Dance in America

http://www.columbia.edu/~jw157/arthur.hall.html

Covers Arthur Hall's life and impact on African American dance and cultural development in America and offers links to broader pages regarding Hall's Yoruba culture of Nigeria.

The Arthur Ross Gallery Homepage

http://www.upenn.edu/ARG/index.html

An exhibition gallery of the University of Pennsylvania, featuring fine art shows from around the world.

Artists and Works

http://lydia.bradley.edu/exhibit/artists.html

Offers the capability to find a particular artist or specific work of art. Describes each piece of art work in detail, including the gallery at which you can find the art on exhibit.

ArtMap

http://wimsey.com/anima/ARTWORLDonline.html

Contains links to the visual arts and galleries, mass media and pop culture, literary arts and online libraries, animation, film and video, performance in the audio arts of music and sound, and architecture, environmental planning, and urban design.

The ArtMetal Project

http://wuarchive.wustl.edu/edu/arts/metal/ArtMetal.html

Includes special stories, movies, graphics, and sound files about metalwork.

Arts: Exhibits

http://www.yahoo.com/Art/Exhibits

Focuses on electronic art topics beyond imagination, and offers artist features, reviews, and critiques, as well as access to comprehensive lists of art galleries and exhibitions around the world.

ArtScape

http://www.ides.com/ArtScape/

Provides a means for artists to display their work, share their philosophies and inspirations, demonstrate techniques, and network with other artists and art enthusiasts who share their interests. Offers artists' samples and networking opportunities, and plans to include a searchable index, QuickTime movies demonstrating technique, information on professional organizations, and art show schedules.

ArtScene

http://artscenecal.com/

Guide to art galleries and museums in Southern California.

ArtServe

http://rubens.anu.edu.au/

Australian National University server. Offers a variety of image collections and small presentations dealing with art history. Includes more than 10,200 images, which include 2,800 prints ranging from the 15th to the 19th century, over 8,500 images of architecture and architectural sculpture from the Mediterranean and beyond, and a small selection of Islamic monuments.

ArtSource

http://www.uky.edu/Artsource/artsourcehome.html

Points you to a variety of electronic art galleries, online exhibits, research materials, and art-related periodicals.

ArtStudio

http://www.vt.com/artstudio/

Offers fishermen and art lovers a unique Game Fish series, including the rainbow trout, cutbow trout, yellowbelly sunfish, and the bluegill, in signed, frame-ready prints. Offers a full-color preview of the series, by Texas artist Norm Browne, as well as an opportunity to order the set or individual prints.

Artworld (ArtMap): Online Links and Listings

http://www.anima.wis.net//ARTWORLDonline.html#VISUALARTS

Indexes a wealth of actual images, as well as artists, magazines, events, and so forth, and overviews current art (including literature) in Canada.

As-Sayf Oriental Dance Home Page

http://www.ivo.se/as-sayf/englishindex.html

Dance group that offers traditional Middle Eastern and North African performances (such as belly dancing).

AS220

http://www.ids.net/~as220/home.html

AS220 is an artist-owned complex that manages two galleries, a performance space, a cafe, 11 artist studios, and 12 residential studios in Rhode Island.

The Ashmolean Museum of Art and Archaeology

http://www.ashmol.ox.ac.uk/

One of the four museums of the University of Oxford, founded in 1683, and regarded as Britain's oldest public museum, and contains the University's archaeological and historical art collections.

Asian Arts

http://www.webart.com/asianart/index.html

Online Asian art gallery, contains exhibitions, galleries, and articles (includes Buddhism-influenced art).

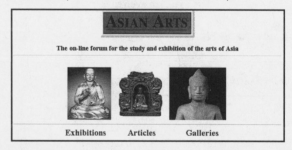

ASIAN ARTS

The on-line forum for the study and exhibition of the arts of Asia

Exhibitions   Articles   Galleries

Asimov, Isaac

http://www.lightside.com/SpecialInterest/asimov/asimov-faq.html

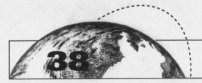
Contains everything you might ever want to know about Isaac Asimov and his works, including FAQs about him, as well as newsgroups in which he is discussed in detail.

Aspiring Artists

http://intrepid.pcnet.miami.edu/aeden/index.htm

Displays art, music, and literature from potentially up-and-coming artists. Submissions welcome.

Atelier Nord

http://www.oslonett.no/home/atelier/index.html

Oslo, Norway site that displays the work of artists in residence at Atelier Nord, including projects on the internet, multimedia, electronic images, computer animation, video, sound, performance, and printmaking.

Auricular Homepage

http://128.218.7.140/Auricular.html

Explores sights, sounds, and beyond and includes collections of computer-generated art, experimental music catalogs, and many links to the alternative and (they say) amazing. Also offers to design Web sites for you.

AusArts

http://ausart.anu.edu.au/ITAAusArts/index.html

Maintained by Australian National University. Contains links to the Institute of the Arts library server, Canberra University, and the electronic library. Offers avenues to information about the arts and higher education in Australia.

Australian Outback Gallery Photography

http://matahari.tamu.edu/People/Ewen/Outback.html

Offers a collection of images from the heart of Australia's arid zone, the outback.

AWID—Association of Women Industrial Designers

http://www.core77.com/AWID

Professional organization devoted to the concerns of women in industrial design. Serves as a forum for speakers and discussion, and as a network for developing collaborative resources.

AXIS Dance Troupe

http://picasso.ucsf.edu/~schmitz/axis.html

Provides information regarding the particular dance troupe (which includes wheelchair-bound dancers), their awards, background, upcoming shows, and provides links to more information on this troupe and others like it.

B.A.W.P.: Spoken Word Audio Recordings

http://www.cs.brown.edu:80/fun/bawp/

Contains downloadable spoken word performances (ranging in theme from computers to love) made in movie-quality sound. Features several artists at a time and updates selections monthly.

Ballinakill Studios

http://gellersen.valpo.edu/~jgordon/art.html

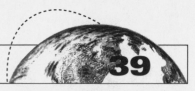
Advertises art courses offered at Ballinakill Studios in Ireland.

Barry Anderson Photography

http://www.eden.com/~alyosha

Presents a selection of photographs from Barry Anderson Photography.

Booth Milton: Sculptor

http://www.alchemedia.net/boothmilton/index.html

Contains thumbnails of the sculptor Booth Milton's metal and wood creations (strictly a virtual gallery—no pricing information—but you can contact the artist).

The Shop Floor

Brookhouse Studio

http://www.ni.net/brookhouse.com/

Offers more than 300 images that reflect Brookhouse Studio's services, which include commercial photography and graphics, 3D models, stock images, and fine art.

Bruce Museum

http://www.primenet.com/art-rom/museumweb/brucemus/brucemus.html

Displays images from exhibits at the Bruce Museum, which is a teaching museum of the arts and earth sciences. Includes crafts and natural history galleries.

Burton Levitsky

http://www.cruzio.com/~scva/blevitsky.html

Features highly detailed oil paintings of California, Ireland, and fantasy landscapes.

Business Volunteers for the Arts—Houston

http://www.fine-art.com/org/bva.html

Provides business expertise through volunteers to nonprofit arts and cultural organizations.

The Butler Institute of American Art

http://www.cisnet.com/butler/

Displays information regarding the Butler Institute of American Art, in Youngstown, Ohio. Includes links to other museums.

BYU Performing Arts Management

http://visitor.byu.edu/pam/homepage.html

Includes links that enable you to order tickets to all performances of all Brigham Young University's performing arts and a schedule of national and international places at which BYU groups perform.

Canadian Heritage Information Network

`http://www.chin.gc.ca/`

Computer-based network that serves museums, libraries, and other heritage institutions internationally. Offers access to more than 20 databases, provides advice on information standards, explores and evaluates multimedia technologies, and offers specialized training in museum practices and Internet use. Contains an online brochure and newsletter through which you can find out more about CHIN.

Welcome to the Canadian Heritage Information Network!

Cette information est aussi disponible en français.

Capacity Index

`http://www.wimsey.com/Capacity/`

Canadian magazine that seeks to expand the boundaries of art and culture (current and back issues available online).

CBC Radio Trial

`http://www.radio.cbc.ca/`

Offers Canadian Broadcasting Corporation radio products, including a complete listing of available program transcripts, aired broadcasts, and digital radio program samples.

Center for Research in Computing and the Arts (CRCA)

`http://crca-www.ucsd.edu/`

Deals with applying computing technology to a wide array of artistic endeavors, including music, visual arts, theatre, literature, and media. Also contains a listing of concerts, seminars, and art-related workshops, as well as links to other sites.

Center on Contemporary Art

`http://www.subpop.com/coca`

Contains Seattle's Center on Contemporary Art's virtual gallery. Also includes membership information, schedule, directions, and more.

The Centre for Contemporary Art in Warsaw

`http://www.nask.org.pl/Others/CSW/`

Features Polish artists and art from the collection at The Centre for Contemporary Art in Warsaw.

CERN MusiClub

`http://www.cern.ch/CERN/Clubs/Music/musiclub.html`

Includes press releases, sounds, and pics from CERN bands.

Chiossone Studio, NYC (Photography)

`http://www.escape.com/~chiosson`

Beauty/Fashion photo studio in New York dedicated to editorial and advertising photography. Includes advertising photos.

Christine Thea Partridge Gallery

`http://www.wimsey.com/~thea/gallery.html`

Contains one artist's gallery of her work. Worth visiting particularly if you're an artist exploring the possibility of

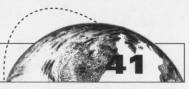
doing art direction and Web page development commercially.

The Chrysler Museum

http://www.whro.org/cl/cmhh/

Provides information about the museum.

Cloud Gallery

http://www.commerce.digital.com/palo-alto/CloudGallery/home.html

Contains 32 downloadable fine art photographs of sky backgrounds. Includes tips on angels and ways to watch clouds, and offers the means to order more sky images.

Colorburst Studios Online Catalog

http://www.teleport.com/~paulec/catalog.html

Offers a catalog of Niobium jewelry, handcrafted by Paul Crabtree and Tess Yevka, for which you can place orders online.

COLORBURST STUDIOS ONLINE CATALOG

This is a catalog of the eye-dazzling handcrafted Niobium Jewelry by Paul Crabtree and Tess Yevka. You will experience the best results using a graphical client such as Mosaic or NetScape which can view GIF files. Alternatively, you may download the GIFs to your home computer for viewing. Many of our designs are available in other color combinations than are shown in the pictures; write for a catalog to see exactly what we offer by mail. The picture files range from 10K to 40K in size, so the speed of your connection will determine how quickly you see the pictures.

Connie Tunick's Paintings in Watermedia

http://www.centcon.com./~atun

Contains a virtual gallery of watercolor and watermedia paintings. Exhibits images of original floral and abstract paintings.

CORE Industrial Design Network

http://www.core77.com

Features articles, projects, designer pages, and a wealth of other industrial design-related information.

Cosmo's Cosmos

http://gvi336.gv.psu.edu

Includes blues, blues, blues; music, jazz, art, philosophy, knowledge, information, search forms, shareware, freeware, religion; Robert Johnson, Muddy Waters, John Lee Hooker.

Crosswire Images

http://cuiwww.unige.ch/Chloe/OtisCrosswire/index.html

Presents a collection of art (an experiment in collaborative art that features starter, manipulated, and finished images, called CROSSWIRE) produced by the organizational efforts of OTIS, an electronic art gallery.

Crucible Chicago

http://www.mcs.net/~poleary/crucible/crucible.html

Contains images of the work of four Chicago artists, primarily sculpture, but also furniture and lighting design.

Cyberkind

http://sunsite.unc.edu/shannon/ckind/title.html

Features publications submitted by viewers in the areas of nonfiction, short fiction, poetry, and art. (All submissions are copyrighted in the author's name.)

Czeslaw Milosz

http://sunsite.unc.edu/dykki/poetry/milosz/milcov.html

Features downloadable poetry (by Czeslaw Milosz, a Lithuanian poet born in 1911) and other readings (including an extensive biography and a selected bibliography) in English and Polish.

Daddazio™—The Bronze Necktie™

http://www.gems.com/showcase/daddazio/

Features sculptures modeled in plaster or wax and subsequently cast in bronze for eternity, and you can purchase the sculptures you want online.

DaliWeb: The Official Salvador Dali Museum Web Site

http://www.highwayone.com/dali/

http://www.highwayone.com/dali/daliweb.html

Presents interactive look at the Salvador Dali Museum in St. Petersburg, Florida. Includes museum history, some of Dali's greatest works, and information on how friends of the museum help it and this site continue to grow and develop.

Dallas Museum of Art Online

http://www.unt.edu/dfw/dma/www/dma.htm

Provides information and images from the museum. Contains approximately 200 digital images of art works owned by the Dallas Museum of Art.

Damascus Productions

http://www.cudenver.edu/~rbergman/index.html

Includes pages for science and math, and an art gallery (for which this site was originally intended).

Dancescape

http://wchat.on.ca/dance/pages/dscape.htm

Offers comprehensive coverage of the world of competitive ballroom dancing and dance sport. Includes a wide range of information, ranging from upcoming competitions to national personals.

Danclink

http://www.cts.com/~danclink/

Point of departure for dance enthusiasts who want more than just Internet connections. Includes not only complete video instructions on how to dance, but also provides a "dating service" (helps you find a dance partner), video dating services such as online chatting with other members, as well as membership in an adult movie club.

Daniel Vogel

http://www.sentex.net/~danvogel/index.html

Displays Daniel Vogel's home page and a series of pages that further display his work. Includes art and graphics accompanied by explanatory text, and an eclectic set of links (heavily Canadian).

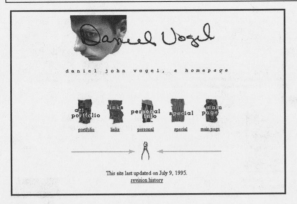

Features "an ever-more-detailed cybernetic-artistic exploration of reality." Also features related Mac links.

Digital Giraffe

http://redshift.com/~cwhit

Online studio/gallery of electronic painting and fun. Exhibition changes every month, as does the artsmart quiz (sassy questions on art subjects designed to challenge your mind and provoke a grin).

Daum On-line

http://www.daum.co.kr

Concentrates only on artistic areas such as photography, cinema, cartoon, and fashion. Provides links to several subsites and several mirror sites for Korean users.

Digital Photography

http://www.bradley.edu/exhibit/index.html

Contains a total of 81 images submitted by artists from 19 different states at the Art Guild Exhibition, sponsored by Peoria Art Guild and Bradley University.

Dia Center for the Arts

http://www.diacenter.org/

Shows exhibitions and the Dia Center for the Arts' permanent collection, and provides links to many other art-related sites.

The Discovery Catalogue

http://prostar-int.com/gogg

Contains a pictorial essay on the journey of Captain George Vancouver to the Pacific Northwest Coast of North America in 1792.

DigiPen Applied Computer Graphics School

http://www.digipen.com/High/DPHP.htm

One page in a series of pages regarding classes and background of Vancouver's DigiPen Applied Computer Graphics School—the page on which the students can display their work.

Donajski's Digital Gallery

http://www.atm.com.pl/COM/Art-Gallery/Art-Gallery.html

Presents a variety of digital arts.

The Digital Cathedral

http://marshall.edu/~stock1/index.html

The Douglas Albert Gallery—State College, PA

http://www.epicom.com/arts/albert/index.htm

Features a variety of works by today's prominent artists. Offers the opportunity to purchase pieces from both local and international artists.

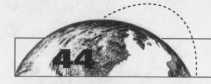
Drama

http://english-www.hss.cmu.edu/drama.html

Contains a number of plays, screenplays, and discussions of drama and dramatic productions. Includes plays from various centuries and by such authors as Aristophanes, Goethe, and Sophocles.

Duane Hilton High Sierra Fine Art

http://www.dnai.com/~antares/hilton/hilton.html

Offers a selection of original miniature oil paintings and limited edition prints of Eastern Sierra landscapes and wildlife.

Duncan Hopkins Web Site

http://www.eden.com/~dhopkins/

Specializes in multimedia and information graphic design, from interactive multimedia to Web site development, as well as animation, 3D modeling, and illustration.

Eagle Aerie Gallery

http://www.advantage.com/EAG/EAG.html

Features the art of Roy Henry Vickers. Offers a catalogue and the means to make online purchases.

Edoardo Villa

http://www.fine-art.com/artist/villa.html

Presents the art of Edoardo Villa, the South African artist.

Edoardo Villa

For almost forty years, Villa has worked mainly in steel, interspersed with short periods of modelling for bronze. In this recent series of steel sculptures, he shows his consummate mastery of the medium, creating powerful, evocative works that evoke the human figure at times.

The full richness of a formal language that he has built up over many decades, comes into play: seemingly mechanical forms, softer curves derived from modelled shapes, the solidity suggested by solid cast bronzes.

Each work has been sensitively finished in subtle color shades, recalling the patina formed on rusted steel.

Abie, steel, 1992
93x30x40cm

The Electric Gallery

http://www.egallery.com/egallery/homepage.html

Offers virtual tours and displays of modern art.

Electronic Art Gallery

http://www.pixelpushers.wis.net//Texindex.html

Offers many thumbnails of the Pixel Pushers, for viewing and for sale.

The Electronic Chronicles

http://www.awa.com/artnetweb/projects/ahneed/first.html

Fictional site that contains a story about a futuristic archaeological dig that finds archaic 20th century electronic documents, and speculates on what the future will think of us.

Enterzone

http://enterzone.berkeley.edu/enterzone.html

Online magazine designed for people who like to read a little bit about everything; an eclectic mix of various forms of art, short stories, and news media. Previous editions available.

Eric Boutilier-Brown

http://www.isisnet.com/empire/ebb/

Black-and-white fine art photography, predominantly of the nude and of archaeological ruins.

eSCENE 1995

http://www.etext.org/Zines/eScene

Furnishes yearly anthology of short fiction published online (available in ASCII, PDF, and PostScript formats).

Exhibition of Paintings by Stanley Pettigrew

http://www.internet-eireann.ie/pettigrew/petpla5.htm

Makes the oil paintings of Irish landscape painter, Stanley Pettigrew, available for viewing and for sale.

The Eye Produce CD-ROM Home Page

http://www.earthlink.net/~rogue/cd.html

Hosts hundreds of royalty free pictures and photographs, mostly backgrounds and textures.

Figure 1: The Visual Sector

http://www.interport.net/~edb

Dedicated to the anonymous pleasure of found photos. Accepts submissions of photos from people on the net, and posts them (see the website for more information). Also maintains a biased listing of photographic sites of passing interest for the web community.

Fine West Photography

http://www.ktb.net/~fadams/

Avails samples and larger GIF format images (scan images from high guality 35mm color slides) for downloading. Categories include scenics, people, animals, and themes.

FineArt Forum Gallery

http://www.msstate.edu/Fineart_Online/gallery.html

Offers electronic art gallery for works by contemporary artists. Requires JPEG viewer for some files.

Flaming Jewels

http://www.prairienet.org/~jjewels/jewel.html

Provides writings by jewel.

Flapping

http://www.slip.net/~atombee

Presents illustrated allegorical sci-fi spoof of Chervil Orbane's saga, including his moment of clarity, the big ideas, the good guys, the bad guys, the gratuitous sex, the great epiphany, the happy ending, and the ipso and the facto, as it were, of fin-de-siecle metaphysical thought.

The Framer's Corner

http://www.traveller.com/mall/hsv/framer

Specializes in limited edition prints by Terry Redlin, Daniel Moore, John Seery-Lester, Alan Hunt, and many others.

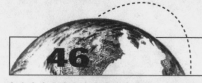

Free Art Website (Laurie McCanna's Home Page)

http://www.mccannas.com/

Lets you view the art work of Laurie McCanna, a freelance illustrator and WWW graphics designer, as well as download icons, textures, and Photoshop tips.

Frida Kahlo Art Pages

http://www.cascade.net/kahlo.html

Showcases the work of Frido Kahlo, provides facts about her life, and points to a bibliography for further reading.

Front Home (Front Magazine's Home Page)

http://www.anima.wis.net//SHELF/FrontTOC.html

Electronic newsletter for a cultural center in Vancouver, Canada. Offers gallery and performance space, as well as a simple meeting place for local artists. Includes pages to the magazine, the place, the artists and their work.

Frozen Music, a Novel by Michael J. Vaughn

http://www.best.com/~iapp/

Even bachelor ducks and shortneck giraffes can't seem to drag Michael Moss out of his self-imposed exile. But then he joins the Westfield Community College Choir and falls under the spell of music and the baton of Amy Fine.

Galeria MexPlaza

http://mexplaza.udg.mx/Ingles/Galeria

Promotes Mexican artists and their work throughout the world.

Gallery

http://www.eciad.bc.ca/~mlabre/gallery.htm

Provides several artists' private images.

Gallery Lainzberg

http://www.gryffin.com

Serves as a source for animated art products for the serious collector of production cells, limited editions, lithographs, sericells, and comic strips.

gallery.html (Edison Gallery)

http://www.wimsey.com/~panic/gallery.html

Elaborates on the gallery's background, upcoming exhibits, and images of previous artists.

Gen Art

http://www.emedia.net/genart/

Displays the work of young artists and provides exhibitions, online catalog, and links to other art-related sites.

Getty Art History Information Program, The

http://www.ahip.getty.edu/ahip/Text_home.html

Disseminates research and information about artistic and cultural heritage. Provides text and graphics versions of pages.

The Graphix Exchange

http://www.rust.net/TGX_WWW_pgs/TGX.html

Growing resource directory of freelance talent from around the world. Furnishes a database of artists (to whom you can send e-mail directly from this site) and links to many artists' personal home pages.

The Great Books of Western Civilization

http://roger.vet.uga.edu/~lnoles/grtbks.html

Provides access to the great literary works of the western world.

The Great Books of Western Civilization

In the early 1980's, Mercer University began the Great Books Program, modeled after the course of study at St John's College, as an alternative to the standard distributional track of basic courses needed to graduate. The program was divided into eight courses that were required to complete the program and an additional ninth course which was optional.

For a better understanding of the goals of the program, we need to refer to the Mercer Catalog:

The Great Books curriculum of nine courses is one of two General Education "tracks "in the College of Liberal Arts. The Faculty of the College believes that careful study in the primary texts of Western thought and belief, guided by committed and rigorous instructors, is a valid means to a good general education.

Through this survey of political, religious, philosophical, and scientific thought, students can increase their skills in disciplined thinking and effective writing, can heighten their moral and ethical reflectiveness, and can understand how the seminal ideas of the past have formed our twentieth and twenty-first century selves. The Great Books thus can provide both a ground and a goal for the specialized disciplines in which students major.

Hal Earp—Graphic Designer

http://www.nando.net/events/dance/hal.html

Offers opportunity to check out Hal Earp, a graphic designer whose work has appeared on several WWW pages.

Hal's Virtual Furniture Gallery

http://www.xensei.com/users/hipjr

Presents handcrafted pieces ranging from grandfather clocks to Belizian deck chairs.

I have been designing and building furniture for the past fifteen years.

I began with traditional cabinetry and furniture techniques and have progress towards more organic, natural pieces.

Some of my early work is pictured below. Please click on image for more information, views and pricing of that particular piece.

Grandfather Clock, 1985

Hans de Kort Photography

http://www.euronet.nl/users/shorty/index.html

Presents fashion and advertising photography.

Harmony Music List

http://orpheus.ucsd.edu/mbreen/harmony.html

Indexes nearly 1,000 music-related links and contains a built-in search engine for finding sources in the Harmony list, including major headings such as Artists, Classical, Cultures, Discographies, Instruments and Equipment, Jazz, Music Magazines, Labels, Radio Stations, Studios, and more.

The Heard Museum

http://hanksville.phast.umass.edu/defs/independent/Heard/Heard.html

Promotes appreciation and respect for native people and their cultural heritage and emphasizes the traditional cultures of the Greater Southwest and the evolving Native American Fine Art Movement. Over the years the Heard Museum (established in 1929) has grown and today boasts a collection of more than 30,000 works of art and artifacts; 45,000 pieces of archival materials including significant papers, books, and photographs; and a membership of nearly 5,000.

Henry's Dance Hotlist

http://zeus.ncsa.uiuc.edu:8080/~hneeman/
dance_hotlist.html#tango

Provides a list of Internet pages, events, supplies, magazines, and more, all related to dance.

Herbert R. Mears, Contemporary American Artist

http://www.wwma.com/mears/

Offers the chance to view Texan artist Herbert R. Mears' romantic paintings reminiscent of Bonnard, Ensor, and Matisse.

Hillustration

http://www.hillustration.com/~mhill/

Samples traditional and digital illustration, along with examples of Web page design and interface design.

Hiway Technologies Graphics Portfolio

http://www.hway.com/sp/

Provides a collection of images created by Hiway Technologies' graphics and logo design department, as well as Web services and Internet consulting.

Hoffer School Home Page

http://cmp1.ucr.edu/exhibitions/hoffer/
hoffer.homepage.html

Presents a collection of pictures, poems, and projects of a grade school class, as part of a five year collaboration with the UCR/California Museum of Photography. Includes sound and video files.

Hollywood Archaeology

http://www.echonyc.com/~hwdarch

Contains five separate subsections, one of which traces the life and career of wrestler and movie heavy, Mike Mazurki: text by conceptual artist Lowell Darling, design by Jim Newman. Includes forty examples of film found in the streets of Hollywood by Darling in the early '70s.

Home Page of Photographer/Sculptor David C. Franson

http://www.eciad.bc.ca/~dfranson/dfranson.htm

Offers images of David Franson's photographs and sculptures for viewing and for sale.

HypArt

http://rzsun01.rrz.uni-hamburg.de/cgi-bin/HypArt.sh

Stands for Hyper-Art, the artistical equivalent to hypertext. Features many pictures created based on the idea that several people create a single picture.

The Identity Box Collective

http://www.mcs.net/~ibc/home/ibc.htm

Showcases the artistic creation of Sam Jennings, including paintings and images from the past three years of his painting career.

The iGallery

http://www.igallery.com

Presents a collection of eclectic art work from around the world, including beaded and metal jewelry, iron furniture, decorated masks, and much more.

ImageKit for the Macintosh

http://smartworld.com/imagekit/imagekit.html

A comprehensive resource of over 1200 royalty-free images collected from artists all over the globe on 10 CD-ROM discs, all cross-referenced and available in low and high resolution versions.

ImageKit was created by Digital Artists
for Digital Artists as the ultimate all-in-one imaging tool
Macintosh Only (PC Coming Soon)

ImageMaker Gifts for Dog Lovers

http://fender.onramp.net:80/imagemaker/

Makes available artist Monique Akar's pen and ink drawings of approximately 150 dogs for imprinting on a variety of quilts, umbrellas, photo albums, or aprons, or simply transferring to nearly anything.

INM Home Page

http://www.inm.de/

The Institute for New Media, a research site and forum for art, science, and technology in new media. Includes four levels of cooperative projects in the fields of audio, video, 3D-graphics, and interactive media.

International Folk Dancers Of Ottawa Home Page

http://lucas.incen.doc.ca/ifdo.html

Ottawa-based nonprofit participatory recreational dance group. Provides links to local and other dance events.

International Masters Group

http://www.fine-art.com/gallery/masters.html

Wholesale fine art distributor. Specializes in limited edition lithographs.

The International Museum of Art

http://www.nettap.com/~iart/

Preserves and promotes rice straw art, an ancient Indian art form. Displays pieces as well as offers them for sale.

International Sculpture Center's On-line Resource

http://www.dgsys.com/~sculpt/

Nonprofit organization devoted to issues related to contemporary sculpture. Publishes *Sculpture and Maquette* magazine, holds technical workshops and conferences, brokers sculpture shows, and administrates Sculpture Source, a database for contemporary sculpture.

Internet Dance Resources

http://www.nando.net/events/dance/dsource.html

A directory of dance resources available through World Wide Web. Links to dance pages already separated by type. Also includes newsgroup and link access.

Israel Museum—Jerusalem

http://www.imj.org.il

Emphasizes the material culture (past, present and future) of the land of Israel and the Jewish people. The Israel Museum (founded in 1965) fosters public education and strives to preserve, study, and display the collections.

Shalom - Welcome

Shalom - Welcome to the Israel Museum, Jerusalem. We are delighted to have you join us for a virtual tour of Israel's major art museum, and we cordially invite you to visit us in person in the near future.

Jayhawk

http://www.klab.caltech.edu/~flowers/jayhawk/

Presents the Jayhawk series, a cyberpunk fantasy by Mary K. Kuhner, serialized in 144 parts and stored in the order in which the author posted them on the Web (except for the story background, an explanatory piece posted partway through the story to help bring new readers up to date).

The Jazz Photography of Ray Avery

http://bookweb.cwis.uci.edu:8042/Jazz/jazz.html

Traces jazz beginnings through records and photography. Also includes Ray Avery's online jazz exhibition, which is grouped into four major areas: The Lighthouse All Stars—Hermosa Beach and Laguna Beach; Nightclubs, Festivals and Concerts; Recording Sessions—Los Angeles; and Stars of Jazz—TV Series.

Joe_Walker's_Page

http://www.oz.net/~jwalk/

Provides a rotating display of Joe Walker's personal art and page design services, as well as links to other pages he has created.

Jordan, Robert

http://www.cc.gatech.edu/ftp/people/viren/www/jordan/jordan.html

Focuses on FAQs (frequently asked questions) about Robert Jordan and presents readings on dreamers, lyrics, and humor. Also offers links to other related sites.

Kaleidospace Home Page

http://kspace.com

Offers a mix of art and publications: you can select where you want to go from a color wheel, relax in the Reading Room, chat with artists online in the Kaleidospeak forum, see what's new in the Art Studio, or check out the new tunes in the Music Kiosk, to name a few of your many options. Also allows you to place online orders for work by Kspace artists.

Kaufman, Karin

http://www.execpc.com/~skaufman/karin.html

Presents a virtual art gallery of Karin's colored pencil drawings, which she calls "illustrated dreams."

Kids' Gallery

http://www.interport.net/kids-space/gallery/gallery.html

Exhibits a gallery of pictures and stories submitted by children aged two to twelve from all over the world; accepts picture submissions in an IBM-compatible format.

Kjell Ringi Art Exhibition

http://www.wca95.org/ringi/

Displays Kjell Ringi's paintings, sketches, graphics, and posters.

Koh-Varilla Guild

http://www.mcs.com/~kvg/

Consists of classical realist artists who specialize in portrait and monumental sculpture, limited editions of bronze and terra-cotta sculptures, still life oil paintings, and fine drawings. Accepts commissions. Offers classes in figurative and portrait sculpture.

Krannert Art Museum

http://www.art.uiuc.edu/kam/

Provides information about the University of Illinois' Krannert Art Museum. Includes exhibition schedules, a guide to the permanent collection, special events at the museum, a virtual tour and shopping at the museum shop. Doesn't offer links to other art-related sources.

Welcome to Krannert Art Museum

Thank you to everyone who responded to our survey. Ann Bishop and Joseph Squier have just released a paper describing the results. Thank you making this a successful step toward a better understanding of how people use on-line art and its potential role in society. The survey is still available if you would like to see it.

 Guide to the Permanent Collection

An electronic sampler of the Museum's permanent collection, including pictures and descriptions of sculptures, American and European paintings, Asian, African, Pre-Columbian American, Near Eastern, and 20th Century art.

 Upcoming Exhibitions and Projects

Information on current and upcoming temporary exhibitions and projects at Krannert Art Museum. "Art as Signal: Inside the Loop" and "Concerned Theatre Japan: The Graphic Art of Japanese Theatre 1960-1980" are currently in preparation. Also information about the Visual Learning Initiative.

Krypton Neon—The Internet's Neon Shop

http://www.neonshop.com

Offers neon signs, neon art, neon special effects, and more. Demonstrates the art of making neon. Includes neon FAQs and more.

La Galéacutérie d'Art

http://www.iway.fr/champs_elysees/html/vitrines/galerie_d_art.html

Showcases French artists and their work.

La Trobe University Art Museum

http://www.latrobe.edu.au/Glenn/Museum/ArtMuseumHome.html

Offers an online view of exhibitions taking place at the La Trobe University Art Museum. Doesn't link to other art-related sources.

Le Ministère de la Culture: Direction des Musées de France

http://dmf.culture.fr/

Displays exhibit, titled "The Age of Enlightenment in the Paintings of France's National Museums," offered by the French Ministry of Culture. Offers complete French version in addition to the English site.

Le WebLouvre

http://mistral.enst.fr/~pioch/louvre/

Gives you Paris at your fingertips. Presents the collection in the medieval art wing, a set of 100 art works at The Cézanne summer, and the Famous Paintings section. Also takes you on a tour of Paris and lets you listen to some classical music pieces in the Auditorium.

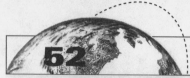

Lectro-Art

http://www.artnet.org/iamfree/IAMFREE/html/elecart.html

Dave Parmley is an electronic art wizard who resides in Monte Sereno, California. Parmley was inspired by eastern philisophical concepts in design as well as his own hand. These elements culminate in his piece, "Seeing Is Not Believing," available for downloading.

Lewis Carroll Home Page

http://www.students.uiuc.edu/~jbirenba/carroll.html

Highlights listings of Carroll's publications online, *Alice in Wonderland* graphics, and links to other related sites, including a *Jabberwocky* translation page.

Lien/Nibauer Photography, Inc. and the Impact Studios

http://www.netaxs.com/~impact/index.html

Features photographic images.

Liros Gallery

http://media1.hypernet.com/liros.html

Specializes in the sale of fine paintings, Russian icons, and prints. Offers many 19th and 20th century Russian icons, as well as American and European paintings, prints, and maps. Also offers details on how to contact Liros Gallery regarding the purchase or sale of fine art.

Los Angeles County Museum of Art

http://www.lacma.org/

Displays the exhibits in the Los Angeles County Museum of Art. You can watch a QuickTime movie, sift through online catalogs, pick out favorite categories in the exhibition schedule, or visit the museum shop. Also offers links to other online art museums.

Lysator Computer Society

http://www.lysator.liu.se

Maintains a collection of books, art works, and literature resources divided into three broad subject areas: The Science Fiction/Fantasy Archive (contains reviews, bibliographies, news lists, electronic magazines, and art work), Anime and Manga (a collection of Japanese comics

and animations), and Project Runeberg (publishes electronic texts in Scandinavian).

Marjan

http://www.cybernetics.net/users/jwkjr/marjhome.htm

Marjan is a belly dancer in Dallas, TX: site includes her photo, but more importantly, links to other pages on belly dancing.

Media West Editions

http://www.wimsey.com/Pixel_Pushers

Features works of original digital art created wholly on computers and works from the Pixel Pushers Exhibition of Original Digital Art.

The Meridian Gallery: Contemporary Art, in the Heart of San Francisco

http://www.homenet.com/meridian/

Presents contemporary art from throughout the Americas, in the heart of San Francisco's gallery district, including exhibitions, visual, literary, and performing artists.

Metaverse

http://metaverse.com/index.html

Offers much in the way of art and entertainment.

Michael C. Carlos Museum, Emory University

http://www.cc.emory.edu/CARLOS/carlos.html

Offers a virtual tour of the museum with downloadable video files.

Michael Rubin

http://www.fine-art.com/artist/rubin.html

Presents the art of Michael Rubin, which he claims represents the next aesthetic stage in pure abstraction.

Mill Valley Film Festival

http://www.well.com/mvff

Offers the 17th Annual Mill Valley Film Festival, a line-up of American and international films, tributes, and a three-day videofest and interactive exhibition.

Millennium Productions

http://www.arts-online.com/

Hosts the home pages of many visual artists, performing artists, and writers.

The Minneapolis Institute of Arts

http://www.mtn.org/MIA/

Provides information on The Minneapolis Institute of Arts, including exhibitions, galleries, events, and shopping. Doesn't link to other art-related sites.

Museum Index

The Minneapolis Institute of Arts
The Minneapolis Institute of Arts is the most comprehensive fine arts museum in the upper midwest. The permanent collection includes outstanding works in seven curatorial areas with 85,000 objects spanning 4,000 years. General admission is FREE, except to some special exhibitions.

MIT Center for Educational Computing Initiatives Virtual Museum

http://abelard.mit.edu/cgi-bin/museum-entrance/

Allows you to search the available database for pictures of interest and view Harold E. Edgerton's high-speed photography, including a variety of photographs from which to select; for example, apples split by bullets, Vortex motion pictures, and birds and balloons in flight.

Motorcycle Collectible Art Gallery

http://www.rwga.com/motor2.htm

Displays a montage lithograph of the history of Harley-Davidson for collectors and provides information on how they can (for a price) paint your portrait into this picture.

The Multimedia Cultural Information Service

http://www.wimsey.com/anima/ARTWORLDhome.html

Provides an online art gallery and links to other related Web sites on visual arts, design, video, literature, and performance.

Musée des Arts et Métiers's World Wide Web (Museum of Art and Craft)

http://web.cnam.fr/museum/

Offers many collections, displays, and unique graphics. Currently, most of this site is in French, with no English translation available.

Musee National D'Histoire Et D'Art

http://www.men.lu/~fumanti/LuxMusee.html

Invites you to take a tour of Luxembourg's National Museum of Art and History and provides many links to other art-related resources on the Web.

Museum Web

http://www.primenet.com/links/graphics.html

Enables you to explore some of the world's most famous art galleries on the Web today, in addition to eclectic sites such as The Shiki Internet Haiku Salon, Shremagraphs, 3D Kinetic Art, and Thant's Animation Index.

Museum Web from Art-ROM

http://www.primenet.com/art-rom/museumweb/

Directory to museum and gallery sites on the World Wide Web.

Museums in the Netherlands

http://www.xxlink.nl/nbt/museums/

Provides links to information about museums in the Netherlands. Supports many languages. Text only.

Na-Te-So Workshop

http://www.qadas.com/nateso

Exhibits original handcrafted Southwestern art works in wood, silver, and paintings created by artists of the Na-Te-So Workshop, which is located in Indian Hills, Colorado.

National Museum of American Art

http://www.nmaa.si.edu/

Presents information and exhibitions for the National Museum of Art.

The National Museum of the American Indian: George Gustav Heye Center

http://www.interport.net/~logomanc/heye.html

Displays information about The National Museum of the American Indian. Provides links to other Native American cultural sites.

NCSA Digital Gallery CD-ROM

http://www.ncsa.uiuc.edu/SDG/DigitalGallery/DG_readme.html

Offers a wide range of NCSA Scientific Software for the Macintosh, IBM PC, SGI, Sun, and X Window servers, along with approximately 250 MB of images and animation sequences produced by researchers around the world. You also can view scientific animations in the Science Theater in the upper level of the gallery.

Netwash!

http://www.umn.edu/nlhome/g023/filmsoc/chris/netwash.html

Exhibits a series of images made of pictures and text collected on the Infobahn during the current week—the trash and treasures you can find along the side of the information superhighway, dressed up like art.

Nico Roos

http://www.fine-art.com/artist/roos.html

Includes 16 one man exhibitions and a retrospective exhibition at the Pretoria Art Museum in 1993, the work of Nico Roos, abstract landscape painter and professor of Fine Art at Pretoria University.

Noel Ford Cartoonist/ Illustrator/Author

http://193.118.187.101/help/extra/people/noel-ford-cart

Features general information about Noel Ford, a UK cartoonist and author.

North Country Arts

http://www.cyberpages.com/db/company&1&197/

Serves as source for native culture and heritage arts and crafts of the Inuit of Baffin Island in Northern Canada. Includes carvings, sculptures, paintings, and handicrafts.

OBD—Organization of Black Designers

http://www.core77.com/OBD

A nonprofit professional association. Addresses the unique needs of African-American design professionals.

Ohio State University, Department of Dance Home Page

http://www.dance.ohio-state.edu

Distributes original material related to dance. Provides information on dance history, dance and technology, and musicians in dance.

Ohio State University at Newark

http://www.cgrg.ohio-state.edu:80/mkruse/osu.html

Exhibits the Art Gallery, established at Ohio State University at Newark in 1968. Enables you to download a movie (Mpeg) of the gallery's interior as well as tour the gallery in German and Spanish.

Okanagan University College, Department of Fine Arts

http://oksw01.okanagan.bc.ca/fiar/home.html

Describes programs, resources, and so forth avaliable at the Department of Fine Arts, and provides useful general information and links to related sites.

On-Line Books

http://cs.indiana.edu/metastuff/bookfaq.html

Offers an index of Internet servers that offer electronic reading materials. Contains archive sites for books and electronic text as well as a list of known books freely available on the Web. Also gives information on related Usenet groups.

oneday

http://www.gold.net/oneday/

Claims to offer some potentially interesting links you might want to check out "while you sip coffee before you return to something more worthwhile."

Online Source Register (Services)

http://www.interstat.net/serv.html

Includes internet advertising, telecommunications, e-mail setups, job lead reports, contracting services, and more.

Optical Illusions

http://www.lainet.com/~ausbourn

Contains a collection of some famous optical illusions.

Origami Club of Pittsburgh

http://www.contrib.andrew.cmu.edu/usr/origami/home.html

Includes a comprehensive set of pointers to origami and paperfolding resources on the Net.

Parallax Gallery

http://www.colossus.net/rwsa/parallax_gallery.html

Includes a collection of art objects, fine art, jewelry, mineral specimens, sculpture, blown glass, and espresso.

Welcome to Parallax Gallery

Parallax Gallery

is one of the most unique and innovative galleries in Washington state. Located in the breathtaking beauty of the Cascade mountain foothills, just 30 miles NE of Seattle, this stoic country church of some 100 odd years was remodelled and renovated over five years by curators Toni Makinaw, her partner-in-art Bill Schicker, and their combined family of 6 children. Rachel, Toni and Bill would like to welcome you to their gallery/home. Inside you will find an unusual collection of outstanding art objects, fine art, jewelry, mineral specimens, sculpture, blown glass, and refreshing espresso.

Click on the photos below to meet the family and to see some art items.

Patrick Gallagher, Celtic Art

http://www.planet.net/celtart

Provides lists of exhibitons, where to learn the art form, bibliogaphies, examples and samples, and a news page.

Pavilion of Polyhedreality

http://www.li.net/~george/pavilion.html

Polyhedreality: an almost magical transformation of the banal (paper clips) into multisided, symmetrical, structures.

PDX TheatreSports

http://www.spiretech.com/~richie/pdxts.html

Offers improvisational comedy with a competitive twist, in which teams of improvisors compete in improvisational games scored by a panel of judges or the audience. Includes plenty of information about TheatreSports, as well as links to other groups and improv pages.

Pearl St. Online Gallery

http://antics.com/pearl.html

Exhibits computer-colored images of the southwestern United States, Colorado Wildflowers by Steven P. Cone, three images from within the Hoh River rain forest, and images from Colorado.

The Photography Spot

http://www.cris.com/~Bubaluba/photo_spot.html

Dedicated to photography and photographers. Links you to the work of photographers around the world. You can add the Web site that shows your work or the work of another. Also visit Photo Stuff to look at or add companies and services that deal with photography.

PhotoServe

http://www.photoserve.com/

Publishes the latest work of professional photographers, their home pages, an industry resource center, a bulletin board, and a new talent section.

Pix Gallery

http://www.nynex.co.uk/nynex/pix/index.html

Includes information on the British Computer Arts Association and Art Technology.

The Place

http://gertrude.art.uiuc.edu/ludgate/the/place.html

Evolving repository of art work created specifically for distribution on the Web. Includes many graphics, very little text.

Poems on the Net

http://www.mind.net/gallery/poems.html

Offers poems: "warm, loving, reflective poetry about life, love, happiness, serenity, peace, and hope."

Poetry SLAM!

http://pubweb.acns.nwu.edu/~ppawinsk/poetry.html

Provides the opportunity to peruse the latest works, submit your own poetry, or critique existing works.

Progress Computer Systems Ltd.

http://www.progress.co.uk

Deals with all the very latest technology from Digital and Oracle.

Project Gutenberg

http://jg.cso.uiuc.edu/PG/welcome.html

Contains complete texts for more than 100 works of literature, ranging from Light Literature (for example, *Alice in Wonderland*, *Through the Looking-Glass*, *Peter Pan*, *Aesop's Fables*, and so on) to Heavy Literature (for example, *The Bible* or other religious documents, Shakespeare, *Moby Dick*, "Paradise Lost," and so forth) to References (for example, *Roget's Thesaurus*, almanacs, a set of encyclopedias, dictionaries, and so on).

A Purgatory of Semiotics

http://www.sonoma.edu/Exhibits/Semiotics

Contains a selection of poems by Michael Mollo of Wine County, California, as well as author information, a searchable table of contents for the poems and other exhibits.

RACE: Research into Artifacts, Center for Engineering

http://brains.race.u-tokyo.ac.jp/RACE.html

Offers images that depict art, technology, and their relationship to the surrounding environment, as well as links to several of the university professors to find out their views and contributions to this and other projects.

Rainbow of Chaos

http://www.indy.net/~gemini/

Serves as an environment in which computer-oriented artists who use primarily the Amiga personal computer can display their artistic accomplishments. Offers pieces of art and displays the graphics capabilities of the Amiga.

Rare Treasures

http://www.ip.net/rt

Presents a gallery of fine porcelains to art collectors, museums, and fine arts establishments.

Rare Treasures

Limited Edition Porcelains

REIFF II Museum

http://www.informatik.rwth-aachen.de/Reiff2/

An electronic art museum available in both the German and English language. Exhibits digitized images and fast frame art.

rEX's wORLd

http://www.cea.edu/rex

Presents pieces of original art work from rEX and friends.

rgaphic design—alex r. mayer

http://www.speakeasy.org/cgi-bin/llama/llama?owner=arm

Presents a digital gallery.

Rice School (Art)^n Laboratory

http://www.artn.nwu.edu/

Documents the historical developments of PHSColograms and (Art)^n Laboratory (in which PHSColograms3D images not requiring special glasses for viewing were created). Explains how the images work and provides access to several hundred PHSColograms, virtual photography galleries, and computer gaming galleries.

The Risk Map of Cultural Heritage in Italy

http://www.uni.net/aec

A project promoted by Italian Instituto Centrale per il Restauro on preventative restoration and programmed maintenance.

Rittners School of Floral Design

http://www.tiac.net/users/stevrt/index.html

Provides workshop courses in floral designing.

Robert Derr's Virtual Gallery

http://www.neosoft.com/~kcderr/rcd.html

Presents the black and white and digital imagery of Robert Derr.

The Roger Whitney Gallery of Artists

http://www.rwga.com/index.html

Displays a selected variety of Roger Whitney's works.

Saaraen Light Universal Dragon Cult Page

http://www.teleport.com/~rfrederi/slu01.htm

Ongoing experiment in story-telling using the wonders of hypertext and the World Wide Web. Includes products of the experiment and links to other Web sites.

Sacred Faces, Sacred Spaces

http://www.artsantafe.com/sfm/jyoung/youngphoto.html

Exhibits polaroid transfer, color, and black and white images of the American Southwest, Australia, Mexico, Greece, and more.

Sample the Dog Design

http://www.teleport.com/~sample/

Slaves to digital imaging, layout, graphical concept, and video.

Santa Fe Fine Art

http://www.sffa.com

Features the work of photographers, painters, sculptors, and printmakers from the southwestern United States.

Scott Freeman's Underwater Photography Page

http://weber.u.washington.edu/~scotfree

Focuses on underwater photography in the northwest, namely Puget Sound.

Sculptor/Stone Carver

http://www.mcs.com/~sculptor/home.html

Contains a variety of sculptures, including gargoyles and grotesques, custom fireplaces, signage and entry panels, and public sculptures.

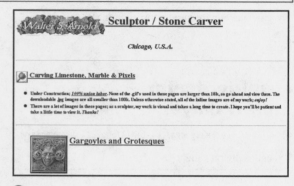

Walter S. Arnold **Sculptor / Stone Carver**

Chicago, U.S.A.

Carving Limestone, Marble & Pixels

- Under Construction; *100% union labor*. None of the .gif's used in these pages are larger than 16k, so go ahead and view them. The downloadable .jpg images are all smaller than 100k. Unless otherwise stated, all of the inline images are of my work; *enjoy!*
- There are a lot of images in these pages; as a sculptor, my work is visual and takes a long time to create. I hope you'll be patient and take a little time to view it. *Thanks!*

Gargoyles and Grotesques

Sculpture Tour

http://loki.ur.utk.edu/sculpture/sculpt.html

Presents over 200 pieces of sculpture on the Knoxville campus of the University of Tennessee as well as links to the other exhibitions.

Shakespeare

http://the-tech.mit.edu/Shakespeare/works.html

Contains the complete works of William Shakespeare. Offers a chronological and categorical listing of plays, Bartlett's familiar Shakespearean quotations, and a section of frequently asked questions.

Sierra Wave Art Gallery

http://www.dnai.com/~antares/wave/wave.html

Showcases the work of photographers, painters, sculptors, writers, and other artists who live in the Eastern Sierra region of California and Nevada.

Sonoma State University Alumni Art Exhibition

http://www.sonoma.edu/exhibits/alumni/

Contains the art work of 16 former students of Sonoma State University.

Sony Pictures Classics Home Page

`http://www.spe.sony.com/Pictures/SonyClassics/index.html`

Distributes foreign films, independent films, and documentaries in North America. Provides information about their latest releases and offers downloadable photos, sound bites, and movie clips.

Spanky Welcome (The Spanky Fractal Database)

`http://spanky.triumf.ca/`

Serves the mildly curious with simple fractal images and challenges the avidly interested with links to in-depth discussions and projects in nonlinearality.

Stained Glass by Steve

`http://www.craftweb.com/org/steve/steve.shtml`

Features stained glass windows and fused glass visual images. Offers opportunity to get in touch with the artist.

The Surrealism Server

`http://pharmdec.wustl.edu/juju/surr/surrealism.html`

Attempts to simultaneously explain surrealism and entertain. Covers surrealism from all angles. Offers links to other surrealistic pages.

Surreomystical Poetry

`http://www.algonet.se/~kelly/dipak/mystical`

Offers the poetry of Dipak, a mystical poet who wanders the Internet.

Surrey Institute of Art and Design's World Wide Web Server

`http://www.surrart.ac.uk/`

Offers, among other draws, links to pages related to graphic design.

Susan Aaron-Taylor: Profile of an Artist

`http://www.cris.com/~greenlak/sat/satmain.shtml`

Profiles Susan Aaron-Taylor, who has had exhibitions at the Detroit Institute of Arts and teaches at the Center for Creative Studies.

Synergy Music and Art Workshop

`http://www.eirenet.net/cork/synergy/`

Promotes music, art, and entertainment.

We wish to invite you to have a look behind the normally closed doors of a busy Multimedia Workshop. See what we do, learn how we do it, listen, look and interact. Find out about our projects and our services to clients, learn who our clients are and how they benefit from our skills. Get lots of free sound samples, images and video clips to use in your own multimedia work. Meet Artists and Musicians, a Wizard, a Salesman and a Teacher. Visit our strange new worlds.

WIN £100.00 IN OUR COMPETITION

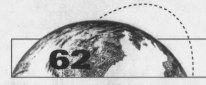

Syracuse University Computer Graphics for the Visual Arts

http://ziris.syr.edu/curriculum/mainmenu2.html

Provides information on Syracuse University and links to students' pages.

Talk about Dance

http://www.nando.net/events/dance/dance.html

Represents the American Dance Festival (ADF), which has sponsored several hundred dance works. Features columns, profiles, and dance reviews originally published in the *Raleigh News & Observer*. Contains the ADF dance schedule and upcoming events, as well as links to other dance sites.

Tallahassee Woodcrafters Society

http://wane-arc.scri.fsu.edu/~tatum/tws.html

Serves as a forum for practitioners of the art of woodcrafting.

Tango Dance Notation Argentina Argentine

http://litwww.epfl.ch/~shawn/tango/

Provides all the information you might ever want to obtain (and maybe more) concerning dancing the Tango, including where to do it, as well as plenty of interrelated (and unrelated) links.

Tati's Page

http://www.lncc.br/tatiana/

Contains personal information and helpful tips for designing pages and surfing the Web.

Techno-Impressionist Art

http://www.interport.net/~tkarp

Features the work of the techno-impressionist artists. Provides information on the origins of techno-impressionism, quotes from the artists, a history of 21st century art, fables, and more.

Techno-Impressionist Art

http://www.digiweb.com/tkarp/

Serves as a gallery of techno-impressionist art. Doesn't link to other art-related sites.

Tel Aviv Museum of Art

http://www.macom.co.il/ta-museum/index.html

Displays the best of Israel's art and sculpture from the 1920s to the contemporary work of today's established and newly discovered Israeli artists. Contains the Museum's graphics collection of more than 20,000 prints and drawings.

Tele-Garden

http://www.usc.edu/dept/garden/

Enables you to control a robot arm to plant and tend a real garden. Provides color images of the garden and detailed logs record the growth of the plants and the social interactions between gardeners.

The Tokugawa Art Museum

http://cjn.meitetsu.co.jp/tokugawa/index.html

Highlights the Tokugawa Art Museum, the third oldest privately endowed museum in Japan. Uses a map of the museum to give a virtual tour.

THE TOKUGAWA ART MUSEUM

Tom Reed/Photographer

http://www.his.com/~reedpix

Tom Reed focuses on image creation analog and digital, location and studio tailored toward advertising, corporate, and editorial use. Specializes in making the familiar strange and the strange familiar, photographing people and technology at the point where they meet.

Travels with Samantha

http://martigny.ai.mit.edu/samantha/travels-with-samantha.html

Depicts writer Philip Greenspun's experiences as he traveled throughout North America. Offers photographs of United States and Canadian landscapes, wildlife cultures, and youthful women.

Treasures of the Louvre

http://www.paris.org/Musees/Louvre/Treasures/

Offers a selection of the art treasures you can see in the real museum in Paris.

Tucson Museum of Art and Historic Block

http://www.primenet.com/art-rom/museumweb/tucartm/tucartm.html

Provides information about the museum and displays images of exhibits and the permanent collection of Roberto Marquez.

Turkish Poetry Page

http://www.cs.umd.edu/~sibel/poetry

Contains a large collection of poems by Turkish poets, both in Turkish and in English, and many articles on the world of poetry in Turkey.

University Art Museum and Pacific Film Archive

http://www.uampfa.berkeley.edu

Contains current exhibitions of film and art from an exciting museum/cinematheque.

University Art Museum: Art Exhibitions

http://www.uampfa.berkeley.edu/exhibits.html

Provides links to the UCB University Art Museum exhibitions. Provides links to artists' work. Doesn't link to other art-related sites.

University of Wyoming Art Museum

http://www.primenet.com/art-rom/museumweb/uwyartm/uwyartm.html

Displays examples from the collections and exhibits of the museum.

Vancouver Arts Index

http://giant.mindlink.net/sloth/arts.html

Provides icon-directed directory to all sorts of arts and events in Vancouver, Canada and allows for feedback.

Vancouver Arts Index

http://giant.mindlink.net/sloth/art/

Serves as directory for the arts in Vancouver, Canada. Includes community, university, and private performances and galleries, as well as a virtual gallery. Contains built-in room for expansion, artists' home pages, upcoming events, and so on.

Vancouver Cyberspace Association

http://www.anima.wis.net//VCA.html

Provides information about the Vancouver Cyberspace Association, an association of arts organizations interested in promoting the visual, performing, and literary arts on the Internet. Offers links to related magazines, events, and so forth.

VCU Arts Home Page

http://128.172.172.6/.SOTASERVER/sota.html

Provides comprehensive information about The School of the Arts at Virginia Commonwealth University (VCU).

A Very Usable Film and Cinema Directory

http://www.movies.net

Contains the best of the best, all the usual, as well as unique features, such as production information and a list of local theatre showtimes called "Now Playing."

VFS Multimedia

http://www.multimedia.edu/

Provides information about the Vancouver Film School's Multimedia Productions department. Contains gallery of digital images. Offers links that integrate other information about the school.

VI&P Animation Art Resources

http://www.earthlink.net/~sworth/

Provides information of interest to collectors of original animation drawings and cels. Includes topics on care and restoration, authentication, appraising, and more.

The Watercolors of Sherry Zuker

http://www.halcyon.com/hzuker/colors/sazpage.htm

Presents Northwest artist Sherry Zuker's bright, bold watercolors and watercolor collages.

The Web Nebulae

http://seds.lpl.arizona.edu/billa/twn/

Introduces a few of the spectacular objects that unfold in the night sky when you have a camera and a telescope.

WebArtWed

http://www.uni.net/aec/waw

Acts as a bulletin board for Italian happenings about art, cultural heritage, research projects, new books, and more.

WebMuseum

http://sunsite.unc.edu/wm/

Exhibits art collections and exhibits primarily from a very famous Paris museum. Provides access to many network points for faster display. Includes downloadable classical music files (.au format). Also provides links to other art-related sites.

WebMuseum

http://mexplaza.udg.mx/wm/

This site is a WebMuseum mirror of Nicolas Pioch, which is now in Mexico.

The WebWeavers

http://www.anima.wis.net//WebWeavers.html

A networked group of artists and computer professionals dedicated to promoting and developing multimedia applications on the Internet. Provides information about and links to the people generating and operating on self-proclaimed "synarchist principles." See also, ANIMA.

Welcome to the aRt_sLab @ UCSD

http://jupiter.ucsd.edu/~webmngr/

Displays examples of student work at UCSD (and maintained by UCSD art students). Provides links to many interesting displays of art.

Welcome to TV Babies

http://val.net/~tvbaby/

Nationally broadcast venue for new experimental and independent film and video. Accepts submissions.

Welcome to VIPER

http://www.viper.ch/viper

Dedicated to the most advanced aesthetic strategies in the audiovisual sphere—a challenge to map the gray area between technological innovation and poetic imagination. Acts both as a public forum for critical discussion and a meeting place for artists, critics, and the public.

The West Australian Virtual Arts Community

http://www.arts.uwa.edu.au/MegsWWW/intro.html

Presents material from various artists and arts companies in West Australia, as well as visual and audio galleries, an arts funding game, pages from the southern hemisphere's premiere cyber-nightclub, a magazine, game reviews—high and low art and culture.

What I Believe by J.G. Ballard

http://www.cnw.com/~miki/index.html

Offers a link-enhanced list of quotations from the work of English science-fiction writer J.G. Ballard.

Whitney Museum Information

http://www.uky.edu/Artsource/whitneyhome.html

Represents the Whitney Museum of American Art in New York, and portrays a listing of exhibitions (dating from 1931 to 1997), as well as of events and performances. Describes all pieces of art in great detail, but doesn't display them. Also features traveling exhibits.

The Will James Art Company

http://www.imt.net/~murphy/mainhomepage01.HTML

Owns all copyrights to Will James art and books, and provides much information about Will James and his work. Reproduces art from the originals and sells a wide variety of high-quality prints. Offers limited edition prints of oils and pencil sketches for sale, as well as the art and books of Will James.

Windshadow

http://www.wimsey.com/~bobg/index.html

Displays images of Canadian Michael Duncan's Windshadow series prints for sale.

Wonders of the World

http://www.eznet.com/wow/ww_intro.html

Wonders of the World is a small shop in an Old Flour Mill located in Spokane, Washington, a purveyor of the ancient and the mysterious, the beautiful and the exotic, the rare and extraterrestrial. Collectors of museum quality art, artifacts, and adornments.

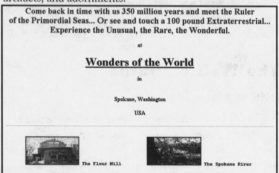

Come back in time with us 350 million years and meet the Ruler of the Primordial Seas... Or see and touch a 100 pound Extraterrestrial... Experience the Unusual, the Rare, the Wonderful.

at

Wonders of the World

in

Spokane, Washington

USA

The Flour Mill   The Spokane River

The WORD—guide to the arts

http://rampages.onramp.net/~voorhees/

Acts as a monthly guide to the arts and literature in Dallas, Texas. Includes listings of events, articles on art-related subjects, book reviews, interviews with artists, and information about the literary and art communities. Accepts unsolicited submissions of articles about art or literature and pays with byline credit and copies. Also accepts submissions of art work for inclusion and for cover art and pays in copies and byline credit.

Yahoo— Entertainment:Dance:Swing Dance

http://www.yahoo.com/Entertainment/Dance/Swing_Dance/

Presents directory page for seven Swing Dance pages, mostly just in the United States. Offers several pages that cover activities in a particular location, but a few pages that offer a full range of other information.

1-800 Roses

http://www.1stresource.com/r/roses/default.htm

Advertises floral arrangements. You can order flowers over the Internet or by calling the toll free number.

1-800-FLOWERS

http://www.800flowers.com/

Advertises the services and products of 1-800-FLOWERS.

2(x)ist Underwear

http://www.digex.net/2xist.html

Provides a virtual catalogue of men's underwear. Includes a closer view of boxers, briefs, tanks, and tees, as well as a size chart and guarantee.

21st Century Web

http://www.hpnet.com/home.htm

Provides companies with an immediate Internet presence via online product information and online advertising services.

3M Innovation Network

http://www.mmm.com

Provides information about 60,000 innovative 3M products for the home, business, and industry.

42 Productions, Inc.

http://refer.com

Presents a sophisticated database of real estate world wide. Features color photographs and advanced search capabilities for commercial/investment properties, vacation resorts, rentals, land, and real estate.

900 Numbers Services

http://www.tc.net/900

Authorized AT&T 900 Number Service Bureau. Offers to establish new 900 number applications or service existing 900 accounts. Provides turn-key 900 number solutions.

AoWEAR

http://www.awear.com/awear/

Clothing Company devoted to creating affordable garments and increasing awareness of individuals of all ages.

à la Gift Basket Headquarters

http://www.gifthq.com/gifthq/

Offers 30 food, wine, and all-occasion gift baskets, nationwide, with secured credit card ordering.

A+ Online Résumés

http://www.hway.com/olresume

Offers a low-cost alternative to posting your résumé on the Internet. Posts your résumé and markets your Web site to ensure that those in the human resources and personnel community make it a regular stop in their Internet travels. Shows prospective employers that you are creative, innovative, and resourceful by placing your information on the Net.

A. D. Bradbury Ltd.: Professional Photographer; Brochure and Lecturing

http://194.72.60.96/www/3b/adb/

Presents A. D. Bradbury: international professional fashion, editorial, advertising, and architectural photograper, brochure, lecturing, and Web page services.

A.S.K. Financial Digest

http://www.cloud9.net/~dkirchen/ask

Helps investors trade stocks, bonds, and mutual funds for intermediate periods of time.

AAA Resume

http://www.infi.net/~resume/

Professional résumé writing service. Includes personal interview, questionnaires, and typesetting. Includes fee information. Lets you upload your résumé to the Internet for a fee.

Aangstrom Precision Corporation

http://www.neosoft.com/users/a/apc/html/homepage.html

Provides the petroleum industry with quality mapping of database solutions. Offers Vortext, a ready-to-use solution for displaying, managing, querying, analyzing, reporting, and mapping geographic information that incorporates user-friendly intuitive functions for the casual user and provides powerful tools for the advanced user.

About Wall Street Research Net

http://www.wsm.com/about.html

Provides information about brokerage firms, third-party research, company documents. Lets you search by company or company string. Lists more than 5,000 companies.

Absolute Media

http://www.maui.net/~absolute/am.htm

Serves as a multimedia content developer. Focuses on CD-ROM titles for Mac and Windows platforms.

Absolutely Fresh Flowers

http://www.cts.com/~flowers/

Online ordering site for fresh flowers.

Accel Partners

http://www.accel.com

Invests in companies of selected technology-driven markets. Provides links for background, strategy, partners, and resources for entrepreneurs.

Access Business Online

http://www.futuris.net/touch/welcome.html

Provides business and professional people with information, communication, and transactions across 20 major maket areas. Offers the capability to navigate to 40,000 locations within three mouse clicks.

ACE Computer Consulting

http://www.azstarnet.com/~jlichty/home.htm

Offers computer consulting with prepurchase decisions, repairs, training on hardware or software, and Internet training.

Adobe Systems Incorporated

http://www.adobe.com/

Includes a permuted index you can use to search Adobe Web page titles; contains hundreds of HTML documents, more than 1,000 PDF files (Portable Document Format used by Adobe Acrobat software), and almost 200 GIFs. Includes links that take you through information about

Adobe, its products, technologies, service, and support, and tips and techniques. Lets you download free Adobe software.

ADS Art Design Services by Chuck Kelley

http://www.spindata.com/ads/

Provides illustration, graphic design, copywriting, and Internet home page development.

Advanced Hair Products

http://www.mja.net/adv_hair

Offers shampoos, conditioners, gels, and sprays. Carries a complete line of hair care products, treatments, and accessories.

Advant Homes

http://www.sccsi.com/Advant/homes.html

Designs custom homes. Presents sample designs and information.

African Sky Video

http://www.active.co.za/~askvideo/

Directory of film production and tourism facilities in South Africa.

PICTORIAL TRAVEL DIRECTORY

After Hours Media Duplication Service

http://www.afterhours.com/

Provides audio CD and CD-ROM mastering, plus replication, audio cassette and video cassette duplication, international video standards conversion, film to video transfer, printed media, packaging, graphics, and distribution services.

After Hours Media Services

http://www.mindspring.com/~afthours/

Provides audio, video, and CD mastering and duplication.

Agents for Buyers Network

http://www.bestagents.com/

Provides information for home buyers. Serves as a network of exclusive buyer agents who become your personal advisors, consultants, and negotiators.

Agora Language Marketplace

http://www.agoralang.com:2410

Provides a place for vendors and consumers of language-related publications, materials, and services to congregate. Offers an online newsletter also available by subscription. Permits people to post their queries directly to the pages that relate to their request, for example, publications, study abroad, language services, business, and so on. Also contains extensive resources for foreign language professionals.

Aircraft Shopper Online Home Page

http://www.sonic.net/aso/

Provides categories related to aircraft-related sales and dealings that include dealers and brokers, maintenance, flying clubs, and flight training.

Allegiance Financial Advisors

http://www.ibp.com/pit/allegiance/

Specializes in asset and money management for individuals and businesses, and in retirement plans and trusts.

Allegro New Media

http://www.allegronm.com/

Publishes interactive business reference and instructional titles. Includes Allegro Home PC Library and the growing "Learn To Do" series of instructional discs.

Allen and Associates, Ltd.

http://www.radix.net/~eallen/

Offers full-service marketing, publication, and graphic design. Specializes in corporate, association, and international development.

Aloha Conferencing

http://sirius.pixi.com/~confrnce/

Provides teleconferencing services to a wide range of companies.

Always in Business— Colorado Area

http://www.always-biz.com/always-biz/

Serves as local business Yellow Pages for Colorado. Includes information on arts, and entertainment, Colorado information, and employment listings.

An Amazing True Story

http://www.roughguys.com/bluegreen

Over the past 20 years, algae has gained tremendous popularity as a nutritious food for health-conscious people. In 1983, the Cell Tech Company began to process and distribute Alpha Sun and Omega Sun, whole and intracellular algae harvested from Oregon's Lake Klamath. Today, Cell Tech is far and away the leading company in the field with an exceptional line of respected, leading-edge products.

The Amber Lady

http://www.xmission.com/~gastown/goldpages/amber1.htm

Features genuine 40 million year old insects in polished honey colored amber, as seen in *Jurassic Park* and featured in *Smithsonian Magazine*. Also offers more traditional amber jewelry.

America's Tall Catalog

http://www.a1.com/shirt/bigtall.html

Offers button-down pinpoint oxfords for tall and big, Web-direct, same day shipping.

American Stock Exchange, the Smarter Place To Be

http://www.amex.com/

Provides all kinds of financially related information, including market information, market news, listed companies, options and derivatives, information exchange section. Claims to be the first stock market on the Web.

American Stock Report

http://www.awod.com/gallery/business/asr/

Newsletter targeted at the busy individual who wants to build equity by purchasing stock in American companies. Provides a review of selected growth stocks rated favorably by established and widely read American financial publications.

American Turbine Pump Company

http://interoz.com/atp/atphome.htm

Vertical turbine and submersible pump manufacturers. Provides engineering catalogs and product literature. Invites feedback from engineers worldwide.

AmericaNet.Com—Coupon Section

http://www.AmericaNet.Com/coupon.html

Serves as host to a growing coupon section. Lets you print the coupons right from your screen.

AmericaNet.Com—Free Classified Advertising

http://www.AmericaNet.Com/classified.html

Provides free national classified advertising, including help wanted, cars, trucks, RVs, commercial real estate, and residential real estate. Lets you submit your ad.

Americans for Tax Reform Home Page

http://beryl.emerald.net/ATR/

Serves as an information source for the conservative grassroots movement for tax reforms. Also acts as a meeting ground for all such movements.

Amnesty International Merchandise Site

http://www.digitalrag.com/mirror/aisale.html

Offers T-shirts, hats, buttons, and stickers to raise funds for Amnesty International's activities.

AMT Multimedia, CD Publishing, Content Development, Video/Audio Production

http://amt.nol.net/amt

Provides cost-effective solutions in Internet marketing, content development, Webtop publishing, CD production, and video/audio production services.

Ancient Galleries

http://innet.com/~ancient/ancient.html

Offers authentic ancient artifacts, including Egyptian, Greek, Roman, Western Asiatic, and Holy Land. Offers Egyptian scenes reproduced on genuine papyrus. Presents a full-color catalog.

The Ancient World

http://www.mindspring.com/~ancient/ancient.html

Manufacturers of archaeological museum reproductions. Displays more than 400 pieces representing classical Greek, Roman, Celtic, and Near Eastern motifs. Also manufactures molds of almost any type of artistic or architectural element to your custom specifications.

Angela Bartz—Image Consultant

http://www.islandnet.com/~cvcprod/bartz.htm

Certified European Image Consultant—provides head-to-toe image makeovers, skin care and cosmetics, wardrobe, fashion and shopping assistance, and business presentations.

Another Victim of Santa Fe Style

http://www.neosoft.com/~victim

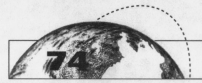

Serves as online curio shop. Offers the art of the late Tommie Macaione, as well as T-shirts, notecards, and posters from some of the Southwest's most singular talents.

Antiquarian Booksellers' Association of America

http://www.abaa-booknet.com

Antiquarian Booksellers' Association of America, national association for rare book and manuscript dealers in the United States. Provides a search service by specialty and location, catalogs and links to other services for over two dozen dealers, current information on book fairs nationwide, links to online public access catalogs at libraries worldwide, and articles of interest to book sellers and book collectors from the *ABAA Newsletter*.

Antiques

http://www.accelerated.com/antiques

Specializes in exquisite mahogany dining sets from the early 1900s.

Antiques World

http://www.webcom.com/~antiques

Features online antiques shops, searchable antiques and collectibles classifieds, new books on antiques, calendar of events, and other resources for collectors and antiquers.

AquaNet

http://www.aquanet.com/aquanet

Serves as an information server for the aquatic world. Includes aquaculture, conservation, education, fisheries, marine science and oceanography, maritime heritage, ocean engineering, and seafood.

Aquarium World Market

http://www.io.com/~kslandry/Aquarium_World_Market.html

Provides the Saltwater and Freshwater mail-order companies and current availability and price lists.

Arabian Connection

http://www.spidergraphics.com/arabian/arald.html

Promotes your farm and horses through Web postings and CD-ROM production, matches stallions at stud with brood mares, sells Arabian horses, and trains horses.

Art of the States

http://www.pol.com/states/

Offers limited edition prints and collector series Christmas ornaments. Features a collection of native birds and wildflowers along with the capital building of its respective state. (All paintings by W.D. Gaither MSB.)

Artisoft, Inc.

http://www.artisoft.com

Serves as a peer-to-peer network for small and growing businesses.

The Artropolis Oasis

http://www.interpage.com/artropolis

Serves as a site for anyone interested in going beyond boring Web graphics. Includes an automatic subscription (for those who register) to the Oasis' electronic newsletter. Also includes downloadable files (backgrounds, graphics, sounds, and interactives).

Artzilla Surf Constructions

http://www.earthlink.net/~Artzilla

A group of designers and illustrators who left the corporations to provide the Web with high-quality graphics.

Asian American Media Mall

http://www.stw.com/amm/amm.htm

Offers more than just media. Meant to further the Asian American presence on the Web. Offers the Asian American Yellow Pages, which contributes to that agenda. Also offers "strictly for entertainment" sites.

Ask Us For...

http://www.webcom.com/~wrsl/askusfor.html

Offers monthly newsletter by e-mail about the international business sector in Bermuda. Also contains reports on other related issues.

AT&T Home Page

http://www.att.com/

Includes information about AT&T technology, news, employment opportunities, and long distance.

Atlas Pen and Pencil Corporation

http://pwr.com/ATLAS/

Presents highlights of 82-page business-to-business catalog: gifts, promotional incentives, awards, and advertising specialties. Sponsors *Creative Times*, an Internet newsletter.

Australian Sharemarket Page

http://www.wp.com/paritech

Covers information and sales on technical analysis and portfolio management software, data vendors, broker contacts, and investment association contacts.

Austrian Worldport®— Database of Commerce

http://www.worldport.co.at/worldport/

Serves as database of commerce, major business sites in Austria, international trade, technology, industry, manufactory, services, tourism, culture, and entertainment.

Auto Buyers Information Guide and Consumer Information

http://www.earth.net/output/abig/index.html

Offers to negotiate your purchase or lease for you or give you enough information that you will never feel intimidated in a car dealership again. Also includes a database of current used cars by area code.

Auto Club: Emergency Roadside Assistance Service

http://www.barint.on.ca/cybermal/autoclub.html

Aims to provide the fastest possible service to members.

AUTO-NET, Your Online Used Car Connection

http://www.webcom.com/~witnet/biz/autonet

Provides listings of cars for sale from all around the United States. Also lets you list your car or cars for sale.

Autobank Autosearch

http://cygnus.igs.net/autobank

Provides automobiles, interactive advertising application, and accepts online query submissions. Covers the majority of United States, and Canada too, especially Toronto.

Automated Business Services

http://www.shore.net/~adfx/1061.html

Offers products and services to reach untapped markets and increase sales.

Automated Graphic Systems

http://www.ags.com

Specializes in commercial printing, desktop publishing, book binding, CD-ROM replication, online publishing, and more. Houses the AutoGraph desktop publishing newsletter and features special offers on free subscriptions and specially priced CD-ROM recordable media.

Autonetwork—Makes versus Models

http://www.autonetwork.com

Lets you advertise cars at $30 per vehicle. Contains more than 400 entries for cars to be bought. Presents sequential selection options by make, year, color, and transmission type. Contains dealer or owner contact address or number.

AutoPages of Internet

http://www.clark.net/pub/networx/autopage/autopage.html

Features full color photographs and detailed descriptions of automobiles and motorcycles for sale across the United States. Also includes information about manufacturers, restorers, trade shows, and auctions.

AutoSimulations: Simulation and Scheduling Software and Services

http://www.autosim.com

Provides 3-D simulation and scheduling software products and consulting services to help solve manufacturing and material handling problems.

AzTech Interactive

http://www.bga.com/aztech

Multimedia CD-ROM and online production company based in Austin, TX.

B.A.A.S. Boating Advertising, Advice, and Service

http://www.dataplace.nl/baas

Specializes in advertising for the marine market: represents yachting magazines, b-to-b and consumer magazines, and Webvertising.

Baby Joy Toys

http://www.pacific.net/~joy/bjt/

Provides children's toys and clothing. Makes clothes and toys.

Baby Net Wear

http://www.hpnet.com/showoff/showoff.htm

Sells baby (infant and toddler) clothing, blankets, and sweaters.

Balancing Tradition and Technology

http://www.webcom.com/~isys

Graphic and digital design company. Works with you to design and implement progams that effectively reflect your mission, products, and services.

Bearbmu's Custom Written Stories

http://web.sunbelt.net/~bearbmu/bearbmu.htm

Offers to write personalized stories for the reader.

BellSouth Mobile Data

http://www.bls.com/bmd

Operates Mobitex wireless data networks worldwide.

The Benchmarking Exchange

http://www.benchnet.com

Dedicates their efforts to benchmarking, reengineering, process improvement, and quality improvement.

Bio-Genesis, Inc.

http://www.bio-genesis.com/browse/craig/index.html

Offers bacillus laterosporus (BOD), a versatile, naturally occurring bacteria that is the active ingredient in several new life-improving products.

BioWorld Home Page

http://www.megalinx.net/bioworld

Supplies molecular biologists with name brand products for DNA, RNA, peptide, and antibody research. Procures and consolidates biotechnology for international shipment purchases.

BizCafe Mall

http://www.bizcafe.com

Serves as a WWW mall. Includes categories such as travel, books, getting ahead, printing, office, home, consulting, business, financial, legal, sports, fitness, gifts, manufacturing, and autos.

Blacklist of Internet Advertisers

http://math-www.uni-paderborn.de/~axel/BL/blacklist.html

One of several blacklists of Internet advertisers. Provides more information on the issue and advice on what to do to avoid getting blacklisted when you advertise on the Internet.

Blue Mountain Graphic Design Home Page

http://www.moscow.com/~bmdesign/bm/bmdesignhome2.html

Contains a neat portfolio of Blue Mountain's work, as well as information on Internet graphics. Provides samples and price lists for companies interested in having Web design work done.

BMW Automobile Information

http://cbsgi1.bu.edu/bmw/bmw.html

Provides information about BMW gathered from different sources. Provides information about BMW clubs, parts suppliers, and a database of frequently asked questions.

Body Doubles—Fine Bathing and Skin Care Products

http://www.primenet.com/~doubles

Offers a line of fine bathing and skin care delicacies created to inspire beautiful healthy skin.

Bonnell Environmental Consulting

http://infoweb.magi.com/~tauceti

Assesses chemical contamination in the environment. Involves ecotoxicology, risk assessment, guideline development, and bioassessment.

Bonté Naturel®— Environmental Clothes for Kids

http://www.catalog.com/corner/bonte

Offers children's casualwear made with environmentally friendly fabrics. For every garment sold, the company purchases 25 square feet of rainforest land to protect it forever against destruction. Gives you deed to property if you send hangtag.

BookLink Discount ESL Books

http://www.intac.com/~booklink

Specializes in distributing ESL and multicultural books. Also sells any British book in print.

Books on Chaos, Neural Networks, Artificial Intelligence, AI, Finance, Stocks, Investing, Derivatives, Consult

http://weber.ucsd.edu/~rtrippi/rtbooks.htm

Provides books relating to applying advanced chaos theory to determine where to invest.

Britain Mall

http://www.Internet-eireann.ie/Euromall/england/england.html

The place to go if you are looking for a British company, product, or service, or just want to relax.

British American Chamber of Commerce Home Page

http://bacc.conpro.org/

Serves as gateway to business development opportunities and trade intelligence in the United States and the United Kingdom.

British-American Chamber of Commerce

Welcome to The British-American Chamber of Commerce - your gateway to business development opportunities and trade intelligence in the United States and the United Kingdom

The Chamber is dedicated to assisting corporations in increasing their business in the largest economic partnership in the world, $190 billion in two-way investment and $48 billion each year in two-way trade.

The Chamber Web Site provides information on our programs and services including publications, events, and information data bases. The UK/US Marketplace lists member products and services. Our Web Site will also direct you to UK and US government Web Sites useful to transatlantic businesses.

BTG Home Page

http://www.btg.com/

Provides solutions for information technology needs from systems integration to software development. Provides access to the products and services of BTG, including the BTGAXP275 RISC computer, "the world's fastest PC." Also features employment opportunities with BTG, links to the BTG Pentagon Computer Superstore, and BTG news releases, among others.

Builders Graphics

http://www.primenet.com/~mrclark/builders.html

Designs dream homes from your sketches. Offers downloadable GIF files from a home project by Builders Graphics.

Bulldog Beach Interactive

http://www.halcyon.com/duwamish/bulldogbeach/welcome.html

Offers writing and expert technical knowledge to help you get an international audience for your WWW page. Also offers their traditional graphic design and paper publishing services, as well as PhotoFloppy and a line of T-shirts and activewear.

Buning the Florist

http://www.paradise.net/flowers

Serves the needs of the flower buying public as one of the largest retail florists in the United States.

Business and Safety Cartoons by Goff

http://www.fileshop.com/personal/tgoff/

Presents four cartoons by professional cartoonist Ted Goff. Geared to people who are responsible for an in-house newsletter, training manual, presentation, brochure, or other publication. Available cartoons have safety, teamwork, quality, management, sales, technology, and computer themes.

Business Directions Home Page

http://www.business.com.au/business/

Ideas exchange site. Contains very good details about how to do business. One very nice feature is a triple indexing system—you can search and locate information by section, subject, and topic.

Business Expo

http://www.bizexpo.com

Exposes Orange County, CA's commercial sites on the Web.

Business Information Resources

http://sashimi.wwa.com/~notime/eotw/business-info.html

Includes magazines and journals, government and law, financial, business services and opportunities, and regional and entrepreneurial organizations and resources.

Business Mart

http://www.mbnet.mb.ca/~cancon/bmart.html

Provides classified listings for Canadian businesses for sale and businesses wanted.

A Business Researcher's Interests

http://www.pitt.edu/~malhotra/interest.html

Provides more than 1,000 sites relevant to contemporary organizational issues related to information processes and information systems, such as electronic commerce, organizational learning, emergent organizations, reengineering, and WWW strategy.

Business-to-Business Exchange Home Page

http://www.btob.wfu.edu/b2b.html

Contains access information about business-related events, research, publications, and job listings.

Byte Elaborazioni srl— Software and Hardware in Arezzo, Italy

http://www.ats.it/byte/index.html

Lets you order online and receive product(s) in two days.

Cadillac Motor Car Home Page

http://www.cadillac.com/

Provides Cadillac-related information. Contains many different categories, including performance information and product-related information. Offers mail order options for some.

California Crafts Marketplace

http://www.catalog.com/giftshop/index.htm

Serves as a guide to crafts and gifts.

Camalgori: A Representative Collection of Fashion Made in Italy

http://www.nettuno.it/btw/cmlgr

Offers the Camalgori collection.

Canada Net Pages

http://www.visions.com

Serves as a resource of Canadian products, services, stock quotes, and mutual fund profiles. Provides full Internet consulting, marketing, HTML, and site development.

Canadian Job Source

http://www.irus.rri.uwo.ca/~jlaw/job_stuf.html

Provides a free, job-seeker maintained database of all Canadian recruiters and human resources deptartments.

Capulin Coffee

http://emall.com/ashcreek/

Offers a special extra-caffeinated coffee grown on Mexico's Pacific Coast. Proceeds from the sale of Capulin benefits a conservation project, which grows and harvests these beans.

CAR-LINK

http://www.bdt.com/car-link/

Lets you view a car for sale. Lets you submit an ad, including a color picture of the car for $5. Offers listings by the month.

Career Action Center

http://www.gatenet.com/cac/

Helps you manage your work life in today's rapidly changing environment. Includes weekly updates on programs, events, and career management issues and provides links to other career management resources.

Career Center

http://www.netline.com/career/

Provides a database about job opportunities in different categories. Offers links to other job opportunities-related sites.

Career Networking and Recruiting

http://www.Internet-is.com/skillsearch/index.html

Links experienced professionals with organizations that need their talents. Lets you explore new career opportunities discreetly. Lets employers locate and prescreen qualified, highly skilled, employed prospects who meet unique requirements, in a cost-effective manner.

Carshow and Event Listing Page

http://www.tiac.net/users/cody/carshow/welcome.html

Provides information about car shows and auctions. Includes a wide range of cars from classic to modern. Lists events and includes contact name, phone, time, date, fees, directions, and a short description for each event.

Carsoft Company, Inc.

http://transport.com/~rose/carsoft

Sells complete race results for all Winston Cup races since in 1973. Provides complete statistics on most subjects.

Cartoon Heaven

http://symphony.ucc.ie/~niall/cheaven.html

Presents an animation art gallery in Melbourne, Australia.

The Castle Attic

http://emporium.turnpike.net/~castle.home/index.html

Offers a selection of swords, daggers, and armor for medieval and renaissance fans, SCA members, or anyone who just likes a good blade.

Catalog Central

http://www.infi.net/commerce.html

Provides links to various mail-order catalogs, such as *careerWEB* and *JewelryNET*, and many others.

Catalogue Production Management Services

http://www.webcom.com/~thames/cpms/welcome.html

Helps United States direct mail companies into Europe, providing sources for the most competitive print and paper prices.

CD-ROM Shop

http://www.cdromshop.com/cdr/

Offers more than 1,500 different titles. Ships anywhere on the planet and offers next day shipping. Catalog organized alphabetically and provides a keyword search engine so you can search the entire database. Provides product information and reviews for more than 500 titles.

Celebration Vineyards

http://www.deltanet.com/intersphere/cv

Offers custom-labeled personalized mini champagne and wine table favors for weddings and other special occasions.

Century 21 Action Realty Service—Andy Leong

http://www.aimnet.com/~ayl/bidnez.htm

Specializes in residential and commercial real estate in the greater San Francisco, California Bay Area.

CEO Access: Across the Street and Around the World

http://www.ceo-access.com/index.html

Provides resources for businesses to grow. Offers advertising and marketing service for a fee. Includes links to newspaper, journalism, and electronic-related sites.

Chancellor and Chancellor, Inc.

http://www.chancellor.com

Serves as a brokerage firm for computer technology professionals. Specializes in services for contractors. Contains useful information for contractors and links to related sites.

Chastain Research Group, Inc.

http://www.best.com/~chastain

Serves as a consulting firm dedicated to meeting the requirements of biotechnology/pharmaceutical companies and professionals.

Chemical Biological Information Analysis Center (CBIAC)

http://www.dtic.dla.mil:80/iac/cbiac/CBIACHP.HTML

Provides chemical and biological information in the defense area, specifically concerning fate and effects,

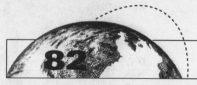

demilitarization, treaty verification, medical effects, toxicology, NBC survivability, technology transfer, decontamination, individual and collective protection, warfare, weapons, and combat effectiveness.

Chicago Mercantile Exchange Home Page

http://www.cme.com/

Contains financial-related information. Offers updates of currency futures and options and a special section on currencies. Also offers exchange-traded futures and options.

Christian Book Connection

http://www.xmission.com/~seer/Christian-Book/index.html

Online Christian bookstore. Features a catalog of nearly 30,000 items including books, Bibles, Bible software, CDs, and cassettes. Also presents the monthly Christian best-sellers lists of books and music.

The Christmas Shop

http://www.ChristmasNet.com

Offers gifts for children year 'round. Specializes in Steinbach Nutcrackers, Department 56, and ornaments of all types, sizes, and shapes. Lets you visit Santa in Long Grove, Illinois.

Citizens for an Alternative Tax System Home Page

http://www.intac.com/~gbaren/cats.html

Houses the national public interest group for an alternative tax system and tax reform. Talks mainly about the group's manifesto and related information.

Classic Car and Auto Database

http://www.primenet.com/~dadalus/classic.html

Contains everything anyone would want to know about classic cars. Includes categories like spare parts, insurance, accessories, restoration services, sales details, and market trends. Also offers a list of upcoming classic car shows and events.

Cleo Ireland Limited— Clothes from Ireland's Past

http://www.adnet.ie/Adnet/topics/cleo.htm

Specializes in clothes made from natural fabrics, wool and linen, of Irish origin. Offers many designs drawn from Ireland's past.

Clip Media in Finance

http://www.cob.ohio-state.edu/dept/fin/clips.htm

Contains pictures and video clips of finance topics. Offers a section on historical pictures related to finance. Also presents quotes and comments from leading financial experts and scholars.

Cobweb

http://www.netresource.com/cobweb/intro.html

Serves small business and retailers. Offers catalog of products offered by small business enterprises. Encourages such companies to contact.

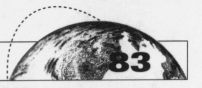
Cockrell Antiques

http://mars.ftech.net/~cockrell/

Deals mainly in furniture, books, and collectables. Contains pictures, prices, and ordering information.

The Codex

http://www.interaccess.com/trc/tsa.html

Specializes in espionage, secret agents, law enforcement, investigators, detectives, electronic surveillance, electronic countermeasures, CCTV, video, counter-surveillance, TSCM, telephone security, encryption, transmitters, receivers, scanners, and *The Codex Newsletter*. Also includes links to interesting security, investigative, and related sites around the world.

Coherent Communications Systems Corporation

http://www.coherent.com

Offers coherent designs and manufactures and markets speech enhancement products for the telecommunications industry, including digital echo cancellers for T1 and E1 terrestrial, satellite and cellular networks, speech enhancement products for digital and analog cellular networks, and full-duplex audio conference systems for conference room and desktop applications.

Color Glo International

http://www.lowry.com/color_glo/

Provides mobile services to aircraft and auto upholstery shops, used car dealerships, and the general public. Also distributes and/or installs after-market door panel, dashpad skins for classic to late model Cadillac, Lincoln, muscle cars, and others.

Comics at Bendigo Books

http://www.prodata.com.au/~benbooks

Comic subscription service. Lets you subscribe to comics direct from the Web.

COMLINE Business Data, Inc.: English News on the Japanese Economy

http://www.twics.com/~COMLINE/home.html

Contains information on accessing a database on Japanese economic reports. Provides services at a price. Also contains links to other Japan related ftp sites. Provides information on other Asian economies too. Updates headlines weekly.

The CommonWealth Opportunity

http://www.castles.com/CWealth

Wants to help you achieve your goals, both personal and financial.

Computer Innovations Home Page

http://www.StarPower.Com

Provides software development tools, including C Compilers, C++ Compliers, text editors, debuggers, and IDEs for Unix programmers. Offers demo downloads. Includes support for sparc, solaris, SCO, UnixWare, QNX, venix, and other operating systems.

The Computerized Networker

http://www.mlmbbs.com

Serves as a common meeting ground for MLMers/entreprenuers around the world. Includes training articles, special reports, and mailing lists.

Confluent, Inc.

http://www.confluent.com

Creates Visual Thought, the multipurpose Unix diagramming and flowcharting tool that has won stellar reviews from journals such as *SunExpert* and *Advanced Systems*: it

creates software design diagrams (Booch, Rumbaugh, Fusion, and others), flowcharts (for ISO 9000, TQM, BPR), plus dataflow, network, organizational, and circuit/logic diagrams for presentation and documentation graphics.

Consumer Fraud Alert Network

http://www.world-wide.com/homebiz/fraud.htm

Provides the latest scams that crooks are using to rob you of your money.

The Consumer Law Page— Introduction

http://tsw.ingress.com/tsw/talf/txt/intro.html

Identifies dangers related to product liability and consumer protection. Offers articles of interest to consumers, contains brochures that feature useful information, and contains useful links to related resources.

Consumer Marketing Guide

http://metro.turnpike.net/metro/tuvok/guide.html

Provides information about marketing management concepts, mostly gathered from class lectures.

Continental Investigative Services

http://www.mja.net/pub/continen/

Private investigative firm. Claims they can find anyone, anywhere.

Copyright Clearance Center Online

http://www.openmarket.com/copyright/

Provides copyright licensing, clearance, and usage services. Contains catalogs for searching for material.

The Copyright Website

http://www.benedict.com/

Provides copyright information for the general public and interested parties. Includes categories of fundamentals on copyrights and issues related to copyright over the Net. Also contains a section for relevant sources and links.

Corporate Agents and Lawyers

http://www.xmission.com/~seer/uslawyer/corp.html

Provides listing for discounted company incorporation services for as low as $25.00 plus state filing fees.

Corporate Agents, Inc. Home Page

http://www.corporate.com/

Contains details of how to form your own corporation in any state.

Cortex Marketing Resources

http://www.netweb.com/cortex/content/mktg/

Compiles marketing resources. Concentrates on listing agencies, suppliers, publications, and so on that are not presently on the Internet.

CraftBase

http://www.cerf.net/vistek

Acts as a source of craft kits, patterns, and information, including one craft catalog for any age and one with fun and learning activities for kids ages five and up. The Kangaroo Korner includes craft tips, links to other craft-related sites, and craft news. Lets you view photos of completed kits or patterns and order them using an 800 phone number.

The Credit Union Home Page

http://www.cu.org/

Serves as a gathering place for credit unions on the Internet, featuring information on credit unions ranging from joining a credit union to running one.

Criminal Enforcement Bulletin

http://www.haledorr.com/criminal_news.html

Provides information for owners and/or managers considering internal investigation into possible criminal activities by employees.

CTX Mortgage Company

http://www.ctxmort.com

Offers a Homebuyer's Quiz, information on the details of purchasing your home, an explanation of mortgage terms and the loan process, and many other sources of information.

CultNet Finland

http://www.cultnet.fi/

Presents home pages of Finnish companies, publishing houses, and bookstores.

Cyber Business Journal Trade Shows List

http://rt66.com/coach/cbj/tradesho.html

Lists business, communications, and information handling trade shows from around the world. Includes all known links for the sites it lists. Listed trade shows deal with business communications, from marketing and in-house computer networking to video-teleconferencing and virtual work groups.

Cyber Grape and Grain

http://www.ari.net/webworks/finewine

Houses The Wine Specialist, an international mail-order and retail Washington D.C. supplier of fine wines, malt whiskeys, and other premium liquors. Contains the monthly newsletter, wine and malt liquor related links, and special offers. Lets you order premium liquors directly from the site.

Cyber Planet Korea

http://www.cpk.co.kr/

Contains a business center, an advertising firm, a bank, a Korean elementary school, a Cyber kid's place, entertainment, and more.

CyberFund

http://www.cyberfund.com

The CyberFund® Investment Account is a managed investment advisory service of Hammer Capital Management, Inc. that is designed to participate in the growth of the computer, telecommunications, and advancing technology industries through individually managed portfolios of U.S. and international equities.

Cyberian Outpost

http://www.cybout.com/

Serves as a virtual computer store. Offers software, accessories, and peripherals at unbeatable prices with overnight delivery. Features a Product of the Day, detailed information on the hundreds of featured products—including reviews, screen shots, and product demos (as available).

CyberPress Communications

http://www.nocdc.bc.ca/cpc/

Offers graphic services for a wide variety of promotional and communications needs on the World Wide Web.

CyberSales

http://cybersales.com/catalog/

Serves as an Internet Mall and includes the following merchants and products: MBNA, 1996 Olympic Games VISA Card, Antiquarian Fossils, Fossil Skull Replicas, Quick Draw Systems, Universal Clip System, San Diego Sheet Metal Works, Laser Crafted World Map, Kangaguru, Driza Bone Coat, Gamble Trading Co., Russian Porcelain, Designs for a Living, and Computer Blanket.

CyberSight

http://cybersight.com/cgi-bin/cs/s?main.gmml

Provides opportunity for interactive promotions by companies. Marketplace for different products and services. Offers a knowledge/information section, as well as good links to creative sites.

Cybertown

http://www.cybertown.com/cybertown

Presents off-world 21st century town with spectacular graphics that load quickly. Offers many areas to explore, including the mysterious Cyberhood.

Cybertoys

http://pages.prodigy.com/CA/rep/cybertoys.html

Presents the latest and most fun products available for ages 8 to 80.

D.J. Inkers

http://www.fiber.net/sensible/djinkers

Contains warm and whimsical things, including clip art software, rubber art stamps, cut and copy books, gift boxes, and stamp videos.

Dakota Engraving, Etc.

http://www.getnet.com/engrave/

Offers custom engraved Internet key tags.

Dallas/Fort Worth Business Yellow Pages

http://www.onramp.net/~mexis/shopdfw.html

Serves as a business directory for the Dallas/Fort Worth/ North Texas area. Offers free listings, as well as http links to other sites and home page design and storage.

DealerNet—The Source for New Car Information

http://www.dealernet.com/

Acts as a source for new car information. Offers links to directly connect you to actual car dealers on the Internet. Also provides information on new and used cars using a searchable interface.

Debt Calculator

http://uclc.com/uclc/debt.html

Lets you give details about outstanding debts—including car loans, mortgage loans, and credit card balances—then

provides calculations and tells you how much you can lower your monthly debt payments.

Defense Technical Information Web

http://www.dtic.dla.mil/dtiw/

Provides information about and related to the United States Department of Defense. Contains information on military products and features.

DeLoayza Associates

http://www.dnai.com/~daprod

Produces CD-ROMs, interactive kiosks, and Web sites.

Dialogic Corporation

http://www.dialogic.com

Supplies components for open systems signal computing.

Dick Williams and Associates

http://www.netrep.com/home/dwa

Specializes in high technology industry recruiting. Looks for company clients and individual candidates for executive/manager positions in sales and marketing, key account, product, design engineers, field and customer service, technical, process and application engineers: photolithography, etch, cvd, pvd, diffusion, implant, wafer, mask, and disk cleaning.

Digital Access Specialists— Leased Lines and Switched Digital Service

http://www.intense.com/digital-access

Provides free service to organizations in the geographic area served by Bell Atlantic.

Digital Café™

http://www.skypoint.com/members/digitalc/

Develops CD-ROMs, screen savers, and Web pages. Lets you explore products and services in entertainment, education, and corporate arenas, as well as download demos.

Digital Technics, Inc.

http://www.access.digex.net/~dti/index.html

Offers Esopus 2000®, a generic switching platform used in a variety of applications, ranging from small office PBX to central office, interactive voice response (IVR), satellite audio-link, and PCS switch.

Digital Techniques, Inc.

http://execpc.com/~digitalt

Provides employment for contract engineers and consultants. Targets the high-tech areas of image and signal processing as well as embedded systems. Also employs various categories of EE, CS, and ME under contract and performs off-site outsourcing projects.

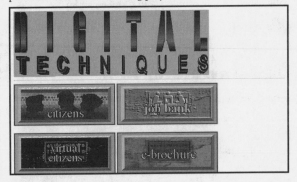

Discover Success with Gary L. Viterise, PhD

http://www.infoanalytic.com/viterise/

Offers a wide collection of presentations that cover motivation, self-esteem, and leadership. Includes programs for stress management, psychology of selling, positive morale development, and leadership models. Also offers audio tapes.

Discreet Boutique

http://www.mbnet.mb.ca:80/flatland/mall/discreet/

Offers a new way to shop for lingerie—online.

Diskovery Educational Systems

http://www.diskovery.com/Diskovery/

Furnishes an electronic pricing guide for a list of categories like computer software, hardware, CD-ROMs, videos, and laserdiscs. Also offers order placing information. Lets you request a printed catalog. Categorizes listings by title, category, and publisher.

Distant Caravans

http://www.greatbasin.com/~caravan/

Serves people interested in the Middle Ages, renaissance, belly dance, drums, ethnic jewelry, amber, and more.

DJO Jewelers, Inc.

http://www.digimark.net/DJO/

Advertises the jewelry products of DJO Jewelers, Inc. of Gaithersburg, Maryland. Also provides information on diamond grades, custom designs, and birthstones.

DOE Energy Efficiency and Renewable Energy Network

http://www.eren.doe.gov/

Provides information about renewable energy and energy-efficient technologies. Contains a resource database. Offers information and assistance to a broad range of users on energy-related issues.

dotSpiegel

http://www.spiegel.com/spiegel/

Spiegel's new online catalog and magazine, including features, merchandise, stories, tips, and contests.

Dowvision

http://dowvision.wais.net/

Lets you access only between 6PM–8AM ET. Offers full text of WSI, Dow Jones Services, *The New York Times*, and newswires. Provides search capability by sources and subjects. Also lets you browse by category.

DPP International Recruitment UK/Europe

http://www.pncl.co.uk/dpp/dpp.html

Serves as UK recruitment agency. Updates contact and permanent positions daily.

DRaG-Net—Internet Trading

http://www.davrich.co.uk

Provides Internet services, trading, and shopping to United Kingdom businesses.

DXI Corporation

http://isotropic.com/dxicorp/dxihome.html

Provides contract services to the information processing industry, updated weekly. Lists positions for contractors in Atlanta and other southeast locations.

Dyewitness

http://nol.net/DYEWITNESS

Advertises Dyewitness, a criminal identifier that leaves a dark green stain on your attacker for up to seven days.

The Econsult Group of Companies

http://www.egroup.com/home.html

Specializes in information technology, economic consulting, market research, executive mentoring, and property development management. Provides offices in Australia, Malaysia, Papua New Guinea, Singapore, and Thailand.

EDNET—Employment Opportunities for Educators

http://pages.prodigy.com/CA/luca52a/bagley.html

Contains online bulletin board where educators can look for jobs in public and private schools.

Electronic Countermeasures, Inc.

http://www.t8000.com/eci/eci.htm

Provides equipment and services to law enforcement, the cellular industry, corporations, legal firms, and the oil and brokerage industries.

Electronic Product Catalog Systems

http://www.intbc.com/ibc2/csad.html

Produces custom business electronic media for sales automation and market expansion and develops modern marketing tools for businesses. Offers an electronic product demonstrator catalog.

Electronic Realty Services

http://www.tyrell.net/~ers

Provides listings of apartments, houses, realtors, and commercial properties across the United States. Features custom layouts and color photographs. Offers free and paid listings.

Electronic Yellow Pages

http://www.webwave.com/yellow.html

Lists with many national and Idaho businesses.

Elegance Network

http://www.elegancenet.com/elegance

Includes aircrafts, antiques, arts, attorney, business opportunity, clubs, dating, employment, escort, executive gifts, exotic animals, florida, food, hardware, hotels, investment, jewelry, marine, medical, miscellaneous, models, money to lend, personals, real estate, Russia, sex, singles, software, travel, vehicles, wines, and Web pages.

Empire Entertainment Promotions

http://fly.hiwaay.net/~prm/empire.html

Provides promotional and booking services for up-and-coming bands or individuals. Offers a variety of services. Also offers Web page development and other computer services.

Employment Edge

http://sensemedia.net/sprawl/employment.edge

Includes job categories of accounting, auditing, engineering, legal, management, programmer, and more. Charges no fee for candidates.

Employment News

http://www.ftn.net/emplnews/

Online version of Canadian employment magazine. Indexes by categories like careers, office, general help, hotel/restaurants, sales/marketing, and skilled/technical. Includes career training and résumés. Includes business franchises for sale and opportunities for self-employment. Also contains online information about trends and employment statistics for Ontario and Canada.

Employment Opportunities and Job Resources on the Internet

http://www.wpi.edu/~mfriley/jobguide.html

Serves as a guide to employment opportunities and job resources on the Internet, emphasizing free resources. Provides job listings for all around the country and world. Lets you search by a specific state, or specify a field or area.

Enrico Ferorelli Enterprises

http://branch.com:1080/enrico/enrico.html

Serves as the photographer for corporate annual reports, special advertising, and even portraits. Enrico Ferorelli is multilingual and ready to help.

The Entrepreneur Network

http://bizserve.com/ten/

Focuses on helping midwestern inventors and entrepreneurs with information and connections. Provides information on business opportunities, new products wanted, private and public sector resources, and details about membership organizations.

Environmental Engineering

http://www.texel.com/home/globeinf/sponsors/env.engr/

Assists companies in environmental cleanup. Also performs research in the broad band radiation arena, doing measurements and analysis.

Environmental Support Solutions, Inc.—HVAC MALL

http://www.hvacmall.com/hvacmall.htm

Provides custom full service WWW listings and links for companies in the heating, ventilating, air conditioning, and refrigeration industry. Specializes in ozone depletion issues, refrigerant regulations, and indoor air quality.

ErgonITe Ltd.—Web Page Design, Authoring and Markup; Scanning/ Retouching

http://194.72.60.96/www/3b/

Provides international Web page design, authoring and markup, scanning and retouching services, ergonomics, human factors, and IT services.

Erre Esse Gifts

http://www.erresse.com/erresse/index.html

Advertises fine silverware, sterling silver, and Ventiuan crystal. Contains prices and images of various pieces, along with ordering information.

Essex Wood Products

http://www.snswwide.com/essex.html

A wood fabrication shop. Combines computerized routing equipment with skilled hand-finishing to provide quality woodworking.

Eureka! The Web Junction

http://www.wilder.com/eureka.html

Offers shops that contain T-shirts, candy, software, and solar powered panels.

Euromall

http://www.Internet-eireann.ie/Euromall/

The European shopping and business mall with national malls for individual countries in your local language. Offers a broad range of products, services, local information, and entertainment.

European Market Entry

http://www.sme.com/lukas.consulting

Specializes in European strategy, marketing, and sales, to help non-Europeans enter the European market successfully. Provides expertise in computer and communications systems, products, services and contents. Emphasizes multimedia. Reaches from Scandinavia to Sicily, from Portugal to the Urals.

Evolving Technologies Corporation

http://www.evolvingtech.com/

Specializes in clinical trials data analysis. Produces CANDAs (Computer Assisted New Drug Applications) integrating data, text, and images for sponsors of new drugs and medical devices/products.

Exotic Hawaiian Flowers, Plants, and Gourmet Gift Baskets

http://www.interpac.net/WebClients/alika/

Advertises the services of a company that delivers exotic flowers and gifts. Presents images of the various types of flowers available.

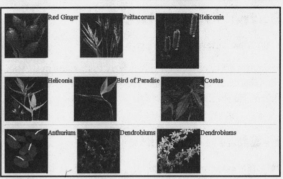

Experimental Stock Market Data

http://www.ai.mit.edu/stocks.html

Provides recent stock market information, including current prices and the previous day's closing prices, one-year graphics of stock movements, and ticker symbols. Also contains links related to finance. Lists categories such as stock and mutual funds, top stocks, and the latest stock quotes.

EXPOguide Home Page

http://www.expoguide.com/

Offers details about trade shows, conferences, exhibitions, and links to related associations and resources.

Exquisite Homes and Properties™

http://www.exquisite.com/index.html

Provides a real estate listing service for residential and commercial real estate. Features exquisite homes as well as exquisite commercial and investment real estate opportunities. Home to Web sites maintained by real estate brokers and salespeople for the display of residential and commercial real estate listings in their geographic area.

Extra Trade, Inc.

http://www.interport.net/~extra

Lists inventory offered for sale mostly to markets in Russia, the CIS, and Eastern Europe. Also ships many goods to Brazil and the Caribbean.

F-Sharp—Music

http://www.mja.net/f-sharp/

Sells karaoke tapes, CDs, and equipment.

Fabrics Online

http://www.fabrics.com/

Sells fabrics and serves as a meeting place for textile and fashion industry professionals.

Falcon Software, Inc.

http://www.falconSoftware.com/falconweb/index.html

Educational software publisher. Specializes in chemistry, electronics, engineering, environmental science, and foreign languages.

Fanco International Corporation

http://www.webcom.com/~stannet/fanco/fanco.html

Imports PVC laundry, storage, and shopping bags. Also imports slippers, luggage carts, and more. Distributes within the greater New York area and wants to expand throughout the United States. Ships same or next day.

FDA Center for Food Safety and Applied Nutrition

http://vm.cfsan.fda.gov

Contains FDA regulations regarding food and nutrition issues like product safety and harmful substances. Also has information about imports and exports of food and cosmetics, and good manufacturing practices in the food industry. Also has a number of links to other related sites.

Feathered Friends

http://www.halcyon.com/featherd/welcome.htm

Produces down sleeping bags and garments in Seattle, Washington.

FEDEX Home Page

http://www.fedex.com/

Features free package tracking with the identification number. Can track packages that are in transit too. Also contains features related to available services, downloadable software.

FFP Securities—Thomas E. Murray

http://awebs.com/33487/ThomasEMurray

Provides services in the following areas: estate planning, trust planing and preparation, pensions, mutual funds (highest ranking by Morningstar and Lipper analytical), annuity products, and fixed income products.

Fin-Atlantic Securities, Inc.

http://www.gate.net/~stocks

Stock brokerage firm. Offers stocks, bonds, options, mutual funds, and new issues. Offers Internet users one free no commission on first trade.

Financial Resource Guide

http://www.libertynet.org/~beausang/

Serves as a financial resource guide to sites dealing with stocks, charts, currencies, exchanges, government sites, search utilities, and more.

Finders-Seekers

http://finders-seekers.com

Assists in locating lost contacts and elusive people. Further specializes in background checks for both business and personal relationships, as well as in locating ex-mates and children.

Flea Market @FUW

http://info.fuw.edu.pl/market/market.html

Serves as an online flea market for products. Lets you place ads, as well as search ads in the long and short form, or search for a specific item.

Fleurs d'Ete

http://www.webguide.com/fleurs.html

Advertises the flowers offered by Fleurs d'Ete of Miami, Florida. Contains product list with images and a price list.

Flora Designs

http://www.nav.com/FDI/flora.html

Advertises the services of Flora Designs, a worldwide fruit, gourmet, and champagne basket delivery service.

Flower Stop

http://www.flowerstop.com/fstop/

Advertises floral arrangements provided by Flower Stop, the Internet's fresh flower market. You can order flowers by using their online order form, calling their toll free number, or sending e-mail.

For Sale By Owner Magazine

http://www.human.com/mkt/fsbo/

Lets you place ads for selling homes. Lets you post your own ad, view property listings, refer to area maps, and see property advertising rates.

Form for Mortgage Payment Query

http://ibc.wustl.edu/mort.html

Calculates mortgage payments when you input details about mortgage and the payment. Also includes a conversion factor for Canadian users. Contains links to other search calculation pages on the Web.

Fortune **Home Page**

http://www.pathfinder.com/@@WseQNgAAAAAAlcs/fortune/fortune.html

Offers a list of the 500 top companies in order of revenues. Also contains *Fortune*'s annual report on information technology.

Four Winds, Inc.

http://www.nicoh.com/fourwinds

A Native American Non-Profit Corporation dedicated to alcohol and drug rehabilitation of native youth, which offers a site for marketing Native American products. Includes an electrical night lamp that accents a 17th-century tepee, video tapes on native ceremonies, historic books, herbs, spiritual healing, drums, and beadwork.

Four11 White Page Directory

http://www.Four11.com/

Lets you search for people and their addresses. Contains more than 1.1 million listings and more than 100,000 registered users. Lets you register and put your name on the directory, too.

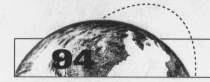

Fox Color and Light Home Page

http://www.microweb.com/jimfox/index.html

Design, manufacture, license, electronic, interactive, fashions, clothing, toys, gifts, musical instruments, safety devices, sculpture, jewelry, art, accessories, props, crystals, stage sets, carnivals, LED, bras, lingerie. Video game programming, cowboy hats. Products include Fireflys, FireFleas, FlashBands. Have designed stage sets for The Grateful Dead, Dwight Yoakam.

FractalNet Real Estate Server

http://www.fractals.com/realestate.html

Offers listings for residential real estate on the Internet and advertising to anyone interested in selling real estate.

France Mall

http://www.Internet-eireann.ie/Euromall/france/france.html

Serves as the commercial center of France. Covers just about all things to do with France (if not all).

Franchise Net

http://www.frannet.com

Provides certain basic information that should aid you in selecting the right franchise. Also includes a listing by category of a large number of franchise opportunities and also a number of franchise home pages that provide more detailed information on certain franchise opportunities.

Franklin Information Group

http://www.execpc.com/~fig

Information search firm. Specializes in backgrounding of individuals and businesses, preemployment and retention screening, business credit, competitive business intellegence, and litigation support.

Free-STUFF Junkies

http://www.getnet.com/~xinh/free.html

Provides information on getting free stuff both on and off the Internet. Includes free offers from anywhere the site creators can find them: magazines, Internet sites, newsletters, TV, and so on.

Fry's Electronics

http://www.fry-s.com

Sells computers, software, audio, video, and electronic components.

FTD Internet

http://www.ftd.com/

Offers FTD's official flower catalog. Also provides international delivery. Advertises the services of FTD International. Contains images of the products available and a free personal reminder service.

FutureMall

http://futuremall.stardate.com

Provides a wide variety of products and services for both businesses and consumers, operated by StarDate Publishing, a full-service electronic marketing and advertising company.

Garden State Laboratories, Inc.

http://www.planet.net/gsl

Certified environmental and food testing laboratory. Analyzes drinking water, wastewater, sludges, biosolids,

soils, solid wastes, hazardous wastes, food, and dairy products for chemical, bacteriological, and microbiological contaminants.

Gateway Design

http://www.main.com/~gateway/

Provides turn-key graphic communications services.

GE Capital

http://www.ge.com/gec/index.html

Provides financial services, including loans, equipment management, computer services, consumer services, and speciality insurance.

Gem Search International

http://www.pixi.com/gem_international/

Advertises the products of Gem Search International. Contains a diamond buying and selling information guide.

General Information Concerning Patents— Table of Contents

http://www.uspto.gov/web/patinfo/toc.html

Provides general information about application for and granting of patents.

The Generator-Set Controllers Company

http://www.datasrv.co.il/wexler

Manufactures generator-set controllers. Specializes in automatic synchronizing, load sharing, and peak shaving generator-set applications.

GEO FORCE

http://apollo.co.uk/a/geoforce/

GEO FORCE is an all natural herbal combination designed to enhance one's five senses and provide for more physical and mental energy.

Geoff's Science Policy Page

http://www.cs.dartmouth.edu/~gdavis/policy/jobmarket.html

Offers statistics and facts on the mathematics job market. Gives future projections and offers links to more information.

George Baker and Associates: International Energy Business Development

http://www.portal.com:80/~gbaker

Studies international energy markets. Assists senior management in the evaluation and development of business opportunities in the energy sectors of Latin America, particularly Mexico, and other emerging markets. Evaluates markets and energy policy frameworks and the development of business plans that reflect a careful assessment of economic and political risk.

German Mall

http://www.Internet-eireann.ie/Euromall/germany/germany.html

Einkaufszentrum Deutschland. The German mall.

Get Organized

http://www.get-organized.com

Provides helpful tips from a professional organizer for keeping your life, work, and home in order. Updates hints weekly.

Giftnet

http://www.demon.co.uk/giftnet/

Lets you purchase novelty gifts over the Net and surprise that special person.

Gilltro-Electronics, Inc.

http://www.giltronix.com

Manufactures remote access systems, which allow remote users (people who work at home, test engineers, MIS Managers, and so forth) to access a number (1 to 16) of devices (PCs, printers, plotters, test equipment, and so on) at the main office.

Global Business Network

http://www.gbn.org/

Includes some of the world's leading companies—our subscribing WorldView members—and individual GBN members from business, science, the arts, and academia and brings these members together in unlikely combinations and intriguing settings to explore the changing business environment and its strategic implications (available to organizations on an annual membership basis). WorldView is designed to enhance learning and to help organizations think more effectively about the business environment and the tools for developing adaptive, successful strategies.

Global Innovations

http://www.icw.com/global/global.html

Online novelty products shop. Carries an Internet watch, *Star Trek* T-shirts, Aura's virtual reality vest, cooling products for those hot summer days, and stereogram posters and software.

Global Recycling Network

http://grn.com/grn/

Provides a guide to recycling information and recycled products. Offers links to recycling stocks quotes, recycling directories, and access to the market place where recycled goods are sold.

Global Trade Center

http://www.tradezone.com/tz/

Provides resources and information for people interested in Global Trade. Provides links to trade resources and sites around the world, trade news, business opportunities, and much more. Features Global Roulette, which might take you on a surprise journey, as well as a list of clickable maps that let you travel on your own.

Glynda Turley Online Catalogue

http://nerosworld.com/www/GlyndaTurley/MainIndex.html

Offers Glynda Turley's romantic prints.

Go Media, Inc.

http://www.gomedia.com

Provides print- and online-information design services. Also offers training and consulting on a variety of Internet- and Web-related topics.

Gold Leopard, Inc.

http://www.airmail.net/~erivers

Distributes gold jewelry made from leaves and other natural items.

The Goodyear Tire and Rubber Company

http://www.goodyear.com/

Doesn't highlight company products. Provides information on specifications and preferences regarding tires. Offers a section on how to prolong tread life on your tires. Also gives contact information to the nearest Goodyear store, including store hours.

Graphics on Call™ by Pacific Coast Software

http://www.pacific-coast.com/GOCDemo.html

Offers discount graphics. Lets you buy just the photos you need, not the entire CD, and use Pacific Coast Software's high-speed search engine for free.

Graphiti

http://libertynet.org/~graphiti

Enables you to create your own T-shirts, sweatshirts, polo shirts, and more. Lets you order as many or as few items as you want.

Greater Phoenix Dog Training Academy, Inc.

http://cyberdog.com

Offers dog training techniques. Résumé includes dogs trained for Phoenix Suns and Phoenix Cardinals players, six feature length television and motion picture productions, and many television commercials. Mr. Andrew D. Luper, training director and author of *Never Never Hit Your Dog*, has been interviewed many times in print as well as on numerous local TV and radio shows.

Greenscreen Anti-Pollution Air Filter Face Masks

http://198.30.116.211/~grnscrn/index.html

Sells high-quality, activated carbon filter-based fashion face masks for people in polluted areas, allergy sufferers, and people with chemical sensitivities or chemical injuries.

Gustafson Glass Studios

http://www.netshopper.com/~fetterly/gustafson

Offers a selection of Tiffany style lamps suitable for tabletops in your home or office.

H & R Block

http://www.gate.net/~gwieser/hrbhome.html

H & R Block tax service in Lake Wales and Fort Meade, Florida. Includes information about H & R Block's Income Tax Training School and electronic filing. Also includes links to IRS tax sites.

The Haight Ashbury Home Page

http://www.best.com/~blholmes/sffind/haight/haight.html

Provides a list of shops and information on San Francisco's Haight street.

Handcrafts Unlimited

http://www.awod.com/gallery/crafts/hu/

Offers a variety of quality handcrafted items, including clothing, halloween costumes, calligraphy and art, lamp shades, baskets, bears and dolls, tole painting, and many other items by request.

Happenings in the Mutual Fund Industry

http://www.ultranet.com/~marla/features.html

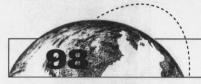

Features articles on what's happening in the mutual fund industry, written by Marla Brill.

Happy Jack Dog Care Products

http://iweb.www.com/jack

Provides animal health products.

Haworth Office Furniture

http://www.haworth-furn.com

Offers a host of resources and insights into the challenging issues of today, from creating alternative work environments to integrating technology in the workplace.

Hayes Microcomputer Products, Inc.

http://www.hayes.com

Provides product information, support, and much more, including monthly features such as contests in which visitors can win free modems or software. Develops, supplies, and supports computer communications equipment and software for personal computers and computer communications networks. Distributes products through a global network of authorized distributors, dealers, mass merchants, VARs, systems integrators, and original equipment manufacturers.

Welcome to

Increasing the Speed of Business™...
and **FUN!**

Headhunters Guides

http://www.universal.nl/jobhunt

Offers a wide range of International Headhunters address guides, employment contacts, and worldwide jobs pages.

Health-Max/Health Technologies Network

http://www.ieway.com/business/max/welcome.html

Strives to be on the cutting edge of technology to improve people's health by supplying best natural, nutritional, health products.

Healthsource Bookstore

http://www.appi.org/healthsource

Serves as a source for books on health, wellness, fitness, allied health, nursing, and mental health.

HERMES, Consumer and Corporate Surveys

http://www.umich.edu/~sgupta/hermes/

Provides free access to results from the project's research on commercial uses of the Web. Currently offers results from two user surveys, based on more than 13,000 responses from 52 countries. Also enables companies who use the Web to communicate with their customers or suppliers to register to become corporate panel members (also free).

Hi-Fish Net-Center

http://etoy.atnet.co.at/etoy.Internet-tank/Hi-Fish

Offers brand new net-style on hi-fashion spacewear. Includes the latest releases and a Phosphorfashion-shoppingshow.

Highland Trail Company— Scotland

http://www.highlandtrail.co.uk/highlandtrail/

Offers interactive online shopping: Scottish food, drink, and gifts covering a range of fish, meat, clothing, and crafts. Includes fresh and smoked salmon, smoked venison, malt whisky, and cashmere and woolen tartans.

Home Business Solutions

http://netmar.com:80/mall/shops/solution/

Includes information related to credit reports, classified advertising, tax issues, office supply sources, and solutions for startup, marketing, and finance.

Home Connections

http://www.trinet.com/homeconn/information.html

Lists hundreds of homes for sale in your area.

Home Mortgage Loans, Calculator, Refi Testdrive

http://www.homeowners.com/homeowners/index.html

Provides the latest interest rates, market trends, featured programs, histories of adjustable rate indices, mortgage dictionary, mortgage calculator, graphical comparisons of loans, and online forms for purchasing and refinancing. Lets you join a mailing list for updates on the latest news in mortgage rates.

HomeBuyers Fair Welcome: Real Estate, Mortgage Loans, Apartment, Relocation, and New Homes

http://www.homefair.com/homepage.html

Contains free housing guides for 23 cities, and offers links to other real estate sites. Provides information on buying, selling, and relocating. Includes a special section for first-time buyers. Also has instructions on getting a mortgage, apartment directions, and locator services.

Homebuyer's Fair Real Estate Classifieds

http://www.homefair.com/class/classified.html

Provides an online format for searching real estate properties by state, type of house, and price range. Includes pictures of houses.

Hot Couture Clothing Company

http://www.hotcouture.com

Designs and manufactures clothing for women. Designs and sews every garment individually to produce distinctive garments that represent the wearer's individual sense of style.

How To Become a Real-time Commodity Futures Trader—From Home

http://www.crocker.com/~futures

Presents a trading guide recommended by *Futures Magazine*. Covers from initial home setup to advanced strategies.

How To Do Business in Mexico

http://daisy.uwaterloo.ca/~alopez-o/busfaq.html

Provides general information for doing business in Mexico, such as about customs, regulations, and procedures.

Human Resources On-line. Direct Links to Human Resources Departments of Several Computer Related Companies

http://www.glue.umd.edu/~vernita/

Provides information for job seekers in computer-related companies. Includes job and company listing. Contains e-mail addresses of human resource development offices in the companies.

Hyper Link Productions

http://iglou.com/hardware_hq/hylp.htm

Offers to provide Web pages with multiple links and an online brochure.

The IBM Home Page

http://www.ibm.com/

Provides information on IBM (also in foreign languages). Contains ordering information about IBM products and services.

IBM/RS 6000 Scalable POWER Parallel Systems Home Page

http://lscftp.kgn.ibm.com/pps/

Serves as a technical site for parallel computing systems. Contains ordering information.

Icelandic HorseNet

http://www.webcom.com/~odyssey2/icehorse/

Educates and informs breeders, buyers, and the curious about this relatively rare breed. Includes pictures, events, and networking.

Ideal Engraving Co., Inc.

http://www.cybercom.com/~rbeir

Manufactures a complete line of marking products, including steel hand stamps, dies, interchangeable type and holders, numbering heads, and bench presses.

Ideal Point Home Page

http://www.ipoint.com

Contains information about Ideal Point, Inc. and links to information related to research and development focusing on technologies that enhance interaction, communication, and learning.

Inc. Business Resources Library

http://nmq.com:80/emgbiznc/cntprovs/products/incbiz/

Provides information about business resources related to a host of categories, including listings for business startup, planning, time management, managing people, and customer service. Provides resources via books, videotapes, and computer software.

Income and Business Solutions

http://www.magi.com/~bizsol/enter.html

Serves as information site for different types of businesses. Includes the following categories: income opportunities, multilevel marketing, products for sale, mail-order business, health products, and business opportunities. Offers many links to different places and contacts for all the listed categories.

Income Taxation Notebook Home Page

http://www.best.com/~ftmexpat/notebook.html

Targets users who are research-oriented on taxes. Contains information about other tax sites, summaries, articles, authoritative references, income tax-related functions, and spreadsheets.

Index to acts section

http://darkwing.uoregon.edu:80/~nfargher/acts/index.html

Very good information site for various reports and links for cost accounting issues. Include activity-based costing, pricing, total quality management. Good as an educational site, can be used by professionals too for information related to cost accounting.

IndustryNET: Industry's Online Mall

http://www.industry.net

Presents up-to-date information about engineering design, automation, and manufacturing news from IndustryNET. Includes application assistance, new products, demo software, online trade shows, tested shareware programs, employment opportunities, and used industrial equipment.

INFOCENTRO

http://www.infotec.conacyt.mx

Provides information about Mexico (commercial, business, tourist, government). Includes a search engine that lets you search all Hispanic written documents that can be reached on the Internet, as well as specialized directories.

INFOMART: Dallas, Texas Home Page

http://www.onramp.net//infomart/infomart.html

Houses more than 100 big name computer companies, such as Apple, IBM, and GTE. Provides access to the home pages of Infomart's occupants, as well as magazines and articles, and a calendar of events.

INFOMART is a 1.6 million square foot market center for computer related products and services located in Dallas, Texas, USA. Its 100 tenants include Andersen Consulting, Apple, AT&T, EDS, GTE, Novell, SAS Institute, Toshiba and Xerox. INFOMART Magazine discusses hot topics for the information systems industry such as client/server, multimedia, ATM, and networking. The INFOMART Directory gives a brief description and telephone number for contacting INFOMART tenants. INFOMART is also the site for many conferences and classes as described in the Calendar of Events.

InfoWell

http://www.infowell.com/~infowell

Offers the most exciting products from around the world, delivered to your door. Includes porcelain dolls, carousels, decorative masks, ancient Egyptian handcraft art on papyrus paper, information about how to check your house for asbestos and lead, money mortgage loans, and electonic marketing programs.

Ingvar's Home Page

http://www.ingvar.is

Covers engineering and designs related to the processing of marine products, waste disposal by incineration (with heat recovery), geothermal and (waste) heat recovery; useful refrigerating and heat-transfer techniques/designs; export of marine and aquatic products, fox pelts, mink pelts and woolen ware; aqua- and mariculture; environmental issues; subjects of general interest.

Installer Direct Pricing for Alarms

http://www.mindspring.com/~ko4ta/alarm.html

Presents an opportunity to purchase alarm equipment. Provides education information about installing security equipment.

Institute for the Study of Business Markets

http://www.psu.edu/isbm/

Contains information related to seminars, research projects, and membership to the organization.

IntelliMatch Online Career Services

http://www.intellimatch.com/intellimatch/

Offers a new concept in employment services. Lets you fill out a WATSON Structured Résumé to enter in the site's database. Makes your profile accessible to dozens of employers and search firms who use IntelliMatch's HOLMES search and profile matching software to quickly identify candidates with the skills they desire.

Interactive Computer Video, Inc.

http://204.209.3.26/

Provides technological solutions, from Internet to desktop video production.

Interactive Employment Network

http://www.espan.com/

Furnishes a database of job opportunities. Provides up-to-date information. Lets you search by keyword, region, industry, date of posting, and job title. Also offers facility for posting résumés to the site.

Intercat

http://www.intercat.com/

Creates multimedia interactive catalogs and Web sites for catalog distribution. Offers custom software design and applications.

InterLAN Consulting, Inc.

http://www.interlan.ca/~jzaidman/

Internetworking consulting firm. Specializes in LAN and WAN technologies. Undertakes short- and long-term projects that involve designing and implementing large enterprise networks anywhere in the world.

International Cigar Club

http://www.magicnet.net/orlando/business/cigar1.html

Invites you to join the club and receive 4–6 cigars a month for $9.95 plus shipping and handling. Also offers humidors and other accessories.

International Competitive Research Asian Business Daily

http://infomanage.com/~icr/abd/

Contains real-time information on financial, political, and economic matters in Pacific Rim countries. Useful for trade, stocks, industry trends and company decisions, or simply as an educational site. Contains a daily section. Lists each section by country.

The Internet Ad Pages

http://netmar.com/mall/ads/

Lets you exhibit your advertisements. Also lets you exhibit, sell, or buy diverse items. Includes categories for real estate listings, employment listings, business/ service listings, business opportunities, software, and miscellaneous. Provides an online order form for placing ads (at a price based on number of words).

Internet Auction List

http://www.usaweb.com/usaweb/auction

Serves as a source for auctions on the Internet. Provides auction listings for automobile, real estate, antiques, collectibles, wines, and much more.

Internet Bankruptcy Library

http://bankrupt.com

Provides troubled company resources for the bankruptcy and insolvency professional.

Internet Business Center

http://tig.com/IBC

Offers many links to information about doing business on the Internet. Good intermediate site for searching for the particular business service. Statistics on Internet usage, best commercial sites on the Net, and much more.

Internet Business Opportunity Showcase

http://www.ibos.com/pub/ibos/home.html

Specializes in franchise offerings, small business opportunities, multilevel/network marketing offers, and business services. Showcases links to many business-related sites.

Internet Business Opportunity Showcase

http://www.ibos.com/pub/ibos/busops.html

Provides information related to small businesses and opportunities and services related to the small business sector. Also contains details about multilevel marketing and products and services.

Internet Consultants

http://www.csn.net/~johnhart/internet.html

Contains a "who's who" directory of Internet consultants. Provides contact information and a paragraph that describes the range of services offered for each person or firm listing.

Internet Funeral Service Directory

http://www.funeral.net/information/ceminetdir.html

Offers a list of cemeteries and crematoria that are on the Internet.

Internet Information Services Ltd.

http://www.demon.co.uk/iisl/

Provides a full Web design, consultancy, and training service to companies in the United Kingdom, emphasizing working with advertising agencies to enable their clients to market using the Internet.

Internet Providers

http://www.csn.net/~johnhart/provider.html

Contains a who's who listing of Internet service providers.

Internet Radio

http://www.medium.com/IRT/ir1.html

Features RealAudio: world news, VOA, music, and more.

Internet Shopping Galleria

http://www.intergal.com/intergal.htm

Includes different categories like corporate services, art, audio books, auto gallery, bikes, computers, jewelry, magazines, sports shop and travel information.

Internet Shopping Network

http://www.Internet.net:80/

Lets you join online shopping club for deals on everything from software to flowers. Provides an alphabetical listing of more than 600 companies.

Internet Web_Business Center

http://www.internetweb.co.uk/centres/business.htm

Contains many useful links to other sites under a number of categories. Includes listings for banking, accounting, stock

market, investment companies, brokers, venture capital, credit cards, and politics.

InterNIC Directory of Directories

http://ds.internic.net/ds/dsdirofdirs.html

Contains an index of links to different business-related resources, products, and services on the Net. Offers a categorize search facility. Lets you add your site.

InterQuote

http://www.interquote.com

Provides a collection of affordable Internet based stock market services; and real-time, 15-minute delayed, and end-of-day information on stocks, options, indices, mutual funds, and futures in most United States and Canadian exchanges.

IntheNet OLS and Virtual Mall

http://www.inthenet.com

Provides the greater Oklahoma City area with a family/business/education-based online service with Internet access provision. Also maintains a virtual marketplace that includes a variety of merchants, products and services, as well as several clubs and organizations and charitable concerns.

Intro-TV Home Page

http://193.135.247.20/introtv.htm

Offers multimedia in Switzerland.

The Investor Channel

http://www.wimsey.com/xr-cgi-bin/select?/0@/Magnet/mc/menu.html

Contains list of featured companies, newsletters and newsgroups, hot stocks, and advertisements related to investments. Provides information for the investor.

IOMA Home Page and Business Directory

http://starbase.ingress.com/ioma/

Offers trial subscriptions to business newsletters. Provides a directory to the Web for business executives responsible for finance/accounting, purchasing, institutional investing, manufacturing, human resources, benefits and compensation, property/casualty insurance, design/construction, law firm management, and CPA firm management.

Ireland Mall

http://www.Internet-eireann.ie/Euromall/ireland/ireland.html

Provides products, information, leisure, and shopping (all Irish).

Island Concepts Shopping

http://www.mpcs.com/islandc

Offers a variety of products for home or office shoppers. Provides a variety of exciting free catalogs. Includes computers, jewelry, giftware, Avon, and Tupperware products.

ISO Easy

http://www.exit109.com/~leebee/

Provides assistance in the details of ISO 9000 quality standards and implementation issues associated with the same. Contains a section of frequently asked questions and related links to other sites on quality and ISO9000.

Italy Mall

http://www.Internet-eireann.ie/Euromall/italy/italy.html

La Zona di Negozi Italia. The Italian Shopping Centre.

J & M Coin, Stamp, and Jewellery Ltd.

http://www.jandm.com

J & M retails and buys coins, stamps, bullion, and jewelry. Offers a current list of products.

J. Crow Company

http://www.ronin.com/jcrow

Offers herbs, spices, essential oil fragrances, Tibet Stamps (approved by the Office of His Holiness the 14th Dalai Lama), Tibet incense, information on Tibet medicine, information on arthritis and folk medicine, books, and J. Crow's Mulled Cider Mix (a blend for spicing apple cider juice or wine).

J.R. Antiques and China Registry

http://www.islandnet.com/~cvcprod/jrantiq.html

Serves as a registry for China. Buys and sells current and discontinued patterns. Provides a list of required items.

J.T. Smith and Associates

http://www.prairienet.org/jtsa/

Serves as a programmers' shop for the Central Illinois community.

Japan Dimensions Research

http://ccnet.com/~jdrinfo/

Provides answers to your questions concerning Japan in the areas of business, medicine, and science and technology.

Lets you search computerized databases, governmental and nongovernmental documents, public and private libraries, and interviews with experts in both Japan and the United States.

JC Penney Home Page

http://www.jcpenney.com/

Contains investor relations, news releases, and information about customer relations. Presents an online catalog that contains many different items. Offers 800 numbers for ordering.

JDG Designs: Work That Works

http://www.jdgdesign.com

Offers graphic solutions for businesses establishing their online presence and showcasing their products and services.

Lift the dropcloth and wander through our blueprint of distinctive corporate and association logos, annual reports, magazines, marketing brochures, collateral and Internet home page design. Glimpse behind the scenes at JDG's idea pages to see how we construct "Work That Works!"

Jesus Fellowship Christian Bookstore

http://www.fiu.edu/~wgreen01/bookstore.html

Provides thousands of titles that you can order direct.

Jewelers of Las Vegas

http://www.manifest.com/Jewelers

Offers a large selection with prices to fit any budget.

Job Opportunities in the Pacific Rim

http://www.Internet-is.com/tko/index.html

Specializes in recruitment and careers in Japan and the Asia-Pacific region. Provides a listing of job openings in Japan, Singapore, Korea, and the United States in the areas of semiconductors, software, and accounting. Provides a list of bilingual candidates in several categories.

Job Search and Employment Opportunities: Best Bets from the Net

http://www.lib.umich.edu/chdocs/employment

Offers categorized links to different job-related sites on the Web in an attempt to make all good job-related locations accessible from a single site.

JobBank USA

http://www.jobbankusa.com

Offers a list of employment sites and resources (United States and around the world). Categorizes job listings by field, location, and company. Provides a résumé database, submission form for job-matching, and distribution to companies and recruiters.

John Charles Antiques

http://www.londonmall.co.uk/antiques

Deals mainly in furniture originating from the 17th century to beginning of the 20th century. Supplies fine oil and watercolor paintings, old and new prints, clocks, chandeliers, china, glass, mirrors, pewter, copper, brass, bronze, silver, and gold.

John Judy's Hypermedia Designs

http://www.mcs.net/~jjudy/

Designs Web sites for corporate customers in the Chicago area. Also offers a rotation of pictures of Nantucket Island,

as well as John Judy's reminder list on the finer points of the golf swing.

Jones Hall Hill and White

http://www.jhhw.com

Practices exclusively in the area of municipal finance as bond counsel, underwriter's counsel, disclosure counsel, special tax counsel, and rebate compliance counsel.

Jordan Manufacturing Company, Inc.

http://www.empgal.com/~jordan

Sells birdhouses and feeders, squirrel feeders, replacement cushions, umbrellas, wooden picnic tables, sawhorses and workbenches, and umbrella frames.

Kansas Careers

http://www.ksu.edu/~dangle/

Discusses career opportunities for women. Contains job listings under unconventional interest categories such as artistic, plants and animals, industrial, humanitarian, and so forth. Focuses on nontraditional careers and information on such resources.

The Kansas City E-Mall

http://www.sky.net/~techno/kcemall.html

Contains links to Kansas City area commercial, educational, nonprofit, and informational resources.

Links to Kansas City area commercial web sites.

Keller's Appaloosas

http://www.babcom.com/keller/

Offers breeding quality Appaloosa horses for sport, halter, and performance. Provides online sales and pedigree information, as well as photos and pricing.

KeyStone Learning Systems Corporation

http://www.keylearnsys.com

Provides video-based training for many business software packages.

Khem Products, Inc.

http://www.khem.com/khem/home.html

Releases Khem modules, which track and report hazardous and nonhazardous chemicals and provide an affordable building block approach to chemical inventory management and EPA regulatory compliance, as well as address the community right to know laws in the areas of EPCRA, RCRA, SARA, and CERCLA.

Kingston Telecommunication Laboratories

http://www.ktl.co.uk/ktl/

Offers a wide range of compliance services for fast market access.

Kittelson and Associates, Inc.

http://www.rdrop.com/~kaipdx/kai.html

Offers depth and expertise across the full spectrum of transportation-related engineering disciplines. Also contains links to other transportation engineering-related resources.

KRAMER Handgun Leather

http://shop-utopia.com/kramer_leather/kramer.html

Sells horsehide concealment holsters and accessories for the armed professional. Offers specialized designs for government covert operations, military special warfare, undercover police, and dignitary protection details.

Laid Back Designs

http://www.travelsource.com/travelstore/lbd/lbd.html

Lets you buy hammocks and sleep systems from the comfort of your own home.

Lane & Lenge

http://plaza.xor.com/lane/start/index.html

Presents a floral wire service. Lets you place orders for flowers, potted plants, and special occasions and gift baskets. Also allows enrollment on the mailing list.

Law Materials by Topical Area

http://www.counsel.com/topical.htm

Contains a huge listing of law-related headings, each of which in turn offer several links to other sites.

Layer Eight Systems for the Derivatives Market

http://www.eight.com/18home.html

Provides software for the financial derivatives market. Overviews Layer Eight Systems' product, potentially of interest to finance professionals who might having trouble pricing derivatives.

Le Parfum

http://www.netview.com/leparfum/

Carries more perfume labels than any other store in California and lets you order some of them online.

Lebow Bros. Clothing

http://www.tiac.net/users/lebow/

Offers fine clothing for men and boys, including sizes for the hard-to-fit individual.

Leonardo Collection Co.

http://www.crl.com/~bidlccca

Features a fine selection of high quality corporate and personal gift items.

Leonardo Park

http://www.hobbies.com

Internet shopping mall for hobbies, crafts, and collectibles, including products, services, and information. Consists of a Web site and related listserv mail lists.

Leverage Technologists Home Page

http://stout.levtech.com/home.html

Specializes in reverse engineering and reengineering. Offers off-the-shelf and in-house training and products on various computer languages.

Levien-Rich Associates Home Page

http://www.brainlink.com/~levien

Services lending institutions through construction management and monitoring.

LEXIS-NEXIS Communication Center

http://www.lexis-nexis.com/

Provides database for retrieval of business- and legal-related information.

LifeTime Filters

http://www.sccsi.com/LifeTime/lifetime_welcome.html

Advertises electrostatic air filters sold by LifeTime Filters. Provides information about these air-cleaning products, including how to order and clean them.

Lighten, Inc.—Advance Business Modeling and Analysis

http://www.lighten.com/lighten/

Suggests a new way to build business models and analyze data in Windows.

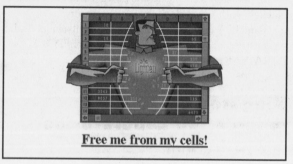

Free me from my cells!

Links to the World

http://dct.com/~gbvcb/links.html

Provides a list of Internet starting points, including movie studios, gambling links, big computer companies, cops and spies, fun government addresses, and the ability to add your own URL.

Little Tree Log Home Miniatures

http://199.6.33.29/cedar/little/little.htm

Presents handmade banks, dollhouses, birdhouses, birdfeeders, and more.

LockNet

http://www.locknet.com/

Serves as a listing service of locksmiths, alarm installers, safemen, and other security professionals who belong to security associations.

London Mall Magazine and HQ

http://www.londonmall.co.uk/_edit.htm

Offers articles and columns on topics ranging from politics to beer.

Lucia's Little Houses

http://media1.hypernet.com/knight.html

Offers Grand Ideas for Small Houses, a portfolio of twelve designs (Lucia's Little Houses).

Lumina Decision Systems, Inc.

http://www.lumina.com/lumina/

Contains sections on software demonstrations and a section on decision risk analysis. Focuses on providing corporate information.

Made in America

http://amsquare.com/america/made.html

Provides access to American made products. Offers separate sections on handmade goods, career and résumé management, and help wanted ads. Lets you post ads for a fee. Also offers great links to other sites.

Magazine Warehouse

http://cdnow.com/mags

Offers subscriptions to more than 300 magazines in more than 80 categories, including art, audio/video, automotive, business, and finance, to name a few.

Main Sequence Astronomical Apparel

http://www.treknet.net/astronomytees

Offers full line of wholesale astronomy T-shirts, sweats, and caps for purchase by planetariums, science centers, and museums.

Malaysian Internet Business Pages

http://www.beta.com.my/biz

Provides an easy entry for Malaysian companies and their overseas counterparts to do business on the Internet. Introduces Malaysian importers and exporters to the world and lists job vacancies and résumés (free service). Also provides full page Internet advertising. Supplies links to the *Malaysian Star* newspaper.

Man's Best Friend Software

http://www.interaccess.com/mbfsi

Presents animal-oriented software. Displays demos, comparisons, and information on product line.

Manufacturers Information Net Home Page

http://mgfinfo.com/home.htm

Good database related to manufacturing of products. Categorized into software, computers, job shops, suppliers, professional services, and machine tool manufacturers.

Manufacturing Resources

http://www.warwick.ac.uk/~esrjf/manufact.html

Provides information for the manufacturing community. Contains links to resources that are relevant to the manufacturing community and that are available on the Net. Serves as a subject guide, but also contains information on professional development and other resources.

Mark Palmer Design Home Page

http://navishow.web.aol.com/lab/m/mpalme/MPDWeb/MPDHomePage.html

Identity and image-building firm that concentrates on corporate identity and logo design, including packaging, advertising, marketing, logos, identity, and so on.

Marketing Solutions Systems Integration and Web Design

http://www.marksol.com/marksol

Offers systems integration and support primarily to the staffing and legal industries. Offers the Recruitment Management System (RMS) and Tempus Fugit database software for recruiting, networking, and Web page design.

Marketing Tools/American Demographics

http://www.marketingtools.com

Provides *American Demographics*, a Dow Jones publication, online, which covers consumer trends and demographics from a business perspective. Also presents *Marketing Tools* magazine, which covers information-based marketing, including database marketing, research, advertising, and media.

Marshall on the Internet

http://www.marshall.com

Contains product information and data sheets from more than 140 electronic parts and components manufacturers. Lets you order all products directly through the Internet.

Master Lock Security Tips

http://www.masterlock.com

Provides information about home and commercial security, Master Lock Company corporate, and product information.

Mastery Services Avatar Deliveries

http://www.starsedge.com/masters/masteryserv.html

Offers information on Avatar (a state of the art nine-day self awareness, self-empowerment course) as well as Mastery Services' corporate trainings.

Maude Asbury

http://www.deltanet.com/intersphere/ma

Presents distinctive photo albums and desk accessories handcrafted in the United States.

Maui Amenities/Maui Island Formula Skin and Hair Care

http://planet-hawaii.com/~amen

Offers Maui Island Formula skin and hair care products with all natural Hawaiian ingredients. Lets you order via a secured line.

Maverick's Shop

http://www.maverickcomm.com

Provides a broad spectrum of services, ranging from complete integration of two-way radios and computer communications, single radios and rapairs, batteries, antennas, hard drives, to specialty knives for police and firemen. Offers special pricing for government, schools, full- and part-time students, and specialty groups.

Mayflower Software

http://www.maysoft.com

Provides specialty products for Lotus Notes.

MBT Architecture

http://www.mbtarch.com/~mbt

Specializes in buildings for science and technology.

McDonnell Douglas Aerospace

http://pat.mdc.com/LB/LB.html

Includes some corporate information as well as information on robotics and 3D modeling. Uses the 3D interactive modelling system to analyze human body fit and function within a geometric structure.

MCI

http://www.mci.com

Takes you on a virtual tour of MCI. Offers links to Internet MCI, Gramercy Press, MCI Developers Lab, and the Small Business Center.

MECC

http://www.mecc.com/

Contains information about its innovative and fun software programs for kids of all ages. Offers technical support and links to various other Internet sites of interest to kids, parents, and teachers. Includes titles such as The Oregon Trail, MathKeys, Storybook Weaver, MayaQuest, and the Muncher product family.

Meetings Industry Mall

http://www.mim.com

Serves as a virtual mall specifically for industry professionals to use. Lets suppliers open shop to meeting planners and buyers throughout the world.

Mega World Media

http://megaworld.com

Provides Web space and Web publishing services. Contains the RV Mall, which provides recreational vehicle information. Also provides résumés and many other businesses that need a Web presence.

Mega-Directory of US/Canada International Exports—United States Trade

http://www.grasmick.com/ustrade.htm

Contains directory of professionals who can assist Canadians exporting to and doing business with the United States. Offers categorized listing.

Menswear Unlimited

http://www.clark.net/pub/menswear/suits.html

Presents a catalog of fine menswear. Lets you browse the catalog and then place an order.

Messages Heavenbound

http://www.golden.org/~startrek

A small group of professional astronomers that has established a firm to send personal messages into space. They have a dedicated radio telescope for this purpose. All messages are absolutely confidential.

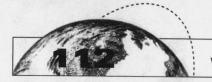

Michele-Shine Media

http://www.internex.com/MSM/home.html

Specializes in your company's graphics and multimedia needs. Creates a presence for your company on the Internet, at conferences, and in print.

MicrOpsys

http://www.cam.org/~apanisse/index.html

Describes a practice management program for ophthalmologists and optometrists.

Microsoft Corporation

http://www.microsoft.com/

Provides information about products, services, help, and the much anticipated Windows 95.

Microswiss-Centre North-South

http://www.mic.htl-bw.ch/~mswiss

Swiss government program that promotes microelectronic applications for small and medium enterprises (SMEs).

Mikrographix, Caught on the Web

http://shop-utopia.com/mikro_site/mikro.html

Specializes in 3-D graphics, digital kiosks, Web pages and sites, professional photo retouching, corporate logo packages, graphic designs, and desktop publishing.

Milne Jewelry Company (Japanese Version)

http://www.xmission.com/~turq/Milne01-sjis.html

Offers Japanese translation of full *Jewelry of the American Southwest* online catalog. Provides exporting information.

Milne Jewelry Company— A Southwest Tradition

http://www.xmission.com/~turq

Presents an exquisite collection of classic earrings and delicate neckwear in traditional Navajo, Zuni, and Hopi designs. Provides an informative "Guide to Southwest Indian Jewelry" and "Care of Silver and Turquoise."

Milwaukee Marketplace

http://www.mixcom.com/

Lists businesses and business-related services in Milwaukee, Wisconsin, categorized under different businesses and services. Also has general information about Milwaukee.

MinisRme

http://rhytech.com/~minisrme

Retailer of fine miniature antiques for doll houses. Specializes in finely crafted works of American and English artisans.

Mississippi Business Information Home Page

http://www.aue.com/MBI/MBIhome.html

Specializes in preemployment screening. Lets you use government databases to provide instant applicant screening nationwide.

Mobile Phones for UK Users

http://www.demon.co.uk/mobiles

Provides information on mobile phone Web pages in the United Kingdom.

Moe's Books

http://sunsite.unc.edu/ibic/Moeshome.html

Contains more than 500,000 titles in stock—at a discount. Includes rare children's books, hard-to-find import titles, old books, new books, and used books. Also searches for you if you can't find the book you want.

Moscow Libertarium

http://feast.fe.msk.ru/libertarium/

Features information and articles on liberalism in Russian and English.

MotoMini Motorcycle Collectibles

http://www.homepage.com/mall/motomini/motomini.html

Presents MotoMini's collectible motorcycles Web catalog online.

Motorcity

http://www.motorcity.com/

Contains information about cars, classifieds, vehicle search, parts accessories, dealerships, and maintenance.

Motorola Information Systems Group

http://www.mot.com/MIMS/ISG/

Offers products in networking technology, including Frame Relay, ISDN, and Leased Line/Dial Modems.

Mousetracks—NSNS Marketing Resources

http://nsns.com/MouseTracks/

Offers links to marketing activities and resources available on the Net for educational, academic, and professional use.

MPEG Information & Resource [Optibase]

http://www.optibase.com

Provides the latest information on MPEG encoding and playback technology for the PC/AT platform. Provides downloadable product information, technical specifications, white papers, and newsletters that cover every aspect of MPEG mastering and digital video integration for kiosks, computer-based training, and multimedia.

MTAC Home Page

http://oracle.mtac.pitt.edu/WWW/MTAC.html

One of six regional NASA technology tranfer centers. Promotes use of NASA technologies in the private sector.

Musicmaker's Kits, Inc.— Catalog Index Page

http://www.primenet.com/~musikit/catalogi.htm

Serves as an index to the catalog pages of the Musicmaker's home page. Lists all of the instruments for which information is provided at this site.

N-Vision Systems

http://www.iquest.net/kiosk/index.html

Specializes in Kiosk production and development. Also serves consulting needs.

The NAFTA Professional, Law Office of Joseph C. Grasmick

http://www.grasmick.com/nafta.htm

Contains procedural instructions for applying for immigration and work permits. Also contains general information relating to immigration and work issues.

The NAFTA Watch

http://www.aescon.com/naftam/index.htm

Contains information and a weekly newsletter.

Narrators, Toastmasters 1398

http://www.earthlink.net/~bizplaner/NarPge.html

One of more than 7,000 Toastmasters clubs worldwide, dedicated to improved communication, leadership, and public speaking.

NASA/Goddard Space Flight Center

http://panza.gsfc.nasa.gov/mod.htm

Contains information regarding procurement and logistics, patents counsel, health, and security.

National InterAd

http://www.nia.com/

Provides information divided into real estate properties and services, and business opportunities. Offers options like city, neighborhood, minimum and maximum price, area, number of bedrooms, garages, amenities. Includes business opportunities such as business for sale, business brokers, and franchise opportunities.

National Locator & Data

http://iu.net/hodges

Specializes in public records retrieval and background verification. Offers links to numerous databases and sources for complete and accurate reports. Includes information on judgements, bankruptcies, liens, criminal histories, asset

information, SSN tracing, medical doctor and stock brokers license verification, marriage and divorce records, national phone number kris cross, address identifiers, asset records, real property, United States detailed business report, banking sections CD4 report, motor vehicle information, and more information.

The National Technology Transfer Center Home Page

http://www.nttc.edu/

Contains information for technology transfer issues. Offers links to different places on the Web.

Navatar Ltd.—Process Engineering and Change Management

http://www.hookup.net/~navatar

Offers up-to-date information on BPR and change management. Offers links to many other sites covering business process reengineering, business process redesign, IT, public service reengineering projects, treasury board IQE, and related subjects. Also presents notification of upcoming BPR seminars and courses.

Nesbitt Burns Inc., Toronto, Canada—Alan Nelson Investment Advisor

http://204.138.60.75

Serves the needs of individuals, corporations, and institutions from a network of Canadian and international offices. Provides investment and related information.

Net Diamonds, Inc.

http://www.bnt.com/netdiamonds/

Advertises products offered by Net Diamonds, Inc. of New York, New York. Provides a catalog, images of specific products, and prices and ordering information.

Net Trader

http://www.sentex.net/nettrader

Offers many trading options. Includes categories of buy, sell, swap, barter, wanted, services, employment, groups, clubs. Lets you place your own ad for a fee.

netViz Home Page

http://www.level.com/netviz

Presents a network diagramming and documenting tool for Windows. Offers a downloadable working demo version.

Network X, Inc.

http://www.clark.net/pub/networx/networx.html

Accesses information from various markets using the Internet.

NeuroSolutions Neural Network Software

http://www.nd.com/

Provides information on NeuroSolutions, a neural network simulation software product for MS Windows.

New England Complete Automobile Page

http://www.tiac.net/users/autoplus/

Provides different car-related information, including a number of links to car enthusiasts in the New England area.

New England Ski and Scuba

http://awebs.com/06066/NewEnglandSkiScuba/

Serves as a full service ski and scuba center. Carries all major brands and offers instruction and service on all of their equipment.

NewAge City

http://www.nads.com/

Offers shopping, a local newspaper, a public library, and more.

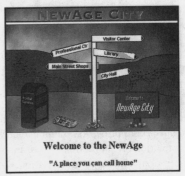

NewMedia Vision

http://www.newmedia.net/newmedia/

Specializes in everything from traditional print photography to WWW design and implementation.

Nijenrode Business Resources—Table of Contents

http://www.nijenrode.nl/resources/bus/

Provides resources, both on- and off-line for students, faculty, and researchers at business schools. Offers links to information about careers, other business schools, and many good links to resources.

Northwest Neon

http://www.peak.org/~omarab/nwneon.html

Northwest Neon designs and builds custom neon signs to fit your needs, including matching logos, generic signs, and 12v auto lighting systems. We are also proud to be affiliated with Stealth Technologies and Affordable Limousine, a Pacific Northwest Limo service (see http://www.peak.org/~omarab). Please check us out!

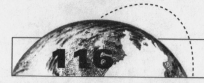

NTDB on the Internet

http://www.stat-usa.gov/BEN/services/ntdbhome.html

Provides information related to exports for international businesses.

ObjectSpace Home Page

http://www.objectspace.com

ObjectSpace is a leading supplier of object-oriented software products, consulting, and training. Our Web site provides information on our training classes and schedule, product descriptions, and support information.

OCEANOR—Oceanograohic Company of Norway

http://www.oceanor.no

Specializes in the marine environment. The company has developed environmental and performance monitoring systems through a combination of expertise in meteorology, oceanography, biolgy, engineering, and instrumentation. Markets these systems worldwide.

Octagon Technology Group, Inc.

http://www.otginc.com

Provides a global platform and infrastructure that allows companies to compete in international commerce. Gives organizations the capability to provide their goods and services across multiple jurisdictions worldwide at a low, predictable cost, by letting them utilize the vast global communications capabilities of the Internet and Octagon's sophisticated technology and corporate infrastructure. Octagon's infrastructure allows for order processing and payments in a wide variety of hard and soft currencies. Distribution of goods can be in virtually every major language.

ODIN Oil Network

http://www.oil.net

Presents an internet network designed for oil companies to put exploration and drilling, production, seismic, and personnel people in touch with the jobbers and services they require.

O'Gara-Hess & Eisenhardt

http://www.ogara.com

O'Gara-Hess & Eisenhardt is the world's leading armorer of automobiles, with a record of excellence spanning decades. Learn more about protecting yourself with the help of O'Gara-Hess & Eisenhardt's team of security specialists.

Ohio State Business Job Finder

http://www.cob.ohio-state.edu/dept/fin/osujobs.htm

Focuses on job search in areas of accounting, finance, and consulting. Contains information about job descriptions, salaries, future outlook, and leading employers. Offers many links to organizations.

Oils of Aloha

http://alohamall.aloha.com/~Oils

Serves as the Hawaiian source for Kukui and Macadamia nut oils.

O'KEEFE WORLD

http://www.okeefe.com

The home of O'Keefe Marketing, a full-service ad agency integrating Web site development with traditional marketing. Ideas worth stealing.

The Old Bookroom

http://www.ozemail.com.au/~oldbook/

Deals in secondhand, out-of-print, and antiquarian books, prints, and maps. Specializes in material on Asia, Africa, and the Middle East.

Olsen & Associates Information System

http://www.olsen.ch/

Develops online predictive information systems for the financial community. Provides a range of products and services, including the profile specific O&A Trading Models and the real-time O&A Forecast and Timing Service.

Online Career Center

http://www.occ.com/occ/HomePage.html

Contains categorized career opportunities with links to different related sites. Includes categories for career assistance, résumés, career canters, links to on-campus sites, and links to company home pages.

Online Design

http://www.corcom.com/pearson/design.html

Provides Web site design, maintenance, and promotional services. Includes a changing collection of Alaska photos.

Online Marketing

http://www.shore.net/olm/

Provides advertising opportunities for small businesses and individuals. Six line ads cost $15 per month. Offers travel related information. Also, contains many ads on vacation resorts and holiday rentals.

On-Line Trader

http://www.onlinetrader.com/closeouts/index.html

Offers products at below wholesale prices. Requires club membership fee. Lets you buy, sell, or trade options. Provides reports on international trade leads and reports like NAFTA and GATT, and government auction schedules.

Rd 3, Brook Road, Suite 835 - Montpelier, VT 05602-9214 - Phone: (802) 223-4707 - e-mail: admin@onlinetrader.com

Opportunity Network

http://www.oppnet.com/ern

Promotes opportunities in all communications media: by mail, through a highly targeted database, through the Internet on the Web, by telephone networking, and by attending major regional trade and consumer expositions.

Oracle New Media Products

http://www.oracle.com/info/products/newMedia/

Provides complete solutions for interactive multimedia applications.

Ovation Software Testing, Inc.

http://world.std.com/~ovation/ovation.html

Specializes in software test automation technology.

P. & D. Collectibles (Coca-Cola, Scale Airplanes & More)

http://www.webcom.com/~gregg/pdgifts

Serves as an online Ma and Pa-type collectible shop. Offers gifts for the young at heart.

Paracel, Inc.

http://www.paracel.com

Provides high-end solutions for text classification (including dissemination, categorization, and text retrieval) by combining highly functional software with a hardware, pattern-matching accelerator.

Paramount Custom Cabinetry

http://www.bizlink.com/paramount

Specializes in custom cabinetry, kitchens, computer furnitures, and wall units. Offers the latest computerized designs and layouts.

Parkleigh

http://www.parkleigh.com

Features the "Guilty Netsurfers Guide To Forgiveness™" to help you return to your loved-ones' good graces, after a "bit" too much time online. Also includes a selection of coffees, fine gifts, and some foods and candies.

Parsons Technology on the WWW

http://www.parsonstech.com/

Specializes in personal software of all fields and offers fully enhanced or nonenhanced sites on the WWW.

Patent Portal: Internet Patent Resources

http://www.law.vill.edu/~rgruner/patport.htm

Serves as an entry point for patent-related information. Identifies resources, links to resources, and sections on new patents issued. Also allows patent search and search of attorneys and agents.

Pawws Financial Network

http://pawws.com

Provides information for investors. Allows quick access to the vast amounts of information necessary for successfully managing a securities portfolio. Seamlessly integrates services for portfolio accounting, securities and market research, and online trading.

PC Index

http://ici.proper.com/1/pc

Lets you ftp to sites on the personal computer, download articles from the best online magazines, and search the American Computer Exchange for the best prices on new and used PCs and equipment.

PC Quote/Spacecom Systems Stock Quote Server

http://www.spacecom.com:8001/Participants/pcquote/qmaster.html

Provides 15-minute delayed stock quotes for any stock on the market when you enter the ticker symbol or the company name.

Perceptics Corporation

http://www.perceptics.com/info

Develops, designs, manufactures, integrates, and supports specialized information systems for applications in document management and imaging.

Perception: Global Market Predictions

http://www.manawatu.gen.nz/pages/business/perception

A Neural Network technically oriented financial market prediction service for global markets. Includes futures, options, and indices.

The Perdido Experience

http://www.perdido.com

Serves as a business and recreation guide for the Perdido Key and Perdido Bay areas of Pensacola, Florida.

Performance Development Corp. Information Strategy Planning Seminar

http://www.sw-expo.com/perfdev/
Information_Strategy_Planning.html

Explains what information strategy planning is and how it forms the basis for making sound business decisions. Teaches you how to align your information strategy with your overall business strategy and how to improve corporate performance through business reengineering and identifying core processes.

Performance Parts, Inc.

http://www.internext.com/mustangs/ppi.html

Helps you outfit your 1979 and later Mustang with the best in Ford Motorsport, SVO, and SVT parts. Also specializes in Mustang special service parts (police parts) and equipment.

Petals Plus Florist

http://www.islandnet.com:80/~igm/

Provides floral services through the American Floral Services network.

PGT Toys

http://walden.mo.net/~mudfish/index.html

Offers a list of antique and collectable toys for sale and/or trade.

Philadelphia Stock Exchange

http://www.libertynet.org/~phlx/

The oldest stock exchange in the nation and the first on the Net.

The Phoenix Business Renewal Site

http://www.phoenix.ca:80/bpr/

Provides information related to business process reengineering. Provides related information on total quality management and process modelling.

PhotoGraphics

http://www.helix.net/octavo/photographics

Features classic cameras of the 20th century—not photographs, but extremely accurate drawings. Reproduces every detail of each camera at twice the actual size. Designed to appeal to serious camera collectors, each 18 × 14 inch print uses a premium acid-free archival paper, a specially mixed metallic ink, and a super-fine 200 line halftone screen.

Photoprotective Technologies

http://www.txdirect.net/corp/ppt/index.htm

Provides a wide variety of products that eliminate the vision and health risks associated with exposure to light by using melanin. Photoprotective Technologies' products eliminate eyestrain and block UV and high energy visible (HEV) light emitted from both natural and artificial light sources. Offers computer monitor light filters, sunglasses, clip-on lenses, fluorescent light filters, contact lenses, and other products that provide solutions to complete eye protection by offering a patented technology that copies nature's own photoprotective pigment, melanin.

Physicians' Guide to the Internet

http://www.netrep.com/home/pgi

Presents a site for physicians who want to take advantage of the many Internet information resources regarding lifestyle, clinical practice, education, and fun.

Planet Greek

http://www.nemonet.com/planet/plntgrek.htm

Offers a selection of Greek apparel.

Point Click and Shop

http://batech.com/cgi-bin/shop/b0index

Offers a new point-and-click shopping experience that includes fun merchandise and graphics.

Points North

http://www.mps.org/~pointsnorth

Offers United States military insignia and emblems reproduced in embroidery on sweaters, sweatshirts, and ballcaps. Also, offers T-shirts and sweaters with bicycling graphics embroidered.

Porsche Club of America (North East Region Server)

http://www.research.digital.com/CRL/personal/hawe/pca-ner.html

Provides stuff for Porsche lovers and owners. Includes joining the club, photo of the month, activities calendar, driving events. Offers links to sites in other regions as well.

Portland Software

http://www.portsoft.com

Develops screen savers and Ziplock, a suite of processing tools that allow companies to sell software or any kind of digital information directly and securely using the Internet, a BBS, or a pay-per-play CD-ROM.

Posters from Your Photos and Computer Files

http://www.pacificrim.net/~bydesign/poster.html

Makes a poster from your photos and computer files.

Power Images' PowerWeb

http://www.pwr.com/

Offers advertising and graphics service of Power Images, a Florida design and graphics firm. Provides clients of Power Images and other forward thinking companies with the means to place professional, effective advertising on the Internet's World Wide Web.

Precision Investment Services, Inc.

http://deepcove.com/powertrader

Presents PowerTrader, a fully integrated, real-time stock quotation, technical analysis and portfolio management software program that runs under MS Windows 3.x, NT, 95, and IBM's OS/2. PowerTrader software reads the data you recieve from your data service and displays the delayed or real-time quote information on your monitor. Enables you to collect data and analyze up to 32,000 instruments in any market: equities, options, futures, indices, bonds, money markets, and mutual funds.

Preziosi—The Italian Style in Jewelry

http://www.inrete.it/preziosi/homepahe.html

Presents online catalog of Preziosi's jewels, all completely handmade in 18 karat yellow, white, and red gold, and each accompanied by its own guarantee certificate.

PrimeCALL

http://www.compumedia.com/~primecal/Welcome.html

Offers callback services to anyone in the world. Bills customers in six-second increments, unlike the major

providers, which tend to bill in 30-second intervals. Requires no monthly fee and bills users only for the calls made and not the initial call to receive callback services.

The Private Source

`http://metroux.metrobbs.com/PrivateSource/index.htm`

Advertises Private Source's collection of personal gifts through an online catalog. Offers images for and/or describes many items.

Process Software Corporation

`http://www.process.com/`

Offers users a complete line of TCP/IP-based solutions for Windows NT, Windows, and OpenVMS platforms. Contains information about the company and its products, including Purveyor, its HTTP server for Windows NT, and its products supporting VMS Internet connectivity and NFS file systems.

Process Technologies Incorporated

`http://www.execpc.com/~pti`

Produces zero defect photo masks and phototooling for the LCD and microelectronics industries. Provides a full range of photolithographic services: artwork generation, laser confirmation plots, substrate coatings, step and repeat, hard surface masters, and working copies up to 24" × 36".

Professional Resource Outlet

`http://nyx10.cs.du.edu:8001/~jrozyck`

Contains database about advertising, business reports and information, buying guides, trade directory, mail order, credit finance, real estate, science, and technology.

Professional Services

`http://www.primenet.com/~laig/proserve`

Provides generic information from attorneys, certified public accountants, and medical professionals. Offers a bulletin section that contains information about tax issues, including an analysis of IRS guidelines for independent contractors and employee status.

The Progressive Business Web Pages

`http://envirolink.org/products/`

Contains a directory of environmentally or socially conscious companies. Also has links to other organizations, publications, government support agencies, and mailing lists associated with environment issues.

Project T1023—METIER Manufacturing Sector Study Summary

`ftp://race.analysys.co.uk/pub/race/economic/metier/manufsum.htm`

Provides summary report for the European manufacturing sector. Contains quantitative portrait, trends and potential problems, and effect of advanced communications on manufacturing. Provides general information for academic, knowledge, or business reasons.

Promptus Communications Web Server

`http://www.promptus.com/promptus`

Manufactures board and box-level solutions for ISDN-switched digital networks. Provides boards that allow OEMs to incorporate ISDN in their own products, and systems that provide ISDN connectivity for video-conferencing and data communications applications.

Punch & Brodie Productions

http://www.pacificrim.net/~lbrodie/punch

Provides live animation for video productions. Specializes in corporate videos and events.

QMI (ISO9000 Registrar) Home Page

http://www.pic.net/qmi/

Provides guidelines for the ISO9000 quality standards. Also offers registration for quality system in companies.

Quadralay MarketPlace

http://www.quadralay.com/home.html

Provides information about everything from the growing computer industry to the University of Texas and St. Edwards University. Also lists places to shop, eat, and be entertained.

Voted "Best Local WWW Site" in the *Austin Chronicle* 1995 Reader's Poll. Thank you for your support, Austin!

Please feel free to sign our Guest Book.

Qualitas, Inc.

http://www.qualitas.com

Develops memory management utilities 386MAX and Bluemax, a memory testing utility called RAMExam, and Qualitas Dispatch—a Windows communications package that allows faxing, Internet mail, printing, and e-mail in one easy step. Includes a link to Qualitas' FTP site free of charge downloadable software and patches, United States, and international sales information available in English, French, and German.

QUORUM

http://205.218.102.223

Provides state-of-the-art consumer electronics, health, entertainment, and self-improvement products. Specializes in home, auto, and personal safety.

QuoteCom Home Page

http://www.quote.com

Provides financial market data to the Internet community, to members (for $9.95 per month), as well as other services.

R. A. Vess Enterprises

http://www.infi.net/~ravess/index.html

Offers computer/software consulting, integration, customization, technical support, and value added services. Also offers desktop publishing, Internet training, and Web page development.

Rachael's Reminders

http://heinlein.k2nesoft.com/~rar/rates.html

Subscription based online event reminder service. Sends reminders by e-mail at one week and three days prior to event.

Radio Marketing Page Menu

http://www.prgone.com/bus/radio3060/menu.html

Provides information about radio advertising. Offers promotion ideas for particular months (July's has information about September). Also offers special dates, safe ideas, and target businesses for the particular month. Provides information about where to advertise and how to write effective radio ads.

Rainbow Rags

http://www.promotion.com/rainbow/

Offers high-quality, durable children's clothing featuring embroidered and appliqued trim for a unique look.

Rainforest Health Project

http://www.mps.org/rhp

Nonprofit international relief organization recognized in the United States and Peru. Sells art and artifacts created by the indigenous peoples of the Peruvian rain forests and reinvests the proceeds into RHP to help fund the organization.

RE/MAX WorldLink

http://iquest.com/~new3/remax/

Serves as a worldwide real estate information source and referral service. Agents list your own personnel pages (USA, Canada, Caribbean, worldwide, international, remax, real estate, home/house/residence/condominium/ land, realty, Realtors, agents, property, listings, relocation, military).

The Real Estate Junction

http://www.valleynet.com/~webcity/

Provides real estate listings by category, including residential, farm and ranch, commercial and investment properties, and coastal/resort/retirement properties.

Real Estate Web

http://www.infi.net/REWeb/

Lets you browse all listings of property for sale on the east coast or simply look up individual reality companies.

Redi-Check—Online Payment Solutions

http://www.redichek.com/redichek

Allows online stores, business, and individuals to accept payment for products and services using a personal or business checking account. Also presents a frequently asked questions section.

Regional Economic Models, Inc.

http://www.crocker.com/~remi/

Constructs models that forecast the economic and demographic effects that policy initiatives or external events might cause in a local economy.

Register Your Domain Name

http://www.netbistro.com/synaptic/domain.html

Offers to register a domain name for your business or organization on the Web. Lets you check which Internet domain names are still available.

The Resource Center for Growing Companies

http://www.halcyon.com/midnight/

Serves as a resource center for growing companies. Presents the online edition of the subscriber newsletter, *Creative Edge Meets the Bottom Line™*.

The Resource Group

http://www.in.net/resource/index.html

Serves as the meeting and management professionals' launchpad to personal and professional growth and development. The group has two main divisions: Technical Resources, a company committed to assisting organizations and individuals become comfortable and profitable using the tools of the information age; The Resource Online Bookstore, which offers books, online newsletters and other material.

ReZ.n8

http://www.rezn8.com/

Hollywood animation company on the cutting edge of comprehensive image branding packages. Offers a partial

list of clients, along with samples of work, including work from *The Flintstones* and *Clear and Present Danger*.

The Rip-Tie Company: Velcro Cable Organizers

http://www.riptie.com/riptie/

Sells cable organizers. Designs Rip-Tie products for maximum speed, flexibility, and safety, letting you easily insert, remove, or rearrange cables as you need without damage.

Roctronics Lighting and Special Effects

http://www.oppnet.com/ern/roctronics.html

Provides lighting and special effects.

Rodex—Manufacturing Technology Showcase

http://www.magi.com/~rodex/

Covers business opportunities that relate to manufacturing technologies.

Rogers Communications World Wide Web Server

http://www.rogers.com

Offers operations in wireless, long distance, cable systems, and multimedia.

RON—Recruiters Online Network

http://www.onramp.net:80/ron/

Offers large directory on recruitment. Lets you post your résumé, subscribe to news digest, and search for particular organizations. Lets members share information about business opportunities and employment positions.

Rose City Darts

http://amz.com/~amazing/RoseCityDarts/

Distributes darts.

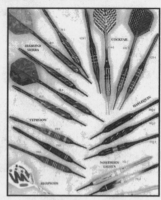

Roslyn Celtic Jewellery

http://www.internet-eireann.ie/Euromall/ireland/roslyn/roslyn.html

Contains a collection of Celtic jewellery, handcrafted in gold and silver. Includes claddagh rings, pendants, brooches, and more. Also presents the history of these items.

Ross-Simons

http://www.shopping2000.com/shopping2000/ross_simon/

Provides information on jewelry offered by Ross-Simons with images and prices for each piece.

Royal Tara China

http://www.euromall.ie/Euromall/ireland/stores/tara.html

Contains a collection of fine bone china.

Royer's Flowers

http://go.flowerlink.com/html/dship/dship.html

Contains images of the various types of floral arrangements, foliage, gift baskets, and specialty items.

S & S Enterprises

http://www.usaweb.com/usaweb/ss

Provides a wholesale sports supplement catalog. Serves the needs of professional and amateur bodybuilders.

S-Cubed Home Page

http://www.scubed.com/

Takes you on a tour of San Diego, California. Includes southern California traffic reports, a missing children database, and positions available at Maxwell Labs.

SABRE Decision Technologies

http://www.sdt.com/SDT

Provides information about SABRE Decision Technologies, which provides business solutions to the travel and transportation industry and related fields. Also lists employment opportunities.

Saint Anne Hospice

http://www.luminet.net/mktplace/stanne

Provides skilled nursing, adult daycare, nursing assistance classes, and trained social workers.

Sales and Marketing Exchange: PR Web

http://www.sme.com:80/prweb/

Lets you search for public relations providers and professionals. Offers to locate related services, share ideas, and find information related to public relations.

Sales Plus

http://www.salesplus.com/

Contains information related to sales. Contains prospecting, video and audio tapes, books and software, trade shows, and consulting type of information related to sales.

Salonwear

http://visi.com/~ibonk/

Offers factory direct beauty supplies, a complete line of uniforms and fashionable career attire for the stylist, capes, gowns, lab coats, and sundries.

SATURN Enthusiasts

http://www.physics.sunysb.edu/Saturn/

Contains model information, sneak previews of upcoming models, company information, and product reviews and comparisons. Categorizes its Frequently Asked Question section under heads like mechanical, electrical, audio systems, accessories. Provides all you need to know about Saturn.

SBA: Service Corps of Retired Executives

http://www.sbaonline.sba.gov/business_management/score.html

Contains information on financing, expanding, and starting businesses. Lets you search for documents and other Internet links.

SBH—Patent Management Group

http://www.inlink.com/~sbh/index.html

Specializes in all aspects of United States patents, including licensing, buying, selling, consulting, and infringement

matters. Recognizes that many inventors and companies have achieved greater success in creating the inventions rather than selling or licensing them. Acts as an agent for inventors, companies, and institutions in marketing United States patents.

Scan/US, Inc. Geomarket Analysis Software for Windows

http://www.scanus.com/scanus/4windows.html

Offers a complete description of the company's Scan/US Streets and Data USA CD-ROM, Scan/US street address geocoder, and business and census demographic data products. Includes Daytime Marketplace, Consumer Spending Potential, Basic Demographics, Income and Education, Census geography and data, and more. Also displays some thematic maps and provides complete product information.

Scarves

http://www.euromall.ie/Euromall/ireland/stores/scarves.html

Offers hand-painted scarves made in Ireland.

Scintilla—Alternative Lighting and Accessories

http://www.mindspring.com/~bart/scintilla.html

Presents a collection of functional art in forms of lighting fixtures, jewelry, frames, and other choice accessories.

Scope Systems—Industrial Electronics Repair and Services

http://www.charm.net/~scope

Specializes in repairing of industrial electronic circuit boards and assemblies. Includes analog, digital, power supplies, AC & DC drives, video monitors, and process control equipment.

Screenwriters Online

http://screenwriter.com/insider/news.html

Offers trade secrets, professional advice, and insider information by major screenwriters who make their living by getting their scripts made into movies. Publishes *The Screenwriter's Insider Report*, a subscription-based industry newsletter that features insider interviews with screenwriters, studio heads, and agents.

SDI

http://www.hardiman.com/malls/rmcm/sdi/index.html

Serves as an advertising page for retailers, business services, and tourism. Features a listing of existing products that need new investors. Charges a fee for advertising.

Seals on Wheels

http://www.acoates.com/seals

Offers mobile notary, small claims, and fingerprinting services in the San Francisco Bay area.

Search Utility

http://edgar.stern.nyu.edu/xtest/seek.html

Provides directory of companies. Offers alternative modes of search. Lets you search by specific SIC codes or by a company's SIC code. Also lets you search by business category. Provides exhaustive listings through the SIC codes.

SeaVision USA

http://www.seavisionusa.com

Offers the finest in underwater vision technology. The underwater world provides a unique and challenging environment for our senses, especially sight.

Second Chair Corporation

http://www.secondchair.com/secondchair

Manufactures legal specific software for the legal research and litigation community. Features a legal specific research RDBMS (The Legal Scholar), a litigation case management RDBMS (The Trial Lawyers Assistant), and a generic non–legal-specific research RDMBS tool (Research Information Manager).

Security APL Quote Server

http://www.secapl.com/cgi-bin/qs

Provides 15-minute delayed stock information. Also offers end-of-day mutual fund NAVs. Provides historical data on the DJIA and S&P 500 as well.

Self-Management Institute

http://www.xmission.com:80/~smi/

Serves clients in the areas of sales and marketing, leadership development, interpersonal skills, business communication, and open enrollment proposal workshops.

Selling Your Products Abroad

http://www.kcilink.com:80/brc/marketing/v2n10.html

Contains general information for product export, market opportunities, and market identification. Also provides financing information for exports.

Seven Technologies— Knows How

http://www.sevent.dk

Provides process visualization, automation tools, graphical user interfaces, supervision systems, transaction systems, security management systems, and information about how to get in touch with us.

SGA Goldstar Research

http://www.sgagoldstar.com/sga/

Presents a daily financial newsletter that offers the opinions and recommendations of successful stock market experts. Contains information on stocks, bonds, options, futures, securities, gold, the NYSE, American and NASDAQ stock exchanges, as well as Dow Jones, over the counter, and Canadian stocks.

Shadow Patent Office

http://www.spo.eds.com/patent.html

Provides information about United States patents.

Shape Memory Applications, Inc.

http://www.sma-inc.com/

Supplies and uses NiTi shape memory and superelastic alloys, including both materials and custom fabricated components.

Sharrow and Associates' Advertising and Marketing Home Page

http://www.dnai.com/~sharrow/register.html

Hosts marketing topics, including an upcoming mail-order catalog and advertising opportunities.

Shell Australia's WWW Graduate Recruitment Site

http://www.next.com.au/shell/

Offers information for university students on graduate recruitment, vacation work, and an insight into the nature of the Shell group of companies.

Shell Oil Web Site

http://www.shellus.com

Offers visitors the opportunity to learn about Shell's activities and businesses, download the 1994 Annual Report, and provide feedback on Shell service station quality.

Shell Oil Company

Service, Safety and Satisfaction

Sholink Corporation

http://www.sholink.com/

Provides a newsletter, seminars, Web design and hosting services, and Web tools that facilitate global competitive business processes by adopting and integrating Internet technologies.

Shopper's Utopia

http://shop-utopia.com

Contains a variety of custom shops, ranging from leather products, fashion jewelry, and salsa to a full-fledged graphics design shop.

Shopping 2000 Home Page

http://www.shopping2000.com/

Offers a wide variety of products. Companies offering products include Brita, Caribbean Software, CDnow, Clifford & Wills, Coffee Anyone, Dakco PC Products Division, Inc., Delta Dream Vacations, Hanover Shoes, J C Whitney, Lens Direct, Omaha Steaks International, Rodale Press, Superflora, 800-GIFT-LINE, Teleflora, and USA Direct.

Silicon Investor

http://www.techstocks.com/

Consists of five innovative areas for technology investors. Includes mroe than 250 technology stocks. Lets you participate in discussion forums, create individual charts and comparison charts, view company profiles, and get quotes and other financial information.

Silver Jewellery

http://www.algonet.se/~marions/akhome.htm

Displays samples of work at Sir John Cass Faculty of Arts, Jewellery, and Silversmithing.

Simple Solutions

http://fbsolutions.com/prieto/simple1.htm

Home-based consulting business.

Small and Home-Based Business Links

http://iquest.com/~coupon/homebased.htm

Offers dozens of small and home-based business links: reference, franchises, marketing, opportunities for home-based businesses.

Small Business Development Center

http://www.bucknell.edu/~sbdc

Provides small businesses and entrepreneurs managerial and engineering assistance.

Small World Software's Development and Consulting Services

http://www.smallworld.com/promotions/
promo_development_and_cons.html

Develops custom applications and consults with clients who work on a variety of platforms, including MacOS, Windows, and Unix. Features Small World XChange, an interactive financial training game.

SmartStuff Software

http://www.teleport.com/~smrtstuf/

Presents SmartStuff Software, maker of FoolProof Security for Macintosh, DOS, and Windows.

Soft "Wear" by ColorTech

http://www.holli.com/colortech

Offers more than 20 T-shirt designs and a wide variety of shirts, hats, and coffee mugs. Also puts your own artwork on a shirt if you e-mail it to them.

Softpro Books

http://plaza.xor.com/Softpro/index.html

Online page for retail computer bookstore situated in Boston and Denver. Contains inventory of software books, and mailing list and ordering information.

Somers & Associates

http://www.jkcg.com/Webmaster/Ispy/index.html

Claims to be "private eyes for the world." Specializes in background investigation, competitor intelligence, financial transaction crimes, and more.

SONY Online

http://www.music.sony.com/

Contains information about Sony products and services. Includes categories of music and films.

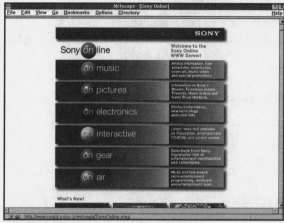

Sotheby's Australia

http://www.com.au/sothebys

Australia's leading auction house online. Provides fine art images, illustrated art sales catalogs, exclusive real estate listings, and other art, decorative art, furniture and jewelry sales information.

Southern Reprographics

http://www.mindspring.com/~srepro/southern.html

Specializes in drafting, computer drafting, blueprinting, plotter, electrostatic, and xerographic products.

Special Electronic Security Products Ltd.

http://sesp.co.il/~tunik

Specializes in the design and manufacturing of surveillance and counter surveillance equipment and systems. Offers direct purchase worldwide.

Specialty Concepts, Inc.

http://www.wp.com/scinc/

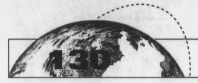

Presents an online catalog that shows Specialty Concepts' complete product line of electronics for the photovoltaic solar industry. Manufactures all types of regulators/charge controllers and monitors for use in PV systems.

Spectra.Net Mall

http://www.spectra.net/

Brings the convenience of home shopping to you. Adds new storefronts, new products, and new services daily.

Spider

http://www.w3spider.com

Offers Spider Technologies' new product, Spider, the visual solution to Web/database applications. Enables you to create and maintain Web applications with absolutely no programming.

SpiralWest Interactive

http://www.spiralwest.com

Specializes in creative user interface design. Excels in 2-D and 3-D animation, animated interfaces, digital audio and video, art design and production, multimedia programming, consulting and strategic marketing for interactive CD-ROMs, floppy disks, kiosks, and Web sites.

SPITE! Books

http://www.ukshops.co.uk:8000/spite/

Carries a wide range of United Kingdom self-published material. Features comics and zines.

Split Cycle Technology

http://www.splitcycle.com.au/~splitcyc

Offers efficient, and enviromentally acceptable technology. Explains Split Cycle's engine technology and why it provides the best solution to automobile pollution. Also explains low emission fuel injector technology and a fan technology that will have applications from vacuum cleaners to jet engines.

Spy Supply Online

http://wbrt.wb.psu.edu/~galt/spy.html

Offers a full product line, including audio recorders, antibugging and tapping devices, covert camera, locksmithing tools, and more.

SrategyWeb: [Commerce/ WWW/Community/ Conferences]

http://www.onramp.net/~atw_dhw/home.htm

Provides information about business strategy related services. Focuses on enhancing the strategy process and a sense of community on the Internet.

STANCOM, Inc.

http://www.mindspring.com/~stancom

Specializes in all types of security systems and equipment.

STAT-USA

http://www.stat-usa.gov/

Provides information about the economy, businesses, social programs, and environmental programs. Provides data from more than 50 federal sources.

Stealth Technologies

http://www.peak.org/~omarab/index.html

Provides wholesale stereo equipment, custom computer programming, hardware sales, computer setup assistance, and is affiliated with Affordable Limousine, a local limousine service provider.

Stephens Graphic Design WebPage Advertising

http://www.opendoor.com/StephensDesign/
StephensDesign.html

Provides information on the company's projects and Web page design. Includes a link to ConsciousMind, a list of businesses operated by spiritually oriented people.

. . . .
StewNet BBS & Internet Services

http://www.stewnet.com/business/StewsServices.html

Provides Web presence, consulting, Web authoring, and training.

. . . .
STI Printers, Toner & Supplies

http://www.itsnet.com/commercial/sti

Offers a wide selection of new and remanufactured imaging supplies for printers, copiers, and fax.

. . . .
Stockdeck Online

http://www.stockdeck.com/

Features corporate profiles on more than 600 publicly traded companies. Lets you request additional information such as financial reports or news releases online as well as 15-minute delayed stock quotes.

. . . .
Strategic Applications for Professional Offices

http://www.ticllc.net/~ccasey/bytewise/bw_welc.htm

Specializes in identifying and implementing strategic applications of technology for professional service providers, such as lawyers, doctors, architects, and so forth. Offers a variety of services, including business analysis and planning, custom application design and development, selection and acquisition of hardware/software, and marketing and management audits.

. . . .
Stratton's Collector Toy Network

http://www.umsi.com/stratton/ctn.htm

Offers a collection of collectible scale replica toys. Includes cars from the sixties, John Deere farm toys, and licensed Coca-Cola toys and banks.

Stratton's Collector Toy Network

For the kid in all of us.
Offering hard to find collector quality toys and scale replicas at discount prices.

Christmas Gifts!
Collector toys may be the perfect gift for that hard-to-buy-for person on your list. And children will always love bright new toy cars, trucks, and tractors.
See details below.

. . . .
Structural Affiliates International, Inc.— Structural Engineers

http://www.saii.com

Specializes in challenging projects that require unique expertise, such as seismic, base isolation, hangars, high-rise, locks and dams, bridges, hospitals, parking garages, commercial, and other structures.

. . . .
Studio One Photography, Inc.

http://www.interaccess.com/studio-one/

Operates six photography studios in Chicagoland, and specializes in photography and video production for weddings, corporate events, commercial uses, and portraits.

. . . .
Sturbridge Yankee Workshop

http://netplaza.com/plaza/strfrnts/1003/storepg1.html

Offers fine home furnishings, including decorating accessories and furniture.

. . . .
subLuminal Designs

http://subluminal.com

Provides graphic design, Web design, 3-D modeling visualization, and creative input for individuals or businesses.

Sun Alliance

http://www.sunalliance.co.uk/sunalliance/

Provides company and product information, quotes, and details of some of Sun Alliance's sponsorship and community projects.

SunFun Collection

http://www.sunfun.com

Offers travel and outdoor catalog.

Sunglasses, Shavers, and More

http://www.shades.com/sunglass/shop

Offers sunglasses, shavers, and more. Includes a large selection of sunglasses.

Sunquest Information Systems

http://www.sunquest.com/

Provides laboratory information systems and computer solutions to hospitals and medical laboratories.

Surplus United States Government Sales

http://www.drms.dla.mil/index.html

Contains information on sale of surplus Department of Defense properties to general public. Shows mostly advertisements but has only a partial listing of the materials available for sale.

Svoboda's Books Online— State College, PA

http://www.epicom.com/svobodas

Specializes in academic and technical titles, but offers access to anything in American Books-in-Print. Lets you place your book orders from your computer.

Tal, Inc.

http://moose.erie.net/~talerie

Offers extensive experience in print, media, multimedia, audio/video, interactive, broadcast, direct mail, and outdoor marketing.

Tampa Machinery Auction, Inc.

http://www.usaweb.com/usaweb/tma

Holds an auction every month. Includes surplus and seized vehicles from cities, counties, sheriffs' departments, utilities, and many others. Offers lists of inventory for next auction.

The Tampa Rico Cigar Company Internet Sampler

http://www.highwayone.com/rico/

Serves as the online version of the Tampa Rico Cigar Company, a family operation that began making handmade cigars in a little factory only 400 feet from its present location, commited to quality by incorporating the finest tobaccos of Central and South America and expert craftsmanship.

Tandy Corporation

http://www.tandy.com/

Encompasses Radio Shack, Computer City, Incredible Universe, and others. Provides corporate information about Tandy and plans for rapid expansion.

TaxSites—Internet Income Tax-Related Information Available on Internet

http://www.best.com/~ftmexpat/html/taxsites.html

Provides income tax–related information. Also contains links to related sites.

Taylor Publishing Company

http://www.taylorpub.com/

Provides sales and marketing information on general and yearbook publishing, as well as an FTP site for distributing publishing information. Also hosts an electronic book store for high-quality hardcover books and provides information for high school and college reunion activities.

TEAMS: Marketing and Sales Assessment Software

http://mtg-teams.com

Offers TEAMS, a sales and marketing assessment software program designed for use by small businesses, small business development centers, and management consulting firms. Provides visitors the opportunity to see samples of the TEAMS questionnaire and report and the ability to download a demonstration version of the software directly. Also provides an electronic order form.

Tech Image, Ltd.

http://www.techimage.com/techimage

Provides public relations and marketing communication support services to high-technology companies in the computer, digital video, telecom, and interactive/multimedia markets. Combines traditional public relations capabilities with emerging online communication tools.

The TechExpo on WWW

http://www.techexpo.com/

Focuses on information about high technology companies and products, related societies, and conferences. Offers comprehensive coverage of the science related high technology sector.

Teleflora—at the Spectra.Net Mall

http://www.spectra.net/mall/teleflora/

Teleflora—because the time is always right for sending flowers.

TeleKachina Productions

http://www.telekachina.com

Provides video and multimedia consulting and production services for local and national clients.

Ten Thirty-One, Inc.

http://www.irc1031.com/1031/

Presents "Real Estate Exchange Frequently Asked Questions," which provide information about the tax saving benefits of Internal Revenue Code Section 1031, and a "Real Estate Exchange Checklist," which helps taxpayers determine if these benefits are available to them.

TENAGRA Home Page

http://arganet.tenagra.com/Tenagra

Internet providing site. Helps clients use Internet to market and advertise products and services and for public relations.

Tessler's Nifty Tools (TNT)

http://www.crl.com/~zallar/tnt/tnt.html

Supplies Tessler's Nifty Tools®, a collection of 35 useful Windows 3.1, 95, NT, and DOS utility programs. Includes a Win GRP file editor, Win95 resource monitor, and more.

The Breyer World of Model Horses

http://www.aa.net/~cascade

Provides a model horse mail-order service that offers many things for the model horse collector. Always has current models in stock.

The Fred Siegel Group

http://www.fredsiegel.com

Specializes in providing financial news analysis and consulting to the broadcast media, primarily to local radio and television affiliates of the national networks.

The Mortgage Manager

http://www.fairfield.com/mindtrek/index.html

Claims you can save dollars and interest on your mortgage and cut your payment time in half. Provides information about managing your mortgage and principal prepayment.

The Mortgage Manager Version 5.00

http://web.idirect.com/~klg

Offers a mortgage and loan amortization program for professionals, used by banks, lawyers, accountants, insurance companies, real estate agents, and mortgage brokers.

The South African Futures Exchange

http://www.safex.co.za/

Offers information on the financial and agricultural derivatives market in South Africa, as well as downloadable statistics and prices.

The Techni-Core Home Page

http://www.traveller.com/~tcore

Specializes in telecommunications equipment operation and repair support for DOD and NASA subcontracts.

The Virtual Press

http://www.aloha.com/~william/vphp.html

Provides global solutions for the world's electronic publishing needs through consulting, full-service e-publishing, and community service.

The Virtual Toy Store

http://www.halcyon.com/uncomyn/home.html

Offers a fully interactive toy store, complete with sound and video clips to enable you to play with the toys in the store. Specializes in unusual noisemaking and mechanical toys, but offers many other lines.

Thomas Register Home Page

http://www.thomasregister.com

Provides instant sourcing and contact information on industrial products and services offered by 150,000 United States and Canadian companies in approximately 52,000 categories. Provides information about Thomas Register's printed and CD-ROM editions. Also provides access to the full Thomas Register database, including company name,

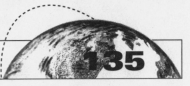

city, state, telephone, fax, and company/product line descriptions. Includes more than 1,500,000 individual product/service sources in all.

Thoroughbred Motorcars

http://www.tnnet.com/thoroughbred/

Offers wholesale auto parts for luxury cars.

Timbergreen Custom Homes—Dallas, TX

http://www.dfw.net/~custmbld/timbergreen.html

Provides information about Timbergreen Custom, which has been designing and building high-end custom homes in and around Dallas, Texas since 1983. Contains information about the company and present homes available. Also contains photographs, floor plans, and elevations of various projects built by Timbergreen Custom Homes.

Time Life Explorer

http://www.timelife.com

Lets you explore the many products Time Life offers in books, music, and videos.

Tipperary Crystal

http://www.internet-eireann.ie/Euromall/ireland/roslyn/crystal.html

Lets you view and order crytal products handmade in Tipperary, Ireland.

Torresen Marine, Inc.

http://www.win.net/~torresen

Serves as an online site for sailors. Provides information concerning Great Lakes Race activity, weather, winter storage, computer sailing simulators, and more. Offers links to many other sail-related sites.

Total Flower Exports

http://www.iinet.net.au/~total/

Provides information about this exporter of fresh and dried flowers. Lets you view some unusual flowers and even order a sampler of dried flowers delivered to your door.

Total Process Consultants

http://udcsco.udc.com/TPC/TPC.html

Specializes in connectivity solutions, software development, Web presence design, marketing, and implementation, and hardware/software growth and expandibility planning.

Tough Traveler Gear

http://www.travelsource.com/travelstore/toughtraveler/toughtraveler.html

Presents Tough Travel gear online. Features soft luggage, packbacks, camera bags, duffel bags, and child carriers.

Toyota OnLine

http://www.toyota.com.au/

Lists new Toyota models, along with an illustrated worldwide motorsport news and photo archive, dealer contacts, and other information.

Traders' Connection

http://www.trader.com

Presents more than 500,000 classified ads online. Lets you browse or search ad papers from all over the United States and Canada. Offers more than 40 publications online. Also offers full BBS services and nationwide full Internet access for as little as $3.95 per month.

Tradtec—Technical Translation

http://www.cyberplus.ca/tradtec.htm

Offers technical translation services to small- and medium-sized engineering firms and information technology companies. Specializes in large projects of a complex technical nature.

Transit-Center

http://www.SmartLink.net/~horizon

Serves as a resource site for public tranportation professionals. Includes vendor information on companies serving the transit industry. Also includes FTA Section 15 tables, bus specifications, sample RFPs, training materials, classified advertising, employment opportunities, conference schedules, training opportunities, and numerous Web links and standard mail addresses.

Trident Data Systems—SunScreen and FileNet Partners

http://www.tds.com

Serves the growing need to secure network connections. Designs firewall systems to provide the required level of protection and assurance to safely connect to networks, ranging from simple packet screening techniques to bastion host and proxy server configurations.

Trusts and Estates Bulletin—June 1994

http://www.haledorr.com/trust_news.html

Contains information on the pros and cons of family partnerships. Specifically deals with the implications of gifts to family members to avoid double taxation.

TSW's Interactive Classifieds

http://www.catalog.com/tsw/classified

Represents a revolution in classified advertising. Serves as a source of classifieds.

The Turning Point

http://www.tpoint.net/

Offers information about The Turning Point, a service that provides connections for Austin businesses. Includes various categories arranged by business or community.

Twinkle Toes!—Socks for Kids

http://www.bonk.com/Twinkle

Provides photos and prices.

The UK Shopping Centre

http://www.ukshops.co.uk:8000

The United Kingdom Shopping Centre. Offers 180,000 books, 56,000 videos, and 14,000 CDs, plus computer software, PC games, CD-ROMs, and more. Offers businesses services, including Internet and interactive advertising as well as joint venture management and referral services, to enable them to reach their market quickly and economically.

Ulster County Development Corporation

http://www.okc.com/ucdc

Provides businesses with information and planning services for Ulster County area office space made available by the downsizing of IBM. Outlines considerable economic and tax incentives.

Ultimate Auto Connection

http://www.wizard.com/uac.html

Serves as a site for new cars.

Uncommon Connections

http://www.mps.org/uncommon/

Offers online marketplace. Includes some unique products and unusual gift items. Provides secure credit card transactions for all online merchants.

United Futures Group, Inc.

http://blackdiamond.com/trading.com/commodities

Provides information on a number of things related to stock market futures and options. Includes information on brokerage firms, brokers, trading advisors, and quotes. Also contains links to other financial sites.

United Lithographers, Inc.

http://www.ul.eznet.com

Specializes in receiving digital information via the Internet for output on UL's Docutech 135 high-speed digital printer. Also provides the capability to repurpose your information for printing on our offset presses.

United States Bank Student Aid

http://usbanks1.com

Presents a comprehensive guide to financing the college education. Covers topics from creating a monthly budget to applying for the right loan. Lets you order materials from U.S. Bank directly online.

United States Business Advisor

http://www-far.npr.gov/VDOB/

Clarifies government's dealings with businesses. Offers assistance listed by categories like regulatory, financial, labor, trade, commerce, and selling to government. Features a personal front page message from the president. Lets you know what the government is doing or planning about business.

United States Council for International Business

http://www.uscib.org/

Contains links to different sources related to international business. Also offers links to other related organizations. Provides a section on ATA Carnet, the merchandising passport for doing business in foreign countries.

United States Tax Code Online

http://www.fourmilab.ch/ustax/ustax.html

Contains the complete text of United States Internal Revenue Code.

Untied Cities Mortgage Company

http://uclc.corn/uclc/quickmath.html

Offers a cash calculator you can use to determine how much money you can save by refinancing your home

Upclose Demographic Summaries

http://www.upclose.com/upclose/demomenu/demomenu.htm

Provides information about population demographics. Includes summaries, updated to 1994 figures, by states, metropolitan statistical areas, counties, cities, and towns.

UPS Home Page

http://www.ups.com/

Contains service information, software, UPS news, and contact information. Also contains a section on package tracking.

Used Car Net

http://www.rezn8.com/usedcars/

Claims to be the largest database for used cars of any type. Lets you list and/or view cars. Includes model, make, year, maximum price you're willing to accept, maximum acceptable mileage.

UTEE

http://utee.com

Offers a team of designers and programmers who develop virtual storefronts and establish a corporate presence for businesses on the Web.

Valentine & Company

http://ireland.iol.ie/~nova/nova1/pages/valentns.htm

Serves as an Internet department store. Supplies linen by Thomas Ferguson, among other high-quality Irish products.

Valore International

http://www.florin.com/valore/

An electronic journal. Covers issues in international trade and development.

Vegas.COM's Electronic Mall

http://www.vegas.com/otherside/elemall.html

Las Vegas–based electronic shopping mall.

Victoria Digital InfoMART

http://interchange.idc.uvic.ca/~vonline

Provides information and virtual shopping. Also offers *Victoria Online NEWS…*, an electronic magazine. Welcomes Webvertisers to participate.

Video Online Fashion Page

http://www.vol.it/HTML_UK/MODA_UK/

Offers a selection of glamour sites of the web: magazines, shopping, fashion shows, jewelry, beauty, and more, updated continuously.

VideoServer, Incorporated

http://www.videoserver.com

Supplies multimedia conference servers for OEMs, VARs, and distributors.

Virtual AdVentures

http://www.virtualadventures.com

Focuses on producing high-quality travel and adventure experiences via CD-ROM and other forms of electronic media.

Virtual Business Plaza

http://zocalo.net/cz/

Presents the Czech and Slovak market, companies, and other information.

Virtual Design Center

http://www.vdc.com/

Presents a corporate communication and marketing system for furniture design and marketing. Contains information about the furniture industry.

Virtual Diamond Lobby

http://www.teleport.com/~raylc/master/diamonds.html

Advertises the products of Associate Jewelers, Inc. Offers resources that include a guide for understanding more about diamonds, gemological information with images, appraisal information, and a diamond price guide. Also offers an Ask the Gemologist section in which you can e-mail questions to a certified gemologist.

The Virtual Forest City (London, Ontario, Canada)

http://emporium.turnpike.net/~athome

Serves as a site of potential interest to inhabitants of London, Ontario, Canada, and surrounding areas, but with entertainment and business sponsors of international appeal.

Virtual Job Fair

http://www.careerexpo.com

Provides resources for the career conscious technical professional. Offers career opportunities, links to high-tech employers' home pages, job fair venues, *High Technology Careers Magazine*, and an online job search/retrieval system. Also lets you send your résumé to potential employers, hiring managers, and more.

Virtually Yours Online Mall

http://www.islandnet.com/~alanb/AJBmall.html

Features a free classified ad section, fine art, and real estate.

Vision Sunglass Eyewear

http://www.opennet.com/hydepark

Provides discounted sunglasses: Ray-ban, Serengeti, Bolle', Gargoyles. Furnishes other brands upon request. Offers specials on a specific pair of sunglasses each week. Lets you send e-mail on models you would like to see as the special of the week.

vMall

http://www.iquest.net/vmall/

Provides product photos, low prices, and a one-year, money back guarantee on all items.

Volvic Natural Spring Water

http://www.volvic.ca/

Presents a pure and natural cyberspace—the cool, the clean, the wet, and the geologically hip world of Volvic natural spring water from France.

VR Cargo International Home Page

http://www.kolumbus.fi/cargo/

Provides information about Finnish railways as a transportation link between the West and East. Includes links to Russian and railroad Web sites.

WaidSoft

http://www.datasync.com/waidsoft

Offers multimedia production and design, desktop multimedia, custom graphics, and Web design.

Walgreen Co.

http://www.walgreens.com

Includes Walgreen's corporate information, career opportunities, company history, store locations, and links to other pharmacy-related sites.

Wall Street Journal

http://www.adnet.wsj.com/

Online guide for advertising on the Net, Web sites, and general Internet directory. Lets you search the directory by category and alphabetically.

Wall Street Net

http://www.netresource.com/wsn/home.html

Provides update-to-date data on financial dealings for issuers, investors, and banks. Contains archival data of the last twelve months.

Wall Street Online

http://www.wso.com/wso/

Presents a collection of daily investment advisory services that include: Prostock, Gabriel Advisory Service, The Seven Percent Solution, Instant Advisor, Fibond, IPO Outlook, and Newby & Company.

Waters Corporation

http://www.waters.com/

Provides chromatographers product information on HPLC instruments, chromatography columns, and chemistries, as well as information about the company and its related technologies.

A Wealth of Information InfoHans Page

http://www.infohans.com/access/by-seller/
A_Wealth_of_Information

Provides database of information for entrepreneurs and small businesses. Contains extensive information on categories like advertising, small business opportunities, home-based business ideas, projects, mail order, financial information, direct response marketing.

Web Designer, Inc.

http://www.webhead.com/~designer/

Designs and builds Internet Web information systems. Offers to design, create, manage, and evolve a complete Internet presence.

Web Digest for Marketers

http://www.advert.com/wdfm/wdfm.html

Offers links to other marketing-related sites. Also offers advertising- and catalog-related information.

The Web Plaza—Online Marketplace

http://www.webplaza.com/

Serves as an online marketplace. Offers categorized listings of various businesses.

Web Warehouse Mall

http://webwarehouse.com

Offers products and services ranging from office furniture, watches, and flowers, to real estate services.

WebReach Advertising & Marketing

http://www.io.com/~webreach/

Offers Internet advertising and marketing.

Welcome to Canadian Business InfoWorld

http://csclub.uwaterloo.ca/u/nckwan/index.html

Provides Canadian business-related information. Includes Canadian business directory, business resource database,

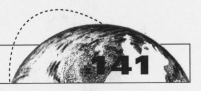

stock market links, business school links, and job-related information. Offers many links to many places.

Welcome to helpwanted.com

http://www.helpwanted.com/

Contains advertisements from companies with help wanted ads.

Welcome to Intel

http://www.intel.com/

Corporate site of Intel Corporation. Very nice design and very easy to use. Lets you sign up online for testing the upcoming P6 processor on your own machine, among other features.

Welcome to Internet MCI

http://www.internetmci.com/

Provides information on products and services offered by MCI, as well as links to other related sites. Also offers shopping links.

Welcome to Molson Canadian Online

http://www.molson.com/canadian/

Focuses on Canada: culture, events, travel in Canada, and hockey. Also offers e-mail, bulletin boards, and a well-developed chat facility.

Western Direct's Home Page

http://www.westerndirect.com

Provides support for a host of different activities, including inbound and outbound telemarketing, internet services, credit card processing, and database and information services.

Who's Who in Luxury Real Estate

http://www.luxury-realestate.com/jbl/

An international network of independent real estate brokers. Specializes in the finest properties in the world. Includes more than 300 brokers representing 45 states in the United States and more than 20 foreign countries. Offers properties online and provides listing information.

WilTel

http://www.wiltel.com/

Provides full domestic and international services.

Winona

http://www.mps.org/~winona.inc/

Offers products to make your life comfortable and enjoyable. Includes a selection of sportswear, sweaters, and unique gifts.

Woman Made Catalog

http://www.megamed.com/womanmade

Features art and crafts made by women-owned businesses. Includes jewelry, pottery, T-shirts, stained and etched glass, and more.

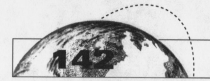
Woodbridge and Associates

http://www.calypso.com/woodbridge/

Offers information on making your money work for you.

WoodWrite Wood Pens

http://www.ip.net/shops/WoodWrite__Wood_Pens/

Offers a variety of wood pens and pencils hand-turned in both traditional and unusual shapes using a variety of hardwoods selected for beauty of color and grain pattern. Offers laser engraving and quantity pricing for corporate gift and promotional item buyers.

[working title(s)], inc.

http://www.gate.net/~wtinc/

Serves as a one-stop shopping source for all your interactive communications needs. Delivery systems range from CD-ROM to the Internet. Creates custom graphics, audio, video, and interactive programming for your marketing, sales, training, or entertainment applications.

The World Bank Home Page

http://www.worldbank.org/

Provides information on current events of the World Bank, country, and projects-related information. Provides general information with respect to World Bank activities.

World Currency Converter

http://www.dna.lth.se/cgi-bin/rates

Lets you choose a currency of the world, and then choose another currency to compare against it, which gives you the exchange rate.

World Stock & Commodity Exchanges

http://www.lpac.ac.uk/ifr/

Provides details of a paper guide to more than 250 exchanges in 65 countries.

World Trade Directories

http://mindlink.net/derek_mailhiot/WorldTrade.html

Offers 10 world trade directories covering more than a 1,000 wholesalers and 20,000 products from around the world.

WRENet—World Real Estate Network

http://www.wren.com

Provides an interactive and searchable real estate database that includes all types of property (residential, commercial, ICI—industrial commercial investment, ranch/land, resort/retirement, and new housing).

WWW Advertising—Directory of Services

http://www.xmission.com/~wwwads/

Provides information related to advertising. Contains many links to different advertising related sites, including categories like computers, financial, florists, food, Internet services, travel, and sports.

Xerox Small Office/Home Office Information

http://www.xerox.com/soho.html

Describes Xerox products and services to the small office/home office. Also provides valuable resources and Web links for the small business person. Adds new resources weekly.

Young Explorers Online Catalog

http://www.aep.com

Shows products carefully chosen to encourage and stimulate the curiosity that comes naturally to kids.

Zanadu Comics

http://www.aa.net/~zanadu

Specializes in alternative and mainstream comics, graphic novels, and more. Features reviews by staff and customers, promotions, a trivia contest, and a virtual catalog.

Adoptee Classifieds

http://www.law.cornell.edu/~shelden/adoption.html

Provides details about the child. Contains more than 150 entries and connected contact addresses. Includes option for posting to the list.

Adoptees Mailing List Home Page

http://psy.ucsd.edu/jhartung/adoptees.html

Provides information about adoption. Includes legal information, links to other related pages, and Canadian resources.

Alice's Adventures in Wonderland

http://www.cs.indiana.edu/metastuff/wonder/wonderdir.html

Lewis Carroll's *Alice's Adventures in Wonderland*, online.

Alphabet

http://www.klsc.com/children/

Offers simple online games that teach the alphabet and counting. Plans to add more educational games.

ASCII ArtGoodies

http://gagme.wwa.com/~boba/otherascii.html

Contains pictures drawn on a computer or typewriter using only typed letters and symbols.

The Asylum's Lite-Brite

http://www.galcit.caltech.edu/~ta/lb/lb.html

Allows you to make your own Lite-Brite-style pictures on the Web and see what other people have made.

Aunt Annie's Craft Page

http://mineral.galleries.com/annie/auntannie.htm

Features a new craft project every week. Emphasizes learning, creativity, and problem-solving, while having the fun of doing crafts. Includes links to related sites, and suggested books for further reading, as well as free craft software to download. Craft projects offer a variety of designs, patterns to print, and illustrated instructions, and many of them could serve to integrate hands-on learning with math and/or science lessons.

Berit's Best Sites for Children

http://www.cochran.com/theosite/KSites.html

Categorizes and rates children's Web sites. Offers links to online projects, interactive exhibits, educational information, and fun.

Bob Allison's Home Page (Uncle Bob's Kids' Page)

http://gagme.wwa.com/~boba/kidsi.html

Lists a few hundred "kid-safe" sites, divided into seven sections full of links to kids' sites.

Boy Scouts of America

http://www.scouting.org/scouting/

Provides information about the Boy Scouts of America and lists of troops online.

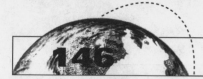
The Canadian Kids Home Page

http://www.onramp.ca/~lowens/107kids.htm

Lists and briefly describes links to educational sites and fun online activities, including icons that reveal whether the link is graphic-heavy, has sounds, originates in Canada, and so on.

Carlos' Coloring Book Home

http://robot0.ge.uiuc.edu/~carlosp/color/

Offers several types of pages to color interactively online using the mouse. Requires a Macintosh program, available for download on the site.

Child Safety on the Information Superhighway

http://www.compuserve.com/new/news_rel/chldsfty.html

Contains the text of a brochure prepared by the National Center for Missing and Exploited Children. Lists ways to protect your child from possible harm on the Internet, and also presents a model "child-parent" pledge for Internet usage rules.

Children Now

http://www.dnai.com:80/~children

Nonprofit children's advocacy group. Provides information related to the education, health, welfare, and safety of American children.

Concertina—Books on the Internet

http://www.digimark.net/iatech/books/

Sports a set of interactive children's books (of which you also can order hard copy versions).

The Cool Word of the Day Page

http://www.dsu.edu/projects/word_of_day/word.html

Offers a new word every day.

Crayola * Crayola * Crayola * Crayola

http://www.crayola.com/crayola/home.html

Provides information about crayons. Also offers a Crayola Trivia game.

Cyberkid's Club

http://mack.rt66.com/kidsclub/home.htm

Offers site where kids can meet and write each other, read, shop, and play games.

CyberKids Home Page

http://www.mtlake.com/cyberkids/

Online magazine for kids. Includes games, fiction, and non-fiction.

CyberKids is a cool place for kids to learn and have fun. Our free online magazine contains stories and artwork created by kids. Have fun doing puzzles, playing games, and more. Tell the world about yourself and find keypals from around the globe in CyberKids Interactive.

 1995 Writing & Art Contest

 CyberKids Magazine

 CyberKids Launchpad

Edible Starchy Tuber Head Animation

http://winnie.acsu.buffalo.edu/potatoe/potatoe.html

Offers a short animation of Mr. Potato Head being put together.

Froggy Page

http://www.cs.yale.edu/HTML/YALE/CS/HyPlans/loosemore-sandra/froggy.html

Provides information about frogs.

Global Show-n-Tell Home Page

http://www.manymedia.com/show-n-tell/

Lets children show their work to kids (and adults) around the world. Consists of links to children's art work on Web pages or ftp servers.

Helping Your Child Learn Science

http://www.ed.gov/pubs/parents/Science/index.html

Provides way for parents and kids to play and learn science together with suggested experiments.

Hotlist: Kids Did This

http://sln.fi.edu/tfi/hotlists/kids.html

Contains categorized links to sites that kids have created and put on the Web themselves. Includes science, language arts, and school newspapers. Searchable.

How Far Is It?

http://gs213.sp.cs.cmu.edu/prog/dist

Enables you to find out the distance to any place in America.

Hull's Home Page

http://www.hipark.austin.isd.tenet.edu/home/teachers/grade.k/hull/main.html

Exhibits dinosaurs created and named by a kindergarten class in Texas. The children drew pictures (or used the computer to create a picture) and described their creations. Also includes poems.

I-Site.on.Canada Presents

http://I-site.on.ca/

A site laid out like a newspaper (if you have Netscape 1.1), its main purpose being creation of multiauthor documents—similar to make-your-own-adventure stories. Serves as a discussion forum for children's literature and movies, a place for kids to post their own reviews of kids' books. Another project here is the KidoPedia—an international project allowing kids to create an international encyclopedia.

IPL Division's Dr.Internet

http://ipl.sils.umich.edu/youth/DrInternet/

Presents science projects and offers a trivia question for kids to answer.

Jason's Web Kite Site

http://www.latrobe.edu.au/Glenn/KiteSite/Kites.html

Provides information about kites and kite-flying.

Jason's Web Kite Site

Joseph Wu's Origami Page

http://www.cs.ubc.ca/spider/jwu/origami.html

Presents images and directions for making your own origami. Offers links to more polygonic creations.

Juggling Information Service

http://www.hal.com/services/juggle/

Provides information on juggling.

Kid's Window

http://kiku.stanford.edu:80/KIDS/kids_home.html

Teaches about kids in Japan.

KidPub WWW Publishing

http://www.en-garde.com/kidpub/

Offers poems and stories written by children.

Kids' Crossing: The Voice of the Rocky Mountain Youth

http://rmii.com/~pachecod/kidsnet/ckids.html

Provides kid-related information. Serves as an online meeting place for kids.

The Kids' Place

http://www.islandnet.com/~bedford/kids.html

Links to various kids' sites.

Kids' Space

http://www.interport.net/kids_space/

Exhibits art work done by children, in English and Japanese. Accepts submissions of stories and art work by children.

KidsCom Home Page

http://www.kidscom.com:80/kidscom/

Serves as a network to which kids can register (free) and choose a personal password, and then on which they can play geography or other brain-teaser games or find a keypal (only other KidsCom registered users), among other available activities. Also includes a section in which parents or teachers can discuss kids, the Internet, schools, and so forth.

KIDSCOM

KidsCom was voted Funky Site of the Day in July, 1995.

Please Click on one of the buttons below:

LEGO Information

http://legowww.homepages.com/

Provides information about new LEGO products and ideas for LEGO fun.

Links for Kids

http://www.webfeats.com/illusion/index.html

Contains more than 30 links to safe sites for children of all ages.

Marcel's Web Mind

http://einstein.et.tudelft.nl/~mvdlaan/WebMind/WM_intro.html

Online version of the game Master-Mind.

Marmaduke®

http://www.unitedmedia.com/comics/marmaduke/

Contains Marmaduke's own Web page, complete with a two-week archive of current strips.

Mentor

http://shasta-co.k12.ca.us/www/telementors/mentor5.html

Lists what are locally considered the ten best Web sites for children; updated monthly. References diverse links.

National Parent Information Network

http://ericps.ed.uiuc.edu/npin/npinhome.html

Provides information about parenting. Includes the full text of many articles about parenting, family life, and urban/minority families, as well as other information for parents, teachers, and counselors.

OUDPS—KidSafety

http://www.uoknor.edu/oupd/kidsafe/start.htm

Provides safety information for kids: Internet safety, fire safety, avoiding fights, and more.

Peanuts Collectors Club Home Page

http://www.dcn.davis.ca.us:80/~bang/peanuts/

Provides information to join the PCC and links to other *Peanuts*-related online pages.

SciTech, Inc.

http://scitech.lm.com/

Presents humor and hands-on activities. Challenges kids to think and reason out the answer to a question. Also offers a catalog of innovative science education products.

SurfWatch

http://www.surfwatch.com/

SurfWatch is a very high visibility Web-access-restriction program company. They make software that is updated once a month and, when loaded on your PC, prevents you (or your kids or whomever) from accessing possibly objectionable Web sites.

The T.W.I.N.K.I.E.S. Project

http://www.rice.edu/~gouge/twinkies.html

Presents an account from two guys who took playing with food to extremes.

Teddy-Bears Mailing List WWW Service

http://www.rhein.de/Mailing-Lists/teddy-bears/

Provides information about teddy bears and for joining a mailing list for collectors.

Totware

http://www.het.brown.edu/people/mende/totware.html

Offers special software just for kids (for PCs and Macs).

Trove Investment Corporation

http://www.netnanny.com/netnanny/home.html

Offers software you can use to help you screen out unwanted material your kids could find on the Internet (PCs only).

Web-Yahtzee

http://wwwcgi.umr.edu/cgi-bin/
cgiwrap?user=nneul&script=webyahtzee.pl

Lets you play Yahtzee online.

Welcome to Burlingame On-Line's PEZ Exhibit

http://www.spectrumnet.com/pez/

Provides information about PEZ candies and dispensers.

Why Ask Why?

http://www.eng.auburn.edu/~rudolmc/why.html

Presents a long list of strange questions about life.

Wierenga Software

http://www.xmission.com/~wwwads/sharware.html

Houses Bert's Coloring Programs Series, Rachel's Fashion Dolls, and Peter's Warbirds. Provides information about these MS-DOS-based programs. Also offers a link to download shareware versions of all different versions of coloring book software.

World Birthday Web (WBW)

http://sunsite.unc.edu/btbin/birthday

Provides lists by birthday.

World-wide Webs

http://www.ece.ucdavis.edu/~darsie/string.html

Teaches Cat's Cradle and other string games.

WWW Index

http://www.delphi.com/young-america/edref/edmenu.html

Offers links to interactive online experiences.

WWW Spirograph

http://juniper.tc.cornell.edu:8000/spiro/spiro.html

Presents a spirograph that draws according to the numbers you input.

Your Lucky Fortune Cookie

http://hci.ise.vt.edu/~kelso/fortune.html

Provides lucky numbers and fortunes.

20/20 Software

http://www.twenty.com/~twenty/

Develops and markets PC-Install, an installation program for developers and consumers. Also offers PC-Loan, a finance software for analyzing mortgages, car loans, and so forth.

2000's Technology (3T), Inc.

http://www.inforamp.net/~hedy/

Provides computer products and services. Also repairs and upgrades PCs and notebooks.

Acorn Computers Home Page

http://www.acorn.co.uk/acorn/home

Contains information about Acorn Computer products. Includes links to the Acorn FTP site, which provides many different patches and drivers.

ActionCall Help Desk Service

http://www.actioncall.com

Offers solutions to your computer hardware and software problems.

Administrative Software from Cogent Computing Corporation

http://www.rt66.com/sjburke/

Specializes in software for departmental administration in public and educational institutions. Lets you use The Budget Director for financial management and CC-Track for task management.

Advanced Computing Systems Company

http://acsc.com

Focuses on advanced technology for distributed, networked client/server systems, including multiplatform environments.

Americomp Computers

http://www.net1.net/comm/acomp.html

Offers computer sales.

NEW INTEL TRITON BOARD

SIGNATURE SERIES

Amzi! Prolog + Logic Server

http://www.amzi.com/

Offers Rubik's cube solver, puzzles, games, rule-based systems prototypes, articles, TechNotes, source code, and other information about prolog, rule-based components, and Amzi! products.

ANDOR Systems (Australia)

http://www.laa.com.au/ANDOR/Andor.html

Offers a full range of business and personal computer solutions. Specializes in Novell NetWare installation and support. Serves as a dealer for OPTIMA Computer Technology.

ANGOSS Software Intl.

http://www.angoss.com

Publishes business-to-business software geared toward providing a total solution set to the enterprise. Provides the Data Analysis/Decision Support Tool, which exposes significant relationships with your operational data. Offers Middleware and Development tools that provide solutions to corporate networks with data warehousing architectures.

The Smartware development environment is a powerful application development system for office and other enterprise operations.

Anyware Fast, Inc.

http://www.anyware-fast.com/

Serves as a small software consulting and development firm, specializing in 2D/3D graphics. Handles all levels of software implementation, from device drivers to window systems to applications.

Apex PCMCIA Modems

http://warrior.com/apex/index.html

Manufactures high-quality PCMCIA modems, Ethernet adapters, and combination cards for notebook computers. Also features a cellular-ready PCMCIA modem that connects directly to your cellular phone.

Apple Support and Information Web

http://www.info.apple.com/

Provides informaion about Apple's products. Includes in-depth descriptions of all the features of Apple's large variety of computers and accessories.

Applix, Inc. Home Page

http://www.applix.com

Develops, markets, and supports Applixware, an integrated family of software applications and tools for real-time decision support and groupware. Applixware runs on most popular Unix platforms, and is soon to be released for Windows NT.

AppWare Developers Association

http://www.adeva.org/

Focuses on educating the public about Novell's AppWare. Also includes a file with frequently asked questions (FAQ) about AppWare.

AppWare Home Page

http://netwire.novell.com/home/appware

Serves as a visual development environment for Windows and Macintosh. Lets you create applications graphically without writing a single line of code. Includes a form that you can use to order a free AppWare demo CD that includes a working version of AppWare, movies, graphics, and sound, and runs on a Windows or Macintosh computer.

AppWrite, Inc.

http://cyber-active.com/appwrite

Provides solutions, connectivity, and expertise to get the information to where you need it, when you need it. Offers software development and consulting services in a multiplatform client/server computing environment.

Apricot WWW Home Page

http://www.apricot.ac.uk/

Provides general information about Apricot Computers. Helps you find a dealer in your area. Doesn't contain much detailed information about the computers.

Archive Comparison Test (A.C.T.)

http://www.mi.net/act/act.html

A monthly report that compares 45 different compression programs (archivers) for speed and ability to compress files. Also includes a checklist of special features some archivers can perform.

ARDI

http://www.ardi.com

Provides information about Executor, a commercial Macintosh emulator for DOS, Linux, and NEXTSTEP. Offers free time-limited demos.

AT&T Global Information Solutions WWW Homepage!

http://www.attgis.com/

Contains information about AT&T computers and other products. Also provides ordering information and product news. AT&T makes and advertises more than just personal computers here. Includes information about LANs and other types of networks.

The ATS Home Page

http://www.mindspring.com/~biggyrat/ats.html

Provides new and used Macs and peripherals, as well as Apple components on a repair/exchange basis.

Austin Software Foundry

http://www.foundry.com/

Seeks to lead business clients migrating to client/server architectures and object-oriented application development methodologies. Focuses on developing components, tools, and techniques. Helps information development teams and managers build large, innovative applications to meet current and emerging processing challenges.

Banyan Systems, Inc.

http://www.banyan.com

Develops networking software for large enterprise networks. Includes products such as enterprise services, messaging, network management and the StreetTalk® naming service, and the popular VINES® network operating system.

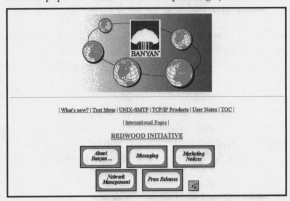

BarCode1—A Web of Information about Bar Code

http://www.adams1.com/pub/russadam/barcode1.html

Online publication about bar code and other automatic identification technologies. Includes extensive, original information as well as a collection of bar code shareware and links to other sites.

Bennett Products— Computer Sales/ Networking/Consulting/ Internet

http://www.bennettpro.com

Provides computer sales, consulting, networking, and Internet access and support. Offers free downloadables section and help in creating HTML Web pages.

Blueridge Technologies

http://www.blueridge.com

Incorporates document imaging, archival, text retrieval, workflow, OCR, and fax capabilities. Supports both IBM-compatibles and the Macintosh.

Bluestone

http://www.bluestone.com/

Builds and resells software development tools, training, and professional services for Unix and cross-platform developers. Includes graphical user interface, database, client/server, and object-oriented technologies. Contains information about Bluestone's product, training, support, and professional services offerings. Lets you browse Bluestone's product and training catalogs, request more information, request a free product evaluation, request a free software skills assessment, or just drop a note.

BMC Software, Inc.

http://www.bmc.com/

Focuses on meeting the needs of corporate IS professionals looking for information on solutions that automate application and data management across enterprise computing environments. Contains the latest product information, demos, seminar and education schedules, announcements, press releases, and partnership details. Provides registered customers access to product documentation, updates, FAQs, and forums for questions and answers with BMC Software's reaserach and development staff.

Bottom Line Online

http://www.dgr.com/

Serves as a virtual marketplace for everything to do with the Macintosh computer. Updates the latest prices and product information on thousands of Macintosh-related products every 15 minutes.

Burnham Park Software, Inc.

http://execpc.com/~burnsoft

Small software development and consulting firm located in Chicago. Offers several shareware releases, from games to business applications, available for download.

BYTE Magazine

http://www.byte.com/

Contains a five year, searchable archive of *BYTE Magazine*. Lets you download *BYTE*'s benchmark tests, code samples presented in articles, and shareware utilities.

C++ Course Book

http://uu-gna.mit.edu:8001/uu-gna/text/cc/text/index.html

Offers an online book that teaches you how to program in C++. Provides plenty of information, but involves significant online reading. Offers sample programs and conversion scripts.

CadSoft Computer GmbH

http://www.CadSoft.DE/

Provides information about CadSoft's EAGLE PCB Layout Editor. Offers information, technical tips, and support; an exhaustive worldwide list of distributors, and lets you download updates, new drivers, and a free, fully functional demo version of EAGLE.

Camellia Software Corporation

http://www.halcyon.com/camellia/

Develops Batch Job Server, batch job management for Windows NT. Offers custom software and consulting.

Catalog of Free Compilers and Interpreters: Introduction

http://remarque.brerkely.edu/~muir/free-compilers/

Serves as an index to sites with information about free computer programming compilers. Contains a couple links, but not very many.

CD Learn: Interactive Audiovisual Training for Popular Applications

http://www.netaxs.com/~irp/cdlearn/cdlearn.html

Offers a series of CD-ROMs that provide audiovisual lessons and reference guides for popular applications such as Microsoft Word, WordPerfect, Excel, and Windows 95.

CD Warehouse

http://www.ecn.com/cd_warehouse

Lets you shop online from more than 1,000 titles at low warehouse prices. Offers new specials each week. Provides an online catalog.

CD-ROM Advisor Home Page

http://cd-rom-advisor.com/

Lets you request a free copy of the new quarterly, *CD-ROM Advisor*. Collects opinons on CDs that users have purchased and includes the ratings.

Cellular Works

http://virtumall.com/Cell/

Features the premiere issue of Cellular Works' online cellular communications and paging catalog. Provides a selection of accessories for all makes and models of cellular telephones and pages.

CELLULAR WORKS

Welcome to Cellular Works, your personal connection to today's digital revolution. We are pleased to present the premiere issue of our on-line cellular communications and paging catalog.

The increased use of cellular telephones and pages for business and personal use has resulted in a wide variety of available equipment and accessories.

Cellular Works prides itself on having the widest selection and lowest prices of high-quality accessories for all makes and models of cellular telephones and pages. Whether you need a hard-to-find or discontinues accessory for an older model phone or the latest in wireless communications equipment, Cellular Works is your primary sourse. We guarantee low prices, high quality, and the widest selection anywhere!

Chicago-Soft, Ltd.

http://www.quickref.com

Markets and sells mainframe software, featuring MVS/Quick-Ref and MVS/Quick-Ref for Windows, instant-access, online

documentation tools that provide information for errors encountered in the MVS operating environment. Contains millions of lines of code representing nearly 40 vendors and over 200 products.

Cimio Ltd CAD++ STEP Data Exchange

http://www.cimio.co.uk/

Focuses on the development of STEP-based CAD/CAM data exchange tools.

The COBOL Programming Language

http://www.cs.indiana.edu/hyplan/cobol/cobol.html

Provides information about COBOL. Includes a list of compilers.

ComCom Systems, Inc.

http://www.intbc.com/comcom/

Offers a complete line of imaging products for your daily and personal needs. Offers scan compression software, desktop management, indexing, form processing, recognition of mark/check boxes, OCR and ICR, and document management.

Command Computer Services—CD-ROMs for Sale

http://www1.aksi.net/~cdrom

Contains more than 500 CD-ROM titles. Includes educational, reference, business, games, adult, and other areas.

CompAdept Corporation

http://www.compadept.com/

Specializes in personal computer and network consulting. Focuses on helping you and your business make decisions

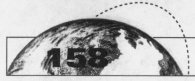
that allow you to use technology effectively and affordably. Also implements these solutions and provides ongoing support and training.

Compaq Computer Corporation

http://www.compaq.com/

Contains information about the Compaq Corporation and its many products. Lets you download FAQs, send e-mail to technical support, download drivers, patches, and utilties. Also lists jobs available at Compaq.

Computer Express

http://cexpress.com:2700

Online computer superstore. Provides a customer service link to help you out if you can't find a specific computer-related product.

Computer Goldmine

http://www.csn.net/~fmills

Buys and sells surplus and used computer systems and parts inventories. Includes micro to mid-range to mainframe systems.

Computer Literacy Bookshops, Inc.

http://www.clbooks.com/

Carries a selection of computer, electronics, high-tech business, telecommunications, mathematics, engineering, and Internet books. Offers free book search and a book recommendation service, as well as worldwide shipping. Lets you order via e-mail.

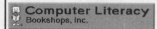

Computer Literacy Bookshops Home Page

Computer-Oriented Abbreviations and Acronyms

http://www.access.digex.net/~ikind/babel95b.html

A glossary of computer-oriented abbreviations and acronyms, updated three times a year (January, May, and September).

Computer Sun Times

http://www.rmii.com/cstimes/

Monthy online computer publication. Features hardware and software reviews and offers numerous feature articles on an everchanging list of topics.

Computer Training Academy

http://www.cta.net

Microsoft Solution Provider Authorized Technical Education Center (ATEC). Serves Hawaii and the Pacific doing end-user and technical training.

SCHEDULE FOR: **SEPT ★ OCT ★ NOV ★ DEC 1995**

Why Should I Choose CTA ?

Computer/Software

http://www.codd.com/vbonline

Provides a Visual Basic catalog of custom controls and other VB productivity tools. Contains overviews, prices, and author names, as well as where you can find a full description of the product's features and how to use it.

Computerized Data Management

http://www1.minn.net/~cdm

Offers training and support for the home user and small business in the Minneapolis and St. Paul areas.

Welcome to Computerized Data Management

The Confederation for Future Computer Professionals

http://tigger.jvnc.net:1000/cfcp/

Includes information about this group, a copy of their weekly magazine, and other information. Also provides a form you can fill in to join their e-mail mailing list.

CONSULTIX, the Unix Training Experts

http://www.halcyon.com/yumpy/

Provides Unix training and consulting services. Includes programming in the C, AWK, Bourne shell, and Korn shell languages, Unix System administration, Unix security, and the Unix look-alike system, Linux.

Continental Resources: Computer Division

http://www.conres.com/ctop.htm

Contains systems and networking integration offered in continental United States and complemented by PC hardware and peripherals sales, rentals, and service (new and used equipment).

Continuum Information Services

http://pages.prodigy.com/GA/continuum_is/
continuum_is.html

Provides business information solutions, consulting, hardware sales, home information solutions, Internet solutions, maintenance, and software sales for churches, home offices, individuals, nonprofit organizations, schools, students, and small businesses. Lets you visit the Continuum IS eXchange, an online Internet Resource Center.

Coptech, Inc.

http://www.oai.com/coptech/

Provides high-quality software media duplication and fulfillment service, fast turnaround, courier service, personalized support, and affordable prices.

CORE Resources Web Site

http://core.cpmc.columbia.edu/

Offers network design tips by displaying the LAN/WAN IP routing layout of the CPMC campus network. Offers other computing resources as well as links to related sites.

CorelNET

http://www.corelnet.com

Serves as the online meeting place for Corelians. Provides discussion areas in which you can post questions, and provides a Corel Corporation presence, with press releases, support files, and product information. Also presents area for third-party vendors of Corel-related products.

Cornell Theory Center

http://www.tc.cornell.edu

One of four supercomputing centers funded by the National Science Foundation.

Cort Directions, Inc.

http://www.empnet.com/cort/

Specializes in payroll and human resources software for client/server (Windows) and the HP3000.

CrossWind Technologies, Inc.

http://www.crosswind.com

Designs and markets workgroup productivity software. Offers Synchronize, a cross-platform scheduling, task and resource management tool designed to meet the needs of the corporate environment.

Crystal River Engineering

http://www.cre.com/cre

Develops and supplies 3D sound technology for entertainment, multimedia, virtual reality, simulator, professional audio, and 3D audio research markets. Provides company, technology, and product information and samples.

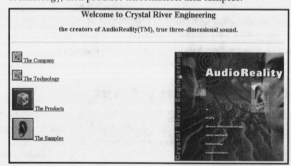

CS-100: The History of Computing

http://calypso.cs.uregina.ca/Lecture/

Presents a copy of a very detailed college lecture given on the history of computing.

Cult of Macintosh

http://www.utu.fi/~jsirkia/mac/index.html

Offers hundreds of links for all Mac users.

CyberMedia, Inc.—PC 911 for DOS and First Aid for Windows

http://www.internet-is.com/cybermedia/index.html

Introduces First Aid for Windows and PC911 for DOS, both of which provide instant support to PC users. First Aid fixes Windows configuration problems fast and automatically, while you work. PC911 keeps track of today's myriad configuration files in a PC.

Databyte

http://www.databyte.com/home.html

Supplies financial and business management software to mid-size businesses. Features Flexx, which provides advanced client/server and relational database technology to address your unique requirements.

DataLink by Timex

http://www.xmission.com/~turq/Timex_DataLink

Offers the award-winning "DataLink Watch" by Timex— wireless PC to watch communication.

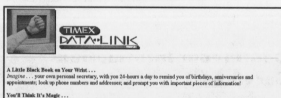

A Little Black Book on Your Wrist . . .
Imagine . . . your own personal secretary, with you 24-hours a day to remind you of birthdays, anniversaries and appointments; look up phone numbers and addresses; and prompt you with important pieces of information!

You'll Think It's Magic . . .
With the *Timex DataLink® Watch*, transferring scheduling and personal information from a PC to your wrist is effortless. Using this revolutionary new communications technology is as easy as pointing your watch at a desktop monitor. The watch sensor reads flashing bars of light on the monitor--that's the data. There are no wires or cables, and downloading takes only seconds!

Dataserv Middle East & Africa Ltd.

http://www.wp.com/dataserv/home.html

Serves the Middle East and Africa, supplying second user IBM and PCM hardware and peripherals.

David Reilly's Programming Page

http://www.moscow.com/homepages/
zz_David_Reilly@macmail.bond.edu.au.html

Contains resources useful to programmers. Supports the following languages on the IBM PC platform: Pascal, C, Delphi, and Assembly. Offers various links to similar sites.

DayStar Digital

http://www.daystar.com/

Contains information about DayStar Digital Corporation. Lets you join the mailing list, go to the ftp site, or register a product. Also includes links to magazines on the Internet about Macintosh computers.

Dell Computer Home Page

http://www.dell.com/

Provides answers to questions about Dell computers. Includes pictures and detailed descriptions of their products. Also contains a copy of parts of Dell Corporation's annual report and employment opportunites.

Demo and Tutorial Builders from MIKSoft, Inc.

http://www.cnj.digex.net/~mik/

Provides information about two Windows development tools—Demo/Tutorial Builders for Windows Applications. Lets you download a copy of StDemo Player—a demo builder. Also includes an opportunity to watch a unique demo-presentation of ShowBasic—a demo/tutorial/CBT/presentation development kit for Windows.

DIGIDRAFT, INC.

http://www.maf.mobile.al.us:80/business/b_dir/digi/

Scans and converts large format engineering drawings into 100 percent CAD-ready vector files for AutoCAD .DWG, Intergraph .DGN, and .DXF files. Also scans and archives raster files into all formats.

Digital Dimensions

http://www.unicomp.net/lantz/

Provides quotes concerning memory and RAM pricing.

Direct Connections

http://www.owplaza.com/dc/dcindex.html

Supplies hard drives, DAT drives, optical drives, monitors, CD-ROMs, scanners, and raid systems.

Domanski-Irvine Book Company

http://www.u-net.com/~dibookco/

Promotes solid analysis design and design—irrespective of the mask of advancing technology.

Dowdell Business Services

http://www.dowdell.com

Specializes in Windows NT/Novell real-time database interfaces. Includes network issues.

Dubl-Click Software

http://www.dublclick.com

Makes products for the Macintosh, Windows, and Newton platforms. Lets you download information, demos, and products for purchase.

Dubl-Click Software welcomes you!

We publish software for Macintosh, Newton, and Windows.
Here you can browse product info, download demos and purchase our products.

Dylan Greene's Windows 95 Home Page!

http://cville-srv.wam.umd.edu/~dylan/win95.html

Provides information on Windows 95. Lets you download Netscape for Windows 95, read the Windows 95 FAQ, and download device drivers.

ECS

http://www.ahoynet.com/business/imart/ecs_home.html

Converts signature and logo samples into scalable TrueType fonts for use with software supporting Microsoft's TrueType fonts, running under Windows or comparable operating system.

Edinburgh Multimedia Home Page

http://www.worldserver.pipex.com/nc/edinmedia/

Offers a full multimedia service.

Elek-Tek

http://www.elektek.com

Provides easy access to a wide selection of merchandise. Carries more than 8,000 products.

EMD

http://www.mps.org/emd

Provides leading-edge technology and quality services. Offers design, prototype, manufacturing, and test services for printed circuit board assemblies and final box build.

EMJ Data Systems

http://www.emj.ca

Distributes computer products and peripherals, specializing in high-performance products for Apple, CAD, Point of Sale, Unix, and Telephony applications.

Exide Electronics

http://www.exide.com/exide/

Manufactures uninterruptible power systems (UPS) and network power management software. Provides company and product information or register to win a free UPS. Also informs you of how to save your company more than $78,000 per hour.

Fineware Systems

http://www.fineware.com

Offers quality software for home or office. Lets you download evaluation editions of all Fineware products, including the Space Hound and Peeper disk utilities.

Fly-By-Day Consulting

http://www.mindspring.com/~cavu

Provides software consulting services in C and Unix, specializing in communications and porting. Also offers many aviation links, including current weather observations and forecasts.

Fujitsu Systems Business of America Home Page

http://www.fujitsu.com:80/FSBA/

Provides software development and technical support for the UGMX family of CAD products.

Future Net

http://www.futurenet.co.uk

Offers more than 10,000 information-packed pages on topics ranging from world news computing, video games, music, sports, and more.

Europe's most popular e-zine - updated daily

- **World news** - All the top news stories, updated every weekday
- **Computing** - Hundreds of features on PC, Mac, ST, Amiga and more
- **Videogames** - Loads of game reviews and features for every platform
- **Music** - Classical reviews, high-tech music making and guitar technique
- **Sport** - Daily sport news, plus great features on football, rugby and cycling

...and much, much more. We've over 10,000 info-packed pages, plus hundreds of links to the world's best Websites. With more than 100 pages added to FutureNet every weekday, there's always something new to see - bookmark FutureNet now!

FutureBASIC Home Page

http://www.ids.net/~paumic/FutureBasic/Index.html

FutureBASIC is a powerful BASIC programming language for the Macintosh. Includes code, a brochure, utilities, a catalog, and more.

Gateway Users International

http://www.mcs.com/~brooklyn/home.html

Contains a link to an ftp site where users can get many different drivers for their Gateway Computers.

Genesys LLC Home Page— Premier Telephony Products for Windows

http://www.teleport.com/~genesys/index.shtml

Invites you to look at some of Genesys's telephony products, like CallerEGO DX, a call management system for Windows, and RACom, a remote agent communicator for the ROLM CBX.

Global Computing, Inc.

http://www.pixi.com/~global/

Offers computer hardware, software, and networking items. Ships, UPS ground, from nine warehouses across the United States. Provides a downloadable electronic price book for Windows, which features more than 25,000 products.

GMT Home Page

http://www.gmtnet.co.uk/gmt1.html

Provides network consultancy services, including development, installation, load analysis, optimization, implementation, and training. Undertakes complete turn-key networking projects, including initial design, cabling installation, implementation, training and ongoing support contracts.

Golden Triangle (Texas) PC Club

http://bmt.cent.com/users/iwilsker/gtpcc.html

PC users group in southeast Texas (APCUG affiliated).

GUIDE International—An IBM User Group

http://www.guide.org/

User group for the management of information technology. Provides information about conferences. Also offers many publications you can order via fax.

GUS Electronic Marketplace

http://www.gus.com/emp/emp.html

A shopping mall with a wide variety of vendors of electronic and computer products, including a shop that makes jewelry from recycled computer parts. Offers a link to an adult shopping mall.

Halcyon Users' Group

http://www.halcyon.com/pdyer/hug/index.html

Offers Internet help and information to customers of Northwest Nexus in Bellevue, WA (and anyone else, for that matter).

Harlequin

http://www.harlequin.com

Provides symbolic processing, electronic publishing, and Harlequin applications. Programs in C, C++, Dylan™, Lisp, ML, PostScript®, Prolog, and whatever else it takes.

Hartford Computer Group

http://www.awa.com/hartford/

Sells, services, and leases a full line of computers, peripherals, and equipment from manufacturers like Apple, IBM, Compaq, NEC, AST, Texas Instruments, and others. Offers free technical support, fast delivery, warranties, and more.

hav.Software

http://www.neosoft.com/~hav/default.html

Provides several C++ class libraries that implement neural networks (PC-DOS, Windows, NT, Unix—IBM, HP, SUN, SGI). Also provides contract and custom software development and project management services to business, scientific, and research interests.

HDS Network Systems

http://www.hds.com

HDS Network Systems manufactures and sells a line of full-featured, high-performance X terminals. HDS X terminals

offer a full suite of audio and video clients, including analog and digital video, IP Multicasting, and live TV/cable displays.

HELIOS Software

http://www.helios.de

Provides high-performance, easy-to-use client/server solutions for Apple Macintosh, DOS/Windows PCs, and Unix workstations; uses Unix/RISC-based systems as the server platform.

Historic Computer Images

http://ftp.arl.mil/ftp/historic-computers/

Contains a small collection of historic pictures of computers that bore names like ENIAC, VAX, and Cray.

HPI's Visual Release Line of Installation Products

http://www.instalit.com/

Specializes in providing high-capability installers for a number of popular platforms. Visual Release is HPI's baseline product, offering a Windows-based environment from which you can develop a sophisticated installation (setup) program. Also offers a number of add-on packages to extend Visual Release's capabilities to include cryptography, Windows NT platforms for the PowerPC, MIPS, and Alpha, client/server capabilities, and a VBX version. Provides product information, as well as technical support and information on other services.

HTA Link

http://www.swcp.com/htalink/

Committed to simplifying the networking process and providing solutions to your specific needs. Offers benefits by effecting practical solutions that impact your bottom line.

IBM 3D Interaction Accelerator

http://www.research.ibm.com/3dix

Workstation-based interactive software product that enables real-time visualization and inspection of large and complex mechanical and architectural CAD models. Provides navigation control through a variety of input devices and a proprietary simplification technique. Allows real-time navigation through models whose complexity significantly exceeds the limit at which the graphics hardware can operate at interactive rates. Enables you to navigate freely through models comprising thousands of parts and millions of faces.

IBM OS/2 Games Home Page

http://www.austin.ibm.com/os2games

Provides information for game developers and game enthusiasts who want to combine the power of OS/2 Warp with PC-based games. Includes announcements related to OS/2 gaming (demo events, new products, articles), developer information, and gaming tips, as well as links to an ftp site and other sources of relevant information.

IBM Personal Computers Home Page

http://www.pc.ibm.com/

Offers a support section and a searchable database for information and solutions to problems about IBM personal computers. Also contains new and old press releases about IBM. Includes a file library filled with patches, software updates, and popular utilities.

ICA Home Page

http://www.gol.com/ica/index.html

Serves as a forum for information and technology in Japan. Provides information about the organization in English, along with a phone number (in Japan) you can use to obtain the most recent copy of their newsletter.

Ice-9 Publications

http://info.pitt.edu/~depst8/

Contains information about how to order hard to find books on a variety of computer-related topics. Also contains a few links to other computer-related sites.

IEEE Communications Society Technical Committee on Gigabit Networking

http://info.gte.com/ieee-tcgn

Provides information on TCGN activities, workshops, conferences, and publications. Offers links to other gigabit networking projects, researchers, and sites.

IEEE Computer Society— Purdue Student Chapter

http://purcell.ecn.purdue.edu/~ieeecs

Strives to educate members about the benefits of professional membership and provide a service to all students at Purdue.

The Image Factory

http://uptown.turnpike.net/I/Image/INDEX.HTML

Specializes in media, multimedia authoring, digital imaging, nonlinear digital editing, and 3D graphics and animation.

IN Jersey

http://www.injersey.com/

Offers the latest in shareware. Provides message boards and resource libraries for Mac, Windows, OS/2, DOS, and Amiga users. Also offers a variety of information that can link you to sports, political issues, current events, and online dating.

Index of /1/perlinfo/scripts/

http://www.metronet.com/1/perlinfo/scripts/

Contains many downloadable scripts written in Perl.

Indiana University's UCS Knowledge Base

http://sckb.ucssc.indiana.edu/kb/

Contains the answers to more than 3,000 questions about computers and computing. Answers general computing questions about hardware and software, as well as questions about how to use and configure popular hardware and software.

InfoImaging Technologies Home Page

http://www.infoimaging.com

Offers free software. Lets you can send password-protected digital files from your PC's fax/modem to any other fax/modem–equipped PC. Lets you compress a 30-page document into a one page fax. Lets you use the global fax network to send digital files faster and for far less money by encoding them as compressed images. Lets you send color documents, executable software, and multimedia files by fax.

Information Builders, Inc.

http://www.ibi.com

Develops EDA/SQL. Also contains LEVEL5. Offers to read, update, or convert your database. Provides information on what Information Builders has to offer.

INFOSEARCH PrintNet©

http://www.xmission.com/~insearch/printnet.html

Serves as a resource directory for graphic designers, computer users, and advertising agencies. Offers links to help users stretch their creative limits.

Intelligent Systems Integration Program

http://www.augusta.co.uk/isip

Joint initiative by the Department of Trade and Industry (DTI) and the Engineering and Physical Sciences Research Council (EPSRC) set up to address the important area of intelligent systems in UK business.

Intergraph Corp.

http://www.intergraph.com/stor.shtml

Offers HSM optical mass storage for Windows NT. Features DiskExtender, from Intergraph, a flexible and efficient storage management software available for Windows NT. Manages jukeboxes and stand-alone devices, WORM, R/W Optical, CD-ROM, and Tape—transparent to the user. Virtually unlimited storage can be used for archive, backup, and data intensive applications at a fraction of magnetic storage costs.

InterWorking Labs

http://www.iwl.com/

Offers Test Suite software products for sale, performs custom testing of networking products, and organizes group interoperability events. Tests products, including SNMP, RMON MIB, MIB II, Printer MIB, Host Resources MIB, X Windows, and Windows TCP/IP products.

Investor's Advantage

http://cyber-active.com/appwrite/iawin.htm

Performs analysis on stocks, commodities, mutual funds, options, and market indices.

IPC Technologies, Inc. on the World Wide Web

http://www.iptechinc.com/

Contains information about Austin computers. Lets you browse their catalog online and order your own copy via e-mail. Contains customer service for their products. Manufactures Austin notebooks and PCs. Lets you register to win a free Austin notebook computer as well as investigate *PC Magazine* Editor's Choice Award-winning Pentiums, the new Austin PowerPLAY based on the Motorola 604/100 Mhz RISC CPU, and other computer products.

Ipsys Software Home Page

http://www.ipsys.com/

Provides client/server development tools. Also contains technical information on developing client/server systems and news on the latest topics in the industry.

ISDN-High Speed On-Ramp to the Digital Highway

http://www.pacbell.com/isdn/isdn_home.html

Introduces the world to IDSN. Contains information about ISDN, rates for business and home use, how to use it, and related products and services.

JUMBO! Shareware Archive

http://www.jumbo.com

Offers thousands of freeware and shareware programs. Includes categories for business, games, personal, programming, utilities, and graphics. Adds new programs weekly.

Laitron Computers

http://www.vistapnt.com/laitron

Provides computer sales and services by mail order. Also provides free technical support to anyone needing help over the Internet.

List of the World's Most Powerful Computing Sites

http://www.mordor.com/~gunter/

Provides a list of the most powerful computers in the world.

Loviel Computer Corporation

http://www.loviel.com

Specializes in digital video, multimedia, and video conferencing. Provides system configuration and technical support.

Mac Talk, Inc.'s WWW Page

http://www.primenet.com/~mactalk/

Full service Macintosh reseller.

World Wide Web Page

Sales/Support/Service/Networking

(800) 622-5557

Macmillan HTML Workshop

http://www.mcp.com/general/workshop

Provides the latest information about the HTML standard. Offers links organized according to users' skill levels. Includes an HTML-oriented hypermail forum and Macmillan's free *HTML Survival Guide*.

168

COMPUTERS

Macola Software from Osiris

http://www.osiris.com/osiris/products/macola/index.html

Combines Macola and network expertise with ODBC SQL client/server solutions for the ultimate in flexibility.

MacZone Internet Superstore

http://www.maczone.com/maczone

Carries a full selection of Macintosh hardware, software, and peripherals. Also offers overnight delivery, secure online ordering, and the chance to win free computer products.

MAEstro Software

http://www.mae.com/

Develops multimedia authoring software for Unix workstations, including a suite of end-user authoring tools, distributed multimedia messaging system, and full developer's toolkit.

MakeMPEG—The Home Page

http://www.zip.com.au/~adf/mpeg.html

MakeMPEG—the key to video for users of Autodesk's 3D Studio—the ultimate way to create MPEG files.

Category	MakeMPEG	Flic	Motion JPEG	PAR
Quality	Highest of any compressed video	High detail; poor colour or frame rate	Moderate detail and colour	Good detail and colour
Compression ratio	Between 20:1 and 200:1, typically 50:1, highest of any compressed video standard	Between 3:1 and 10:1	Between 5:1 and 50:1, typically 15:1	Around 1.5:1
Amount stored in 500MB	Around 40 minutes	Around 5 minutes	Around 15 minutes	Around 4 minutes
Standard	Yes - ISO/CD11172	Yes, proprietary	Yes	No

Mantissa Computer Systems

http://www.hpnet.com/mantissa/mantissa.htm

Serves hardware, software, and networking needs. Stocks all standard equipment and provides a variety of surplus goods.

Maui Software

http://hookomo.aloha.net/~mauisw

Develops applications for the Macintosh and to some degree for Windows. All programs are shareware and can be downloaded. Features TimeTracker, an easy-to-use application for recording time tasks on the Macintosh, and a sneak preview of TimeSlice, a commercial product that takes up where TimeTracker left off.

Image copyright Virtual Magic 1995

Aloha and Welcome to Maui Software's home page

Megabytes Radio Show

http://www.ns.net/megabytes

National radio show about computers. Provides a program schedule listing and lets you browse through the online newsletter.

Meiko WWW Server

http://www.meiko.com/

Contains product and technical information about Meiko's scalable, parallel computing systems. Explains why this company believes that scalable, parallel computing is a better solution for large organizations to adopt than using "old iron" mainframe computers.

Meridian Computers and Consulting, Inc.

http://WWW.MeridianInc.com

Provides businesses with the right computer solutions. Includes services for network design, sales, and installation; service, repairs, consulting, and training.

MetaCenter Computational Science Highlights

http://www.tc.cornell.edu/Research/MetaScience/

Contains descriptions of some of the 10,000 scientific research projects that have used the resources of National Science Foundation supercomputing centers, ranging from astronomy to zoology, including scientific breakthroughs on black holes, how the heart works, pollution control, and modeling the oceans. Also provides images with the reports, and animations and sound with many of them.

Micro-Frame Technologies, Inc.

http://www.microframe.com

Specializes in Windows-based client/server project management, resource management, and time management software.

Micron

http://www.micron.com/

Contains links to all of Micron's Web sites, including Micron Technology (DRAM and memory products), Micron Electronics (Micron and Zeos computers), Micron CMS (custom manufacturing), Micron Internet Services (Internet provider), and Micron Construction (building construction management services). Each site features information about Micron's products and services and technical support.

Micropolis Corp.

http://www.micropolis.com

Produces high-capacity, high-performance storage products, including AV-optimized hard disk drives, RAID subsystems and controllers, and video-on-demand systems.

Microsystems Software, Inc.

http://www.microsys.com

Lets you download demo copies of Microsystems products, read company publications and press releases, and enter a monthly drawing. Lets customers who have support contracts submit problem reports. Also offers an online e-mail list.

The Millennium Solution

http://www.prairienet.org/~dwcollin/millen.html

Provides information on an inexpensive solution to the year 2000, when computer date systems expire.

The Molloy Group, Inc.

http://www.planet.net/molloy

Features the Cognitive Processor™ for intelligent problem resolution.

Music Screeners

http://www.sony.com/Music/Screeners

Lets you view and download Sony Music Video screen savers. Also provides installation instructions and troubleshooting tips.

NEC Home Page

http://www.nec.com/

Provides information about NEC computer products (in English or Japanese). Includes a list of events and trade shows at which NEC will be displayed. Also discusses the many research and development projects with which NEC is currently involved.

Net Guru Technologies, Inc.

http://www.internet-is.com/netguru/index.html

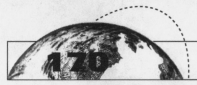

Offers hands-on training classes in client/server computing, security for Unix and TCP/IP networks, connecting to the Internet for businesses and end users, TCP/IP internetworking, Unix internetworking, SNMP, frame relay, ATM, and more. Lists sites at which classes are held.

Net-One System's Personalized CDs

http://www.primenet.com/~net-one

Offers to make personalized CDs (data, music, and so on).

NetEx Unofficial Windows 95 Software Archive and Discussion Forum

http://www.netex.net/w95

The famous Windows 95 page with the user-submitted tips, tricks, software, and now HyperNews-threaded discussion forums.

Netplan ApS. Consultants in Telecommunications

http://www.netplan.dk/netplan/

Consultants company in the field of tele- and datacommunications. Netplan is involved in several international projects and currently participates in standardizations work.

Network-1 Software and Technology, Inc.

http://www.iu.net/n1

Provides network and security software products, consulting, and training. Tells you how to secure your Internet connection easily and economically, using FireWall/Plus. Also offers Network-1's NET1-AccessPlus. Offers and explains other products and services as well.

New Wave Computers

http://www.neosoft.com/~synergy/

Offers upgrades, repairs, and services for the small business owner and indivuals. Also offers parts for your PC.

New World Graphics and Publishing

http://www.primenet.com/~newwrld/

Distributes Spanish language software. Features PFS: WindowWorks, which seeks to provide the answer to all your computing needs in Spanish, and the Key Translator English-Spanish for Windows, which translates documents between Spanish and English or vice versa.

Nightware Energy Saving Switch for Laser Printers

http://www.nightware.com

Details energy-saving Nightware product.

North Carolina Supercomputing Center Home Page

http://www.mcnc.org/HTML/ITD/NCSC/ncschome.html

Provides information about supercomputers. Describes the different types of computers at the NCSC in detail.

The Novell Smithsonian Innovation Network

http://innovate.si.edu/

Honors recent Computerworld Smithsonian Awards Program winners such as Gordon Bell, Linda Roberts, and Dr. Andrew McCammon. Explains how these leaders and shapers of the Information Age have used computer technology to make all our lives better. Also contains a database of award-winning, innovative uses of information technology.

O/S Boot Select

http://www.prz.tu-berlin.de/~wolf/os-bs.html

Provides a customizable boot menu with a timeout and the capability to automatically set the active partition before booting, which avoids boot problems on some UNIX systems.

OAK Software Repository

http://www.acs.oakland.edu/oak/oak.html

Contains thousands of downloadable software titles for DOS and Windows. Lets you search the directory by subject area.

OC Systems AdaMania Page

http://ocsystems.com/

Produces software. Develops Ada compilers and tools for numerous platforms and targets.

The One-Stop Windows 95 Site

http://www.win95.com

Provides links to virtually all of the Windows 95 resources on the Internet. Also contains *Win95User Magazine*.

Onion Peel Software Home

http://www.ops.com/

Designs and develops network management applications for the Hewlett Packard OpenView Network Management platform. OPS is an HP OpenView Premier Solution Partner. Products include the Productivity Series for HP OpenView, RoboMap for HP Open View, and ROVE for HP OpenView.

Ornetix Network Computing

http://www.ornetix.spacenet.de/index.html

Offers software solutions to share local resources like CD-ROMs, MOs, storage media, and printers in Novell NetWare networks. Offers links to sites in Munich.

The Ottawa Microsoft Users Group (TOMUG)

http://www.icons.net/tomug/

Users group to complement the interest in Microsoft products and cultivate the free exchange of related information among all interested persons through means such as presentations, discussions, educational sessions, and distribution of educational materials.

Pacific Animated Imaging

http://www.pai-west.com

Specializes in designing software products that are engaging as well as affordable.

Packard Bell

http://www.packardbell.com/

Lets you look up dealers in your area. Offers a trial link to the Packard Bell ftp site, which provides updated drivers, patches, and software.

Pages INK, Inc.

http://www.pinki.com

Specializes in the creating and/or maintaining of Web sites.

PARC: Xerox Palo Alto Research Center

http://www.xerox.com/PARC/default.html

Performs research that covers a broad spectrum of research fields, ranging from electronic materials and device research through computer-based systems and software, to research into work practices and technologies in use. Lets you retrieve research documents as well as interact with online projects.

PAROLE Software—BBS Doors and Utilities

http://www.cris.com/~dmaidon

Lets you download the latest versions of PAROLE Software Doors and Utilities. Offers links to other sites.

"The home of PAROLE Software"

The Parole Board BBS
Clayton, NC
(919) 965-4696

Parsytec Computer GmbH

http://www.parsytec.de

Supplies cognitive systems based on scalable high-performance parallel computers for industrial and research applications.

People-Planner Labor Management Software

http://www.imb.com

Reduces labor costs, improves customer service, and increases operating efficiency. Products include People-Planner Forecaster, which projects business and labor requirements based on sales history and user defined labor standards for each job in the store; People-Planner Scheduler, which creates optimium employee schedules by matching employees to shifts based on hundreds of user-defined criteria, such as productivity and seniority, while minimizing over- and understaffing; and People-Planner Time & Attendance, which captures employee work time using electronic time clocks or other devices and calculates work time for payroll.

Perl reference materials

http://www.eecs.nwu.edu/perl/perl.html

Offers links to other sites that deal with the Perl program-ming language, including archives, newsgroups, FAQs, and online guides.

Perspectives of the Smithsonian: Smithsonian Computer History

http://www.si.edu/perspect/comphist/computer.htm

Provides information about computer history available. Contains many pictures as well as transcripts of interviews of many well-known computer people, including Bill Gates.

PhotoModeler

http://www.wimsey.com/PhotoModeler/

Converts photographs into 3D computer models. Provides documentation describing PhotoModeler, photo-to-model projects done by users, and links to other 3D-related sites.

PoolWizard for Windows

http://www.getnet.com/~microw/poolwiz.html

A new Windows-based application that helps homeowners maintain their swimming pools.

PR101: An Introduction to C

http://www.cit.ac.nz/smac/cprogram/default.htm

Online tutorial for people who want to learn to program in C. Includes interactive tests and many examples.

Praxis International

http://www.praxisint.com/

Provides software and consulting for database, data replication, and data warehouse applications. Products include Model 204 for IBM, S1032 for VMS, and OmniWarehouse, and OmniReplicator (Unix).

PRC, Inc. Home Page

http://www.prc.com/

Uses information technology to help customers manage change. Offers business process re-engineering, manage-ment consulting, software development, application

products and systems engineering, computer system integration, facilities management and outsourcing, and environmental- and energy-related engineering services.

The Preferred Net.Shopper

http://www.preferred.com/shop/index.html

Offers hundreds of computer systems, softwares, and parts available at discount prices.

ProSoft Consulting

http://www.zelacom.com/~prosoft/consult.htm

Offers Web page design, remote technical support, and consulting services.

Psion

http://www.londonmall.co.uk/psion/

Psion organizers let you send faxes, connect to Windows on a PC, play games, compute your finances, and even read advice on fine wines. Lets you order a Psion organiser over the Internet.

PurePower: A Magazine for PowerBuilder People

http://www.magicnet.net/purepower

PurePower contains information for anyone using PowerBuilder, including testing tips, advice, product information, and market direction. Lets you download the first issue free.

Quadrillion: Data Analysis Software for Semiconductor Manufacturers

http://www.quadrillion.com/

Develops data analysis software and training for semiconductor manufacturers. Features Q-YIELD, used by engineers to help determine the causes of yield loss and production problems.

Questicon, Incorporated

http://www.questicn.com/questicn/

Provides services, from application modernization and support of legacy business applications through complete outsourcing, and products that can improve utilization of existing systems, reduce costs of information, and increase profits.

QuickMedia—Living Album

http://www.quickmedia.com

Develops and publishes multimedia software, Living Album for the Macintosh and Power Macintosh. Living Album allows any color Macintosh users to quickly and easily assemble multimedia albums with each entry linked to photo, audio, video, text, and text-to-speech.

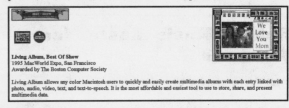

Living Album, Best Of Show
1995 MacWorld Expo, San Francisco
Awarded by The Boston Computer Society

Living Album allows any color Macintosh users to quickly and easily create multimedia albums with each entry linked with photo, audio, video, text, and text-to-speech. It is the most affordable and easiest tool to use to store, share, and present multimedia data.

Restaurant Technology, Inc.

http://www.rti.atlanta.com/

Provides accounting and restaurant management software for fast food restaurants.

RIGAL—A Language for Compiler Writing

http://www.ida.liu.se/labs/pelab/members/vaden/rigal.html

Provides RIGAL, a compiler construction language developed at the University of Latvia.

Safetynet, Inc. AntiVirus and Security

http://www.safe.net/safety/

Provides software evaluations and information covering computer security, anti-virus, and network management software for DOS, Windows 3.x, Win95, OS/2, NetWare, Vines, NTAS, LAN Server, Pathworks, and other operating environments.

SAIC Los Altos Home Page

http://losaltos.saic.com/

Develops risk, reliability, and safety methodology, and applies the techniques on processing plants, aircraft, and other large engineering systems.

School Music Master for Windows

http://www.profile.net/~cmp101/smm.html

A complete School Music organizer. Lets you catalog every aspect of your music program, including music, personnel, publishers, equipment, recordings, CDs, videos, sheet music, and more.

Scientific Computing and Automation Magazine

http://gordonpub.loyola.edu/

Serves the computing and automation needs of more than 70,000 scientists, engineers, and managers who specify and buy computers, instruments, and peripherals.

Scientific Visualization Sites

http://www.nas.nasa.gov/RNR/Visualization/annotatedURLs.html

Offers images on the Web. Claims to offer an annotated bibliography of every visualization Web site.

SEYMOUR—300,000 Images Shot Over the Net

http://WWW.pniltd.com

Offers search, browsing, pricing, licensing, and delivery. Features more than 300,000 pictures from more than 40 sources worldwide.

Shana Corporation

http://www.shana.com

Offers a variety of information and software relating to the company's line of forms processing software, including product information and specifications, recent press releases, pricing, corporate profiles, success stories, complete up-to-date listings of informed consultants, software demos, and extra files. Covers all aspects of the forms process, including design, revision control, filling, digital signatures, routing, approval, tracking, and database links.

SoftInfo Software Information Center

http://www.icp.com/softinfo/

Contains full descriptions of more than 16,500 software products and profiles of 4,500 suppliers. Covers all platforms from PCs to supercomputers. Includes full contact information, including e-mail and Web addresses when available.

SoftLinx, Inc. Web Page

http://www.softlinx.com

Defines network fax solutions, highlights various network fax configurations, and provides help for purchasing a network fax solution (pricing, local distributors, and so on).

Software Publishing Corporation Home Page

http://www.spco.com

Provides business productivity software for Windows, including the Harvard visual communications product line.

Software Surplus Corporation

http://theyellowpages.com/software_surplus.htm

Serves as a clearinghouse for publishers, distributors, and retailers of overstocked, over-produced, or distressed inventories. Offers current version and previous version packages.

Software Tools for Logistics Problem Solving

http://primal.iems.nwu.edu/~levi/tools.html

Provides software and consulting services for solving various logistics and scheduling problems utilizing sophisticated algorithms and information technology.

Software Translation Tools

http://www.netusa.net/~mpsinc

Lets you view the data sheets for the ASM360/370, ASM86, MASM, Cobol, PL/I, and PL/M to C software translators. Also lets you download demonstration programs of these conversion and migration tools.

Starvector Software

http://www.wolfe.net/~svector/

Sells discount CD-ROM titles on a retail and wholesale level. Covers such categories as games, reference, educational, edutainment, shareware, mapping, religion, and more.

Welcome to *Starvector Software's* Online SuperStore!
Your "One-Stop" CD-ROM Shop!

Sterling Information Group

http://www.sterinfo.com

Specializes in client/server and object-oriented custom software development as well as systems integration engagements.

Storage Computer Corp. Presents

http://www.storage.com/

Provides standards-based open RAID 7 disk arrays from gigabytes to the terabyte range. RAID 7s are widely used in over 20 countries worldwide, providing significant I/O acceleration for users of Sun, SGI, IBM, HP, DEC, Cray, Unisys, Prime, Wang, and many other host systems.

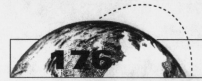

StrandWare Home Page

`http://www.morsepr.com/sw/strandware.html`

Provides bar code design and printing software for the personal computer. Includes a corporate profile, product fact sheet, and ftp high-resolution photos.

Stryder Communications, Inc.

`http://www.strydr.com`

Specializes in open systems technology.

Stylus Innovation, Inc.

`http://www.stylus.com/stylus`

Sells Windows-based tools for building computer telephony and voice processing applications, such as interactive voice response (for example, touch-tone banking), fax-on-demand, and voice mail sytems.

Welcome to Stylus Innovation's World Wide Web Server!

Stylus Innovation, Inc. is dedicated to the development of easy-to-use toolkits for computer telephony , voice processing, and faxing. Stylus markets software and hardware products used in a variety of telephony applications including interactive voice response (IVR), fax-on-demand, and voice mail. Stylus Innovation's Visual Voice is the leading telephony toolkit for Windows.

Sunbelt Software Distribution, Inc.

`http://www.ntsoftdist.com/ntsoftdist`

Distributes utility software for the Windows NT environment. Also offers disk management and client/server utilities.

Sunshine Computers

`http://sunshinec.com/`

Provides state of the art computer systems and custom software development.

Swan Technologies

`http://www.tisco.com/swan/`

Contains product specifications and sales information on Swan Technogies' line of IBM-compatible computers. Lets you use the Config-o-Matic to custom configure and price the PC you want.

Synapse Communications, Inc.

`http://www.synapse.com`

Provides 5250 conectivity to the IBM AS/400 computer system from the Windows environment. Presents product information and company history, as well as a way to contact Synapse to receive a free working demo copy of its software.

System Optimization Information

http://www.dfw.net/~sdw/index.html

Focuses on helping people get the most out of their systems.

TCP3270/NET3270 for Windows

http://www.3270.mcgill.ca/

TCP3270 for Windows is a tn3270 protocol terminal emulator specifically designed for superior IBM mainframe access from the Windows desktop. TCP3270 is a fully featured emulator, specifically designed for Windows developers to produce desktop applications to remotely re-engineer mainframe applications without disrupting mainframe operations.

TechTools Home Page

http://www.techtools.com

Offers specialized MS Windows application development software that programmers and nonprogrammers can use to develop business software applications.

TENET Computer Group, Inc.

http://www.tenet.com

Specializes in Novell NetWare, multiplatform connectivity, and e-mail integration. Offers links to computer manufacturers and provides price lists.

Terminate Home Page, the Final Terminal

http://www.gpl.net/terminate/

Offers Terminate, an advanced DOS communication software with support for Internet and many other features.

THE
TERMINATE HOMEPAGE

Texas Micro Home Page

http://www.texmicro.com

Makes computing products.

TGV Software, Inc.

http://www.tgv.com

Offers a line of products designed to meet the growing need for platform-independent, professionally managed IP products.

Thomson Software Products

http://www.thomsoft.com

Supplies ADA compilers, GUI development tools, and database development and reporting products.

Time Crafter (shareware)

http://www.goldinc.com/Tour/LongBeach/Businesses/ASR/TimeCrafter.html

Adds the ability to have up to 50 waves, 50 signals, and 200 text objects. Also adds the slanted edge option, which lets

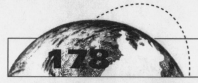

you create professional-looking waveforms. Also now lets you add and delete signal edges by using the delete and insert keys when an edge is highlighted.

. . . .
TimeLess Technologies Schedule Wizard Software

http://www.isn.net/~jmacleod

Creates balanced schedules for sports leagues in minutes.

. . . .
Tosoft Children's Educational and Quit Smoking Page

http://www.teleport.com/~tosoft/

Contains free software to help people stop smoking. Also offers a shareware game available for children.

. . . .
Total Systems, Inc. (TSI) Home Page

http://www.lynqs.com/TSI/

Sells supercomputer equipment, such as Silicon Graphics (SGI) Hardware and Software solutions. Also specializes in Novell Networks, design, and complete WAN and LAN implementations. Carries more than 30,000 hardware and software names.

. . . .
TRG, Inc.

http://www.trglink.com

Lets you explore issues impacting colleges and universities. Shows how TRG's partner institutions are using innovative technology solutions to respond to these issues.

. . . .
Tumbleweed Software Corp.

http://www.twcorp.com/

Develops software to enable people publish and consume documents electronically.

. . . .
Unforgiven Productions '95 Home Page

http://www.xmission.com/~unfo

Provides such items as DOOM I/II Utilities, RealAudio clips, and pictures.

. . . .
Used Computers, Etc.

http://www.xmission.com/~gastown/goldpages/used1.htm

Sells used, warrantied computer hardware and software, from the XT to the 486. Also repairs equipment, upgrades PC compatibles, and accepts consignments.

. . . .
Victoria Macintosh Users Group

http://www.islandnet.com/~vmug

Represents the Macintosh Computer Users Group.

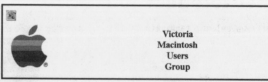

Visual CADD Home Page

http://www.numera.com

Numera Software is the creator of Visual CADD, the open architecture CAD program for the '90s. Visual CADD is the first affordable, professional-level CAD program to combine ease-of-use, speed, and user programmability into a single unlimited package. Created by the programmers that developed Generic CADD®, Visual CADD is ideal for architects, mechanical engineers, industrial designers, space planners, surveyors, and electrical engineers.

VRML Repository

http://www.sdsc.edu/vrml

The Virtual Reality Modeling Language (VRML) is a developing standard for describing interactive three-dimensional scenes delivered across the internet. The VRML Repository is an impartial network resource for the dissemination of information relating to VRML.

Welcome to Apple Networking and Server Products

http://abs.apple.com/

Provides information about Apple's networking products. Tells about current promotions and special deals. Lets you update your old client/server software.

Welcome to The Computer Museum

http://www.net.org/

Lets you participate in a variety of online interactive exhibits about computers.

Welcome to the Lotus Selects Catalog

http://nyweb.com/lotus/

Provides Lotus-related product information, including CD-ROMS, upgrades, books, and video.

The Well Connected Mac

http://www.macfaq.com/

Online guide to everything Macintosh, including FAQ lists, vendor contacts, software, Web sites, mailing lists, and more.

Windows Utilities Page

http://home.ptd.net/~dkt/util/utility.htm

Contains a large collection of windows utilities programs available for downloading, broken down by category. Describes and rates each individual program for effectiveness and usability.

Word Master, Inc.

http://www.interaccess.com/wordmaster/

Specializes in client/server application development.

World's Fastest Desktop Computer

http://www.infotrends.com/system.htm

Explains how you fit a 64-bit 275 MHz supercomputer on your desk.

Xebec Corporation Online Imaging and Supplies Superstore

http://www.servint.com/Xebec

Offers printer and typewriter ribbons, inkjets and refills, laser toners, laser drums, photocopier toners, office supplies, and cellular items.

XPRO Systems

http://www.conres.com/xtop.htm

XPRO Systems are manufactured by Continental Resources. Desktop, tower, notebook, and industrial/rackmount units are available from 486 CPUs and up.

Yost Serial Device Wiring Standard

http://www-scf.usc.edu/~khendric/info/yost.html

Describes the Yost serial device wiring standard.

COOKING

Ann Hemyng Candy, Inc.'s Chocolate FACTORY

http://mmink.cts.com/mmink/dossiers/choco.html

Provides a wide selection of nut, cream, fresh fruit, and gift assortment options. Lets you order a solid chocolate personal computer with a white chocolate mouse and personalized screen.

The Bagel Page

http://jaka.nn.com/~scott/bagels/

Recipes and other information about bagels.

Beamish & Crawford Brewery

http://symphony.ucc.ie/~niall/beamish.html

Brewing Beamish Genuine Irish Stout in Cork for more than 200 years.

CORK CITY | BEAMISH | POURING | CARING FOR | HISTORY | REPORT | BRANDS

BEAMISH GENUINE IRISH STOUT
EXCLUSIVELY BREWED IN CORK SINCE 1792

Beerman's Place

http://www.webknx.com/hafenbrack/

A site where you can talk about beer, breweries, and the world of beer.

Boston Restaurant List

http://www.osf.org:8001/boston-food/boston-food.html

Provides reviews of recommended restaurants in Boston. Lets you search for your favorite restaurant by name alphabetically, as well as by type of cuisine or location.

Includes a list of recently added or closed restaurants. Lets you submit your own reviews.

Bread

http://www.vuw.ac.nz/who/Amy.Gale/recipes/bread/bread.html

Provides index of bread recipes.

Brew Hawaii Magazine

http://www.hypermedia.net/brew/

Discusses beer, wine, whiskey, sake, brewing, and cigars in Hawaii, the Pacific, and Asia.

Cafe MAM

http://mmink.cts.com/mmink/dossiers/cafemam.html

Cafe MAM coffee beans are organically grown by a cooperative of native Mayan farmers living in the highlands of Chiapas, Mexico. Environmentally conscious and socially responsible, Coffee MAM donates 20 cents to the Northwest Coalition for Alternatives to Pesticides for each pound of coffee sold. Place your order for natural or decaf roasts and blends before noon Pacific Time and Cafe MAM will ship your coffee beans the same day.

Callahan's Cookbook

http://www.ruhr-uni-bochum.de/callahans/cookbook.html

Contains recipes contributed by readers of the newsgroup alt.callahans.

Candy

http://www.vuw.ac.nz/who/Amy.Gale/recipes/candy/index.html

Provides a small index of candy recipes.

Cape Breton Pictorial Cookbook

http://137.186.188.131/cbcookbook/home.html

Contains a compilation of recipes from the various cultures that have settled on Cape Breton Island in Nova Scotia. Displays many graphics, using them to present both the foods and the land.

CheeseNet 95

http://www.efn.org/~kpw/cheesenet95/

Find out all about cheese: how to make it, its history, the different variations, a picture gallery, cheese literature, and cheese language. Features a cheese-making demonstration.

Chile-Heads

http://www.netimages.com/Chile-Heads/

Provides information about chile recipes, restaurants, festivals, and trivia.

Chile Today Hot Tamale

http://eMall.com/chile/

Offers Chile and Hot Sauce of the Month Clubs, as well as dried chiles and exotic sauces from around the world.

Chili!

http://www.tpoint.net/~wallen/chili.html

Offers four different chili recipes, each one with a unique twist. Also offers a few tips for preparing any style of chili.

ChocolateTown U.S.A.

http://www.microserve.net/~hershey/welcome.html

Hershey's own tempting Web site, replete with information and recipes and a shopping spot for cybersurfers.

Chocolatier Recipe Index

http://www.godiva.com/recipes/chocolatier/index.html

Chocolate-philes lookout: Godiva has recipes online.

Chocolatier RECIPES

Welcome to the deliciously rich recipe archive of Chocolatier Magazine. We want to help you create the most decadent chocolate masterpieces imaginable, so dig in and enjoy!

- Caramel: The Consummate Candy
- Bread & Chocolate -- Comfort & Joy
- Bountiful Bakeries
- Eclairs: Piping New Life Into the Classic French Dessert
- Super-Outrageous Ultra-Decadent Mega-Chocolate Desserts
- Paradise Lost: Sinful Chocolate Temptations
- Le Chocolat Poiver
- Sweet Surprises
- Chocolate to the 10th Degree
- Special Desserts For The Ones You Cherish
- The Flavor of Brazil
- Chocolatier's Best Brownies
- Desserts from Guimas
- Scoop Du Jour

Coffee Houses in Seattle

http://www.seas.upenn.edu/~cpage/mothercity.html

Provides reviews of coffee brands and Seattle coffee houses.

Cookbook on Friends and Partners

http://solar.rtd.utk.edu/friends/life/cookbooks/master.html

Offers Russian and American recipes.

Cooking Recipes of the Institute of Nuclear Chemistry

http://dkcmzc.chemie.uni-mainz.de/~FRANZ/recipes.html

Contains recipes collected and translated into English by German scientists. Includes a metric conversion chart.

Cooking_Mushrooms

http://www.igc.apc.org/mushroom/cook.html

Part of a larger page of mushroom information.

Creole/Cajun/etc. Recipe Page

http://www.webcom.com/~gumbo/recipe-page.html

Provides recipes and information about getting the ingredients.

A Culinary World Tour

http://www.webcom.com:80/~gumbo/world-food.html

Recipes from all over the world (largest recipe groups are Caribbean/Southern United States, French).

Department of Food Science & Nutrition

http://fscn1.fsci.umn.edu/fscn.htm

Provides information on the programs and courses offered by the University of Minnesota. Offers links to sites relating to food law topics.

Dessert Recipes, etc.

http://www.aus.xanadu.com/GlassWings/food/recipe.html

Provides a list of desserts.

Directory of /pub/rec.food.recipes

ftp://ftp.neosoft.com/pub/rec.food.recipes/

Archives every recipe posted in the moderated newsgroup rec.food.recipes.

Directory of /pub/Vegetarian/Recipes/FatFree

ftp://ftp.geod.emr.ca/pub/Vegetarian/Recipes/FatFree/

FTP site of vegetarian and fat-free/lowfat recipes.

Dole 5 a Day

http://www.dole5aday.com/

Provides information on health and nutrition. Also offers a "Fun Stuff" page of games, and another page that contains a short list of nutrition resources especially for teachers.

Earthrise Spirulina Home Page

http://www.earthrise.com/spirulina/

Offers a natural food product catalog of spirulina blue green algae, green superfoods, and nutriceuticals. Also

offers a spirulina scientific reference library. Explains how spirulina is ecologically grown at Earthrise Farms in California.

The Edinburgh Malt Whisky Tour

http://www.dcs.ed.ac.uk/home/jhb/whisky/

Provides information here about the history and manufacturing of this popular malt beverage. Contains descriptions and pictures of Scotland's malt distilleries. Also categorizes and rates various whisky brands and distilleries.

The Electronic Gourmet Guide

http://www.2way.com/food/egg/index.html

Provides several informative monthly features, book reviews, Web site links, and regular columns—all devoted to food and drink.

The English Server

http://english-www.hss.cmu.edu/Recipes/html

Contains a listing of Web servers that specialize in recipes. Divides listings into three categories: vegetarian, dead animals, and things that possibly contain dead animals. Also offers lowfat vegetarian recipes.

English Server Recipes Folder

http://english-www.hss.cmu.edu/Recipes.html

Devoted to vegetarians but offers some recipes for everybody.

Eric's Simple Fermented Beverages

http://www.mcp.com/people/ericg/ferment.html

Contains information about making ciders, meads, and fruit wines out of ingredients from the grocery store.

FATFREE Vegetarian Mailing List Archive

http://www.fatfree.com/

Fat-free and very low-fat diets from the FATFREE mailing list.

Filipino Cuisine

http://pubweb.acns.nwu.edu/~flip/food.html

Provides information on restaurants, substitutions for hard-to-find ingredients, and recipes.

Food Gatherers

http://garnet.msen.com:70/1/causes/fgs

Presents a system of gathering and distributing safe and edible perishable food items that are discarded every day by supermarkets and restaurants. Includes tips on starting a food rescue organizaiton in your community.

The FoodPlex

http://www.gigaplex.com/wow/food/index.htm

Offers food-related humor and some interesting recipes thrown in for good measure.

Frito-Lay Main Menu

http://www.fritolay.com/

Sells snacks and offers a few recipes.

FYNet's Collection of Malaysian Recipes

http://ucsee.eecs.berkeley.edu/~soh/recipe.html

Offers links to three collections of Malay food.

The Garlic Page

http://broadcast.com/garlic/garlic.htm

Provides garlic information on how to grow garlic, how to prepare garlic, garlic recipes, the different varieties of garlic, and what makes the variations of garlic specifically special. Also explains how you can use garlic to improve your health.

"What garlic is to salad, insanity is to art." Augustus Saint-Gaudens

Godiva Online

http://www.godiva.com/

Presents the online catalog of the world famous Belgian chocolatier. Lets you shop for chocolate creations, as well as discover new recipes to try out. Also provides a free gift reminder service.

Grapevine

http://bighorn.terra.net/grapevine

Online magazine. Provides reviews and information on various international wines and vineyards.

Grapevine

Welcome to **Grapevine** at TerraNet, Inc. Grapevine is the Internet's first Web-accessible magazine dedicated to the wine lover.

Hacienda Flores Salsa

http://shop-utopia.com/flores_salsa/flores.html

Provides a salsa recipe.

Hawaii's Favorite Recipes

http://hisurf.aloha.com/Recipes.html

Aunty Leilani posts new recipes each week for those who like the flavor of the islands.

Hawaiian Electric Kitchen

http://www.hei.com/heco/ekitchen/ekitchen.html

A Web site based on the TV show by the same name. Features Hawaiian and other types of recipes and does a sales pitch for the show.

Herbs & Spices

http://www.teleport.com/~ronl/herbs.html

An index of herbs and spices with recipes and information about growing and storing your own stuff.

Hot Hot Hot

http://www.presence.com/hot/

If you like your food hot, hotter, and nuclear meltdown, Hot Hot Hot is the online hot sauce source for you. Over 100 varieties of sauces from around the globe can be searched by various criteria, including heat level, origin, ingredients, or name.

HotHotHot!

http://www.hot.presence.com/g/p/H3//h3-home.html

Check this out if you love your food as hot as you can get it. This places carries almost any hot sauce imaginable.

Index to Gluten-Free and Wheat-free Diets Pages

http://www.demon.co.uk/webguides/nutrition/diets/glutenfree/index.html

Information about gluten-free diets and Celiac condition.

The Internet Wine Rack

http://www.clark.net/pub/wine/home.html

Offers a wide variety of wine, beer, and other drinks. Although the expensive wines you'd expect are available, also offers alternatives—such as the "Italy on a Pizza Budget" category—for more modest incomes.

Janet Starosta's Recipes

http://metro.turnpike.net/J/jrs/janet.html

A decent-sized recipe batch considering that this is a personal collection.

Java Hut

http://www.vegas.com/mall/java

Culture and coffee collide.

Ketchum Kitchen

http://www.recipe.com/

Offers cooking tips and an easy-to-use searchable recipe index.

Krema Nut Company

http://www.infinet.com/~schapman/mwow.cmh/krema/homepage.html

Peanuts are the only ingredient in Krema's old fashioned peanut butter. Other nuts and nut butters are available through the online catalog as well. Try out some of Krema's mouth-watering recipes.

La Comeda Mexicana

http://www.udg.mx/Cocina/menu.html

Read about the history of Mexican food, and try out recipes for salsas, huevos, ensaladas, and antojitos.

La Pagina dela Salsa Mole

http://www.slip.net/~bobnemo/mole.html

Mole is a spicy chili-chocolate sauce used in traditional Mexican cooking.

Lotsa Hotsa Salsas, Hot Sauces, and more

http://www.nbn.com/starving_artists/lotsa-hotsa

Gourmet hot sauces, salsas, recipes, and more. Color photos, descriptions, and online order entry.

Malt Whisky Tour

http://www.dcs.ed.ac.uk/staff/jhb/whisky/

Provides a Malt Whisky Tour. Presents descriptions, historical notes, and pictures of Scotland's malt distilleries.

Mama's Cookbook

http://www.eat.com/cookbook/index.html

Provides Italian-style recipes using Ragu products.

Medieval/Renaissance Food Home Page

http://fermi.clas.virginia.edu/~gl8f/food.html

Offers references and recipes for anyone who wants to make a medieval feast. Includes references for European and Islamic dishes.

MenuNet FoodFinder

http://www.foodfinder.com

A restaurant directory that displays menus and advertising for Midwestern restaurants.

Myer's Gourmet Popcorn

http://www.aus.xanadu.com/GlassWings/arcade/myers/mgp.html

Lets you order popcorn in a variety of flavors.

Napa Valley Virtual Visit

http://www.freerun.com/cgi-bin/home.o

Enables you to explore various Valley wineries, as well as purchase wines and wine management software. Lets you stay up with current events in the Valley, get Valley sightseeing, dining, and catering ideas, and receive information on various Valley lodgings.

NAPA VALLEY VIRTUAL VISIT

It's 8:12 a.m. on Thursday, August 31 in the Napa Valley.

What's New
Free Stuff
Editorials
Napa Valley
Send a Comment
Other Virtual Visit Sites

Image supplied by Louis M. Martini Winery

Neu Coffee

http://www.iea.com/~neucof

Provides gourmet Arabica coffee and espresso from the world's most renowned coffee producing countries. Includes bulk order discounts, wholesale, retail, espresso, and office accounts.

New England Lobster

http://www.nelobster.com/

Offers fresh lobster, guaranteed overnight delivery. Provides online ordering through a secure server.

Nomius Eye-Sasa Recipes

http://www.nomius.com/~sasa/sasarec.htm

Recipes from Eastern Europe. Some recipes have metric measurements while others do not rely on exact measurements at all.

The Notte's Cookbook

http://www.niagara.com/~mnotte/cookbook.html

A personal collection of recipes.

Over the Coffee

http://www.cappuccino.com/

Lets you express your personal opinions about a good cup of joe, read the opinions of your fellow coffee lovers, or access other coffee-related sites on the Internet.

Paolo's

http://www.acoates.com/paolos

Features a seasonal menu and wine list.

Parrot Head Bar & Grille

http://tiger.cc.uic.edu/~toby-g/dixie.html

Offers recipes of all kinds related to Jimmy Buffet and life in the Keys and the Southern United States.

This page is dedicated to the food of Parrot Heads.

It contains recipes, from the islands, the Keys, the Southen United States, and other food related somehow to Buffett and/or his music.

It is now arranged with a general index which will take you to a more specific index. This was done because I'm adding more recipes and the page is getting crowded.

```
Tried to amend my carnivorous habits
Made it nearly seventy days
Losin' weight without speed, eatin' sunflower seeds
Drinkin' lots of carrot juice and soakin' up rays

But at night I'd had these wonderful dreams
Some kind of sensuous treat
Not zuchinni, fettucini or bulghar wheat
```

Pedro's Kitchen

http://superior.carleton.ca/~pwigfull/pedro.html

A collection of authentic Brazilian recipes.

PizzaNet

http://www.pizzahut.com

Lets you order your Pizza Hut pizza via the Web.

Queen's Kitchen & Pantry

http://www.pantry.com

Internet retail shopping of unusual and exotic foods and related products and services.

Quick Learning Center

http://www.korea.com/SIGHTSEE/recipe1.htm

Korean recipes and pictures of several dishes.

The Real Beer Page

http://and.com/realbeer/rbp.html

Provides a microbrewery tour, tips about brewing, brewspapers and brew magazines, drinking games, and fellow beerdrinkers' audio submissions on the Burp Me page.

Recipe Archive Index

http://www.vuw.ac.nz/who/Amy.Gale/recipes/

A master recipe archive for rec.food.cooking.

Recipe FAQ Collection

http://homecheese.eas.asu.edu/recipes.html

Provides a list of Web and Internet sites that focus on the art of cooking. Links include VEGLIFE, a sourdough mailing list, and cuisine from South India.

RecipeNet

http://www.indi.net/welcome.html

Offers many products and services, including, *RecipEmail*, a weekly recipe newsletter.

Recipes

http://www.marketnet.com/mktnet/kosher/recipes.html

Kosher recipes for Passover.

Recipes

http://www.ece.ucdavis.edu/~darsie/recipes.html

A personal collection of vegetarian recipes.

Recipes for Traditional Food in Slovenia

http://www.ijs.si/slo-recipes.html

This site is in English and offers a translation table for Metric/English conversions.

Recipes from Kathy

http://cyspacemalls.com/cook/recipe.html

Recipes from the AARestaurant. Lets you submit your own recipes for another section of this Web page.

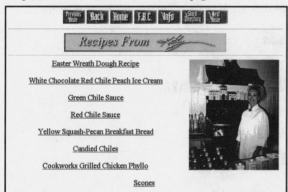

Recipes-Table of Contents

http://www.umich.edu/~babyfish/recipes.html

This small but growing page has vegan recipes and a brief explanation of veganism.

Restaurant Le Cordon Bleu

http://sunsite.unc.edu/expo/restaurant/restaurant.html

Provides recipes and menus from the French Le Cordon Bleu. Offers seven full menus—one for each day of the week.

Ridiculously Easy Recipes

http://www.sar.usf.edu/~zazuetaa/recipe.html

An amusing site for the college crowd. As the title says these recipes are easy.

Rosswog Farm Distillery

http://medianet.nbnet.nb.ca/medianet/atlantic/rosswog/rosswog.htm

Provides information on the traditional schnaps, as well as the blueberry and maple liqueurs, made by the Rosswogs. Dealer inquiries welcomed.

S.P.S. Beer Stuff

http://www.netins.net/showcase/spsbeer

Presents an online catalog of homebrewing (beer making) equipment and supplies. The catalog includes over 100 varieties of malt extracts from around the world. Also offers a selection of more than 30 brewing books.

Sauces and Marinades

http://www.vuw.ac.nz/who/Amy.Gale/recipes/sauces/sauce.html

An index of sauces and marinades.

Single Malt Scotch Page

http://www.intersource.com/~doug

Describes and rates approximately 30 different single malt scotches. Includes a brief history of the people and their orginization. Also, provides several anecdotes about their experiences and words of wisdom to those first-time scotch drinkers or experienced imbibers.

Spencer's Beer Page

http://www.umich.edu/~spencer/beer/

Tells you how to brew your first beer, provides reports on brewing experiments, and gives you links to other beer-related Web pages.

Strawberry Facts Page

http://www.wimsey.com/~jmoot/sbfacts/

Recipes, gardening, and trivia about strawberries.

Stuart's Chinese Recipes

http://www-hons-cs.dcs.st-andrews.ac.uk/~sab/Chinese_Recipes.html

Chinese recipes have been submitted to this site by people from all over the net.

The Tamilian Cuisine

http://www.cba.uh.edu/~bala/tamilnadu/food.html

Collection of Tamil recipes and links to Tamil/vegetarian newsgroups.

Texas Foods

http://www.microserve.com/~duane/TexasFoods.html

A small collection of Texan foods.

Truly Special Gourmet Foods

http://www.netline.net/~kathy/special/special.html

Offers a wide variety of specialty foods and condiments and provides an unparalleled opportunity to enjoy the American Dream.

Turkish Cuisine

http://www.metu.edu.tr:80/~melih/recipes.html

Authentic recipes from Turkey. Posted in English.

USENET Cookbook (Metric)

http://www.astro.cf.ac.uk/local/Recipe/

Online archive of recipes posted in various newsgroups. Offers a link to a nonmetric version.

Veggies Unite!

http://www.honors.indiana.edu/~veggie/recipes.cgi

A searchable recipes archive with information about nutrition. Readers can submit their own recipes.

The Virginia Diner

http://www.infi.net/vadiner/index.html

Provides information about the Diner's history, a catalog of gifts, some Southern peanut recipes, and explanations of the differences between Spanish and Virginia peanuts.

Virtual Health

http://health.net/Virtual/

Provides some healthy and delicious-looking recipes.

Virtual Kitchen

http://www.pathfinder.com/@@6I@xFQAAAAAANcR/twep/kitchen/index.html

Provides recipes and cooking tips.

Virtual Pub

http://lager.geo.brown.edu:8080/virtual-pub/

The place where Web beer aficionados exchange information on their favorite brews. Virtual Pub patrons are encouraged to link their personal Web pages to this site.

VNO: Food—Cooking and Recipes

http://www.yatcom.com/neworl/food/cooktop.html

Offers New Orleans-style cooking.

Watkins Recipes

http://www.polaris.net:80/user-www/mande/recipes/index.html

Fans of the Watkins company can get recipes for those products here. Offers links to Watkins order forms.

What's for Dinner?

http://www.gezi.com:80/gzworld/recipe.html

Thai recipes with a little cooking humor mixed in. You can submit recipes to this page through e-mail.

Whole Foods Market

http://www.wholefoods.com/wf.html

A national food chain of more than 40 natural food supermarkets in 10 states. Provides information on organically grown foods and gives you an opportunity to try out recipes. All household and personal care items have been proven safe through nonanimal testing methods. Also offers links to agricultural, vegetarian, homeopathic, and humanitarian sites.

Wines on the Internet

http://www.wines.com/

Provides information on your favorite wines and wineries. Contains news, articles, and reviews about your favorite wines. Presents a list of wine-related events you can use to keep your entertainment calendar up-to-date.

YACB: Yet Another Cookbook

http://www.csrd.uiuc.edu/koufaty/yacb/

This site is mostly in Spanish and has several Venezuelan recipes. Some recipes are translated into English.

zima.com

http://www.zima.com/

Contains most of what there is to know about Zima Clearmalt.

A.Word.A.Day Home Page

http://lrdc5.lrdc.pitt.edu/awad/home.html

Provides information about the listserv AWAD, which sends a new vocabulary word a day to your e-mail address. Also offers links to other word-related Internet resources.

About the NDLC

http://www.occ.uky.edu/NDLC/NDLCexplain.html

Serves as a free resource for K–12, higher education, and adult education, distance learning. Offers a free telnet database. Explains how to use the database, who to call for help, and NCLD's mission.

Academic

gopher://cwis.usc.edu:70/11/
Other_Gophers_and_Information_Resources/
Gophers_by_Subject/Gopher_Jewels/academic

Categorizes the best of all gophers by subject. Breaks education-related gophers into nine distinct areas.

Academy One

http://www.nptn.org:80/cyber.serv/AOneP/

Provides resources for students, parents, and K–12 educators and administrators. Sponsors Internet projects throughout the year, including a Mousetrap-Powered Vehicle Competition, the TeleOlympics, and the Math Olympics. Also offers a curriculum database and an index of other online projects.

Accept_Use_Policies

gopher://inspire.ospi.wednet.edu:70/11/
Accept_Use_Policies

Provides information about samples of K–12 acceptable use policies.

Adult Education (Education)

http://galaxy.einet.net/galaxy/Social-Sciences/Educa-tion/Adult-Education.html

Offers links to several resources on adult education. Enables the combination of distance education, adult education, and the Internet to deliver instruction. Also invites contributions to the collection of resources.

AIMS Education Foundation

http://204.161.33.100/AIMS.html

Presents the world of hands-on science and math investigations for K–9 students. Integrates the study of mathematics and science in a meaningful manner, which prompts students to quickly realize the value of mathematics and learn to "work like scientists."

Ainsworth Keyboard Training Systems

http://www.qwerty.com

Teaches keyboarding skills. Includes special warm-up exercises to improve efficiency and end writer's block.

Alabama Supercomputer Authority

http://sgisrvr.asc.edu/index.html

Provides state-of-the-art technology in supercomputing and networking to educational institutions, government agencies, and private industry.

Alpine Valley School— Home Page

http://www.well.com/user/artbrock/avs/

A K–12 independent day school located in Denver at which the students completely design their own education and participate in governing the school. Provides detailed information about the school's philosophy, mission, enrollment process, and generally presents a very bright picture of the school.

American Association for the Advancement of Core Curriculum

gopher://mercury.cair.du.edu:70/11/gophers/public_policy/

Provides information from the American Association for the Advancement of Core Curriculum. Covers relevant book reviews, leadership issues, core knowledge initiatives, educational policies, and funding. Also offers curriculum resources.

Ameritech Education Resources

http://www.aads.net:1081/education/

Features the Schoolhouse, which contains a Recreation Area (information on hands-on projects and hobbies), a Teacher's Lounge (lesson plans and curriculum guides), and a Student Activities Center (online activities and projects). Also features the Internet InfoCenter.

The Amistad Research Center

http://www.arc.tulane.edu/

Archives African-American history and culture. Also contains information about many other minority groups. Offers links to the center's manuscript collection, several art collections, traveling history exhibits, and library.

The Anesthesiology Educational Server— Anesthesiology Manuals

http://www.anes.ccf.org:8080

Includes anesthesiology manuals for neuroanesthesia, orthopedic anesthesia, latex allergy, and ENT anesthesia. Also sponsors the Society for Education in Anesthesia (SEA) home page.

Apple Higher Education: The Apple Virtual Campus

http://www.info.apple.com/hed/

Showcases Apple's vision of the campus of the future, while strengthening the technologies of today. Lists learning technologies such as distance learning, talks about collaboration and information access, and the mobile student. Also contains a link to Highway 1, a nonprofit organization formed to support innovative use of new technologies in the legislative environment and democratic process.

The Area Cooperative Educational Services Gopher

gopher://cs.aces.k12.ct.us

Focuses on national and local education. Contains policy and legislation, technology assistance, software and connectivity to government servers. Also offers links to other useful educational gophers.

Aristotle

http://aristotle.isu.edu

Includes an online newspaper, links to Macintosh software, and a graphical interface.

Arizona State University

gopher://info.asu.edu/11/asu-cwis/education/other

Serves as an educational resource from pre-K to higher education, and covers how to get money (grants) and how to spend it (products). Offers links to many other resources.

The Arkansas K–12 Gopher

gopher://hp.k12.ar.us

Features an "I'm New Here" section, which gives the new Internet user practical online help. Includes education news and documents, government information, teaching workshops, reference materials, and connectivity to FTP sites.

Armadillo's WWW Server

http://chico.rice.edu/armadillo

Provides resources related to Texas history, culture, life, and so on. Offers links to information supporting an interdisciplinary unit with a Texas theme. Also offers links to many other education-related Web and gopher sites.

Arrow Publishing

http://www2.interpath.net:80/spadion/arrow/

Lists videos, software, and publications designed to increase literacy. Produces literacy-oriented educational materials.

Also offers an order form that you can print out and fill in to receive more information or materials.

ArtsEdge Network

http://artsedge.kennedy-center.org/artsedge.html

Focuses on using technology to increase access to arts resources and increase arts education in the K–12 school environment. Features an online newsletter, an information gallery, curriculum guides, and links to other arts-related online information.

The AskERIC Virtual Library

http://ericir.syr.edu

Contains select resources for both education and general use. Includes lesson plans, ERIC digests, information guides and publications, reference tools, government information, and educational listserv archives.

Association for Educational Communications and Technology

gopher://sunbird.usd.edu:72/1

Focuses on informational technology. Provides information about the inner workings of the AECT, but also offers a solid collection of upcoming conferences and calls for papers. Also lists employment resources and general IT information.

Banned Books Online

http://www.cs.cmu.edu:8001/Web/People/spok/banned-books.html

Discusses literary censorship and offers links to each work mentioned that is available in electronic format. Also offers a Most Frequently Challenged Books of the 1990s page, as well as links to other sites dealing with censorship.

Biology(Science)

http://galaxy.einet.net/galaxy/Science/Biology.html

Offers links to all things scientific that might be of use to K–12 or university teachers and students. Categorizes sections by subset of biology, most recent additions, software, and collections, to name a few.

Bond University

http://Bond.edu.au

Describes Bond University, a private and independent university in Australia. Enables students to request further information relating to the possibility of studying at Bond.

Book Nook

http://i-site.on.ca/Isite/Education/Bk_report/

Presents book reports by kids on kids' literature. Links reports world-wide into one central point of reference.

Brooke High WWW Server

http://168.216.219.18

Provides information about Brooke High School, located in the northern panhandle of West Virginia, 40 miles southeast of Pittsburgh. Includes the *Babbling Brooke* (school newspaper), information about the school system and surrounding coummunities, information on how to install a Web server and slip servers. Also offers thousands of educational and shareware files for ftp/gopher transfer.

Brunel University Artificial Intelligence Area

http://http1.brunel.ac.uk:8080/depts/AI/

Features information on artificial intelligence, including artificial life and genetic algorithms. Also contains many links to other AI sites.

Burlington High School

http://198.247.53.2/homepage.html

Offers numerous student pages, the history of Burlington, Iowa, and computer projects including a complete tutorial on how to build a Macintosh WWW server.

Buros Institute of Mental Health

http://www.unl.edu/buros.home.html

Includes a Test Review Locater, a catalog of Buros publications, digest articles, and a reviewer application form.

Busy Teachers WebSite K-12

http://www.gatech.edu/lcc/idt/Students/Cole/Proj/K-12/TOC.html

K–12 Internet resource for teachers. Organized by subject area with annotated links to sites that lead directly to source materials.

CALI: The Center for Computer-Assisted Legal Instruction

http://cali.kentlaw.edu

Nonprofit consortium of more than 155 United States law schools. Supports the production, distribution, and use of computer-based instructional materials.

California State University

http://www.co.calstate.edu/ITPA/Info_Tech.html

Develops policy guidelines to facilitate the effective uses of learning resources and instructional technology.

Calvary Lutheran School

http://www.sunflower.org/~calvary/index.html

Presents information concerning the mission, goals, standards, programs, and curriculum of the school. Highlights church and school events, along with current newsletters and other information.

Canadian Institute of Applied Learning, Inc.

http://www.inforamp.net/~canial/index.html

Offers courses in hardware and software training. Carries courses to train students to become certified Novell Engineers and Administrators (C.N.E and C.N.A certification). Also offers courses on PC repair and service.

Canadian Kids' Page

http://www.onramp.ca/~lowens/107kids.htm

Serves as a starting place for parents and children exploring the Web together.

Career Blazers NAEC

http://www.cblazers.com/class/novell.html

Offers up-to-date training at a Novell Authorized Education Center.

Carnegie Mellon University's College of Humanities and Social Sciences

http://hss.cmu.edu/

Provides information concerning Carnegie Mellon University's College of Humanities and Social Sciences and its departments.

Carrie's Sites for Educators

http://www.mtjeff.com/~bodenst/page5.html

Provides a table of contents to make browsing easy. Offers a collection of resources, from humanities to math, and science to software.

Cartoon Laws of Physics

http://abacus.bates.edu/~jburke/open1/physics.html

Adds humor to the standard laws of physics. Illustrates each law using cartoon characters.

CASAA Student Leadership Resource Centre

http://www.sentex.net/~casaa

Focuses on providing fresh student leadership materials, ideas, and support for the student activity advisor.

Center for Talented Youth (CTY) of the Johns Hopkins University

http://www.jhu.edu:80/~gifted/

Serves the gifted population with special programs, job opportunities, and other resources. Provides details about all the CTY programs, and also offers links to other resources.

Center for Technology Studies

http://www.mngt.uleth.ca/deprtmnt/tech/tech.htm

Provides information about CTS's own research projects, links to interesting resources on the Web for business, research, teaching, as well as fun and games/humor.

The Centre for Alternative Transportation Fuels

http://www.bcr.bc.ca/catf\default.htm

The Centre for Alternative Transportation Fuels is operated by BC Research Inc.(BCRI) in Vancouver, B.C., Canada. Maintains a database of technical papers to support the technical and business community in this rapidly moving technological area.

CEPS/NASM Smithsonian Institution

http://ceps.nasm.edu:2020/homepage.html

Serves as a jumping-off point for exploring planetary and other astronomical data from the Center for Planetary Studies, Regional Planetary Image Facility, and the National Air and Space Museum. Offers links that provide information useful for classes such as activities, images, and calendars of events.

Chemsoc Homepage

http://www.chem.ed.ac.uk/chemsoc/chemsoc.html

Provides information, a calender, and latest news of the Edinburgh University Chemical society.

Childaware

http://www.inetcom.net/test/index.html

Offers positive interaction with other parents of preschoolers. Includes a manual for preschoolers to help check readiness for first grade.

Children's International Summer Villages

http://www.altair.it/cisv/

International nonprofit organization (promoted by UNESCO) that promotes peace around the world by organizing summer villages for kids of different parts of the world from 11 years to 99.

Children's Literature Web Guide

http://www.ucalgary.ca/~dkbrown/index.html

Catalogs Internet resources related to books for children and young adults. Lists recommended books, recent awards, new authors, resources for parents, teachers, and story tellers, movies based on children's books, and much more. Provides information on how to get your children or class involved in online publication, so the whole world can enjoy their creativity.

ChronicIllnet

http://www.calypte.com

Focuses on chronic illnesses, including groundbreaking research articles, a nationwide calendar of events, news articles, and an In the Community section.

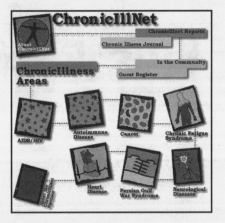

CIC, Center for Library Initiatives

http://www.cic.net/cic/cli.html

Provides information for librarians, educators, and institutions, particularly those within the CIC (Big Ten universities, plus the University of Chicago).

Cisco Educational Archives and Resources Catalog

http://sunsite.unc.edu/cisco/edu-arch.html

Provides information to help educators and schools connect to the Internet. Provides technical information (because Cisco produces networking hardware), but also offers examples of school networking projects. Also offers the Virtual Schoolhouse.

Classroom at the Internet Schoolhouse

http://www.packet.net:80/schoolhouse/inside.html

Offers a collection of educational and interactive resources. Includes Internet projects, art, civics, interactive games, and science.

Classroom Connect

http://www.wentworth.com/classroom

Online magazine for K–12 educators using the Internet in the classroom. Both in print and online, *Classroom Connect* has become a source of pointers and features related to using the Internet in formal education for more than 8,000 monthly readers.

Classroom Connect on the Net

http://www.wentworth.com/classroom(Netscape)

Includes a listing of schools with Web pages organized by country and a page that contains reviews and information from major educational conferences. Also offers a searchable educational resources page with links organized alphabetically or by subject, as well as links to educational vendors and relevant newsgroups. A very useful page.

CNN

gopher://ericir.syr.edu:70/11/Lesson/CNN

Offers a collection of daily CNN downloads with lesson plans and curriculum guides. Archives lesson plans for 1993, 1994, and 1995.

Cold Spring Harbor Fish Hatchery and Aquarium

http://www.okc.com/fish

Offers a wide variety of hands-on educational programs for K–12 students. Presents indoor and outdoor displays. Provides trout and other fish to lakes and streams throughout the region.

College Prep Page

http://www.tpoint.net/~jewels/college.html

Presents a collection of resources for planning your education. Provides information on financial aid, admissions, career planning, and more.

College SAT and Financial Aid Planning Service

http://www.tiac.net/users/oline/college

Offers valuable help for sophomores, juniors, and seniors. Includes family contribution calculations, FAF forms, college planning, Plus Loans applications, and SAT courses.

Columbia Public Schools Home Page

http://www.ims.columbia.k12.mo.us

Serves 15,000 K–12 students. Features student and staff work and technical information for other schools.

The Comer School Development Program

http://info.med.yale.edu/comer

Provides information about the School Development Program, a national school reform project directed by James P. Comer, M.D., the renowned child psychiatrist at the Yale Child Study Center.

The Community Learning Network

http://cln.etc.bc.ca

Provides information pertinent to United States education as well. Includes distance learning resource information, connections to other educational and Canadian government gophers and CLN software.

Computer as Learning Partner

http://www.clp.berkeley.edu/CLP.html

Gives information on integrating computer use to improve middle school science instruction. Provides curriculum guides, software links, and project information.

Concepts in Science through Molecular Modeling

http://www.nyu.edu/pages/mathmol/modules/modules.html

Contains many activities for use in the classroom. Includes a section for teachers and for students.

Cornell Computer Science Graphics Course

http://www.tc.cornell.edu:80/Visualization/Education/cs418/

Plans to develop an online service for the students to review lab procedures and results, as well as present lecture material and project animations for all to view.

Cornell Theory Center Math and Science Gateway

http://www.tc.cornell.edu:80/Edu/MathSciGateway/

Provides links to resources in mathematics and science for educators and students in grades 9-12. Divides the resources into standard subject areas and includes links to online field trips and museums. Also offers journal and research articles.

Council of the Great City Schools Online

http://www.cgcs.org

Nonprofit organization that represents the nation's largest public school systems.

Curtin University, Department of Chemical Engineering

http://www.cage.curtin.edu.au/chemeng/

Offers links to and information about the department and its courses. Also offers a set of pages that describes what a chemical engineer does. Also provides an index of related links.

CyberKids Home

http://www.woodwind.com:80/cyberkids/

CyberKids was created as a place for kids to learn and have fun. Offers a free online magazine that contains stories and artwork created by kids, as well as online puzzles, games, and more. Also provides keypals from around the globe in CyberKids Interactive.

The Cyberspace Middle School

http://www.scri.fsu.edu/~dennisl/CMS.html

Contains links to science fairs, *Midlink Magazine* (for kids by kids), and Virtual Bus Stops (links to online middle schools). Also offers many helpful links for students, such as an online Periodic Table, how to read a map, and so on.

CYBERSPACE MIDDLE SCHOOL

Deaf

gopher://porpoise.oise.on.ca:70/11/resources/IRes4Ed/resources/deaf

Provides a collection of deaf and hearing-impaired educational resources. Lists social issues in deafness, legal issues, educational issues, and teacher and student resources.

Deafed

gopher://gopher.educ.kent.edu:70/11/edgophers/special/deafed

Focuses on deaf education. Provides information on curriculum, instructional strategies, and employment opportunities.

Department of Clothing, Design, and Technology, MMU

http://www.doc.mmu.ac.uk/hol/cdt.html

Details courses, staff, students, and the work done in this department. Contains examples of designs produced by students and staff and also details some of the conferences and shows scheduled.

Department of Computing, Manchester Met. Uni.

http://www.doc.mmu.ac.uk/

Contains pages that describe the activities of the Department of Computing, Manchester Metropolitan University. Describes the courses (including higher education and short courses for business), research and research groups, work with national and international parties, students, and the department in general. Also offers a number of webs for other departments. Manchester is particularly interested in hearing from prospective students, as well as academic and business partners.

The
Manchester
Metropolitan
University

Department of Computing

Department of Informatic at University of Santiago of Chile Pages

http://www.inf.usach.cl/

Contains information about academics, curriculums, internet services, and so on.

The Digital Frog

http://www.sentex.net/~dfi

Focuses on producing high-quality educational software. Features The Digital Frog CD-ROM. Describes DFI and contains a full-featured Web version of The Digital Frog.

Digital Tradition Folk Song Database

http://web2.xerox.com/digitrad/

Offers a searchable database of international folk songs, including children's songs. Includes a table of contents for browsing the titles, tunes, or keywords.

Distance Ed

http://www.cudenver.edu/~mryder/itc_data/distance.html

Offers several links to good distance education resources, especially for colleges and universities. Serves as a good starting point for researching distance learning examples and practices.

Distance Education Clearinghouse

http://www.uwex.edu/disted/home.html

Gathers information on teleconferencing technologies, instructional design, programs and courses, and other distance learning resources.

Distance Education Resources

http://tenb.mta.ca/disted.html

Offers links to international distance learning resources for community and higher education.

Distance Learning Directory

http://199.125.205.20/WebPages/dll/DIST-LRN/dld.htm

Provides a listing of web sites, gopher sites, listservs, and newsgroups associated with distance education.

Distance Learning on the Net by Glenn Hoyle

http://www.interaccess.com/users/ghoyle/

Organizes information like chapters in a book and covers all aspects of distance education from "What is it?" to online and print resources, to grants and funding. Addresses K–12, higher education, and corporate/private industry uses of distance learning.

Distance Learning Resources

http://www.crl.com/~gorgon/distance.html

Offers a list of links (all resources for distance education) that have Internet support of distance learning included in the definition. Also describes each link.

disted%3Aellsworth

gopher://una.hh.lib.umich.edu:70/00/inetdirsstacks/
disted%3Aellsworth

Updated version of *Dr. E's Eclectic Compendium of Electronic Resources for Adult/Distance Education*. An especially good handout for use when teaching novice distance educators about the Internet.

Division of Hearing and Speech Sciences, Vanderbilt University

http://vumclib.mc.vanderbilt.edu/vumcdept/hear.html

Offers both Master's and Doctor of Philosophy degrees, emphasizing speech-language pathology or audiology. The graduate program includes academic, clinical, and research activities.

Dole 5-A-Day Home Page

http://www.dole5aday.com

Offers educational nutrition information and delivers it in a clever and fun way: 36 fruit and vegetable characters host the site and make eating five fruits and vegetables a day fun for everyone. Provides nine areas: 5 A Day Program,

CD-ROM, Nutrition Center, Fan Mail, Fun Stuff, 5 A Day at School, Newsroom, and Dole.

DPI InfoWeb

http://www.dpi.state.nc.us

Provides access to ERIC, employment opportunities, and the state standardized curriculum. Also offers an online telephone directory for the DPI, and a nice teacher and administrator resource page. Features an outline that shows exactly what information links off which page.

DreamLink

http://www.iag.net:80/~hutchib/.dream/

Contains current information and resources on dream translation techniques and different theoretical orientations regarding dreams. Provides a journal to post dreams and receive feedback. Features an archive and guest dreamer.

Dynamy, Inc.

http://www.iii.net/biz/dynamy

Nonprofit organization in Worcester, Massachusetts, which offers a one year internship program to students ages 17–22.

Eagle Ridge

http://www.primenet.com/~eaglerg/

Offers many links related to education, Native Americans, kids, wildlife, and the environment.

Ed Web Home Page

http://edweb.cnidr.org:90/

Centers on resources showing technology and its role in school reform. Lets you hunt down online educational resources around the world, learn about trends in education policy and information infrastructure development, and examine success stories of computers in the classroom.

Education

http://www.lib.umich.edu/chouse/tree/edu.html

Provides a listing of Internet resources, and rates the linked sites to help Internet users plow through the vast amount of information.

Education (Social Sciences)

http://aw.com/educatio.html

Provides a listing of Internet educational resources, organized by topic and type of resource.

Education Sites

http://www.fn.net/education.html

Serves as a subject-oriented guide to Internet resources. Categories include art, health, online museums and libraries, math, science, social sciences, and other resources. Offers art and health links.

Education Virtual Library— Primary School

http://www.csu.edu.au/education/primary.html

Alphabetically catalogs several interesting K–12 curriculum resources from around the world. Helps you research trends in education and creates multicultural or foreign language units. Also highlights links to a Web site created in Russian using the Cyrillic alphabet.

Educational Online Sources

`http://netspace.students.brown.edu/eos/main_image.html`

Plans to become a central "welcoming" and jump station for educators on the Internet. Contains links to educational conferences, policy and reform archives, and subject guides to online resources.

Educational Software Institute

`http://www.bonsai.com/q/edsoftcat/htdocs/esihome.html`

Calls itself a "one-stop educational software resource center," and hosts a large collection of K–12 educational software divided into 19 categories. Also features the "Product Finder," a search tool for finding specific products as opposed to browsing the online catalog. Lets you fill up your "shopping bag" with products and figure shipping along the way.

EDUCOM—Home Page

`http://educom.edu:80/`

Offers searchable archives of *EDUCOM Review*, archives of the listserv *EDUPAGE*, and other online documents. Supports EDUCOM's focus on educational technology in higher education. Also offers links to several other telecom/educational technology-related site and programs.

Welcome to Educational Software Institute Online!

eduMall

`http://edumall.com/`

Offers education products. Includes mall locations: Mall Central for mall events, freebies, and latest information; the Learning Center; Bookstore; Administrator's Connection; Campus Shops; Stadium; and Kiosk. Sells education products.

The Edutainment Page

`http://www.edutainment.com.au`

Contains reviews and discussion of educational software. Offers more than 120 independent reviews and links to other sites.

The Egyptian Gallery

`http://www.mordor.com/hany/egypt/egypt.html`

Provides information on the modern state, such as the national anthem, pictures of modern cities, and sound clips. Also presents pictures and text about ancient Egypt.

Death Mask of Tutankhamen

election.html

`http://buckman.pps.k12.or.us/election/election.html`

Presents the Toon Town Election Page, an example of an online interactive project. Students from about 50 classes sent in their votes on which cartoon should be 'Mayor of ToonTown', and one class posted the results on the Web. They used e-mail ballots, and accepted write-in candidates.

The Electronic Prehistoric Shark Museum

`http://turnpike.net/emporium/C/celestial/epsm.htm`

Features fossil shark teeth (photos and descriptions) from the prehistoric Great White to the jaws of a modern-day

shark. Also offers links to other paleontological sites and posts additional shark sightings on the Internet.

ELTI Charlotte's English Aids

http://www.coe.uncc.edu/~brmattin/adds.html

Lists several sample letters for different situations, intended to be models for ES/FL students or others learning written English.

EMLRL Home Page at the Medical College of Georgia

http://emlrl.mcg.edu/

Focuses on ongoing research projects conducted by the Emergency Medicine Section of the Medical College of Georgia.

English as a Second Language

http://www.ed.uiuc.edu/edpsy-387/rongchang-li/esl/

Brings together resources for teaching ES/FL, such as matching audio to text to help comprehension. Also offers links to the Word a Day vocabulary building e-mail service, and Idiom of the Week.

The Environmental Education Network

http://www.envirolink.org/enviroed/

Serves as a jumping-off point for using the Internet to research the environmental issues. Offers categorized links to resources for teachers, resources for students, and also for higher education.

Environmental Training Group Inc's ENVIROPAGE

http://www.etg-inc.com

Provides United States environmental and occupational safety and health regulations. Emphasizes on training. Contains updates on agency interpretations and regulations. Offers links to related sites.

eslbeg.html

http://www.ed.uiuc.edu/EdPsy-387/Rongchang-li/eslproject/eslbeg.html

Provides instruction. Each link at launches a reading and listening activity geared for ES/FL or other beginning readers.

The ESU #16 Gopher

gopher://esu16.esu16.k12.ne.us

Nebraska's K–12 information network. Contains lesson plans, K–12 resources and connectivity to Nebraska Online, VERONICA, and other services. Also features an acceptable use policy archive and art education resources.

Ethical, Legal, and Social Issues in Science

http://www.lbl.gov/Education/ELSI/ELSI.html

Tackles tough issues that face scientists every day. Discusses basic versus applied research, breast cancer and genetic screening, and more.

eWorld on the Web: Learning Community

http://www.eworld.com/education/resources

Provides educators, students, and parents with a way to find extensive educational information on the Web. Offers information from a wide variety of sources, including

content from Apple's education division, learning institutions, educational publications, and museums.

Exchange—Learning. English Language Culture

http://www.ed.uiuc.edu/exchange/

Serves primarily ES/FL students, but also works for multicultural lessons or thematic units. Consists of contributions from international students, such as "Did you know?" about little cultural differences. Also serves as a place to publish your writing (for ES/FL students).

Exploratorium Home Page

http://www.exploratorium.edu/

Features, among other exhibits, "Diving in to the Gene Pool," "Remembering Nagasaki," "Ask Us A Question," and a digital library. Also offers The Learning Studio, a collection of science resources for parents, teachers, and kids.

Explorer Home Page

http://server2.greatlakes.k12.mi.us/

Acts as a curriculum resource. Contains a searchable database of lesson plans and curriculum guides aimed at math and science. Also categorizes lists of Web classroom resources.

Faculty of Asian Studies, Australian National University

http://online.anu.edu.au/asianstudies/

Provides Asian Studies teaching-and-learning resources, pointers to a vast wealth of Asian Studies research material,

information about the programs of the Faculty of Asian Studies at the Australian National University, pointers to information about the University, Australia, and studying in Australia.

Federal and State-Run Servers

http://edweb.cnidr.org:90/gophwww.gov.html

Lists all current federally- and state-run gopher and Web servers with an educational focus. Lists a link to each site along with a brief description of the site.

Financial Aid Information Page

http://www.cs.cmu.edu/afs/cs.cmu.edu/user/mkant/Public/FinAid/finaid.html

Offers a collection of financial aid information on the Internet. Includes links to all online scholarship and fellowship databases and information about grants and loans, as well as links to university financial aid Web and gopher servers and a link to the online version of Octameron Associates' book *Don't Miss Out: The Ambitious Student's Guide to Financial Aid.*

The Florida Department of Education Gopher

gopher://gopher.firn.edu/11/doe

Contains extensive information on state and local education initiatives. Also offers links to professional development services, Florida private K12 schools, and public and private colleges and universities in Florida.

Florida Institute of Technology—School of Aeronautics

http://www.fit.edu/soa

Offers five accredited degree programs in aviation management, aeronautical science, and aviation computer science. Offers FAA-approved flight training.

Florida Vedic College

http://www.owplaza.com/fvc/

Offers courses on Yoga, Vaishnava philosophy, Sanskrit, and Vedic literature over the Internet.

FredNet MOO

http://www.fred.net/cindy/frednet.html

Lets you attend Lincoln's assassination, visit a biochemical laboratory, examine ancient artifacts at the Iceman Museum, and more. Provides a tutorial for new MOOers. Also contains a handy MOO Command Index for reference.

Friends and Partners

http://solar.rtd.utk.edu/friends/home.html

Promotes understanding between Americans and Russians. Provides information on almost every aspect of life in the two cultures, and also links to learning and using the Cyrillic alphabet. Offers a related listserv that you can join or access.

Friends and Partners

FYI, RFC #1578-Schools, and Internet

http://chs.cusd.claremont.edu/www/people/rmuir/
rfc1578.html

Provides an Internet FAQ on the Internet and K–12 schools. Offers a clickable table of contents for ease of browsing, and contains useful information for anyone considering putting the Internet into a K–12 environment.

Galileo

http://www-hpcc.astro.washington.edu/scied/galileo.html

Offers a downloadable collection of science lesson plans for K–12 science teachers for classroom use.

Garfield Co. Public Library System

http://www.colosys.net/garfield.html

Provides access to online books, magazines, and reference tools. Includes searchable library catalogs.

GCRIO Online Student Activities

http://www.gcrio.org/eduStd.html

Offers a collection of links to online science-oriented interactive projects that students can participate in. Also offers subject guides to resources and grant information.

The GEB Web—Home of Guiding Eyes for the Blind in Cyberspace

http://www.cloud9.net/~jdunn/gebhome.html

Nonprofit provider of professionally trained guide dogs. Offers a better means of mobility for blind, deaf/blind, and blind with special needs persons. Offers extensive information about the school, dog training, and other resources available through GEB Online.

Genetic Engineering Taught Through Telecommunications

http://kadets.d20.co.edu:80/~lundberg/index.html

Genetic Engineering is taught to 36 other schools in the state of Colorado using the Internet.

GENII Home Page

http://www.deakin.edu.au/edu/MSEE/GENII/GENII-Home-Page.html

Teaches teachers how to utilize the resources of the Internet so that they can incorporate the technology into their lesson plans. Lists the mission, virtual faculty, and other relevant data for this project.

Genome Educators of the San Francisco Bay Area

http://www.lbl.gov/Education/Genome/Genome-Ed.html

Group of education professionals from the San Francisco Bay area who have an active interest in all aspects of genetics education. Focuses on sharing information and resources to further the understanding of current advances in the field of genetics.

The Geometry Forum

http://forum.swarthmore.edu/

Focuses on geometry and math education. Offers links to resources such as the Coalition of Essential Schools, a Web-based lesson on vectors, a geometry listserv, and more. Also offers a section on projects for students, such "Ask Dr. Math."

Gifted and Talented (TAG) Resources Home Page

http://www.eskimo.com:80/~user/kids.html

Describes many resources for talented and gifted children, their parents, and educators. Overviews giftedness, and lists mailing lists, schools with TAG programs, summer programs, and publications to name a few. Also offers a keypal contact page.

Glendale Community College

http://www.gc.maricopa.edu

Delivers information about the campus. Also contains student, faculty, and staff Web pages. Contains several campus departments, including the Innovation Center, Network Services, Training and Employee Development, English, Business, and *The College Voice* newspaper.

Global Ecology Study Abroad/IHP

http://world.std.com/~ihp/ihp.html

Study global ecology and travel around the world to England, India, Philippines, New Zealand, Mexico. Earn college credit, live with families, small group, international faculty. Offers courses in anthropology, biology, ecology, and economic development. Provides an online catalog, slide file, and application.

Grolier Interactive

http://www.grolier.com

Presents Grolier Interactive, the international CD-ROM multimedia reference and entertainment publisher of the Grolier Multimedia Encyclopedia, Encyclopedia Americana, Guinness Multimedia Disc of Records, Science Fiction encyclopedia, World Cup Soccer, and Modern Art.

GROW—Opportunity Wales

http://194.72.34.100/grow/

Nonprofit organization that administers a variety of placement schemes and internships (some United Kingdom government-sponsored) for graduates and undergraduate students seeking experience of working for UK-based small- and medium-sized enterprises.

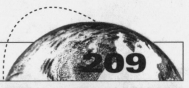

Guidelines for Educational Uses of Networks

http://www.ed.uiuc.edu/Guidelines/guidelines.html

Offers a collection of several different works related to setting up and managing an educational network, mostly philosophical and focused on educational outcomes.

Harry Singer Foundation

http://www.redshift.com/~singerf

The Harry Singer Foundation was created to get people, especially high school and college students, more actively interested in public policy. Provides free information such as books and pamphlets, as well as points of contact for further interest.

Heinemann World

http://www.heinemann.co.uk

Offers news on educational books, events and technology, guides to relevant sites of use for class and coursework, and sample material to download.

Hello India!

http://www.helloindia.com

Serves the Indian community. Contains information about Indian food, music, culture, entertainment, events, and the online version of *India Today*.

Heritage Map Museum

http://www.carto.com

Displays hundreds of original 15th to 19th century antique maps. Focuses on displaying and selling original works of the masters of cartography. Offers the works of Schedel, Munster, Ortelius, Mercator, Blaeu, Hondius, and many others.

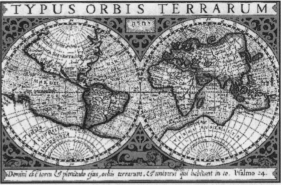

Hillside Elementary School

http://hillside.coled.umn.edu/

Contains activities and projects. Lets students make their own home pages and have e-mail addresses, and use the Internet for research.

Hole Family School Virtual Reference Library Links

http://execpc.com/~wycklend/holy/html

Provides reference information and links to online encyclopedias, including a link to the *Encyclopedia of the Mouse Genome 3.0*.

Holocaust

gopher://info.asu.edu:70/11/asu-cwis/education/other/
k12resources/holocaust

Contains several different curriculum created for teaching about the Holocaust.

Home Growing Automated Systems

http://www.mbnet.mb.ca/~djansen

Contains information on indoor gardening, hydroponic systems, computer-controlled equipment, and mail order of related merchandise.

Homeschooling Resources

http://www.eskimo.com/~billb/home.html

Contains home schooling resources, divided into home schooling Web sites, relevant educational directories, and ERIC information guides.

The Homework Page

http://www.tpoint.net/~jewels/homework.html

A general subject guide page. Categorizes links by subject matter and by age group.

Hoover's Online

http://www.hoovers.com

Provides in-depth profiles of 8,000 public and private companies in the United States, compiled by The Reference Press.

HotList of K–12 Internet School Sites

http://toons.cc.ndsu.nodak.edu/~sackmann/k12.html

Contains links to all United States K–12 schools with Internet access, divided by state, and lists the level of access each school currently has (gopher, Web, e-mail only, and so on).

HotList: Virtual Exhibits

http://sln.fi.edu/tfi/jump.html

Offers links to many online interactive exhibits, where you control the action on the other end, such as a robot or telescope. Also offers links to online exhibits, such as the Amazon jungle or the Louvre.

http://www.widdl.com/ MediaPro/

http://www.widdl.com/MediaPro/

Features the Magic Carpet series of interactive learning software (in English or Mandarin Chinese). Provides ordering information and information on a 30-day free trial basis.

The Hub

gopher://hub.terc.edu:70/1

Serves as a resource for math and science educators. Contains links for many different online math and science resources, as well as conference announcements. Also contains resources from the Eisenhower Regional Alliance, a group that supports math and science education. Features a searchable database.

The Human-Languages Page

http://www.willamette.edu/~tjones/Language-Page.html

Focuses on bringing together information about the languages of the world. The language resources listed here come from all around the world, and range from dictionaries to language tutorials to spoken samples of languages. Offers the page in several languages. Provides Quick-Jump links for easy navigation, and should soon be searchable.

I*EARN

http://www.igc.apc.org/iearn/

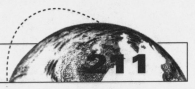

I*EARN is the International Education and Resource Network, composed of teachers and young people working together in different parts of the world via a global telecommunications network. The purpose of I*EARN is to enable participants to undertake projects designed to make a meaningful difference in the health and welfare of the planet and its people. Contains information from all the international projects, as well as entry points for the I*EARN member newsgroups.

ICBL Video Conferencing CASE Studentship Page

http://www.icbl.hw.ac.uk/~cjs/vidconf.area/index.html

Provides information about using video conferencing in the classroom. Includes technology, how-to's, integrating it into the classroom, current projects, and more.

ICDL

http://acs-info.open.ac.uk/info/other/ICDL/ICDL-Facts.html

Offers links to a free telnet database, a quarterly publication about distance learning, and the ICDL gopher server.

IDEAnet—The Indiana Department of Education Network

http://ideanet.doe.state.in.us

Provides Indiana teachers free access to local projects, peer referral, employment information, and classroom resources. Also offers non-Hoosiers a wide variety of connections to educational networks and examples of school home pages.

ILTweb: LiveText: Index

http://daemon.ilt.columbia.edu/k12/livetext/

The LiveText project is based on the belief that the educational applications enabled by networked multimedia technologies will provide the opportunity for educational reform. Provides supporting curricula, lesson plans, and instructional design resources.

Image Analytics Corporation

**LiveText Educational Resources
(Grades 4-12)**

http://www.imsworld.com/image

Provides cost effective hardware and software systems for microscopic and macroscopic image analysis. A full system performs morphometric cell analysis (length, area, velocity, and shape), currently used for AIDS, neuroimmunology, and biological research. Includes ftp Demo file. Offers basic software and frame grabber board. Also offers color analysis.

IMD International Institute for Management Development

http://www.imd.ch/

Offers a solid reputation for pioneering the development of executive education, bringing a truly international perspective to management development in cooperation with some of the most successful companies around the world.

Impact! Online Home Page

http://www.ed.uiuc.edu/Impact/impact_homepage.html

Consists of hypertext documents in English, with links giving pronunciation, parts of speech, and meaning.

InfoList Home Page

http://www.electriciti.com:80/~rlakin/

Helps teachers begin using the Internet as an educational tool. Contains back issues of the *InfoList Digest*, to which you also can subscribe free via e-mail.

InforMNs

http://informns.k12.mn.us

Includes teacher discussions, lesson plans, and a collection of gopher lists.

Inkspot

http://www.interlog.com/~ohi/dmo-pages/young.html

Offers a collection of useful resources for young writers, and anyone teaching young writers. Includes references to workshops, online style guides, publications accepting submissions, and contests.

inQuiry Almanack, March 1995

http://sln.fi.edu/qanda/qanda3.html

Monthly magazine for educators interested in using the Internet to support inquiry-based learning in the classroom. Offers Internet "hunts," online puzzles, and experiments. Focuses on science education.

Integrating Technology Schools Home Page at University of New Mexico

http://www.unm.edu/~jeffryes/its.html

Helps teachers both in the field and preservice learn how to integrate technology into the classroom. Offers online project ideas, subject guides, and how-to's for the Internet.

The Interactive Frog Dissection: An Online Tutorial

http://curry.edschool.Virginia.edu:80/~insttech/frog/

Uses photographs and QuickTime movies to illustrate step-by-step the dissection of a frog. Provides tests along the way to help the student judge mastery of the content.

Interactive Multimedia Education Resources

http://www.ems.psu.edu/Earth2/E2Top.html

Contains images and other multimedia files related to earth science. Offers an online tutorial to learn how to use the resources.

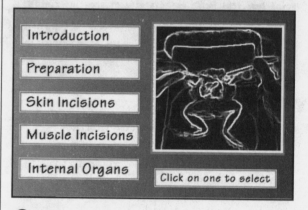

Intercultural E-Mail Classroom Connections

http://www.stolaf.edu/network/iecc/

Provides listings of teachers and classes needing keypals for cross-cultural exchanges and partners for online projects at the K–12 and the college level. Also offers links to listservs and other collections of keypal requests and online projects.

International Federation of Library Associations and Institutions (IFLA)

http://www.nlc-bnc.ca/ifla/home.html

Provides librarians around the world with a forum for exchanging ideas, promoting international cooperation, research and development in all fields of library activity.

Presents members and interested individuals an evolving range of electronic information resources and services through the use of Internet technologies.

The Internet Educational Resources Guide

`http://www.dcs.aber.ac.uk/~jjw0/index_ht.html`

Offers a searchable collection of educational links, but offers more than just links to school subject areas. Also reviews online magazines and books about the Internet, and has information about gophers, FTP sites, telnet databases, and listservs.

The Internet Wiretap

`gopher://wiretap.spies.com`

Presents an archive of electronic texts, ranging from the common to the obscure. Contains hundreds of digitized works of literature, as well as a government archive.

Invitation to Join Internet Projects

`gopher://nysernet.org:3000/11/`
`Assembly%20Hall%20for%20Projects%20and%20Discussions/`

Helps teachers new to the Internet answer the question, "Now what do I do?" Includes listings of past and present inter-school and international Internet projects with open invitations to join the fun and learning. Also helps you create your own local projects.

IPL Building Directory

`http://ipl.sils.umich.edu:80/bldg.dir/`

Consists of four main divisions: reference, youth services, services for librarians and information professionals, and the education division. Contains resources, interactive exhibits, and discussion areas.

ISN KidNews

`http://www.umassd.edu/SpecialPrograms/ISN/KidNews.html`

News service for students and teachers around the world. Lets you use stories from the services as long as you credit the author, and lets you submit stories. Encourages comments about news gathering, teaching, and computer-related issues in the Discussion sections for students and teachers.

Issues

`gopher://gopher.oise.on.ca:70/11/resources/IRes4Ed/`
`issues`

Offers links that discuss issues facing Internet use in the classroom, including censorship, age-appropriateness of materials, setting up a network, and so on.

IUB Libraries: Research Collections and Services Department

`http://www.indiana.edu/~librcsd/`

Serves the humanities and social sciences. Builds the printed and electronic collections, instructs classes and individuals, and offers general and specialized reference and research assistance to the students, faculty, and staff of Indiana University. Also presents some guides which we have created, and select, and monitor information on sites around the world which we think is of potential value and importance to the students and faculty we serve.

IUP-Miages de France

http://miage.isi.u-psud.fr/

Includes computer sciences and management and information systems.

JASON Project

http://seawifs.gsfc.nasa.gov/scripts/JASON.html

Collaborative learning experience for students around the world. Each year, a two-week scientific expedition is mounted in a remote part of the world and broadcast in real-time, using state-of-the-art technology, to a network of educational, research, and cultural institutions in the United States, Canada, Bermuda, and the United Kingdom. Lets participating students at the interactive downlink sites "go live" (using *telepresence*) to the expedition, operate the scientific equipment being used, and talk directly with the scientists at the expedition site.

Jefferson-Scranton Community Schools

http://molebio.iastate.edu/js/homepage.html

Provides high school students the opportunity to explore the Internet through the Web.

John and Janice's Research Page

http://k12.cnidr.org/janice_k12/states/states.html

Provides continually updated education-and-the-Internet and other telecom-related statistics. Provides numbers to convince anyone not sure that the Internet really is useful in a learning environment. Lists information in a summary document, and also by state.

John Suler's Teaching Clinical Psychology Page

http://www.rider.edu/~suler/tcp.html

Focuses on sharing ideas and resources about teaching clinical psychology, especially undergraduate courses.

The Johns Hopkins University Department of English

http://www.jhu.edu/~english/

Serves three primary functions: 1) to disseminate public information about the department, its faculty, programs and resources; 2) to provide links to other online resources in the humanities; and 3) to serve as an anchor for the development of other online resources in the field.

Jon's Home-School Resource Page

http://www.armory.com/~jon/hs/HomeSchool.html

Provides information about home-schooling. Offers links to other web pages, online curriculum guides, listservs, newsgroups, and so on.

Judi Harris' Network-Based Educational Activity Collection

http://www.ed.uiuc.edu/Activity-Structures/

Offers a collection of 236 network-based educational activities, collected by Judi Harris.

Junior Achievement Purpose/Facts

http://www.baynet.com/junior/intro.html

Provides information about Junior Achievement, such as the purpose, mission, goals, and national contact information. Also lists answers to commonly asked questions and tells why you should volunteer to help this worthwhile organization.

K–12 Education (Education)

http://galaxy.einet.net/galaxy/Social-Sciences/Education/K12-Education.html

Offers many K–12 links, searchable and subdivided into primary and secondary education, and also into document type.

K-12 Technology

http://www.cvu.cssd.k12.vt.us/K12TECH/K12TECH.HTM

Describes what is called "Simple School Internet Protocol"—that is, a way to get schools online.

Kidding Around

http://alexia.lis.uiuc.edu/~watts/kiddin.html

Offers links to the Internet designed for middle-school age students. Features current affairs, celebrity information, movie and music reviews, and educational links.

Kids Web—A World Wide Web Digital Library for Schoolkids

http://www.infomall.org/kidsweb/

Provides a collection of multimedia and other resources useful in education. *Caution:* The fun and humor link leads to a general Internet humor archive, an area that might not be entirely appropriate for children.

Kids' Space

http://www.interport.net/~sachi

Kid's Space has been planned for children to enhance basic computer skills through their real participation and use of the Internet.

Knox Junior High Home Page

http://www.geopages.com/CapitolHill/1444

Provides important links for research and training students and teachers to use the vast resources of the Internet.

Landegg Academy Online

http://www.landegg.org/landegg/

Serves as a learning environment in which people from all parts of the world can gather to search for new answers to the needs of contemporary society.

The LaserNet Web Server

http://www.rli.com

Offers education and information on the topic of laser. Includes subtopics for laser applications, tutorials, laser safety, research and development, online newsletters and laser-related links.

Le Coin des Francophones et Autres Grenouilles

http://www.cnam.fr/fr/

Offers links to almost all other French-related sites. Includes pointers to popular tourist attractions, learning and using the language, and more.

Lesson Plans and Activities

http://www.c3.lanl.gov/~cjhamil/solarsystem/education/index.html

Provides information for educators trying to incorporate astronomy into their curriculum.

Little Toy Store on the Net

http://www.suba.com/~chicago/lts.html

Specializes in fun and educational toys for children. Offers a list of resources for educators, parents, and kids on the net.

Live from Antarctica

http://quest.arc.nasa.gov/livefrom/livefrom.html

Connects students and teachers to Antarctica. Includes field journals of scientists, teachers guides, Q & A forums, links to resource materials, and so on.

Macroscale Land Surface Hydrology Modeling at the UW

http://atlas.ce.washington.edu/~lettenma/mlshm.html

Applies the VIC-2L model, a soil-vegetation-atmospere transfer scheme (SVATS), for macroscale hydrologic simulations of the water and energy balance.

Magic Learning Systems

http://www.xmission.com/~stageone/mls.html

Develops and markets educational and self-improvement software and shareware, combining the latest technologies with time-tested educational methods for the individual, the classroom, and the home.

Mark Twain Library, The

http://hydor.colorado.edu/twain/

Provides electronic texts of Mark Twain's works. Offers several works. Also lists other pages with Mark Twain resources.

Maryland Department of Education, The

gopher://sailor.lib.md.us/11/GovInfo/.md/.agency/.exec/.educ

Provides a collection of educational documents and resources. Includes a variety of information on educational development, special education, vocational training, and library management.

Massachusetts Education Computer Information Network Gopher, The

gopher://gopher.mass.edu

Focuses on local public universities. Contains general educational information. Includes college planning and resource information, as well as access to Mass Ed Online

and other educational and information servers. Also offers information on PALMS—a project to improve math and science education.

Math and Science Gateway (Cornell Theory Center)

http://www.tc.cornell.edu/Edu/MathSciGateway/

Provides a wide range of educational services to the national community. Provides links to resources in mathematics and science for educators and students in grades 9–12.

Math Education Resources

http://www.teleport.com/~vincer/math.html

Offers links to many good online math sites. Lists lesson plans, curriculum guides, and interactive links such as the Gallery of Interactive Geometry. Also offers listings of math-related newsgroups.

MathMagic Internet

http://forum.swarthmore.edu/mathmagic/

Seeks to involve teachers and students in problem solving. Pairs up registered teams from all over the world to discuss and find ways to solve the challenges posted in each of four categories: K–3, 4–6, 7–9, and 10–12.

MATHMOL—K-12 Mathematics and Molecules

http://www.nyu.edu/pages/mathmol/

Provides students, teachers, and the general public information about the rapidly growing field of molecular modeling. Also provides K–12 students with basic concepts in mathematics and their connection to molecular modeling. Contains supporting materials for this project, such as a hypermedia textbook, a library of 3D molecular models, and online challenges for students.

MDEnet—The Michigan Department of Education Gopher

`gopher://gopher.mde.state.mi.us`

Focuses on education policy and reform efforts. Includes legislation and government information, as well as classroom resource materials. Also lists information on grants, educational technology, and professional development.

The Media Literacy Online Project Home Page

`http://interact.uoregon.edu/MediaLit/HomePage`

Provides information and resources to educators, producers, students, parents, and others interested in the influence of electronic media on children, youth, and adults. Contains a database on media literacy, as well as links to Internet resources related to the topic.

Medical/Clinical/ Occupational Toxicology Resource Home Page

`http://www.pitt.edu/~martint/welcome.htm`

Provides information for practitioners, educators, and researchers in medical, clinical, and occupational toxicology. Also provides poison information.

MEOL

`http://meol.mass.edu:70/0/home`

Serves as a cooperative gateway to all of Massachusetts' educational agencies and organizations. Offers easily accessible FAQs, listings of current online projects, and job postings.

Microsoft Focus on K-12

`http://www.microsoft.com/pages/services/education/k-12/mainpg.htm`

Provides information on Microsoft products and services geared to helping you integrate technology into your district, school, and classroom.

Middle School Science Library

`gopher://scholastic.com:2003/11/ScholasticInternetLibraries/MiddleSchoolScienceLibrary`

Offers a sample collection of middle school science information from the Scholastic Internet Center Ultimate Learning Libraries. Contains science lesson plans for teachers as fun science fact sheets for kids. Also includes a listing of other online resources for science educators, a list of science-oriented organizations, and information about setting science standards.

Middlebrook's Structured Analog Design

`http://www.ardem.com/middlebrook/`

Offers techniques to help improve design quality and save design time in the analog world.

Mining the Internet Columns

`http://www.ed.uiuc.edu/Mining/Overview.html`

Presents articles (in HTML) written by Judi Harris for "The Computing Teacher," including tips and information on using computers, telecommunications, and the Internet in the classroom.

Minnesota Center for Arts Education

`gopher://gopher.mcae.k12.mn.us:70/1`

Contains many links to arts education. Most of the information originates from the Minnesota Arts High School, but then branches to resources from other locations. Offers resources for all forms of arts education (music, dance, theater, art, and so on) as well as grant information.

Missing-Link Page for Missing Children

http://www.cris.com/~altoren/

Focuses on raising public awareness on the missing children issue. Provides several information sections, including a gallery of missing children. Also features in-depth news on the issue and information on how you can help.

Money for College

http://emporium.turnpike.net/D/dcservice/wg/lenn4.htm

Offers assistance in finding money for higher education. Loans, grants, and scholarships are available if you know where to find them and we do.

Monterey Academy of Oceanographic Science

http://205.155.54.2/maos/home.html

Student-driven pages from a school-within-a-school on the campus of Monterey High School, along California's Central Coast.

Mount St. Helens

http://volcano.und.nodak.edu/vwdocs/msh/msh.html

Provides image maps more than 1,490 still images of the mountain before, during, and after the eruption. Provides information about the people, Mount St. Helens and other volcanoes, other Mount St. Helens resources, plants and animals, and curriculum.

MU CoE Links to Education Resources

http://tiger.coe.missouri.edu/Resource.html

Offers many links on education and resources. Includes an entire section devoted to mathematics, science, and technology.

NASA Education Sites

http://quest.arc.nasa.gov, http://k12mac.larc.nasa.gov

http://www.nas.nasa.gov/HPCC/K12/edures.html

http://www.lerc.nasa.gov/Other_Groups/K-12/K-12_homepage.html

Offers a collection of servers specifically geared for teachers, students, and administrators. Offers a selection of math and science education resources, connectivity to numerous education servers, journals, and grant and project participation information.

NASA Spacelink—An Electronic Information System for Educators

http://spacelink.msfc.nasa.gov/

Contains NASA's public online library of lesson plans, satellite and shuttle images, and more. Also offers information on space careers, interdisciplinary units, and software.

National Association of Mortgage Brokers Educational Foundation

http://www.vegas.com/nambef

Provides access to information about education and training opportunities in the mortgage finance industry.

National Science Foundation World Wide Web Server

http://stis.nsf.gov

Provides information for educators and administrators. Contains information on NSF education projects, grants, and publications.

National Teachers Enhancement Network

http://www.montana.edu/~wwwxs/index.html

Offers graduate-credit science and mathematics courses to teachers nationally. Lets teachers participate in the telecomputing courses from convenient home or work locations by using dial-up modem connections or Internet access. Provides teachers with high-quality graduate science courses taught by university scientists, engineers, and mathematicians.

Natural Resources Defense Council (NRDC)

http://www.nrdc.org/nrdc

Nonprofit environmental organization with 170,000 members nationwide and a staff of scientists, lawyers, and environmental experts. Features the latest news from the Hill, plus information everyone should have on the state of our air, water, land, and health. NRDC's mission is to protect the world's natural resources and improve the quality of the human environment.

Naval ROTC—The University of Mississippi

http://www.olemiss.edu/depts/naval_science

Provides information on scholarships, the faculty, the battalion, and the university.

NCSA Education Program

http://www.ncsa.uiuc.edu/Edu/

Seeks to bridge the gap between scientific research and education and make the tools for computation available in the classroom (K–12). Offers jumps for teachers looking for resource materials.

Network Nuggets

http://www.etc.bc.ca/~tcoop/index.html

Shares information about educationally relevant Internet resources. Provides list members with a message each day during the school year to help them find resources on the Internet. Offers an organized main index, and the listserv is one way to keep up with the Internet one day at a time.

The New York Open Center

http://www.panix.com/~openctr

Nonprofit center for holistic learning and culture in New York City. Offers nearly 1,000 courses annually on topics of alternative health and bodywork disciplines, depth psychologies, sociocultural issues, spiritual and meditative teachings, and multicultural arts. Includes program information and a preview of the center's journal.

Newton's Apple Educational Materials!

http://ericir.syr.edu/Newton/welcome.html

Contains 26 lessons from the 12th season of the television show, Newton's Apple. Topics range from brain mapping to

bread chemistry includes activities, questions, and further investigation suggestions.

The Nine Planets

http://seds.lpl.arizona.edu/nineplanets/nineplanets/nineplanets.html#to

Presents a multimedia essay about the solar system, using text, pictures, sounds, and an occasional movie. Briefly describes each of the planets and major moons in the solar system, and illustrates them using pictures from NASA spacecraft.

Noha's Arc

http://www.ios.com/~edell/NohaArc.html

Advertises Noha Edell, owner of "Noha's Arc," a multiplatform trainer and hardware integrator located in Clifton, New Jersey.

Norm's Home Page

http://www.together.com/home/norm

Explores the use of High Tech Construction Materials like Epoxy Methacrylate. Provides educational information on waterproofing, concrete repair, and restoration.

North American Historical Re-Enactor Web Site (West Site)

http://www.webcom.com/~custer/

Contains a register of societies and clubs dedicated to re-creating historical events for preservation of artifacts and experiencing other periods of history.

North Central Regional Educational Laboratory

http://cedar.cic.net/ncrel/

Nonprofit organization devoted to researching and implementing the best practices in public schools so that all students achieve standards of educational excellence. Contains an online newsletter, educational resources you can order, and other useful resources. Provides standards information.

The North Dakota ICICLE Project

http://calvin.cc.ndsu.nodak.edu/wayne/icicle.html

Offers a library of reviewed K–12 curriculum and instructional materials (lesson plans, pictures, subject matter, and so on) available on the Internet, indexed according to subject area.

Northwest Service Academy Page

http://www.teleport.com/~nwsa

Addresses unmet environmental and community needs. Also contains an application.

NYSERNet

http://nysernet.org

Offers a wide variety of K–12 tools. Includes class projects, teaching tools, discussion groups, career guidance, reference information, and school reform plans.

The Ohio Education Computer Network K–12 Gopher

gopher://nwoca7.nwoca.ohio.gov

Presents a subject database. Offers access to dozens of electronic books (from Aesop to the Book of Mormon), census records, and government documents, along with educational and research materials.

The Old School House Studio

http://www.pikeperry.co.uk/ppp/pd/courses.htm

Offers inspirational personal development workshops. Also offers the one-year, part-time dramatherapy certificate course, which commences every September and spans six weekends, as well as a summer school (validated by Worcester College).

OMNi WWDC (OMNi WorldWide Distribution Centre)

http://www.cs.msu.su/

Distribution center for various fields of human behavior.

Online Books

http://www.cs.cmu.edu:8001/Web/books.html

Contains an index of hundreds of books. Lets you browse or search by author or title for any book you want. Also offers a new books page you can use to keep up to date.

Online Reference Works

http://www.cs.cmu.edu/Web/references.html

Lists several different online reference sources, such as a hypertext Webster's dictionary, a thesaurus, and an acronym dictionary. Also offers several foreign language dictionaries, and computing dictionaries.

Ontario's Information Resources

http://www.io.org/~kconway

Indexes Ontario's information resources by type and by city. Focuses on nonprofit services that seek to better the human condition.

The Open University

http://www.open.ac.uk/

The British institution that pioneered distance education as a way to broaden educational opportunities across the country. Offers a comprehensive program that serves as a model for other programs. Also offers links to other online resources.

Optometry at the University of Melbourne

http://www.optometry.unimelb.edu.au/

Includes the Department of Optometry and Vision Sciences, the Victorian College of Optometry, and the National Vision Research Institute.

Oregon Online

gopher://gopher.state.or.us:70/11/.d26.dir

Focuses on state and local education activities. Includes school district data, as well as resources for home schooling and nonpublic schooling. Also offers information on public and private K–12 institutions, as well as links to Oregon public and private colleges and universities.

The OSPI Math, Science, and Technology Server

http://www.ospi.wednet.edu/

Contains a collection of online math and science resources, as well as information on WEdNet. Also offers links to

public and private online schools and Washington state colleges and universities.

OTPAD

`gopher://unix5.nysed.gov`

Serves as a resource for K–12 education (especially its foreign language collection) and telecommunication policy research. Contains education news, telecom policy briefs, and a collection of classroom resources divided by subject. Also offers links to FTP sites.

Parenting Skills on Video

`http://www.novia.net/~video`

Contains parenting enhancement skills that you can use throughout your impressionable child's life. Presents guidelines for raising happy, healthy children.

PBS K–12 Learning Services on the Internet

`http://mumford.pbs.org/learning/k12/`

Serves as a front-line resource for PBS member stations, supplying information and support services for the effective use of K–12 educational television and related technology. Provides information about instructional television, and a public television database divided alphabetically or by curriculum.

Penn State University Weather Pages

`http://www.ems.psu.edu/wx/`

Offers a virtual reality interactive weather information program, as well as hourly United States weather statistics. Also offers offshore weather information, and a place to enter your own local weather report into a database.

Persimmon Software for Children

`http://www.dnai.com/persimmon`

Chooses a different monthly aspect of the arts and humanities to create an interactive, multimedia presentation that engages children and promotes creative learning.

Peterson's Education Center

`http://www.petersons.com:8080/`

Seeks to catalog all United States K–12 schools, colleges, and universities, both public and private, as well as community and technical colleges. Also plans to offer transcript services and scholarship information.

Placer County Office of Education

`http://placercoe.k12.ca.us`

Lists California K–12 and community colleges.

The Political Science Department at Oregon State University

`http://www.orst.edu/Dept/pol_sci/`

Presents links of interest to political science students and educators.

Political Science Department Home Page— Indiana State University

`http://www-isu.indstate.edu/polisci`

Provides information about the department, faculty, programs (undergraduate and graduate), admissions procedures, financial aid, career resources. Includes forms to request more information and application materials.

Polyurethane Foam Association

http://www.pfa.org/foam

Provides a collection of fire safety materials including INTOUCH bulletins, radio announcements, and television public service spots designed to help prevent household and industrial fires.

Princeton Review

http://www.review.com

Offers information on undergraduate colleges and universities, business, law and medical schools, and other graduate schools. Also provides financial aid tips, and offers a free sample of any standardized entry exam (i.e., SAT, GMAT, GRE, LSAT, and so on).

Private School Resource

http://www.brigadoon.com/psrnet/

Presents a collection of many resources for private, independent, and religiously affiliated schools. Includes separate sections for organizations, school home pages, private school resources guides, and vendor information.

Private Schools Online

http://www.thinkthink.com/schools/

Provides students information about private preparatory schools directly from the institution. Offers listings from several private schools.

Project LEAP (Learn Earn and Prosper)

http://www.olemiss.edu/depts/project_leap

Provides basic skills, GED, job skills, and life-coping skills to a wide range of programs including literacy programs, family literacy, and workplace literacy.

Project Libellus

http://osman.classics.washington.edu/libellus/libellus.html

Contains free classical Greek and Latin electronic texts. Offers pointers to other classical etexts found at other archives, organized by institution or archive.

Ralph Bunche School

http://mac94.ralphbunche.rbs.edu/

Contains an online school newspaper and many other examples of student work.

Reading and Language Arts Library

gopher://scholastic.com:2003/11/ScholasticInternetLibraries/ReadingandLanguageArtsLibrary

Contains a collection of information from the Scholastic Internet Center Ultimate Learning Libraries. Contains brief biographies of several popular authors of children's books, as well as articles on portfolio assessment in literature. Also includes lesson plans for teaching with literature.

Reed Interactive's Global Classroom

http://www.ozemail.com.au/~reed

Offers online projects centering around specific themes, and encourages international participation. Also offers an international keypal search and find center and access to education-related newsgroups.

Research at BYU Integrated Microelectronics Lab

http://www.ee.byu.edu/ee/iml/research/research.html

Innovative research takes place in the BYU Integrated Microelectronics Lab, including MEMS, IC processing techniques, MCMs, and TCAD.

SafetyNet Domestic Violence Resources

http://www.interport.net/~asherman/dv.html

Contains domestic violence resources, including bibliographies, statistics, and a domestic violence handbook with a warning list and safety plan.

The Salmon Page

http://www.riverdale.k12.or.us/salmon.htm

Focuses on all things salmon, including how to catch them, cook them, and save them.

save.org

http://www.save.org

Seeks to educate about suicide and to speak for suicide survivors.

Scholarly Electronic Forums Web Page

http://www.oise.on.ca/~arojo/forums.html

Offers contextualized information on scholarly electronic discussion groups. Provides information for potential and present users and listowners. Serves as a resource for electronic communication scholars, practitioners, and students.

Scholastic Central

http://scholastic.com:2005/

Lists information available through Scholastic Central, such as three online publications and reviews of children's movies. Also offers links to interactive online projects and interviews with popular children's book authors. Provides searchable information.

School and Community Networking Resources

http://www.nas.nasa.gov/HPCC/K12/EDRC21.html

Contains several pointers to good technical guides to getting your school online. The links reference FAQs, lists of Internet providers, and technology plans from other online schools.

School District of Philadelphia

http://www.philsch.k12.pa.us

Consists of more than 250 schools, K–12, servicing approximately 210,000 children.

Schoolhouse Videos and CDs (CD-ROMs)

http://www.nando.net/ads/gift/school.htm

Offers hundreds of topics and thousands of videos and CD-ROMs, from algebra to music to gardening.

SciEd: Science and Mathematics Education Resources

http://www-hpcc.astro.washington.edu/scied/science.html

Offers an organized math and science virtual bookshelf. Offers pointers to online scientific and mathematical reference works and charts, as well as links to the usual science and math subject areas. Also includes information on ethics in science and software and equipment suppliers.

Second Nature

http://www.2nature.org

Nonprofit environmental organization that helps institutions of learning, such as colleges and universities, produce graduates who will become environmental leaders. Provides information about Second Nature's unique educational philosophy.

SERESC

http://reg.seresc.k12.nh.us/

Contains links to a short list of very useful educational Internet resources. Also offers information on grants, government agencies, and museums.

Shakespeare Homepage

http://the-tech.mit.edu/Shakespeare.html

Maintains a complete electronic hypertext collection of all Shakespeare's plays and poems, an index, and a glossary. Also offers a Bartlett's quotations, and links to other Shakespeare resources on the Internet.

The Complete Works of William Shakespeare

This is a server of the complete works of William Shakespeare, provided by The Tech. New features are under development, so check the What's New page periodically.

The original electronic source for this server is the Complete Moby(tm) Shakespeare, which is freely available online. There may be differences between a copy of a play that you happen to be familiar with and the one of this server. Don't worry, this is a very common phenomenon. You may want to read a brief note on these differences.

There are several pages available here:

- About the glossary
- Search the texts

Small is Beautiful

http://www.nas.nasa.gov/NAS/Education/nanotech/nanotech.html

Lists resources on nanotechnology. Includes DNA nanotechnology, molecular manufacturing, and computational nanotechnolgy.

The Smithsonian Institution Home Page

http://www.si.edu/

Features links to What's New (exhibits), Perspectives, Activities, and Resources, which all provide information on a variety of subjects.

The Society Of Cartographers

http://www.shef.ac.uk/~sc-web/

Seeks to support the practicing cartographer and encourage and maintain a high standard of cartographic illustration by providing information and opportunities to meet and exchange views and techniques with fellow practicing cartographers.

Society of Yeager Scholars, Marshall University

http://www.marshall.edu/yeager/

Provides information on Marshall University's Society of Yeager Scholars, a scholarship and enhanced academic program. Includes program description, alumni news, and application information.

State Council of Higher Education for Virginia

http://www.schev.edu

Provides information about the agency and Virginia's colleges and universities, public and private.

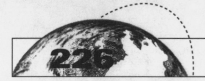

Street Cents Online

http://www.screen.com/streetcents.html

Tied to the Canadian television show "Street Cents," which teaches young people how to be informed consumers. Covers all of the highlights of the week's program, and also offers a kids club and discussion list.

The Study in the USA Online Directory

http://www.studyusa.com/

Serves as a resource for international students seeking to study at a quality American university, college, or English language institute. Lets you browse informative articles and program descriptions, and use the online request information forms to e-mail the school in which you're interested for more information.

Sylvan Learning Centers

http://www.magicnet.net/cge/sylvan/

Offers supplemental education to every type of student. Provides information on their services and locations.

Teacher Talk

http://www.mightymedia.com/talk/working.hmt

Provides resources for the teacher using technology in the classroom. Includes open discussion forums, school reform, parental involvement, and social action/service learning. Features a link from the technology and schools section that leads to useful tips, questions, and answers from other teachers.

The Tech Classics Archive

http://the-tech.mit.edu/Classics/

An archive of 184 works by 17 classical authors (in translation). Provides texts in HTML format and as raw text files. Segments each work into the different books, sections, parts, and so on, whenever possible.

The Technology and Distance Education Branch

http://www.etc.bc.ca/etc.html

Focuses on the development of a community learning network. Also offers links to other good distance education sites and guidebooks.

Technology for All Americans Project

http://scholar.lib.vt.edu/TAA/TAA.html

Seeks to create a forum for developing national standards for K–12 technology education. Contains press releases, consensus building workshops, and a newsletter.

The Tecla Home Page from Birkbeck College London

http://www.bbk.ac.uk/Departments/Spanish/TeclaHome.html

Text magazine written for learners and teachers of Spanish, produced weekly during the school year. Provides text in Spanish, with vocabulary listed below the text.

TEIS

gopher://state.virginia.edu:70/11/TEIS

Explores the ways in which the Internet could benefit teacher education programs around the world. Offers training on developing instructional materials, tips for preservice teachers in several subject areas, and software archives. Also offers links to grants, workshops, and other professional development activities.

TENET

http://gopher.tenet.edu

Serves as a web site and gopher for state educators and general use. Includes state educational news, policies, and reform information. Also offers college planning, field trip plans, and connectivity to educational gophers around the world.

TERC

http://hub.terc.edu:70/hub/owner/TERC

Researches, develops, and disseminates innovative programs in science, mathematics, and technology for educators, schools, and other learning environments. Contains information for educators interested in trying new ideas in learning environments.

TESFL

gopher://cunyvm.cuny.edu:70/11/
Subject%20Specific%20Gophers/teslfl

Includes a wide range of information relevant to teaching English as a second/foreign language. Lists resources for those preparing future ES/FL teachers, as well as resources for those already in the field. Also offers links to employment opportunities, helpful in any field.

TESL-EJ Master Page

http://www.well.com/user/sokolik/tesl-ej.html

Online journal. Covers teaching English as a second/foreign language from many perspectives.

Theodore Tugboat

http://www.cochran.com/

Based on a Canadian TV show, "Theodore Tugboat," and designed for young children. Lets kids send a postcard to a friend, download a coloring book page, and help write an interactive story. Also offers a parent/teacher area.

Thomas Pitre Associates

http://www.hooked.net:80/users/tpitre/homepage.html

Lets you take professional courses by e-mail or correspondence from MSRI.

TIESnet

http://tiesnet.ties.k12.mn.usandgopher://
tiesnet.ties.k12.mn.us

Technology and Information Educational Services of Minnesota, the older sister of InforMNs. Includes access to numerous ongoing school projects, as well as lesson plans, research information, and connectivity to InforMNs.

Total Recall

http://www.demon.co.uk/sharpsw/total.html

Presents an amazing online training course that teaches you how to dramatically improve your memory powers—improve exam grades, learn foreign vocabulary, and more.

Traveler's Japanese with Voice

http://www.ntt.jp/japan/japanese/

Uses the Internet to teach basic language skills. Divides modules by subject. Plays an audio clip that provides proper pronunciation of any word you click. Also provides historical and cultural information.

Turner Adventure Learning

http://cee.indiana.edu/turner/tal.html

Contains information about Turner Adventure Learning, electronic field trips for K–12. Contains text documents, graphics, and web links related to each field trip.

UEWeb

http://eric-web.tc.columbia.edu/

Provides information on and for urban students, their families, and the educators who serve them. Includes manuals, brief articles, annotated bibliographies, reviews publications, and conference announcements in urban education, among other features.

The United States Education Department/OERI

http://gopher.ed.gov

Offers an information server that acts as a reference desk for all things educational. Includes educational software, Goals 2000 information, as well as primary, secondary, and vocational information.

United States Naval Sea Cadet Corps

http://www.tucson.com/nscc

Provides a year-round Naval youth education program for young men and women ages 11–18 years old. Learn new skills and gain confidence while aboard Naval ships or air stations.

United States Two-Year Colleges

http://www.sp.utoledo.edu/twoyrcol.html

Offers a comprehensive list of community and technical colleges in the United States. Provides links to colleges that have Web pages or gophers and links to state community college boards. Includes all types of two-year colleges.

Univ. of Okla. Dept. of Public Safety

http://www.uoknor.edu/oupd/

Contains many online information documents on public safety topics, including crime prevention, personal safety, fire safety, and more.

Universidad de Chile, Santiago

http://www.uchile.cl

Contains admission requirements, research, teaching and cultural activities in medicine, astronomy, literature, philosophy, chemistry, political science, economics, mathematics, biology, Nobel Prize winners, Chilean poets, Chilean sites, and so on.

University of Kentucky College of Dentistry

http://www.uky.edu/Dentistry

Provides information about the University of Kentucky College of Dentistry.

University of Northern Colorado: Educational Technology

http://www.edtech.univnorthco.edu

Serves as a site where educators, administrators, students, and teachers can get together to discuss, work with, and implement educational technology.

University of Waterloo Electronic Library

http://www.lib.uwaterloo.ca/

Serves as a service for information seekers. Provides information on current events, resources by discipline, facts about the UW Library, and so on. Projects include Scholarly Societies, Ejournals, Walking Tours, Web to catalog interface, and resources by academic department.

Upena Hawaii

http://kalama.doe.hawaii.eduandgopher://
kalama.doe.hawaii.edu

Focuses on internetworking between Hawaiian schools and distance education in general. Contains educational resources for teachers and students, interesting Internet server links, and a good collection of state and local education information from the department of education.

Valhalla—The Princeton City School District Home Page

http://www.iac.net/~tdugan

Offers links to other district schools, student work, teacher pages, and so on.

Valparaiso Community School District

http://www.valpo.k12.in.us/

Designed and operated almost entirely by students, the Valparaiso Community School District WWW Site is a K–12 organization in northwest Indiana.

The Vermont Educational Telecommunications Consortium Gopher

gopher://vetc.vsc.edu

Acts as an educational gateway to servers around the world. Offers links to math and science resources, Internet guides, and Goals 2000 information. Includes connectivity to state and local gophers, K–12 gophers, and governmental gophers.

Videodiscovery

http://www.videodiscovery.com/vdyweb

Provides information about interactive CD-ROM and laserdisc multimedia for science and math education, plus cool science facts, a guide to Internet education resources, educational technology primers, and more.

violence.prev

gopher://gopher.edu.gov.on.ca:70/11/english/schools/violence.prev

Provides information on school violence statistics and prevention programs. Also lists educational policies related to the topic.

Virginia Tech English Department Home Page

http://athena.english.vt.edu

Provides curriculum and departmental information, Web-based teaching, and an online writing lab.

The Virtual English Language Center

http://www.comenius.com/index.html

Provides information for ES/FL teachers and students. Includes such resources as interactive exercises and text/audio playback. Also features "Idiom of the Week," a keypal registry, and a recommended software listing. Also offers links to related Internet sites.

Virtual Frog Dissection Kit

http://george.lbl.gov/ITG.hm.pg.docs/dissect/info.html

Provides a learning tool instead of dissecting a real frog. The program uses 3D and MRI images that you can manipulate to see the various parts of the body. Includes online tests.

Visual Impaired

gopher://gopher.educ.gov.bc.ca:70/11/.specialed/.gopher/.visualimpair

Offers specific information on teaching the visually impaired. Covers an introduction to the topic, emotional considerations of visually impaired children, how to talk to parents/guardians, and so on.

Voices of Youth Home Page

http://www.iisd.ca/linkages/un/youth.html

Contains messages from the World Summit for Social Development. Pertains to topics discussed at the Summit, and although the server doesn't currently accept new messages, you can browse and search old messages by topic.

VOTEC Home Page

http://www.ed.uiuc.edu/COE/VOTEC/home.html

Provides information about vocational/technical education. Includes information on workplace literacy, tech prep, thinking skills, and training.

Walter Cronkite School of Journalism and Telecommunication, ASU

http://cronkite.pp.asu.edu/

Offers information about the school, student work, the alumni newsletter, and tools to help journalists explore the Internet.

Warsaw University, Department of Genetics Home Page

http://zguw.ibb.waw.pl

Contains description of Warsaw University's research and offers many links. Focuses on fungal genetics (Aspergillus nidulans and yeasts).

Washington Center for Internships & Academic Seminars, The

http://www.fga.com/twc

Propones the idea that the key to student success is active involvement in the educational process. Provides internships and academic seminar programs to college students that challenge them personally and professionally. Students apply academic theory through practical experience, discover their professional strengths and weaknesses,

question chosen career paths, interact with students from across the country, and develop a broad sense of civic and professional responsibility.

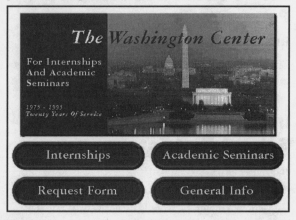

Waterford Institute

http://www.xmission.com/~waterfrd/index.html

Provides the latest in educational research and products for the home and school.

Web 66

http://web66.coled.umn.edu

Seeks to be a catalyst that integrates the Internet into K–12 school curricula. Facilitates the introduction of Internet technology into K–12 schools by helping them set up servers, design home pages, and find other online schools.

Web66: K-12 Schools Registry

http://hillside.coled.umn.edu/others.html

Consists of a clickable map of the United States, Canada, and Mexico, and each click takes you to a different region's online schools. Provides the same information in a text

format. Also offers school listings by country. Helps find keypals or partners for an online project.

WEdNet—The Washington Education Network

gopher://sitka.wsipc.wednet.edu/

Maintains a gopher server of educational and computing resources. Contains a variety of public domain software. Also offers links to the Electronic Frontier Foundation and other Internet links.

Welcome K–12

http://www.gatech.edu/lcc/idt/Students/Cole/Proj/K-12/K12wel.html

Focuses on teachers learning to use the Internet while online, as well as those who have very limited access time. Arranged alphabetically by subject area with two different tables of content—one with subheadings and pictures for those who want to browse and the other with just plain text links to resources. Addresses the real problem of teachers and time.

Welcome to MegaMath

http://www.c3.lanl.gov/mega-math/welcome.html

Aims bring unusual and important mathematical ideas to elementary school classrooms so that young people and their teachers can think about them together. Provides an online workbook with activities for teachers and students, as well as lesson plans and curriculum guides.

Welcome to TEAMSnet

http://teams.lacoe.edu/

Offers information on both distance education and Internet in the classroom. Lists online projects, links to resources, and professional development information. Also offers a page on preservice teacher preparation.

Welcome to the Council of the Great City Schools Online

http://www.cgcs.org/

Nonprofit organization that represents the United States's largest school systems. Offers "legislative alerts," information on instruction, curriculum, and standards, as well as other information necessary to the functioning of large urban school systems. Also provides hypertext versions of the council newsletters, council reports, and conference highlights.

Welcome to the DeweyWeb

http://ics.soe.umich.edu/

Provides information to students and attempts to provide them a chance to contribute their own observations, findings, and reflections.

Welcome to the GOLDMINE!

http://goldmine.cde.ca.gov

Includes information on state educational legislation, reforms, and curriculum, as well as state educational agendas and California Department of Education publication information.

Welcome to the United States Civil War Center

http://www.cwc.lsu.edu/

Serves as a clearinghouse for all Civil War materials. Offers links to many Civil War exhibits, continuously updated. Seeks to be objective, and looks at the causes, events, and aftermath from every viewpoint possible.

Welcome to Virtual FlyLab

http://vflylab.calstatela.edu/edesktop/VirtApps/VflyLab/IntroVflyLab.html

Lets you play the role of a scientist investigating genetic inheritance: manipulate the matings of different fruit flies and see the genetic results of the matings.

Whales: A Thematic Web Unit

http://curry.edschool.Virginia.EDU/~kpj5e/Whales/Contents.HTML

Focuses on K–5 kids. Contains images, activities and project ideas.

Window-To-Russia Home Page

http://www.kiae.su/www/wtr/

Offers resources in both Russian and English, as well as links that tell you how to install a Netscape-readable Cyrillic font. Offers online art exhibits, an interactive Russian-English dictionary, basic country information, and more.

Winston Churchill High School Web Server

http://lancelot.chs.lane.edu/

Hosts various WWW documents written by Churchill High School students or about Churchill High School.

WisDPI—The Wisconsin Department of Public Instruction

http://badger.state.wi.us:70/0h/agencies/dpi/www/dpi_home.html

Includes on resources about education and libraries. Contains a variety of K–12 projects, lesson plans, and educational links.

Wolfe County (KY) Public Schools

http://wolfen.wolfe.k12.ky.us/

Provides educational resources, local and regional information, and announcements, message boards, links, student works, search pages, and more.

Women in Higher Education

http://www.itis.com/wihe

Presents *Women in Higher Education*, a monthly newsletter for women university administrators, faculty, and staff. Includes news and articles and current job listings.

World Kids Press Home Page

http://www.webpub.com/worldkids/

Offers audiotape/coloring book packages designed to introduce the concept of foreign languages to children from preschool level to age 8 or 9 through fun with music, read-along, and coloring.

The World Lecture Hall

http://www.utexas.edu/world/lecture/

Offers links to faculty world-wide who use the Web to deliver class materials. Includes syllabi, assignments, lecture notes, exams, multimedia textbooks, and resource materials on almost any subject.

The World of Benjamin Franklin

http://sln.fi.edu/franklin/rotten.html

Provides multimedia information about Ben Franklin using pictures, documents, and movies. Covers his family,

inventions, diplomacy, philosophy, and leadership. Provides a bibliography for further study of Franklin, his accomplishments, and the time period.

The World of the Vikings Home Page

http://www.demon.co.uk/history/vikings/vikhome.html

Provides information about the World of the Vikings CD-ROM and research project. The CD-ROM includes two separate resources—the Research Database, created for academic researchers, libraries and schools, and Evidence Boxes, which collect together the best resources from the main archive for younger children. Also offers links to other Internet Viking resources.

The World-Wide Web Virtual Library

http://www.w3.org/hypertext/DataSources/bySubject/Overview.html

Cross-references everything from aboriginal studies to zoos. Details the links by alphabetical order, by era, and by region. Offers clickable maps of the world and specific information about many countries. Also offers a list of other online resources.

Writing at MU

http://www.missouri.edu/~wleric/writery.html

Online discussion site for writers. Offers four direct links to information exchange with other writers. Includes other links to assorted Internet sites, mostly related to writing, as well (*note*: a few might not be appropriate for children).

440: Satisfaction

http://www.aloha.net/~hijohn/

Focuses on where the DJs, newspeople, and unsung radio people from out of our past are now.

A.M. Productions

http://www.vt.edu:10021/S/sideout/amhome.html

Independent film company involved in all aspects of the film making process, from screenplay writing, directing, acting, cinematography, and editing.

A1 Children's Videos, Movies, Audio Tapes, and CDs

http://www.nscnet.com/llm001.htm

Children's entertaining and educational videos for both home and school. Presents children's classics, cartoons, sing-alongs, animated learning, stories, animals, and more.

A1 Classic Films and Video Library

http://www.nscnet.com/clsc001.htm

Provides original classic films at incredible savings. Offers films in categories ranging from comedy to western to romantic to adventure.

ABAA booknet/rmharris_ltd

http://www.clark.net/pub/rmharris/booknet1.html

Specializes in rare and antiquarian books, maps, and prints. Helps you locate and contact ABAA-affiliated booksellers, check out current book catalogs, and obtain information about ABAA book fairs.

AbFab.welcome

http://online.anu.edu.au/ArtHistory/TOR/

Provides information about the offbeat British comedy show *Absolutely Fabulous*.

Above the Rim Collectibles

http://www.rt66.com/olworld/mall/mall_us/c_gifts/m_abover/index.html

Carries all major brand sports cards for all professional sports and some collegiate items as well.

The Academy of Motion Picture Arts and Sciences

http://www.ampas.org/ampas/

Provides listings of Academy Credits online. Also tells what the Academy does in addition to giving out awards.

ACES (Asses): The Associated Computer Enthusiast Society

http://www.dashing.com/dash/aces/index.html

ACES' statement of purpose reads: ". . . we wish to waste your time with stupid pictures of us, bad jokes about Atari, and the sounds of ACES."

Adventure Online Gaming

http://www.gameworld.com

Monthly fantasy fiction web magazine featuring original art and fiction. Includes exciting interactive graphical hypertext adventures. Describes a human and computer refereed true role-playing game. Features intelligent talking monsters, multiple players, 3D graphics, and advanced chat.

AirPage

http://trex.smoky.ccsd.k12.co.us/~dlevin/air/air.html

Provides information about airplanes and helicopters. Covers many aircraft from different countries and different time periods. Each AirPage entry features an aircraft description, brief history of the aircraft, technical data, and (if possible) images of the aircraft. AirPage currently features more than 170 aircraft.

Akers Mic

http://www.oslonett.no/uh/am/

Online CD store. Presents a catalog and other offerings within multimedia, surround-sound, and high-end HIFI.

Alaska Porcelain

http://www.xmission.com/~patco/alaska.html

Provides images of some examples of Alaska porcelain works, along with information about receiving the catalog.

All My Children

http://www.teleport.com/~grand/amc/amc.html

A good front door to the world of the soap opera *All My Children*. Includes spoilers and late breaking news.

All TVs Center

http://www.netcenter.com/netcentr/entertain/tv.html

Provides TV on your desk, all your favorite shows, and all the networks direct.

Amateur Radio Books and Open Repeater Database

http://www.earthlink.net/~artsci

Produces amateur radio books, including *Radio Modifications*, *Repeater Mapbook*, cartoon license manuals, frequency guides, and reference manuals.

American Cinema Page

http://www.netcenter.com/netcentr/entertain/cinema.html

Previews, reviews, and critics.

American Flyer Home Page

http://158.93.29.52/AmericanFlyer.html

An excellent site for anyone into model railroads.

The American Saddlebred Horse

http://www.wmwoods.edu/asb/asb.htm

Provides breed information, including videoclips of gaits, history of the breed, a photo gallery, and more.

Amethyst Galleries' Mineral Gallery

http://mineral.galleries.com

Provides information source and an ordering point for minerals of all types.

Andy Hawks Home Page

http://benji.colorado.edu:8080/

Presents the home page of the guy who created FutureCulture (hip alternative virtual community), Tribe (global rave community), Tribevibe (rave/cybercafe culture over CU-SeeMe), and "right on." Includes productions, among other noteworthy projects.

Andy Richter: King of the Couch

http://www.well.com/user/xkot/andy.htm

Fans of Andy Richter know he's not just another sidekick gathering moss. Includes pictures and biographical information.

Animal Sounds

http://information.fuw.edu.pl/multimedia/sounds.animals

Lets you download and play back your favorite animal sounds and noises. Offers a wide selection.

Animaniacs

http://www.cs.cmu.edu/afs/cs.cmu.edu/user/clamen/misc/tv/Animaniacs/Animaniacs.html

Includes episode guides, Pinky and the Brain text files, and much more.

Animation Station

http://www.rt66.com/olworld/mall/mall_us/c_gifts/m_animat/index.html

Provides an address to obtain a catalog of production cels and Limited Edition cels, ranging from American to Japanese animation and includes superheros, cult classics, and more.

Animations

http://pmwww.cs.vu.nl/archive/animations/mpeg/.html/

Online archive of animations and digitized movies. Includes all kinds of topics, but primarily nature and jet airplanes.

Anne of Green Gables Mercantile

http://www.peinet.pe.ca/homepage/anne/homepage.html

Offers toys, gifts, books, dolls, and collectibles pertaining to the fictional Canadian character Anne of Green Gables.

Antiques and Collectibles Related Sites on the Web

http://kbc.com:80/html/antiques.htm

Presents a page of pointers to other collectible- related sites. Offers a variety of pointers.

Appalachian Outfitters

http://www.olworld.com/olworld/mall/mall_us/c_gifts/m_appala/index.html

Specializes in hand-carved mallard duck decoys, although you can commission other carvings. Introduces you to the process of carving the decoys.

AquaLink

http://weber.u.washington.edu/~aqualink

Focuses on tropical fish. Includes fresh, brackish, and marine fish, as well as plants and invertebrates.

Argonauta Productions

http://www.eden.com/~argonaut

Produces videos and CD-ROMs to bring the underwater world and vivid life of a coral reef to young people who have not had the chance to experience a journey to a coral reef. Offers photographs and video clips from trips through the underwater world, as well as descriptions of dive trips. Also provides more information about Argonauta.

The ArtsNet Theatre Sites Listings

http://artsnet.heinz.cmu.edu/Artsites/Theater.html

Provides a smaller listing of mostly American theater. Includes a cross section of different types of theater. Also provides a postcard question forum.

Asian Story Theater

http://www-tep.ucsd.edu./people/gingerlily-lowe-brisby/ast.html

Nonprofit Asian American educational theater company that uses live theater as a medium for education as well as entertainment. Broadens multicultural awareness by dramatizing modern and classic Asian tales for families, children, and educators. Includes information, curriculum, references, and other resources for teachers and students.

Asian Trading Co.

http://www.rt66.com/olworld/mall/mall_us/c_gifts/m_asiatr/index.html

Focuses on Chinese country-style antiques. Provides images of the items and offers to send an information pack on request.

The Asylum

http://www.galcit.caltech.edu/~ta/cgi-bin/asylhome-ta

Provides the interactive online WWW Lite-Brite, saved Lite-Brite images, and the Scratch Pad.

The Atlanta Opera

http://isotropic.com/atlopera/ophome.html

The Atlanta Opera on the Web. Continues its mission to bring opera to Atlanta, and now the world, by enriching the community with music and drama.

Atlantic Lottery Corporation

http://www.alc.ca/alc/

Provides general information about the corporation, description of games available in Atlantic Canada, winning numbers, and more.

Auntie Q's Antiques and Collectibles

http://www.teleport.com/~auntyq/

Includes some pictures and thorough descriptions of items for sale.

Austin Anime-Niacs Association

http://www.io.com/~count/anime.html

Focuses on enjoying Japanese animation and the company of others who also enjoy this art form.

The Austrian Cabaretater and Musical

http://hpbeker.roma1.infn.it

Presents artists and events in the field of cabaret, theater, and musical in Austria.

AVRO Television and Radio

http://www.omroep.nl/avro/

Offers TV and radio in a "Dutch" broadcasting system.

Babylon 5 Files

http://www.hyperion.com/b5/

Provides information about the science fiction TV show *Babylon 5*.

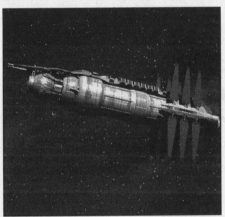

Back Row Productions

http://www.webcom.com/~backrow/

A theatrical production, development, and touring company based in New York, London, and Melbourne. Advertises current and future productions.

Bamsemums MC

http://www.powertech.no/~morteas/index.html

Presents a small motorcycle club located in Oslo, Norway, called Bamsemums MC.

Battlestar Galactica Home Page

http://mcmfh.acns.carleton.edu/BG//

Fans of the old science fiction television show *Battlestar Galactica* might want to visit this site. Includes sounds, images, and more.

Bay Area Improv Listings

http://www.san-fran.com/improv/improv.html

Includes Bay area improvisational theatre listings—upcoming shows, group profiles, calendar, and schools.

The Beam

http://www.interport.net/~lfranke/

Provides a collection of sites combined with ongoing projects involving photography, writing, and literature and graphics experiments.

Before They Were Stars

http://www.spe.sony.com/Pictures/tv/before/before.html

Based on the television show of the same name. Includes pictures of television and movie stars before they were famous.

Beginner's Guide to Star Trek, A

http://tahoma.cwu.edu:2000/~peterson/warnings/trek_warning.html

A beginner's guide to the *Star Trek* universe. Offers a simple tour through the universe of Trek.

BJS Enterprises— Collectibles, Crafts, Cards

http://www.cato.com/bjs/

Provides sports collectibles, cards, comics, and crafts. Lists stock and price information.

Black Adder Page

http://www.unit.no/~chrisvik/blackadder/

Contains graphics, sound, and full dialogue.

Blossom

http://pmwww.cs.vu.nl/service/sitcoms/Blossom/

Provides interviews with Mayim Bialik, Jenna Von Oy, episode guides to *Blossom*, and more.

BMG Ariola Studios— The Complete Production Network

http://www.bmgstudios.de

Exhibits a virtual studio. Specializes in high-end digital audio, video, and computer graphics.

Bob's Rock Shop: Introduction

http://www.rtd.com/~bkeller/rockshop/rockshop.html

Contains an extensive mineral collection. Provides information about mineral collecting, and lets you compare pieces to your own or get in touch with other mineral collectors.

Boyd Gaming Corporation Casinos

http://www.vegas.com/hotels/stardust/instar.html

Presents all the Boyd Gaming properties, including the Stardust, Las Vegas; Sam's Town, Las Vegas; the Fremont Hotel, Las Vegas; the California Hotel, Las Vegas; Joker's Wild, Las Vegas; the Eldorado Casino, Henderson, NV; Sam's Town, Tunica, MS; Treasure Chest, Kenner, LA; Silver Star, Philadelphia, MS; and coming soon, Sam's Town, Kansas City, MO.

Brandoland/Ryan's World of Music

http://www.best.com/~wcleere

Presents Brandoland, an amusement park devoted entirely to Marlon Brando, done entirely with a Brando background, for example, the Streetcar Named Desire takes you all around the park. Features Don Juan DeMarco's Tunnel of Love and many more attractions and shows. Also provides information about one of the best actors ever, including interviews, pictures, sounds, and links to Brando-related sites.

The Breeze 97.9 FM

http://www.kbzn.com/breeze/

A smooth jazz radio station based in Salt Lake City, Utah. Offers music, concert, and local event information.

Brent Alberts' Radioland

http://hightech.iadfw.net/brent.htm

Examines the life and radio adventures of Brent Alberts. Includes pictures and audio airchecks from radio stations dating back to the late '60s.

Bridge Player Live

http://www.londonmall.co.uk/bplive

The software behind the world's largest online bridge club. Lets you play with people from all over the world through a range of abilities. Lets you download the software, sign up, or try the free trial.

Broadsword

http://modjadji.anu.edu.au/steve/broadsword

The Web page for *Doctor Who: the New and Missing Adventures*. An e-zine extension of a small publication that focuses on the new and missing adventures. Includes guidelines for prospective authors.

Broadway World-Wide

http://www.webcom.com/~broadway/welcome.html

Provides information on Broadway shows in the United States and around the world. Provides information on theatre, listings, trivia, books, and interviews.

Buena Vista MoviePlex

http://www.disney.com/

Disney's homepage. Provides movie trailers and information. Includes graphics and videos. Also features the text-based PressRoom.

The C-Span Networks

http://www.c-span.org/

Provides information about C-Span programming and the like. Also includes a nice audio clip archive.

The Cabinet of Dr. Casey

http://www.ee.pdx.edu:80/~caseyh/horror/horror.html

Includes some audio samples. Features the "Horror Timeline."

Cable Movie Guide

http://emporium.turnpike.net/W/wto/tvguide.html

Provides free cable/broadcast movie and sports coverage for American TV. Also features low cost advertising in both Web and e-mail formats.

California Hotel, Casino, and RV Park

http://www.vegas.com/hotels/california/

Recently completed its third expansion, to more than 780 rooms and suites. Only property downtown with a 222 space RV Park. Includes four restaurants and more than 85,000 sq. ft. of gaming on two levels. Features many Hawaiian specialties.

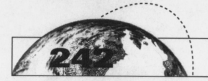
Calling All Cars

http://cacars.com/cac/cachome.html

Provides online car classified ads with pictures, cars for-sale-by-owners. Also presents magazines and other services and products.

Campus Collectibles

http://www.umich.edu/~webspin/cc-ind.html

Carries all sorts of unique gift ideas from autographs to comics to fantasy role-playing games. Primarily advertises, but does provide some information and a catalog.

Canadian Guinness Drinkers' Page

http://www.eng.carleton.ca/chat/~tcusolle/page2.shtml

Provides information about Guinness. Also includes a listing of Canadian pubs that serve Guinness. Welcomes new submissions.

Cape Cod Teddy Bear

http://virtumall.com/cgi-bin/shop?/CCTeddyBear/main.html

Contains a catalog of bears (including pictures) and lets you order items over the phone.

Capitol Ballroom

http://www.harborside.com/cdp/ballroom

Live concert/dance venue in Washington, D.C. Lists upcoming shows, pictures, and sounds.

Card Stores in UK/Europe

http://www.attistel.co.uk:8000/jnp/cardstores.html

Contains a list of stores in Europe that sell collectible card games (CCGs). Provides information supplied by people who have visited the stores. Also offers a link to a list of these stores.

Casa Noel

http://www.olworld.com/olworld/mall/mall_us/c_gifts/m_casa/index.html

Offers a wide range of gifts and items that have a south-western flair.

Casecrafters

http://www.pic.net/uniloc/casecrafters/

Makes and sells display cases for collectibles, such as dolls, trains, and sports memorabilia. Offers premade and custom cases. Lets you order by phone, fax, or mail. Makes all cases from fine hardwoods and lets you choose the finish style.

Cash Box Magazine

http://www.silence.net

Contains music charts and reviews, film and entertainment reviews, country music and radio broadcasting, pop, rap, urban, jazz, rhythm and blues, Latin film and video charts, and reviews.

Casting Online

http://hookomo.aloha.net/~wrap/

One stop cybercasting site for the performing arts industry. Serves those looking for work in the entertainment world or who want to announce a casting.

Cellophane Square

http://www.pacificrim.net/~drvinyl/

Online music store. Features new and used collectible editions of albums, autographs, and other memorabilia.

Centre of Theatre Practice

http://ctp.murdoch.edu.au/

Contains information on all aspects of performance research in a wide range of catagories. Offers author bios, papers, images, and other performance-related links. Also offers a MOO for artists to communicate in a virtual theatre environment.

CG Publishing Inc. Home Page

http://www.icom.ca/cgpinc/

Offers collectibles from *Star Wars* and various musicians, including Elvis Presley. Accompanies each product with a picture to give you a better feel for the product.

Cheers Home Page

http://s9000.furman.edu/~treu/cheers.html

Online fan site the TV show *Cheers*. Includes an archive of pictures, as well as a digitized theme audio file, FAQs, and more.

The Chicago Former Prince Nation

http://www.mcs.net/~ibc/home/cpn.htm

Serves as a resource to Chicago-Area Artist Formerly Known As Prince fans and collectors. Also shows the entire Former Prince community what Chicago has to offer.

Chisholm Prats Gallery

http://www.panix.com/~jerry/chisholm

Focuses on posters and poster design. Presents some of Chisholm's favorite exhibitions.

Christian Dramas

http://www-comp.mpce.mq.edu.au/~mpole/christian/

Good place to find a drama containing a moral message. Offers a small listing of dramas, all hyperlinked and accompanied by instructions on play requirements and set needs, as well as the entire script. Also offers other links to Christian sites.

CinemaSpace

http://remarque.berkeley.edu:8001/~xcohen/

Focuses on film and film theory. Provides information and links to film sites, as well as film and sound clips.

CineMaven Online Information

http://useattle.uspan.com/maven/

Provides movie reviews on current movies, as well as some movies coming out on video.

Citylife Magazine Brussels

http://www.demon.co.uk/cityeurope

A magazine for Brussels. Covers every aspect of young Brussels—from bars to nightclubs and concerts to films.

Also contains classified advertisements for Brussels/Belgium and Europe.

WELCOME TO CITYLIFE ONLINE

welcome://to.citylife.online/

Clarissa Explains It All

http://www.ee.surrey.ac.uk/Contrib/Entertainment/Clarissa/

Provides episode guides, interviews, and other relevent information pertaining to the young adult situation comedy *Clarissa Explains It All*, which airs on Nickelodeon.

The Classic Angler

http://www.gorp.com/bamboo.htm

Contains classic fishing products for collectors and products and information for today's fly fisherman.

Classifieds—Collectibles—Selling

http://www.wwcd.com/classified/collect_sell/collect_sell.html

Provides a collection of ads for collectibles (including toys, sports-related merchandise and stamps) for sale. Lets you read or post ads.

CNN Newsroom

http://www.nmis.org/NewsInteractive/CNN/Newsroom/contents.html

CNN goes online with up to the minute news. Offers current news, as well as backlogs of up to several months.

Collectible Advertising

http://iquest.com/~cws/free_ads/

Serves as an online classified section for collectors looking for something in particular, just browsing, or who want to put some of their own items up for sale.

Collectibles by R&T

http://www.rt66.com/olworld/mall/mall_us/c_gifts/m_colrt/

Features gift items, such as jewelry boxes, music boxes, and sculpture. Also offers an extensive collection of miniatures for the doll house enthusiast. Lets you view and order products.

Collecting

http://www.wiso.gwdg.de/ifbg/collect.html

Contains an extensive list of pointers to collecting-related sites.

Collector Online Website

http://together.net/~collect/

Focuses on antiques and collectibles. Offers classifieds, collector e-mail listings, and file-exchange libraries.

The Collectors Index

http://www.bdt.com:80/home/k55k

Provides collectors of everything a way to locate and network with each other. Lets you register yourself as a collector of a variety of items or just browse to find others with similar interests in your area. Also includes a calendar of upcoming events.

The Collectors Network

http://www.xmission.com/~patco/collect.html

Provides information on submissions, including addresses and requirements, and on subscription. Also offers a list of collector-related events and new releases in the realm of collecting. Offers a variety of resources for a wide range of collecting topics.

Columbia Music Video

http://www.sony.com/Music/VideoStuff

Provides music video resources, including networks and programs on the Web.

The Column that Nobody Reads

http://www.londonmall.co.uk/thecol

The new column in the *London Mall Magazine*. Mixes contemporary politics and the quirks of life in an attempt to entertain you, whatever your mood.

The Comedy Store (at the London Mall)

http://www.londonmall.co.uk/comedy

Advertises The Comedy Store, where audiences can see live comedy performed by established and up-and-coming performers.

ComedySportz Improv Comedy Home Page

http://www.cse.ogi.edu/Interactive/CSz/

Nationwide league of improvisational comedy groups in over 20 cities. Performances are fast-paced, funny, and appropriate for all ages. Offers links to CSz teams across America, including information on performances and workshops.

Comic Book Depot

http://www.insv.com/comxdepo

Provides information about collecting comic books. Features a different comic book dealer from around the country each month. Also provides notes about upcoming books, conventions, and more.

Comics on the Net

http://www.demon.co.uk/IMM/Comics/comics1.html

Magazine for comic book collectors. Contains articles ranging from sensible to bizarre.

COMIX.World

http://www.comix-world.com/

Offers directories of dealers, "Best of COMIX.Web," comic shows, and conventions.

Complete Gaming Headquarters

http://host.yab.com/~macgyver

Offers links to Doom, Descent, Quake, and other games. Also offers radio scanners and links to other sites.

Cottage Catalogs

http://www.olworld.com/olworld/mall/mall_us/c_toys/
m_cotcat/index.html

Features collectible porcelain dolls, each of which are accompanied by a picture and complete description. Includes an enlargement feature that lets you look at the pictures in greater detail.

Cran & Lerma

http://www.moreinfo.com.au/cranlerma/

Cartoon strip that deals with the trials and tribulations of new Internet and computer users.

Crazy Horse Restaurant, Saloon, Concerts

http://www.primenet.com/~proclaim/crazyhor.htm

Advertises the Crazy Horse Steak House and Saloon. Offers beef and seafood and a post-dinner party at the saloon. Provides concerts, western music, and dancing.

The Creative Internet Home Page

http://www.galcit.caltech.edu/~ta/creative.html

Interactive playground for the Internet. Claims to offer links only to fun things.

Creative Places

http://www.ionet.net/~tommiles/index.shtml

Place to relax, read, and perhaps even see some of your own poems or short stories posted.

The Critic Sounds

http://www.phoenix.net/~lsimon/critic.html

Offers sounds from the Fox show *The Critic*.

CTN

http://www.phoenix.net/USERS/ace/ctn.html

Computer Television Network. Produces and distributes television programs about business and personal computing,

including the weekly call-in public television series *Computer Workshop*.

The Cult Shop

http://lasarto.cnde.iastate.edu/Movies/CultShop/

Provides information about movies that have cult followings, such as *Pulp Fiction*, as well as the directors and writers of these movies.

Culture Shock Cafe

http://www.cultureshock.com/salon/

Presents an interactive environment where you can chat with people, relax, check out some new art, and maybe even do a little dancing.

The Cute Kids Page

http://www.prgone.com/cutekids/

Lets you tell the world about your cute kid or tell your cute kid stories via online submission. Also provides reading material consisting of stories from parents all over the world.

The Cyber Psychic

http://www.quantum.net/cyber-psychic

Offers several minilectures on various topics, such as astrology, positive thinking, numerology, hypnosis, dreams, and meditation.

CyberCinema

http://www.indirect.com/www/jonbrown/cinema

Movie poster store. Features interactive movie poster catalogs, movie poster images, movie information, movie links, and the top 10 movie posters in the United States every week.

CyberDiner Internet Cafe Systems

http://www.cyberplace.com/cyberdiner.html

Offers a turnkey system that can be installed virtually anywhere and operated by virtually anyone.

Cyberpet

http://www.cyberpet.com

Provides pet information.

The Cyberplex Theatres

http://tribeca.ios.com/~cyberplx

Multiplex cinema on the Internet. Equipped with RealAudio.

CYMBA's Home Page

http://www.shore.net/icc/cymba.html

Contains pointers to beverage sites, as well as a pointer to a bottle opener society. Provides a pointer to order products.

Danger Mouse

http://www.charm.net/~altera/dm/dm.html

Focuses on Danger Mouse, based on a Nickelodeon cartoon. Includes pictures and sounds.

Darrell Volentine Co.

http://www.olworld.com/olworld/mall/mall_us/c_gifts/m_darrel/index.html

Offers items for sale ranging from beer steins to Egyptian wallets and boxes. Also offers a full-color gift catalog.

Dave Hall's Simpsons Page

http://www.mbnet.mb.ca:80/~davehall/

Offers links to a Simpsons episode guide, the Simpsons archive, as well as other resources about television's favorite animated family.

David Letterman

http://www.cbs.com/lateshow/lateshow.html

The official home page for *Late Night with David Letterman*, complete with the most-recently aired Top Ten list.

Days of Our Lives Page

http://weber.u.washington.edu/~pfloyd/days/index.html

Complete online information site for the soap opera *Days of Our Lives*.

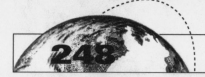

DC Restaurant List

http://www.ngen.com/nextgen/restaurant/index.html

An interactive, searchable listing of restaurants in the DC metro area. Includes links to restaurant sites and a chance to post reviews.

Desiderata—The Reststop

http://www.dfw.net/~custmbld/desid.html

Features an annotated version of Desiderata, the guide for life.

Dewayne DeBerry's Motor Sports Page

http://home.texoma.com/personal/dewayne

Offers various links to motor sports pages on the Internet. Also offers a list of links from A to Z that covers about everything else on the Internet.

DHC Welcome Page

http://www.teleport.com/~dhc

Offers information about current Dark Horse Comics, products, and even employment opportunities in the comics industry.

The Difference with Todd Rundgren

http://www.roadkill.com/cgi-roger/difference

Includes the archives for the syndicated radio show, *The Difference with Todd Rundgren.*

Discovery Toys Products

http://idgroup.com/discovery

Offers fabulous toys, books, and games. Also offers clothes for kids.

Dive USA: Underwater Schools of America

http://www.florida.net/scuba/diveusa

Provides a curriculum of courses for diver continuing education, instructor development, nitrox/deep air diving, rebreather training, aquatic imaging (both video and photo), emergency management, and environmental education.

Dolmax Home Page

http://emporium.turnpike.net/C/cytech/dolmax.html

Offers customers a complete line of the world's finest hand-made collectible musical dolls. Features more than 150 styles and provides information about obtaining a catalog.

DominO Magic

http://www.iceonline.com/home/wayner6/domino.html

Home Page for Martin DominO, magical entertainer extraordinaire in Vancouver, British Columbia, Canada.

Don Ho Home Page

http://www.spacestar.com/donho

Presents "Tiny Bubbles" in sound, as well as video and comedy from Don Ho. Helps you to get anything from Hawaii.

Doneckers At Home Catalogue—Gifts and Collectibles

http://go.flowerlink.com/html/doneckers/catalog/gifts/gifts.html

Provides various items related to lighthouses, including miniature lighthouses and apparel with lighthouses on them. Also offers patriotic candles and a city board game.

Welcome To EPSONE.COM

The Inbound Port of Entry for All Net Travelers to The Many Worlds Of EPS Inc.

The Doom Patrol!

http://www.rpi.edu/~bulloj/Doom_Patrol/DoomPatrol.html

Includes images and annotations of the DC comic book written by Paul Kupperberg, Grant Morrison, and Rachel Pollack.

The Dramatic Exchange

http://www.cco.caltech.edu/~rknop/dramex.html

Serves as a clearinghouse for new plays. Focuses on the up-and-coming playwright or producer looking for new materials.

The Dove Foundation's Home Page

http://www.dove.org

Nonprofit organization whose mission is to encourage and promote the creation, production, and distribution of wholesome family entertainment.

Duckman!

http://bluejay.creighton.edu/~jduche/duckman.html

Provides information on the animated series. Includes episode guides, cast information (the voices behind Duckman), and sound bites.

Dr. Wax

http://www.metamor.com/drwax/

Offers new and used CDs and LPs, as well as collectibles pertaining to music albums (unreleased versions and more).

Early Motion Pictures Archive

http://lcweb2.loc.gov/papr/mpixhome.html

The Library of Congress' archive for early movies. Includes some great QuickTime™ movies, as well as links on early movie history.

DramaSource

http://www.io.org/~dramasrc/

Provides one-stop shopping for drama-related source material. Includes the educational material and a catalog from which you order online.

East Coast Cards and Collectibles

http://www.wwcd.com/eccc/eccc.html

Specializes in sports-related trading cards.

The Electric Playground

http://www.elecplay.com/productions/

Focuses on the exploding world of video games. Based on the upcoming television show of the same name.

electric saloon

http://www.st.rim.or.jp:80/~liliko/e-saloon.html

A virtual saloon where you can meet whimsical characters.

Ellison Webderland: A Web Page Dedicated to the Writer, Harlan Ellison

http://www.snider.net/ellison

Provides information about the author Harlan Ellison. Includes pictures, resources, bibliography, biography, and more.

The Enterprise City Home Page

http://www.xmission.com/~gastown/enterprise/ec_home.htm

Offers a virtual or indexed tour of the fictional town of Enterprise City, which includes a collection of characters, stories, and essays by Dominic R. Villari. Also offers a number of links to other Web sites.

The Entertain-Net

http://userwww.sfsu.edu/~jkafer/welcome.html

Focuses on movies, music, graphics, games, and improvisational theater. Includes the EntertainLink of the Week.

The Entertainment Detour

http://www.kaiwan.com/~paulsd

Provides links to television show Web pages and newsgroups. Includes top 10 weekly film grosses, film Web pages, and newsgroups, video and humor links, gopher and ftp sites, film and TV show reviews, and more.

Entertainment Magazine On-Line (EMOL)

http://emol.org/emol/

Offers hundreds of pages on entertainment, music, film, Arizona tourism, and information and connections in Phoenix and Tucson.

Entrance to the Shakespeare Web

http://www.shakespeare.com/

Focuses on Shakespeare. Features a Shakespearian Insult Service and a Shakespeare feedback forum, as well as a quotation contest.

EPSONE.COM

http://www.epsone.com

Provides multimedia production management, international concert tour support, and business theater and trade show exhibits requiring high-technology integration.

Eric's I Ching Page

http://www.mcp.com/people/ericg/ching

I Ching hexagram generator made for the Web. Lets you ask the I Ching a question and provides a cryptic answer for you to ponder.

Eric's Link-O-Rama

http://www.mindspring.com/~edge/home.html

Offers links to topics including finance, consciousness, games, guitar, fitness, and miscellaneous cool stuff.

Esquireb2b

http://www.esquireb2b.com

An interactive service provided by the publishing operations of *Esquire Magazine*.

The Everyday People's Page

http://www.seanet.com/Users/dphil420/421.html

Offers links to Seattle area bands page, with Phat Sidy Smokehouse and Kilgore Trout.

The Extraterrestrial Biological Entity (EBE) Page

http://sloop.ee.fit.edu/users/lpinto/index.html

Contains pictures and documents on ETs, UFOs, and related topics.

Fashion Net

http://www.fashion.net/

The global meeting point for the world of fashion.

Fil Brown's HomePage—Wet and Messy—Star Trek—Sega—and—Doom

http://www.lookup.com/Homepages/37342/home.html

Provides many links to *Star Trek*, Wet and Messy, and, Sega, Doom, PC Games, and Raytracing sites.

The First Internet McChurch Tabernacle

http://mcchurch.org

Replaces complicated religious dogma with a new and improved EZ McWorship interface. Join McChurch today and be permanently and irrevocably redeemed.

Folklorama 1995

http://www.folklorama.ca/

Folklorama is the world's largest multicultural festival. It's been named the #1 Event in Canada by the American Bus Association and the festival best depicting Canadian culture by the World Tourism Organization.

Foundation Sports Collectibles

http://www.sol.sarasota.fl.us/golf2.html

Lists golf collectibles sponsored by the Sarasota County Youth Foundation. Features autographed pictures of classic and contemporary golf greats, golf wear, and more.

Fremont Hotel & Casino

http://www.vegas.com/hotels/fremont/

Gaming action and superb dining await visitors of the downtown Las Vegas resort. Located in the heart of 'Glitter Gulch' at Casino Center. More than 450 comfortable rooms provide you a restful atmosphere and great restaurants for your enjoyment.

Friends

`http://www.nbc.com/entertainment/shows/friends/index.html`

The official *Friends* home page.

- **Courteney Cox** Monica
- **Jennifer Aniston** Rachel
- **Matthew Perry** Chandler
- **Lisa Kudrow** Phoebe
- **David Schwimmer** Ross
- **Matt LeBlanc** Joey

Frostbite Falls

`http://www.pomona.claremont.edu//frostbite/frostbite.html`

Provides information about the Rocky and Bullwinkle cartoons, their creator, and other creations by the same creator.

The Fruit Bowl

`http://marg.ntu.ac.uk/marg/john/fruit.html`

Offers a collection of fruit stickers. Provides a variety of viewing methods (graphics-heavy, graphics-light, graphics-minimum).

The Funny Pages

`http://www.cs.virginia.edu/~bah6f/funnies`

Provides humor. Includes categories of general humor, lists of stuff, online comic strips, computer-related humor, and Pentium jokes.

Funtiques Antiques Home Page

`http://rivendell.com/funtiques/`

Offers collectibles to fit your budget. Provides a collection of books, magazines, and small items.

Gaffer Tape Anonymous

`http://www.londonmall.co.uk/gta`

Offers a complete event lighting and sound package—from design and conceptualization to implementation.

Galaxy Quest Catalog

`http://virtumall.com/cgi-bin/shop?/GalaxyQuest/gq_cat.shoppingcart.html`

Presents an online catalog that features prop replicas, card sets, posters, software, and other collectibles that relate to science fiction television shows and movies.

Gargoyle in a Tinfoil Hat Home Page

`http://www.primenet.com/~arneson/`

Specializes in links to Minnesota Web sites, reviews of local coffeehouses, images, and links to RA sound sites.

Gary C. King— Author/Lecturer

`http://coyote.accessnv.com/garyking`

Focuses on true crime. Contains sample chapters of Gary King's published books (*Blood Lust, Driven To Kill, Web of Deceit,* and his most recent *Blind Rage*), essays, opinion pieces about the genre, photos of crime scenes, victims, autopsies, and more.

The Gigaplex

http://www.gigaplex.com/wow

Presents an arts and entertainment Webmagazine with departments for film, TV, music, books, theater, photography, food and restaurants, and more. Includes celebrity interviews with actors, musicians, authors, playwrights, directors, and photographers.

A billion pleasures await you!

Girard's

http://www.umich.edu/~webspin/gi-ind.html

Provides addresses, phone numbers, and fax numbers of the Girard's two watch dealerships. Buys and sells new and used watches.

Glass Insulators

http://dc.resilience.com/insulators

Contains pictures, history, and information about collecting glass insulators.

Glen Johnson Coins

http://www.intac.com/~wb2mpk

Contains Glen Johnson's mini-coin auctions. Includes many collectible and rare coins, coin sales, and links to other numismatic sites.

Glen Murphy's Home Page

http://www.geopages.com/RodeoDrive/1220

Consists of several sections, including a TV section, movie section, and more.

Global Art Marketing

http://vvv.com/IslandArt/

Provides information and services to art collectors as well as artists and people who want to buy reproductions of fine art. Offers open market listings, reproductions for sale, and original art.

The Godfather Trilogy

http://www.exit109.com/~jgeoff/godfathr.html

Focuses on *The Godfather* trilogy.

Golf Scorecard Archives

http://www.traveller.com/golf/scorecards/

Presents a collection of images of golf scorecards from courses around the United States and beyond. Also contains a database of information about golf courses all over the world.

Groo the Wanderer

http://www.cs.hmc.edu/~jjones/groo/

Features Groo the Wanderer, perhaps one of the funniest comic books of all time.

Gulliver Film Productions

http://www.uq.oz.au/gulliver

Presents documentaries on wildlife, natural history, and environmental subjects. Includes stock shot film library, Kodak negatives, and more.

Hair: The Musical

http://www.mit.edu:8001/people/spwhite/Hair/hair.html

Features not only information about *Hair*, but also offers links to other musical-related pages.

Hardee's Walnut Creek Amphitheatre

http://www.walnutcreek.com/wca/'

A 20,000 seat concert facility that caters to music fans on the East Coast. Presents top name entertainment from April to October. Offers links to a complete and up-to-date concert listing, directions, ticket information, seating locations, and most importantly, to your favorite artists' home pages.

HeadQuarters Entertainment

http://www.fleethouse.com/fhcanada/western/bc/van/
entertan/hqe/vrhq-shw.htm

Provides information on the latest original cultural productions. Includes a small synopsis on each new endeavor. Also provides links to other theatre/drama-related places based in Canada and abroad.

Hero's Headquarters

http://iquest.com/~cws/heros

Offers autographed 8 × 10 and 16 × 20 pictures of sports figures from most major sports in the United States. Provides an online list of pictures and prices.

Hershey's Collectibles

http://go.flowerlink.com/html/hersheys/collectibles/
collectibles.html

Presents a catalog of gifts and collectibles from the Hershey Chocolate Company.

The Hitchcock Page

http://www.primenet.com/~mwc/

Focuses on director Alfred Hitchcock. Includes a list of Hitchcock's films, a list of his cameos, information about the television show *Alfred Hitchcock Presents* and more.

Hobbytyme Hobby Dealer Locator and Classified

http://www.hobbytyme.com

Enables hobbyists on the Internet to locate hobby shops by state. Offers a classifieds service that enables dealers to promote hobby products.

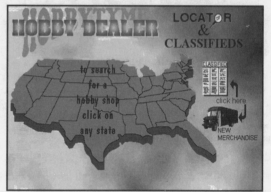

Hollyweb Online Film Guide

http://www.ingress.com/users/spease/hw/hollyweb.html

Presents industry news and film reviews. Provides information on what's coming out on the big screen, as well as on video, and how the critics think they'll fare.

HOLOPHONICS™ Virtual Sound that is Literally Turning Heads

http://www.xspot.com/HOLOPHONICS/holo.html

HOLOPHONICS™, the aural equivalent of holography, records and plays back sound so listeners perceive it as a

three-dimensional entity. Technology mimics the human hearing process and makes listeners feel as if the recorded action is happening to them in actuality. The new sound technique broadcasts directly to the brain rather than through normal acoustical channels. This is NOT surround sound, Q-sound, binaural stereo, or anything related—this technology is infinitely more realistic.

Homepage of Theatre

`http://www.cs.fsu.edu/projects/summer94/group4/group4.html`

Arranged like an index with many links to a number of theatre sites. Includes images along with broad subject areas.

Horizons Technology, Inc. Interactive Home Page

`http://www.horizons.com`

Specializes in digital video compression, multimedia authoring, interactive marketing, digital map-based geographic information, network management, and government applications.

Hot Platters

`http://www.gina.com/~oversight/HotPlatters.html`

Serves as a place for record lovers to look for that hard to find LP or 45. Also offers posters, buttons, and other music

memorabilia. Includes instructions on how to bid, and lets you submit bids by e-mail, fax, or the postal system. Also invites you to send an order or a want-list to Hot Platters.

Hot Wheels Web Site

`http://www.paccon.com/hotwhl/hotwheel.htm`

Provides information and fun stuff on Hot Wheels cars.

Houston Theater District Performance Schedule

`http://www.cent.com/orris/cominfo/theater.html`

Furnishes unofficial Houston theater district performance art exhibition schedule.

HSS Wholesale Home Page

`http://www.direct.ca:80/hss`

Offers a collection of more than 200 life-size stand-up cardboard posters of famous movie stars, singers, *Star Trek* characters, and more. Provides a complete index.

Hyperlight Enterprises

`http://www.iceonline.com/home/roxanneb/www/hyperlight.html`

Offers many science fiction and fantasy products, including card games and autographs.

ICR Interactive

`http://www.icr.com`

Provides complete coverage of the PPG Indy Car World Series. Includes complete race results, current news from the series, an extensive photo gallery, and more.

Ilene & Wayne Productions: Collectibles

http://www.aloha.com/~shakacat/

Offers some Hawaii collectibles and provides information on collectible POGs (milk caps).

Illumination

http://www.yourteam.com/~jon

Provides animation, applied HTML 3.0, information on Arcadia—a MOO, hot lists, pick of the day, and much more.

Incredible Collectibles Home Page

http://rivendell.com/antiques/stores/IC/

Includes a catalog of antiques (contains many pictures) as well as an antique museum online. Includes a form-based survey.

Instrument Jokes

http://www.mit.edu:8001/people/jcb/other-instrument-jokes.html

What's the difference between a banjo and a chain saw? The chain saw has greater dynamic range. Includes dozens more, arranged by instrument. Includes so many viola jokes that they have their own page.

Intergalactic Garage

http://www.intrepid.net/igg/igg.html

Contains music collectibles. Specializes in artists like Kate Bush and Tori Amos. Also carries hard to find T-shirts, vinyl, CDs, posters, books, and magazines that deal with the music of today.

The Internet Auction List

http://ssi.syspac.com/~usaweb/auction.html

Enables the serious collector to keeps tabs on many auctions that occur around the country. Lists the times and locations for these auctions, and includes at least a partial list of items to be auctioned off.

Internet Classifieds: 1500–1599 Collectibles Index

http://ad.wwmedia.com/classified/indexed/1500.1599.html

Lets you view or place advertisements. Lists ads under a variety of subjects. Includes a miscellaneous subject for subjects not listed specifically.

Internet Entertainment Network

http://HollywoodNetwork.com/

Offers information about movies, film, music, news, and more.

Welcome to the Internet Entertainment Network, Inc.

Where you will discover the coolest entertainment cybervillage:

The Internet Karaoke Store

http://www.primenet.com/~karaoke/index.html

Services the Karaoke industry with hardware (amps, players, and more) and software (LaserDiscs and CD+Graphics).

The Internet Movie Database

http://www.msstate.edu/Movies/

Provides a database of information about hundreds of thousands of popular (and not-so-popular) movies.

Interrobang?!

http://www.moscow.com/homepages/hhoffman@ucla.edu.html

Interrobang is a revolutionary print magazine/e-zine, dedicated to perfection in the art of writing. Welcomes submissions of quality articles, poetry, essays, and short stories (requests 3,000 words maximum).

Island Imports, Ltd.

http://www.rt66.com/olworld/mall/mall_us/c_gifts/m_islan2/index.html

Features handcrafted Jamaican walking canes.

The ITA Off Ramp

http://www.ita.org/~dokk

Provides links to interesting things on the Web. Lets you visit the All Wise Oracle, Cafe KidFree, and more.

Jack's Blues Party House

http://www.geopages.com/SunsetStrip/1064

The center of the blues universe in Los Angeles. Provides club information, band information, and blues links.

James Atkinson's Page-o-Thrills

http://espsun.space.swri.edu/~atkinson/jam.html

Includes sex, drugs, rock, cheese, and a great MadLib program to boot. Also provides information on Texas A & M and computer resources at Texas A & M.

James Bond 007

http://www.mcs.net/~klast/www/bond.html

Focuses on 007.

Jan-Ken-Po—The Trading Card Game for Kids of All Ages

http://www.aloha.com/~hollis

A collectible trading card game for kids. Features Manga style artwork with socially responsible storyline.

The Jaunt

http://www.gate.net/~scottm/

Lets you navigate using a simulated window to After Hours Support, What's New, and File of the Week. Also includes links to Florida, Canada, Internet resources, magazines, sporting news, and entertainment.

JB's Jelly Donuts

http://www.moscow.com/homepages/KLEINR@UWPLATT.EDU.html

Provides a unique perspective on Jelly Donuts, including weird stories, dos and don'ts of donuts, games to play with jelly donuts, popular donut names, donut songs, and more.

The Jihad to Destroy Barney on the World Wide Web

http://deeptht.armory.com/~deadslug/Jihad/jihad.html

Serves as a forum for all the people who despise that purple dinosaur the kids worship.

Jim's Rant of the Week

http://www.ids.net/~combat/rant.html

Features a weekly monologue that pokes fun and stimulates thought on the most timely of issues to most Americans. Jim takes the news story that irks him the most and discusses it with a unique mixture of thought, philosophy, and sometimes irreverant satire.

Joe DeRouen's Home Page

http://www.crl.com/~jderouen/index.html

Offers links to all sorts of things on the Web, ranging from folk music to electronic postcards.

Joe's Internet Page

http://atc.ameritel.net/lusers/wrstler/joe/joe.html

Includes magic, the gathering links, Joe's personal magic trading list, airplane links, hockey links, and sounds.

Jogle's Favorite Theatre-Related Resources

http://pscinfo.psc.edu/~geigel/menus/Theatre.html

Provides a wide range of theater-related information. Covers Broadway, regional, and campus theater. Also represents professional organizations. Includes staging and lighting sources as well as theater-related software.

Jokers Wild Casino

http://www.vegas.com/hotels/jokers/home.html

Home of the famous Wild Card Buffet and the fantastic Paycheck Tower, where you can win up to $5,000 and many other prizes when you cash your paycheck at the Joker. Furnishes many exciting slots and table games.

Joseph E. Huston Distinguished Playwrights' Award

http://bsuvc.bsu.edu/~00tekowalsky/contest.html

An annual competition for original scripts. The winner receives a monetary award and production of their play.

Joseph Luft's Philatelic Resources on the Web

http://www.execpc.com/~joeluft/resource.html

Offers many postal links. Includes stamps, postcards, and even some antique links.

K102 Radio

http://www.k102.com/

Provides links to country music, information on K102 Radio, and a chance every month to win great prizes, such as a chance to go backstage with your favorite stars at FanJam.

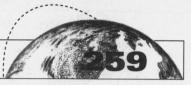

KA9FOX Web Site for Contesters and DXers by Scott Neader

http://www.infoanalytic.com/ka9fox/

Includes photos, contest score rumors, reflector summaries, and some great contesting and DXing-related links.

Kay's Kid's Collection

http://fox.nstn.ca/~tmonk/kayskids/kay.html

A collection of sites for Kids, both young and young at heart.

KCRWWW

http://www.kcrw.org

The Web home of KCRW, 89.9 FM, National Public Radio for Southern California. Features an eclectic mix of music, news, public affairs, and radio drama. Offers RealAudio clips.

Kingswood Kranium

http://www.kingswood.com

Lighthearted humor magazine from the minds at Kingswood Advertising, a full-service marketing communications agency located in Philadelphia.

Irrefutable Evidence That First Cousins Shouldn't Marry...
Volume 1 - Issue 4 - August 8, 1995

Kringle Kottage Collectibles

http://www.prairieweb.com/kringle/

Features Christmas items and collectibles from Christmas past. Includes pictures and descriptions for each item, and offers to send you more information via e-mail.

Lance's Home

http://www.con.wesleyan.edu/~lparsons/lparsons.html

Offers links to many good OS/2 and computer-related sites. Includes links to some sports information pages.

Las Vegas Outdoors

http://www.vegas.com/vegas/outdoors

Provides information on what Las Vegas has to offer outside the Strip.

Lemur's Home Page

http://lemur.acs.umbc.edu/

A source of network service interfaces, various HTMLized texts, documentation, and general fun stuff.

The Lounge of Self Indulgence

http://w3.nai.net/~viktrola/tc/lounge.html

"Where chaos meet lounge there is a fractal in my mai tai." Offers random thoughts on life, music, chaos, and other useless things.

Lucasfilm Archives

http://bantha.pc.cc.cmu.edu/

Industrial Light and Magic, Skywalker Sound, and LucasArts online. Provides sounds, clips, timelines, lists, and information about the projects of these related companies.

Lucasfilm's THX Home Page

http://www.lum.com:80/thx/

Caters to the audiophiles amongst the movie enthusiasts. Provides information about the THX sound system.

Welcome to the Lucasfilm THX Home Page!

Lunds Auction House

http://www.lunds.com/~lunds

Features items currently up for auction. Lets you sign up to be notified when a certain piece comes into the auction house.

The Lurker's Guide to Babylon 5

http://www.hyperion.com/lurk/lurker.html

Provides information on the show, plus spoilers for individuals who might have missed a show.

Madison Wisconsin Scottish Country Dancers

http://sprott.physics.wisc.edu/mscd/home.htm

Describes the Scottish country dance group. Includes a calendar of events, member names, directions to Madison Wisconsin, and links to other dance and regional sites.

Main Page: The Internet Movie Database at Cardiff, UK

http://www.cm.cf.ac.uk/Movies/

Provides movie clips, movie reviews, or any movie information.

Makin' Waves Studio

http://cyberzine.org/html/Waves/wavepage.html

Offers to make a personalized sound file for you to use on your PC, home page, or telephone answering machine. Can even do a full scale, broadcast quality commercial voice over.

Mangar's Home Page

http://www.ksu.edu/~mangar

Provides writers' resources, fiction, music, movies and TV, gothic stuff, humor, esoteric subjects (philosophy, consciousness, paranormal, and so forth), politics, art (fractals, Escher, and so forth), and more.

Manmademedia

http://www.manmade.com

Interactive Record Label fusing experimental electronic music and images. Producers of the HeadTravel series of Enhanced CDs/CD-Plus. Part of the Pacific Collective. Linked to natural music and management.

Mariam's Cyberspace Park

http://www.skypoint.com/members/mariam

Offers nine subparks, ranging from entertainment to global culture, from world religion to ancient stories, within which you can learn and enjoy yourself.

The Marijne Page

http://www.wirehub.nl/~martijn/marijne.htm

Provides information about the Dutch alternative (female) singer, Marijne van der Vlugt, and her Anglo/Dutch band, Salad. Contains pictures, lyrics, and audiofiles.

The Marilyn Pages

http://www.ionet.net:80/~jellenc/marilyn.html

Presents Marilyn Monroe in a tour of her life, films, and images. Includes memorabilia resources.

Marjorie Rose Antiques

http://www.best.com:80/~spectrum/antique/marjorierose/marjorie.html

Focuses on antiques. Offers a list of items for sale. Also offers a map to the showroom, a phone number, and ordering information.

Martin Family Home Page

http://iquest.com/~jsm

Contains pages on astronomy, genealogy, olympics, sports, space, parents' stuff, kids' stuff, *Star Wars*, *Star Trek*, model rockets, travel, search engines, shopping, and more.

MASH Archives

http://www.best.com/~dijon/tv/mash/index.html

Includes cast photos, the opening theme, a FAQ, and more.

Match.Com—"We Met on the Net"

http://www.match.com

Lets you meet other singles by posting a profile, exchanging e-mail, and conducting personalized matches (all anonymously).

MediaNet Online

http://www.medianet.co.uk/medianet/index.html

Offers resources and services for film, television, and multimedia professionals.

Memorabilia — Memorabilia — Memorabilia

http://www.wwcd.com/mem-mem/mem-mem.html

Presents entire stock and price lists, as well as ordering information.

Mentos—The Freshmaker

http://www.best.com/~dijon/tv/mentos/

A site for all the people who loathe and despise the cheesy Mentos commercials on TV.

Metaverse

http://metaverse.com/

Adam Curry's (formerly of MTV) Web page that offers links for information on television shows, movies, and

music.

Mike Mac's DOOM! Page

http://www.nauticom.net/users/mccollum/doom.htm

Doom page where you can download patches, wads, and the game itself. Offers many links.

Minsky Online Home Page

http://www.avsi.com/minsky

Focuses on the works of creative artist Richard Minsky. Also features a selection of limited edition books and prints for sale.

Miramar Productions/ Recordings

http://www.uspan.com/miramar/

Specializes in producing long form visual music and unique audio products. Features artists such as Thomas Dolby, Tangerine Dream, and Jan Hammer. Includes entire audio/ video catalog, product profiles complete with video and audio files, and news/information about Miramar artists.

Model Horse Web Page

http://www.metronet.com/~kira/model-horse

Provides information about collecting model horses. Lets you ask questions about the hobby or request specific information.

Moms-at-Home

http://iquest.com/~jsm/moms/

Geared to homemakers, housewives, househusbands, and anyone else who has decided to forgo paid employment to devote their skills and intelligence to raising their children.

Monolith BBS

http://130.89.228.12/~bbs/

Provides information about the Monolith BBS, as well as a partial interface. Includes dozens of forums for discussion about all kinds of subjects, and a chat facility.

MOODY'S Sports Autographs and Memorabilia

http://www.wwcd.com/moodys/moodys.html

Provides sports cards, autographs, and collectible items.

The Moose's Guide to Northern Exposure

http://www.netspace.org/~moose/moose.html

Online guide to *Northern Exposure*. Includes graphics, sound bites, FAQ, episode guides, and more.

Movie Mom's Guide to Movies and Videos for Families

http://pages.prodigy.com/VA/rcpj55a/moviemom.html

Lists movies suitable for their kids. Provides in-depth reviews on the movies.

The Movie Poster Page

http://musicman.com/mp/posters.html

Exhibits a digital gallery of images of collectible movie posters. Also serves as an online educational resource for people interested in collecting movie posters.
Provides information about pricing, preservation, and poster sizes. Features special sections devoted to James Bond and Disney.

The Movie Sounds Page

http://WWW.netaxs.com/people/dgresh/snddir.html

Provides sounds from many of the zaniest and most popular movies.

MovieLink 777-FILM Online

http://www.movielink.com

Provides movie information, showtimes, previews, and even tickets. Provides local theater locations and up-to-the-minute showtimes for every movie theatre in 25 cities, as well as previews, other information, and the capability to purchase advance tickets in most cities.

The Movies Cliche List

http://www.well.com/user/vertigo/cliches.html

Contains a hilarious list of movie cliches on dozens and dozens of topics.

MPEG Movie Archive

http://www.eeb.ele.tue.nl/mpeg/index.html

Lets you download minimovies to play on your computer. Arranges the movies by content.

MPEG Movie Archive

http://www.eeb.ele.tue.nl/mpeg/

Contains an archive of movies in mpeg format, arranged by topic. Includes R-rated movie snips.

Mr. Showbiz

http://web3.starwave.com/showbiz/

Offers pure fluff on movies and gossip. Perhaps silly, but quite fun.

MuchMusic—The Alternative Medium

http://www.muchmusic.com/muchmusic.html

The Canadian MTV-like site. Provides information on the music industry.

Muppets Home Page

http://www.ncsa.uiuc.edu/VR/BS/Muppets/muppets.html

Offers information about everything Muppet, from *The Muppet Show* to *Fraggle Rock* to *Sesame Street*.

Muse of Fire Productions

http://leonardo.net/musofire/index.html

Develops, packages, and produces intelligent, offbeat, and occasionally Euro-oriented movies. Includes hot list, notes on copyrighting screenplays, an actor/agent/quote list, and more.

Mushroom Comics

http://www.insv.com/mushroom

Offers sneak peaks. Presents images from Araknis, Innercircle, and Futuretech, along with ordering information and some other stuff.

The Music Wars Home Page

http://www.xmission.com/~gastown/MusicWars

Name That Tune, with a twist. Any fan of any type of music should love Music Wars. Features a music trivia contest.

My So-Called Life

http://www.umn.edu/nlhome/g564/lask0008/mscl.html

Focuses on a television show about teenagers and high school.

National Gemstone's Home Page

http://www.primenet.com/~rgenis

Contains information for gem collectors, including dealers, price lists, past price charts, and newsletters. Also offers a collection of gem photographs from the Smithsonian Gem and Mineral Collection.

natural music

http://www.manmade.com/natural.html

Independent vinyl-only record label. Specializes in uncategorizable music for movement and meditation.

NBC HTTV

http://www.nbc.com/

NBC's home page. Provides NBC shows, stations, news, sports, and the Peacock Park, where you can sign up for a newsletter, download a screensaver, and more.

New Comic Book Releases

http://www.mnsinc.com/hyworth/comics/new.html

Provides a day-to-day listing of new comic book titles released. Lists books according to publisher, title, issue number, and price. Also offers previous dates.

New Dramatists

http://www.itp.tsoa.nyu.edu/~diana/ndintro.html

Focuses on serious drama. Contains links to playwrights, agents, and other theatre-related sources. Also provides a script-share program.

New Mexico Market Source Home Page

http://www.rt66.com/nmmarket/welcome.htm

Offers all types of western styles, from watches to prints.

The New Web Site of Love

http://www.usgcc.odu.edu/~ty/mst3k/MST3K.html

Focuses on the cult TV show *Mystery Science Theater 3000*. Includes episode guides, FAQs, and more.

New York Film and Animation Co. Ltd.

http://www.okc.com/nyfac

A high end computer graphics firm working with advertising agencies and other clients. Employs a collection of images and information from recent works to introduce people to the New York Film and Animation Company.

Niccolino's Melrose Place Page

http://www.gate.net/~ninboy/melrose/

Offers some cast biographies, as well as magazine articles about the show. Also includes a pictures archive of the cast members.

NL7J Amateur radio page, DX and SSTV

http://www.alaska.net/~buchholz

Emphasizes DX and SSTV. Lists Alaskan clubs. Includes some difficult-to-find SSTV and support programs.

NOVA

http://www.wgbh.org/Pages/NOVA/NOVAhome.html

Excellent educational site. Contains excerpts from the NOVA program. Features the KnowZone, which contains science facts and figures.

Nuke Home Page

http://www.nuke.com

Offers video games, computer entertainment software, movies, television, comics, trading cards, and more. Contains more than 2,000 pages of editorial content.

NYPD Blue Home Pages

http://src.doc.ic.ac.uk/public/media/tv/collections/tardis/us/drama/NYPDBlue/index.html

Provides information about ABC's show *NYPD Blue*. Includes pictures, FAQs, and extensive episode guides.

O'Bannon Oriental Carpets

http://www.ibp.com/pit/obannon

Provides information about how hand-spun wool and vegetable dyes create unique handmade carpets in time-honored folk tradition. Offers a number of carpets for viewing and lets you order many of them. Also provides information on weaving.

October Films Presents, Nadja

http://www.inch.com/user/october/nadja/index.html

Presents Michael Almereyda's *Nadja*, a spellbinding brew of droll comedy, hallucinatory fantasy, and lush eroticism.

Off the Beaten Path

http://www.interport.net/~dolphin

Provides information, including travel destinations, a movie database, humor, and Internet information.

The Official Casper Merchandise Cyberstore

http://www.atlas.co.uk/casper

Offers products for sale. Displays yet-to-be-released products and lets you order them securely.

OLWW: Gifts and Collectibles: Sun Tile

http://www.rt66.com/olworld/mall/mall_us/c_gifts/
m_suntil/index.html

Features sun tiles. Also offers online ordering and a complete catalog.

ONSALE Home Page

http://www.onsale.com/

Features a broad selection of collectible items and offers bidding and buying options. Lets you browse and check out the merchandise.

Order Form

http://www.cris.com/~Masters/souvenirs.html

Offers a series of souvenirs from the Masters Golf tournament. Features golfwear and collector's pins.

Oren's Spam Shirt Surprise

http://www.xnet.com/~doh

Focuses on Spam and llamas. Includes information on cult TV, movies, music, and books, and offers many links.

Osmond Family Theatre

http://www.branson.net/branson/osmonds

Presents the Osmond Family Theatre in Branson, Missouri.

Painted Label Pop Bottle Collecting

http://www.netaccess.on.ca/~mhall

Provides information for anyone interested in painted pop bottles from Canada and elsewhere.

Paramount Pictures Online Studio

http://www.paramount.com/

Provides information on upcoming and current Paramount movies and television shows.

Party of Five

http://www.csua.berkeley.edu/~byron/PartyOf5/Pof5.html

Focuses on the new Fox television show *Party of Five*. Provides information for fans of the show, including an episode guide and background information.

patch.html

http://www.engin.umich.edu/~tpruss/patch.html

Provides information about patch collecting on the Web. Displays pictures of some patches, includes many links to other sites.

Patrick's Musicians' Page

http://www.crl.com/~patrickk/music.html

Contains information about Patrick's musician's referral service and Web page service. Also provides information about Patrick's band and offers links to other regional/unsigned bands of all types.

Pennington's

http://iquest.com/~cws/penningtons/

Offers sports-related collectibles. Also offers products for racing, comic book, and POG collectors, as well as Magic players. Also furnishes a selection of collecting supplies you can use to keep your valuable cards and comics from being damaged.

Perplexity

http://www.bajan.com/prplxty/prplxty.html

Presents an exciting board game wherein players race to collect letter tiles, stealing and swapping with each other as they are challenged with cyptic crossword puzzle clues.

Personal fX: The Collectibles Show

http://www.delphi.com/fx/fxperson.html

Provides a show synopsis and various promotional items. Includes a programming schedule and a page of pointers to collectible-related sites. Also offers information on the two hosts of the show.

Petite Princess Page

http://deeptht.armory.com/~zenugirl/barbie.html

Contains pictures, history, and information about the world of adult fashion dolls.

Pigs in CyberSpaaaaaaaaaace...

http://www-leland.stanford.edu/~rosesage/Muppet.html

Celebrates all things Muppetational and contains pictures and descriptions of Muppet collectibles. Provides information, history, and trivia about the Muppets as well.

Planet Anchorage

http://www.alaska.net/~rwarner/mypage.htm

Provides music, MOO, government resources, and Netscape images.

Planet StarChild

http://streams.com/starchild

Serves as a music resource for artists and new music fans around the world. Offers home pages and Internet marketing help for independent artists and labels.

Planet X

http://www.geopages.com/WallStreet/1114

Variety page. Includes a *Star Trek* page, a daily unknown site of the day, a new site of the day, and many other goodies. Also includes an image map that takes you to hundreds of sites that constantly change.

PM Zone—The Jukebox

http://popularmechanics.com/popmech/frep/JUKE.html

Contains information about classic jukeboxes and their history.

PoochNet

http://www.aescon.com/poochnet

Provides personalized services as well as current real-time information to the public. Offers advertising services for dog breeders. Creates individual Web pages for dog breeders and posts them in classifications such as breeder classified, puppies for sale, stud services, and accesssories and related items. Also posts breed information for free as an educational service. Posts magazine advertising and lists dog clubs and organizations.

Portal Disney FANtasEARS-Mouse-Sell-aneous Forum

http://www.portal.com/~rkoster/sell.html

Provides information about Disney, Disney collectibles, souvenirs, merhandise, news about WDCC new releases, and Disneyana discussions. Also offers a link to a Disney discussion room to chat with other Disney fans.

The Postcard Page

http://www-iwi.unisg.ch/~mmarchon/postcard/index.html

Features information contributed from postcard enthusiasts from around the world.

The Power Ranger's Home Page

http://kilp.media.mit.edu:8001/power/homepage.html

Provides information about the Mighty Morphin Power Rangers.

Professor Neon's TV and Movie Mania

http://www.vortex.com/ProfNeon.htm

Targets the bizarre side of television, movie, and theatre. Based on Professor Neon's TV and Movie Mania radio show and includes audio bits of the show online.

The Puzzle Post by Pinnacle Solutions

http://iquest.com/~pinnacle/index.shtml

Offers online entertainment with crosswords, board games, puzzle books, shareware archives, and trivia teasers. Features puzzle skill contests for free prizes.

Puzzler

http://www.thought.net/jason/puzzlestart.html

A unique twist on "put the picture together" puzzles. Presents two different kinds of these puzzles: one number-based and one a perplexing cat puzzle.

QuickTimeVR World Wide Web Site

http://qtvr.quicktime.apple.com

Apple Computer brings the award winning QuickTimeVR technology to the Web. Provides a variety of compelling QuickTimeVR content, a free player to interact with it, and technical information on how it all works.

The R.M.P.S.S.

http://ugweb.cs.ualberta.ca/~stuart/monty.cgi/

Presents a randomly selected Monty Python sketch from *Flying Circus* each time you enter.

Rage Page

http://student-www.uchicago.edu/users/cls6/rage/rageindex.html

Focuses on one of the newest collectible card games, Rage. Provides more information about the game itself and lets you order cards and supplies.

Railroad Scripophily

http://www.dnai.com/~tcarson/pages/scrip.html

Scripophily is the hobby of collecting old stock and bond certificates. Introduces interested individuals to the stocks and bonds of old railroad companies, shares the history of scripophily, and reviews books on the topic.

RandyZ's Cartoon Corner

http://lpage.com/randyz/ccorner.html

Presents a collection of original cartoons (all are computer/Web/technology-related), updated weekly.

Rapid 13

http://www.wps.com/KAOS

Contains a variety of links to art, drama, and culture-related areas. Also offers a list of miscellaneous links, some very mainstream, some not.

The Reader's Corner

http://www.quake.net/~autopen

Focuses on classical romance, historical, fantasy, mystery, countryside fiction, and biography. Includes new online short stories, reviews, and related articles. Offers free online mailings of new and classical short stories and serialized stories.

RealTime

http://realtime.cbcstereo.com

Radio show heard across Canada. Includes music and guests. Features a great deal of RealAudio.

Recycler's World

http://www.motive.com/recycle/

Provides information about secondary or recyclable commodities, by-products, used and surplus items or materials, and collectible items. Lists the collectibles by type and subject. Includes cards, stamps, and memorabilia from *Star Trek* and the Beatles.

Red Herring Productions

http://www.bayne.com/wolfBayne/mystery/

Stages audience-interactive murder mysteries, westerns, and melodramas for your corporate or personal special event needs. Offers catalog of original plays online.

Redundantly, Online

http://www.unt.edu/~price/red/

Presents online version of the printed literary magazine. Concentrates on multimedia and using cyberspace creatively and the print version focuses on the humanities.

Reviews of Independent and Alternative Comix

http://weber.u.washington.edu/~keb/comix.html

Kathleen Bennett's reviews of comic books from small-press and self-publishers, including Fantagraphics and many others.

Rhythm and Hues Studios

http://www.rhythm.com/

Projects have included a number of motion pictures, television shows, and commercials—including the world-famous Coca Cola polar bears. Features company information and job listings.

Ricardo Menendez's VFR750 Page

http://www.eng.iastate.edu/~ricm/homepage.html

Provides information, pictures, and aftermarket product reviews (via e-mail by users around the net) for the VFR750 motorcycle.

Richard Kay's Home Page

http://www.moscow.com/homepages/
richardk@delm.tas.gov.au.html

Presents a land use planner's view of the world. Offers links to environmental, philosophy, planning, and sustainable development-oriented sites.

Rippin' Good Yarn

http://www.3rdplanet.com/rippin.html

Online magazine of science fiction and fantasy.

Rob Mayfield

http://wattle.itd.adelaide.edu.au/~mayfield

Includes a collection of amateur radio links and more.

Roger's Collector's Marketplace

http://iquest.com/~cws/rogers/

Lists current in-stock items and information for receiving the *Marketplace* newsletter. Provides information about just about every sort of collectible imaginable, from Armani to Waterford Crystal and more.

Rox Quarry

http://www.rox.com/quarry/

Provides information about a public access television show in Bloomington, Indiana: *J and B on the Rox*.

Rubber Chicken: The Improvisational Comedy Troupe

http://www.conline.com/~chicken

Provides information about a Dallas-based improvisational comedy troupe.

Rudyard Kipling's The Jungle Book

http://bvp.wdp.com/BVPM/PressRoom/JungleBook/
JungleBook.html

Showcases various video and image clips from Disney's rendition of the Kipling *Jungle Book* tale.

RW Books Home Page

http://www.langsys.com/djackson/rw.html

Specializes in out-of-print books and collectible editions. Offers to perform book searches for hard-to-find editions as well.

The Salem Tarot Page

http://www1.usa1.com/~arachne/home.html

Provides online psychic consultations. Features a multimedia introduction to tarot, witchcraft, and Salem.

Santa Fe Southwest Artists Marketspace

http://www.artsantafe.com/sfm/sfmhome.html

Provides a collection of works from fine southwestern artists, musicians, photographers, and weavers. Includes a wide variety of products to browse.

Santa Fe Traditions, Inc.

http://www.rt66.com/olworld/mall/mall_us/c_gifts/m_sftrad/index.html

Features Native American jewelry and crafts from the Southwest. Includes pictures and an online ordering form.

Sarasota Collectibles

http://iquest.com/~tstevens/sarasota/

Contains mostly science-fiction collectibles, especially role-playing games. Also offers fossil-brand watches and includes pictures.

Saturday Night Archives

http://www.best.com:80/~dijon/tv/snl/

Provides information on *Saturday Night Live*. Includes FAQs on everything from the original cast to recurring characters. Also offers a link to the "Deep Thought of the Day."

The Schoolhouse Rock Page

http://hera.life.uiuc.edu/rock.html

Offers audio clips, pics, and more from the old television show *Schoolhouse Rock*.

Sci-Fi Channel

http://www.scifi.com/cgi-bin/rbox/incgif.prl

The science fiction channel online. Offers tidbits about science fiction original movies and the like.

Scientific and Medical Antiques

http://www.duke.edu/~tj/sci.ant.html

Provides information about scientific and medical antiques and serves as a place you can buy and sell items. Provides information about these antiques. Includes an extensive collection of catalogs and classifieds so you can buy and sell your own.

Scottish's Scooby Doo Home Page

http://www.rit.edu/~skm7386/scooby.html

Focuses on Scooby. Provides episode guides, FAQs, pictures, and more.

Scrambled Word/Crossword Solver

http://odin.chemistry.uakron.edu/cbower/jumble.html

Provides a CGI program for solving scrambled word puzzles and helping solve crossword puzzles by suggesting words when only some letters are known.

Screensite Reference Shelf

http://www.temple.edu:80/~pryluck/index.html

Serves as an online encyclopedia of information on actors and actresses, as well as information on books and writing.

The Script Emporium

http://www.cs.tufts.edu:80/~katwell/

Provides a collection of movie screenplays online.

Sea Creations

http://cyberactive-1.com/sea-creations/

Features gifts from the sea, such as jewelry (shark tooth products) and collectible lighthouses.

Seinfeld

http://www.engr.wisc.edu/~heinj/seinfeld.html

Includes FAQs, episode guides, sounds, and pictures related to the *Seinfeld* show.

SHAQ_IT

http://www.wwcd.com/shaqit/shaqit.html

Offers many collectible cards, featuring the Orlando Magic's Shaquille O'Neal.

Sherpa Aircraft Manufacturing, Inc.

http://www.teleport.com/~sherpa

Tells about the Sherpa, a new Bush Plane capable of short take-offs and landings (STOL), enhanced cargo capacity and handling, and ease of loading, unloading, and maintenance.

Sierra Online

http://www.sierra.com/

Lets you choose your own look and feel as you explore different game genres, the latest titles, deals, multimedia downloads, chat rooms, and behind-the-screens news and special events at SierraWeb, the official site of Sierra Online, a world-wide developer of interactive software.

Sinotiq

http://204.253.80.8/Sinotiq/

Serves as an outlet for collectible items from China. Provides information about the shop itself and the means to receiving more information about the shop and ordering.

Sirius Entertainment

http://www.insv.com/sirius

Publishes *Dawn*, *Animal Mystic*, *Poison Elves*, and more.

The SITCOM Home Page

http://www.ccp.uchicago.edu/grad/Dan_Goldstein/sitcom.html

Provides a blend of structuralist literary criticism and artificial intelligence, a live show that converts audience suggestions into full-length, improvised TV sitcoms that unfold live on stage. Produces completely improvised sitcoms that are startlingly accurate and take account of real sitcom length, real sitcom theme music, real sitcom joke structure, and include improvised furniture and improvised commercials.

Sliders

http://www.east-tenn-st.edu/~lucast/sliders/sliders.html

Focuses on the Fox television show, *Sliders*. Provides information about episodes and the actors, and houses an archive of *Sliders* pictures. Includes links to other *Sliders* sites.

The Smurfy Home Page

http://www.umich.edu/~starchld/hannabarbera/smurfs/

Provides pictures and a few QuickTime movies of the little blue creatures from Saturday morning cartoons.

Soap Links

http://www.cts.com/~jeffmj/

Provides in-depth coverage (scoops, cast list, filmographies) for daytime drama fans of *General Hospital*. Provides many links to other soap pages spanning the United States and abroad.

The Social Cafe

http://www.social.com/social/index.html

Serves as a place for people to meet and have some fun. Lets you join conversations on the People Are Talking Page. Offers sports and social club listings (United States). Also provides daily world news, Dr. Fun Oldies, and other stuff.

Softelligence

http://www.deltanet.com/users/litebug

Web management company with advertising specialists for specific web design. Focuses on bringing a new kind of information net to the public. Offers an entertainment guide for various cities, including dining, nitelife and amusements.

Something Special

http://www.wimsey.com/Magnet/shop/index120.html

Contains many Canadian-made specialty products, such as decorative items for the house and clothing. Also lets you register for periodic updates by e-mail.

Songs of the Blue Bird

http://www.iquest.net/~jeneric/songs.html

A virtual 'zine and news source for fans of the CBS television drama *Beauty and the Beast*.

Sony Pictures Entertainment Page

http://www.spe.sony.com/Pictures/index.html

Provides news about Sony Pictures movie, theater, and television projects.

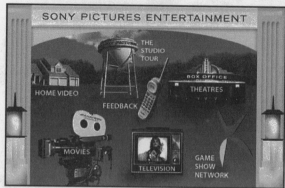

Southborough Players

http://www.ultranet.com/~dlwarren/sobo.htm

Nonprofit community theater group that has been bringing live theater to the Massachusetts Metro West area since 1969.

Space Adventure II

http://www.presence.com/space2/

Space Adventure II is a vibrant, noisy, sometimes silly look at our universe; a place of beauty and of danger; a place of endless variations and possibilities; a place where the same simple rules that make a pencil roll off a table can link whole galaxies in intricate dances and in colossal battles.

SportsCards, Etc.

http://www.nauticom.net/users/sce/

Deals in all kinds of cards. Offers sports cards and nonsports cards in factory-sealed wax boxes. Also offers Magic: The Gathering cards and other collectible card games, as well as complete sets of cards.

ST:CCG

http://129.21.204.63/HTML/STCCG_Home.HTML

Focuses on the *Star Trek: The Next Generation* collectible card game. Offers links to rules, questions, and images of cards.

The Stage Door

http://www.stagedoor.com

Offers links to theatre and stamp collecting.

Star Saga Page

http://www.infohaus.com/access/by-seller/Star_Saga

Presents a newsletter that discusses astrology with current world trends and the significance of planetary transits, eclipses, lunar phases, and various cycles in the charts of people, places, and events.

The Star Wars Collectors Home Page

http://www.cs.washington.edu/homes/lopez/collectors.html

Features information about all kinds of (not for sale) *Star Wars* collectibles, ranging from toys to original movie props. Features many pictures.

Star Wars Home Page at UPENN

http://stwing.resnet.upenn.edu:8001/~jruspini/starwars.html

Provides *Star Wars* information. Includes information on the *Star Wars* trilogy, collectibles, books, and more.

A long time ago in a galaxy far, far, away...

The Star Wars Home Page

Star Wars Humor Page

http://www.epix.net/~killando

Focuses on *Star Wars* humor.

Star Wars Multimedia WWW Page

http://bantha.pc.cc.cmu.edu:1138/SW_HOME.html

Includes digitized movies and sounds available for viewing and/or listening.

Starship Portfolio

http://www.mag-net.co.uk/Starship/

Presents a collection of *Star Trek* fine art, all prints from the original paintings by English artist G. W. Hutchins.

Starship Store

http://www.halcyon.com/uncomyn/startrek.html

Offers home shopping for *Trek* enthusiasts. Provides complete ordering information online.

Steve's Ant Farm

http://sec.dgsys.com/antfarm.html

Presents live ants building bridges and moving mountains.

Stinette Donahue Artists

http://www.xmission.com/~quinnbj/opera/opera.html

The distinguished African American baritone, Ed Pierson, has a rich performance background in opera, oratorio, and concert. He has been soloist with the major orchestras of the United States in the important concert halls from New York's Lincoln Center to DC's Kennedy Center to Salt Lake City's Mormon Tabernacle.

Studio Artico— Photographers Since 1900

http://www.cdrom-paradise.com/artico/

From the beginning of the activity of Giovanni Artico (1868-1930) the firm become famous among the "cultural elite" of the beginning of the century. Includes portraits of conductor Arturo Toscanini, the tenor Enrico Caruso, and the writer Giovanni Verga. Also portrays three Popes: Pius X, Benedetto XIV, and Pius XI.

Sunshiny's Home Page

http://www.ecn.bgu.edu/users/gsunny/monhp.htm

Presents some poetry and offers a few links.

Superman & Character Collectibles

http://www.primenet.com/~proclaim/superman.htm

Provides information on the DC comics hero, Superman. Lists an address, telephone, and fax number for getting in touch with a Superman memorabilia authority. Offers services including buying and selling as well as appraisal and evaluation services.

The Surrealist Compliment Generator

http://pharmdec.wustl.edu/cgi-bin/jardin_scripts/SCG

Provides a surrealist compliment when you connect.

Sylvia's Art of This Century

http://iweb.www.com/vatl/shops/sylvia

Atlanta area coffeeshop, art gallery, and acoustic music venue. Offers live performances Friday and Saturday nights. Includes maps, information, and current art.

Synthesis: Electronic Dance Music Page

http://www.isisnet.com/spacelab/synthesis/wel.html

Focuses on the rave/techno scene, electropop, house, new beat/hardbeat, industrial, and experimental music.

Tales Twice Told Gaming Page

http://www.paranoia.com/~klmac/TalesHome.html

Provides deck designs, FAQs, and card lists for collectible card games. Features Magic: The Gathering, Ultimate Combat, Wyvern, RAGE, and Illuminati: New World Order.

Taz-Mania Page

http://www.realtime.net/~lthumper/taz-mania/index.html

Focuses on the Looney Toons character Taz, the Tazmanian Devil. Includes links to Taz FAQs, images, and other Taz data.

Tech-Rock Cafe

http://www.tcs.co.at/cafe/home.html

Offers a wide range of information, like sports news, TV, and movies, the 'Web-side' of the week, and updated newspapers.

Telkamp Theatres

http://www.iac.net/~mtelkamp

Provides listings of Telkamp Theatres' current films. Also includes pages devoted to specific films.

Ten Eyck Design Studio

http://www.inch.com/~kteneyck/

Web page of a set design studio based in New York. Provides a graphical interface. Includes links to current projects and a large group of previous projects. Provides information on the behind-the-scenes work involved in theater and drama.

The Ten Pound Fiddle Coffee House—East Lansing, Michigan

http://www.msu.edu/fiddle

Presents concerts and dances in the folk tradition.

The Theatre Central Web Page

http://www.mit.edu:8001/people/quijote/theatre-central.html

Provides coverage of amateur professional and scholastic groups. Contains links to international resources as well. Includes topical organization with reference icons.

The Tick Page

http://www.cipsinc.com:80/TICK/tickpage.html

Home of the alternative superhero Tick. Changes the main graphics each time you load it. Includes links and graphics.

Tim's Home Page

http://www.compusmart.ab.ca/warf/tim.htm

Discusses Tim's computer games, fish keeping, and the current state of Canadian politics.

Tiny Toon Adventures

http://www.dur.ac.uk/~d20kku/tta/tta.html

Serves as a place for the fans of Fox's *Tiny Toons*. Includes FAQs, episode guides, and more.

Tooncers Web Page Fantasmic

http://www.mind.net/worksj

Contains the Internet Cola Page, the "UnOfficial" WWIV Web server, and the Internet Animation gallery. Also features the WWIV type network, FANTASYnet.

Trader: 800 Trekker

http://www.scifi.com/trader/trekker/trekker.html

Offers memorabilia of various movies and television shows for sale.

Trading Cards Now Available

http://www.teleport.com/~filmnw/tradingcards.html

Offers sports-related trading cards. Provides a detailed description and an image with each card.

Transient Ratings Page

http://www.cais.com/jpadgett/www/ratings/ratings.html

Provides an online list of television ratings. Lets you submit TV habits to contribute to the ratings system online.

TreasureNet

http://www.halcyon.com/treasure/welcome.html

Provides information on treasure hunting, gold mining, gold panning, and prospecting. Contains photos and book reviews, contacts and literature.

Trek Reviews

http://www.mcs.net/~forbes/trek-reviews/home.html

Provides information on the *Star Trek* television series, as well as books, movies, and more.

Trek-in-Time Star Trek

http://www.wwcd.com/trek-in-time/trek-in-time.html

Features clothing, autographs, posters, tapes, games, uniforms, and more. Also contains a list of *Star Trek* conventions.

Triad Productions Presents

http://www.wizard.com/~patrick/triad.html

Tells about the current activities in Triad Productions' presentation of White Wolf Game Studios' Live Action Gaming systems. Also gives some background on the games.

Tristero—The Online Magazine of Creative Arts and Entertainment

http://superlink.com/tristero

Offers a collection of creative writing, essays, music, art, and entertainment. Welcomes and encourages submissions.

The Truth is Out There

http://www.neosoft.com/sbanks/xfiles/xfiles.html

Provides information on the *X-Files* TV series. Includes bloopers, as well as audio and video clips, and an episode guide.

TV Net

http://www.tvnet.com/TVnet.html

Provides information on TV Net's software, which allows you to use the Web to find out what's on TV. Also contains a unique collection of links to TV shows that maintain a home page. Provides breaking news on TV shows coming out.

TV-5

http://www.tv5.ca/eng_tv5.html

Provides information on TV-5, the all French news channel that covers news in countries around the world.

Tyler Rustic Art

http://www.olworld.com/olworld/mall/mall_us/c_arts/m_tyler/index.html

Features fine hydrostone sculptures, each with a southwestern theme.

U of C Bolo Home Page

http://student-www.uchicago.edu/users/vboguta/bolo/bolo.html

Offers links to other bolo pages, and provides other information.

Ubi Soft

http://www.ubisoft.com

Develops, publishes, and distributes video games and computer entertainment software.

Welcome to the world of Ubi Soft!
Where would you like to visit?

UFO The Pleiades Project

http://www.earthlink.net/~pleja/

Offers UFO information and photos. Includes books, tapes, and videos, as well as updates on the latest Pleiadian UFO contacts in America.

UK Premiership Fantasy Soccer/Football Game

http://www.cybersports.co.uk/soccer/

Enables you to play cyber-soccer over the net against thousands of others. Lets you follow your team's progress from week to week as the real stars battle it out in the United Kingdom Premier League. Includes prizes for manager of the month and the big one for manager of the year.

UK Theatre Web

http://www.nag.co.uk/0/Homes/RobertI/Theatre.html

Focuses on UK theatre. Offers lists and links to information on upcoming events, and companies. Covers amateur groups in addition to professional ones.

Ulti-Mate Dating Service

http://www.primenet.com/~jekagan/dating/

Serves as a resource for intelligent singles. Offers descriptive multimedia member profiles and a database search engine.

Universal Pictures

http://www.mca.com/

Contains MCA/Universal Pictures creations. Includes pages for TV and movies, as well as other Universal interests, such as Spencer's Gifts.

The Unofficial ReBoot Home Page

http://www.best.com/~inwap/Reboot.html

Focuses on the Saturday morning cartoon show, *ReBoot*, on ABC. Features 100 percent computer generated imagery (CGI). Offers a complete episode guide, descriptions and pictures of the main characters, and a collection of press releases.

UnReal Estate Cartoons

http://mindlink.net/Rick_Carlsen/unreal.htm

Ongoing cartoon series that takes a humorous look at the meaning behind the wording in a real estate listing.

Upper Hand Collectibles

http://www.micron.net/~uhc/

Provides an inventory that covers the recent trends in card games, comic books, and comic paraphernalia. Focuses on role-playing card games.

The Usenet Oracle Resource Index

http://www.pcnet.com/~stenor/oracle/

Humor WWW site that focuses on that famous Net diety, The Usenet Oracle. Contains topics related to the Oracle, from archives of past "Oracularities," searchable by number or keyword, to a Web interface for submitting your most burning or puzzling questions to the Oracle.

Vanderbilt Television News Archive

http://tvnews.vanderbilt.edu/

Presents Vanderbilt University's extensive archive of nightly news programs. Lets you request tapes for reference, study, and research.

Vantage Home Page

http://www.insv.com/vantage

Provides comic book dealer advice and assistance, as well as comic-related products. Offers a monthly newsletter, autographed issues of books, and lists of hot new picks in the comics industry. Great for browsing or for the serious comic collector.

Varia Textile Limited

http://www.demon.co.uk/blaah/vtl/index.html

International speciality fabric wholesaler and supplier, dealing mainly with flameproof and fire-retardant textiles for the entertainment industry.

VCV Stunts—Stuntmen on the Net

http://www.procom.com/~daves/vcvstunt.html

Offers professional stunt actors for live action, motion pictures, and video.

VH1

http://here.viacom.com/vh1/index.html

This is the home page for VH-1, the adult contemporary music channel. This is the official site from Viacom. Provides information on artists and their music.

Virtual Bookstore

http://199.99.210.80/

Provides books on modern fiction, history, science, medicine, mathematics, economics, americana, horror, science fiction, mystery, classic literature, art, manuscripts, maps, and children's books. Lets you search the online catalog or browse the list of authors.

The Virtual Headbook

http://www.xmission.com/~wintrnx/virtual.html

Provides access to resumes, photos, video clips, and sound clips of actors looking for work.

Virtual Studio

http://www.infint.com

Provides special effects how-to, interactive comics, art, and the virtual studio.

Watch Out! You're about to Enter Hugh's Web Site!

http://www.electriciti.com:80/~hugh/

Offers links to movies, music, education, and Macintosh.

WAVE—Wognum Art's Virtual Exchange

http://www.pi.se/wognum-art

Tells where Wognum Art is going with interface design, CD-ROM programming, corporate profiling, typography, graphics, 3-D modeling, and animation.

Web Mill Business District—Bears By The Sea

http://webmill.com/web/mill/bears

Includes pointers to other bear-related site, including the Web Bear Orphanage.

Web Mill Business District—Teddy Bear Directory

http://webmill.com/web/mill/bears/dir

Offers a collection of teddy bear manufacturers and retailers, organized by region and by state so that teddy bear enthusiasts can find a source close to home.

The Web Voyeur— Live Images

http://www.eskimo.com/%7eirving/web-voyeur/

Provides live snapshot type images of various items linked to the Internet. Includes live pictures of a Berlin bus terminal, Notre Dame's Golden Dome, and more.

Welcome to Fiasco Comics

http://www.insv.com/fiasco

The online home of Don Simpson, previously a freelance professional illustrator for Marvel, DC, Image, and many more. Details previous, current, and upcoming works from Fiasco and allows fans to order back issues of favorites, post questions, and read information.

Welcome to PBS

http://www.pbs.org/Welcome.html

Provides information about PBS, national programming, and the PBS store. Lets children look up information about their favorite PBS shows and people.

Welcome to the Barrett-Smythe Collection

http://www.ag.com/Barrett/Lighters

Lets you order artistic Zippo™ lighters. Presents an online catalog complete with pictures of the lighters. Also provides online order forms and a comment box. Provides a shopping bag feature that allows you to buy more than one item per visit.

Welcome to the BBC

http://www.bbcnc.org.uk/

The British Broadcasting Corporation on the Web. Provides BBC television and radio information.

Welcome to the GM Pro Shop

http://www.GMProShop.Com/

Features automotive collectibles and clothing. Also provides information about engines and parts.

Welcome to the Mississippi Gulf Coast

http://199.201.186.116/index.html

Provides information about local businesses, tourism, hotels, and more. Includes points of contact to the major businesses.

Welcome to Twin Peaks

http://pogo.wright.edu/TwinPeaks/TPHome.html

Focuses on the television show *Twin Peaks*. Provides information on cast, characters, David Lynch, and more.

WFSU/WFSG-TV—Public Television for North Florida and South Georgia

http://www.fsu.edu/~wfsu_tv

Broadcasts PBS programs and locally produced programs to educate and entertain people in the panhandle of Florida, southern Georgia, and southeast Alabama.

What's on TV

http://prod7.star.niu.edu/jeff/tv.html

Offers television listings for most areas and time zones.

Whose Line Is It Anyway ?

http://metro.turnpike.net/T/TD5584/WLiiA.html

Focuses on the improvisational game show, *Whose Line Is It Anyway?* Provides information about the show, games, players, and more.

Wild Hare Welcome

http://www.teleport.com/~filmnw/

Lets you order the newest line of collectible phone cards, including the new floral pattern line.

Wild Wild West

http://www.phantom.com/~cybersin

Includes information and links to cowboys, cowboy poetry, music, catalogs, magazines, cowfolk, horses, and cowgals, as well as information about Native American Indians, pueblos, Indian arts, and other areas.

The Witches Lair

http://www.apci.net/~weaver

Offers links to personal occult material such as the *Book of Shadows*. Contains material on White Wolfs games.

World of Paths Headquarters

http://www.aloha.com/~william/vpdest1.html

Presents a new fantasy world just now coming to life on the Web, from the creator of The Destiny Chronicles.

World-Wide Collectors Digest—Your Collectibles Outlet

http://www.wwcd.com/hp/collectibles.html

Provides collectibles, but also serves anyone interested in any of the following: baseball, football, basketball, hockey, nonsports, comic cards, trading cards, memorabilia, comic books, autographs, stadiums, sports arenas, seating charts, events, figurines, classifieds, chat, toys, *Star Trek*, milk caps, pogs, standings, schedules, trade shows, trains, baseball cards, price guides, shopping malls, conventions, games, odds, racing tickets, and more.

Worldguide Online

http://www.worldguide.com

Provides travel and health and fitness editorials. Features nutrition, mountain biking, and risk sports. Lets you download interactive 3-D maps and Flightpath video clips. Also offers and lets you preview a line of AtlasCD products.

The X-Files Archive Home Page

http://www.cs.nmt.edu:80/xfiles/

An unofficial *X-Files* page.

X-Files Briefing Room

http://www.delphi.com/XFiles/xfbrief.htm

Serves as the "Official" *X-Files* page at Delphi, but the links aren't assembled as clearly as other "unofficial" *X-Files* sites.

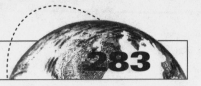
You Can't Do That On Television

http://cctr.umkc.edu/user/rbarrow/ycdtotv.html

Focuses on Nickelodeon's long running program *You Can't Do That On Television*. Provides information on the show and actors.

Zollar's Page

http://www.rt66.com/olworld/mall/mall_us/c_gifts/
m_zollar/index.html

Specializes in Southwestern and Native American art and craftwork.

The Zone—101.5 FM KZON

http://www.kzon.com/www/kzon/store.html

Focuses on the radio station. Also focuses on collectible CDs.

ZOOM San Diego

http://w3.thegroup.net/~zoom/

Presents an electronic 'zine from San Diego, California, focusing on arts and entertainment events and news in the San Diego area. Includes complete listings of theatre, concerts, movies, and sporting events, as well as a guide to local attractions and museums.

The Addventurers!

http://www.addventure.com/

Provides a MOO-style text exploratory game on Web pages in which you can decide what happens next. Describes the situations and environments to you and lets you respond to a menu of choices.

Advanced Squad Leader (ASL) Home Page

http://www.cco.caltech.edu/~erimli/asl.html

Provides information on Advanced Squad Leader, a tactical level World War II board game, as well as links to other ASL sites and tournament information.

Avatar—A Multi-User Dungeon Adventure

http://www.ifu.net/~avatar

Contains more than 9,000 rooms to explore. Offers 7 character classes, 13 races, 50 mortal levels, and numerous Hero and immortal levels.

Avatar   Merc-Diku MUD

telnet: ifu.net 3000

Bigben and Avalons Abode

http://web.sjsu.edu/a/u/bblaust/home.html

Focuses on to real-time communication over the Internet. Provides numerous ways to access Talkers, MUDs, IRC, and Webchat sites.

Bomberman WWW Page

http://fas-www.harvard.edu/~hsieh/bomber.html

Covers Bomberman in deeee-tail. Includes an e-mail form for you to use to comment on it or offer information to other fans. Also includes an archive of the mail that other people send.

BradyGAMES Gamer Connection

http://www.mcp.com/brady/connect

Attempts to list the toughest gamers on the Web—sort of an elite gathering of the best, all in one place. Lets you sign up so you can get in touch with gamers in your area to arrange a game by modem (or network, if you happen to work at the same place).

BU's Interactive WWW Games

http://www.bu.edu/Games/games.html

Enables you to hunt a mysterious and smelly beast called the Wumpus, play a game of strategy (Pegs) against the computer, do a mine sweep, do a 9 Puzzle, or play good old Tic Tac Toe. Offers Wumpus and mine sweep games in a text-only version and offers several links to versions for differing levels of Web browser complexity.

Cat & Mouse

http://www.ecst.csuchico.edu/~ian/cnm.html

Provides instructions and rules for this transmitter location game played in cars using CB radios.

Chess Informant Home Page

http://www1.usa1.com/~chess/index.html

Chess Informant, online. Also features chess books by top-rated grand masters, anthologies, and monographs. Offers links to other chess-related sites.

CICA Index: Windows Games, Educational Software, and More

http://www.ege.edu.tr/CICA/cica_index_games.html

Offers many downloadable games for Windows. Lists and briefly describes each game. Ranges from old favorites, such as Solitaire and Checkers, to mysterious names like Squirmer and Rangoon.

Companies (Welcome to the Usenet Roleplaying Game Companies List)

http://www.cqs.washington.edu/~surge/gaming/companies

Lists the names, telephone numbers, and the e-mail and snail-mail addresses of game companies.

Computer Exchange (England)

http://www.cex.co.uk/cex/

London's funkiest videogame/computer store now offers everything from cool Playstation stuff to second-hand hard drives, online.

Connect!

http://csclub.uwaterloo.ca/u/kppomaki/c4/connect_www.cgi

Provides a graphical Connect Four game. Offers several options to make play more challenging. Serves as a "free-time" site for the kids.

Conquest! Home Page

http://www.misha.net/~conquest

Provides information related to the game. Includes all the manuals for the game, as well as other information needed to play.

Dan's Poker Dictionary

http://www.universe.digex.net/~kimberg/pokerdict.html

Provides a dictionary of poker terminology cross-referenced heavily and alphabetized with links.

Dig Zone

http://ugweb.cs.ualberta.ca/~hubick/digzone/digzone.cgi

Presents a multiuser-shared environment Web game in which you battle the hazards of gravity in search of valuable coins. Interactive live game.

DigiTar WWW Link

http://www.hooked.net:80/users/williams/digitar.htm

Provides information on current and future gaming projects of the DigiTar Corporation, developers of 3-D action and adventure games.

Dinosaur Slammers and POGS™

http://www.tagonline.com/Ads/dinoslammers

Exhibits mirror-finished pure copper and silver dinosaur slammers—collectors' coins you can enjoy for a lifetime.

Fantasy Roleplaying Archives

http://fys-hp-1.risoe.dk/petersen/oldftp.html

Offers roleplaying games in the tradition of Dungeons and Dragons. Includes a listing of a wide variety of downloadable file sites on the Web as well as other Web sites on the same subject.

FutureNet—Videogames

http://www.futurenet.co.uk/games.html

Tells you which video games you might like to have. Covers Amiga, Atari, NeoGeo, Nintendo, Sega, and Sony. Includes a set of pages called "Are You All Clued Up?" which access from a link called "Bluffer's guide to videogames."

Gamer's Den

http://www.den.com

Moderates two games for play via e-mail: Odyssey (heroes and armies in a fantasy setting) and Phoenix (space conquest and diplomacy).

The Gamer's Ledge

http://www.medio.net/users/mgodsey/games.html

Focuses on the gaming crowd. Presents reviews of new games; lets you access the most complete list of online games-related magazines; lets you download demo/shareware copies of many games; and lets you visit the Web sites of all the game makers/producers.

Games (Part of Multimedia File Formats on the Internet)

http://ac.dal.ca/~dong/games.htm

Serves as a site for the Internet newcomer who wants to download and play games. Explains the basics in simple language and supplies some ftp sites from which to download.

Games Domain—Games-Related Information Site

http://wcl-rs.bham.ac.uk/GamesDomain

Serves the new *and* the experienced game developer. Strives "to be the link to the most comprehensive information available pertaining to the creation and development of computer-based games." Acts as a detailed and complete

source for people intrigued by the process of game creation. Also offers lists of frequently asked questions (FAQs), links to ftp sites, and discussion groups.

Games Guide

http://www.ozonline.com.au/gamesguide

Online guide to computer entertainment. Features game reviews and hints and cheats on platforms including PC, SNES, Megadrive (Genesis), Saturn, Gameboy, PlayStation, and 3DO. Also provides the latest gaming news and links to gaming sites.

Games on the Internet

http://happypuppy.com/games/lordsoth/

Provides indexed and alphabetized list of sites for DOS and Windows games. Describes and offers ftp links you can use to download the game for each game in the list. Features a list of the 25 most-frequently accessed games.

GAMES Section (CSUSM Library Technical Services Windows Shareware Archive)

http://coyote.csusm.edu/cwis/winworld/games.html

Includes almost 400 downloadable games for Windows. Numbers and lists each file and includes a description, file size, and date.

GameWeb—A Web Gaming Resource

http://www.iquest.net/~wil126/gameweb/index.html

Contains about 2,500 links. Adds new games and game sites regularly.

Hangman at COMMA in Cardiff

http://arachnid.cm.cf.ac.uk/htbin/RobH/hangman

Presents the classic word guessing game.

History of Game Theory

http://william-king.www.drexel.edu/top/History.html

Offers a detailed and thoroughly linked timeline that notes important papers, schools of thought, and events related to the study of game theory and its relation to the study of economics.

Index of Computing, Systems, IBM-PC, and Windows 3.x Games

http://src.doc.ic.ac.uk/computing/systems/ibmpc/windows3/games

Lists more than 400 files by date and size. Originates at SUNSite Northern Europe.

Josh & Eric's Incredible Choose Your Own Adventure

http://minerva.cis.yale.edu/~davisj/choose/first.html

Presents a game in which the object is to get through the day without being kicked out of school and/or killed. You wake up too early for your French test at the beginning and run through a series of adventures.

Magic: The Gathering— Overview

http://www.itis.com/deckmaster/magic

Focuses on the card game Magic. Provides information on every aspect of the game, including a basic overview.

Michael Moncur's Quotations Page

http://www.xmission.com/~mgm/quotes/

Offers quotations galore. Features quotes of the day, a random quote generator, and a searchable database. Also offers links to other online quotation sources.

Microcraft

http://www.primenet.com/~mcase

Provides a variety of services, ranging from providing software engines for use in other developers' game products, to the development of complete games. Specializes in fast, real-time 3-D graphics rendering, optimized for a particular game design category. Features the Atlantis game engine, a powerful and more general-purpose DOOM-style engine, capable of displaying realistic architectural elements. Lets you download a demo.

NEXUS

http://www.nada.kth.se/~d94-llu/NEXUS

Contains the NEXUS roleplaying-game club. Provides information about NEXUS and offers links to roleplaying, conflict simulation games, live roleplaying, films, comics, manga, anime, and more.

Oh No! The Lemmings Games Web Page

http://stud1.tuwien.ac.at/~e8826423/Lemmings.html

Focuses on the game of Lemmings. Provides information on the game. Includes the sound, presumably, of a lemming. Includes downloadable demos.

PHT's Game Page of the Universe

http://www.pht.com/games.html

Aims to maintain "the hottest list of game links from all over the Internet." Offers a series of "best of" lists and, of course, downloadable files, and lets you preview and comment on the company's newest game products.

Play by Mail (PBM) Games Links

http://fermi.clas.virginia.edu/~gl8f/
pbm_links.html#freeg

Enables you to fight the evil Arch-Druid of Ulom, wrestle, play cricket, design new species, or just fight for galactic domination—all by e-mail.

Radnor's Page O' Fun

http://www.geopages.com/SiliconValley/1070

Provides information on the Warcraft line of games from Blizzard.

Real Beer Page: Games

http://www.and.com/realbeer/rbp.games.html

Includes witty directions on many different, amiable ways to pickle yourself and your friends while having a good time. Urges surfers not to drink and drive.

Rock Paper Scissors

http://virtumall.com/fast/rockpaper.html

Presents Rock Paper Scissors, the ancient childhood game of choice—online at last. Provides hours of fun playing against your imaginary friend.

Roleplaying Games, Collectible Cards, Games, and Hobby Supplies

http://tradingcards.com

Specializes in collectible card games, roleplaying games, board games, and hobby supplies.

Roleplaying Games (Welcome to the Usenet Complete Role-Playing Games List)

http://www.cqs.washington.edu/~surge/gaming/rpgs

Provides information about the ins and outs of roleplaying games. Includes a detailed discussion of the many types of games and information on whether games are still being produced and by whom. Supplies sources and suggestions for further roleplaying game investigations.

RPG and CCG Resource Page

http://mxn117.rh.psu.edu/~spud/gamer.htm

Provides information on and links to many companies that produce roleplaying games and cards. Includes links to pages with survey forms, lists of upcoming releases of games, order information, and more.

RPG International

http://www.isomedia.com/homes/rpgi

Sells roleplaying games through the mail. Offers a large collection of product reviews and links to other RPG-related pages.

Sanctuary Woods Multimedia

http://www.sanctuary.com

Creators of Buried in Time, a game that immerses its players in a complex web of mystery, betrayal, and deception. Covers coming attractions and offers downloadable demos of their games.

Sights and Sounds—Home of the Internet Magic Tricks

http://www.teleport.com/~jrolsen

Presents self-working magic tricks, in which the computer is the magician and you are the audience.

Software Creations

http://www.swcbbs.com

Implements the best of both worlds. Enables you to use all the features of the popular Software Creations BBS on the Web. Features full file sections, fast text search, an online order door, bulletins, and hot news releases, among other features that combine BBS technology with the Web. Supporting thousands of virtual nodes allows large corporations to put up support, and marketing sites that integrate easily and safely with the Internet and gives them the interaction and power they need with little hardware.

Strands—An Earthdawn Web Page

http://rhic2.physics.wayne.edu/sheen/home.html

Enables fellow players to share Earthdawn (a fantasy roleplaying game by FASA Corp.) related material. Includes sample character sheets, reviews of FASA Earthdawn products, and aids for gamemasters and player characters.

Theala Sildorian's Unofficial Champions Home Page

http://www.intercom.net/user/theala/hero.html

Focuses on playing Champions and other Hero System Games. Contains links to all major Champions/Hero System ftp archive sites, a special discussion project previous available only on AOL, gossip and upcoming product announcements, software reviews, and exclusive comic commentaries on the Hero System from the warped mind of Chris Avellone.

Tic Tac Toe

http://www.bu.edu/Games/tictactoe

Lets you play tic tac toe on the Web against the computer. You can choose to go first or second.

Transformers 2005 MUSH

http://www.liii.com/~tf2005/TF2005.html

Contains the Transformers 2005 MUSH, an online interactive roloeplaying game, is set in the Transformers universe in the year 2005 and concentrates on cooperative roleplaying in a faction-based environment.

Wargamers Directory

http://tetrad.stanford.edu/Players.html

Serves as a directory for finding wargaming opponents. Lets you add your own contact information and gaming interests, as well as browse the list of gamers.

Welcome to Connect Four

http://csugrad.cs.vt.edu/htbin/Connect4.perl

Lets you play Connect Four against the computer. Provides two versions—one for graphical browsers and another for text browsers. Uses your e-mail address to keep track of your personal record.

Welcome to Nintendo

http://www.nintendo.com/

Provides access to graphics or a mostly-text version of the same. Provides information on Nintendo products, including sample screens. Invites you to suggest things that Nintendo should put on their "Gimmicks" page, jump into real time Webchat, or go to other places.

The Wonderful Team17 Home Page

http://www.team17.com

Provides many things to look at, touch, feel, or do with as you please. Provides a complete Wonderful Team17 softography.

World Wide Web Ouija

http://www.math.unh.edu/~black/cgi-bin/ouija.cgi

Offers an online Ouija board.

The XystMUSH Home Page

http://katz.wcula.edu/xyst/

Offers XystMUSH, "one of the most exciting Internet games around." Presents a virtual reality world in which players can build and program new things into the environment. Also offers an adventure game in which players solve puzzles to reach rewarding goals.

Zarf's List of Interactive Games on the Web

http://www.cs.cmu.edu/afs/andrew/org/kgb/www/zarf/games.html

Offers links to several pages of games on the Web itself. Supplies an icon set to identify games that use forms, in-line images, image maps, color display, audio, tables, and autorefreshing pages.

Access to Sleep and Psychology

http://web.sjsu.edu/c/s/hawkins/public_html/index.html

Offers basic how-to and self-help information. Also provides sleep research and psychology information. Provides abstracts on melatonin in sleep, health, and development.

Acclaim Professional Counseling

http://www.mindspring.com/~brydaguy/acclaim.html

Offers links to short self-help articles on marriage, better sex, recovery from depression, and other happy thoughts.

Actual Natural Source

http://floralsnw.ark.com/health.html

Focuses on the uses of bee pollen extract for different ailments of the body.

Acupuncture Home Page

http://www.demon.co.uk/acupuncture/index.html

Provides information about acupuncture.

Advocare Nutritional Products

http://www.southwind.net/IMS/advocare/

Offers weight loss, sports nutrition, and skin care products from Advocare International. Supplies complete product information along with product graphics and order forms. Also offers a business opportunity to people who might want to distribute the products.

AIDS Walk Los Angeles

http://www.bonsai.com/LAAIDS/

Lets you register for the AIDS Walk.

Alexandra Health Center

http://www.aescon.com/alexandra/index.htm

Provides knowledge about natural medicine and homeopathy. Also provides concise descriptions on the medicine for sale.

Alliance Health Products

http://www.websrus.com/websrus/alliance/

Offers a complete line of health food products to improve your health and diet, including vitamins, herbal health care products, and a natural weight loss program.

Alternative Care

http://www.servint.com/altcare/whatsnew.html

Online newsletter. Focuses on consumers, professionals, and students who want to know more about various forms of alternative health care. Includes a consumer section, which contains articles that describe a wide range of alternative therapies and offers links to other pages that deal with specific disciplines. Also includes a professional section that contains research, news, and other information.

The Alternative Medicine Home Page from Falk Library of the Health Sciences—University of Pittsburgh

http://www.pitt.edu/~cbw/altm.html

Serves as a jumpstation for sources of information on unconventional, unorthodox, unproven, or alternative, complementary, innovative, and integrative therapies.

Alzheimer Disease Web Site

http://med-www.bu.edu/Alzheimer/home.html

Serves as a reference site for clinicians, investigators, and caregivers interested in Alzheimer's disease and other related dementias.

The American Cancer Society

http://charlotte.npixi.net/acs

The American Cancer Society, online.

APP's Home Page

http://www.advancednet.com/app

Specializes in delivering prescriptions to HIV and transplant patients. Provides full prescription services, including drug interactions, disease management, and patient reimbursement. Also supplies infusion services for physicians, clinics, and home care agencies.

Arkansas Children's Hospital

http://www.ach.uams.edu/

Private, nonprofit institution. Offers children comprehensive medical care from birth to age 21, from every county in Arkansas and from many nearby states, regardless of a family's ability to pay.

Atlanta Reproductive Health Center

http://www.mindspring.com/~mperloe/index.html

Provides information in areas of women's health, including infertility, endometriosis, contraception, sexually transmitted disease, menopause, stress management, and PMS. Also provides information about the doctor's purpose and credentials regarding opinions within the Web site.

Avon's Breast Cancer Awareness Crusade

http://www.pmedia.com/Avon/avon.html

Provides information about breast cancer and breast health. Includes a list of more than 250 breast cancer support groups across the country.

Back-2-Nature

http://netmar.com/~back2nat/TTOIndex.html

Explains the many uses of Australian tea tree oil.

Basic Health and Medicine Home Page

http://www.nova.edu/Inter-Links/medicine.html

Offers general resources and links to information on certain questions.

Blind Children's Center, Inc. Home Page

http://www.primenet.com/bcc/

Nonprofit organization. Provides resources and assistance to visually impaired children and their families. Provides information on an educational preschool program, family services, the current newsletter, and a calendar of upcoming events. Also lists links to other related sites.

BONES: The Biomedically Oriented Navigator of Electronic Services

http://bones.med.ohio-state.edu

Provides faculty, staff, and students in the health sciences with a starting point for Internet exploration.

Breast Cancer Information

http://nysernet.org/bcic/

Provides information for breast cancer patients and their families.

Bright Innovations

http://www.earthlink.net/~bright/

Focuses on those interested in developing new products for the medical field that require research and development and use of the latest computerized tools to reach the market. Provides information that can help you achieve these goals.

Cardiovascular Institute of the South

http://www.cardio.com/

Center for the advanced diagnosis and treatment of heart and circulatory disease. Offers a wide range of reports covering the full spectrum of prevention, diagnosis, and nonsurgical and surgical treatment of circulatory problems.

Catholic Health Association of Wisconsin

http://www.execpc.com/~chaw

Nonprofit state association that serves more than 100 Catholic health care facilities in Wisconsin. Provides information about the association's purpose, educational programming, newsletters, and ethical information.

CCP's AIDS-Related WWW Pages

http://www.seanet.com/Users/jbrian/aids.html

Offers AIDS-related links to information provided on the Web.

Cell Tech Super Blue Green Algae

http://www.gate.net/~clever/home.html

Provides information about Cell Tech Super Blue Green Algae.

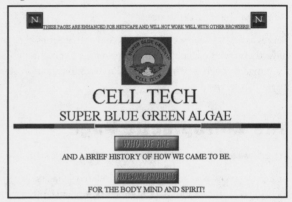

The Cenikor Foundation, Inc.

http://www.neosoft.com/~cenikor

Nonprofit organization. Focuses on assisting people develop skills they need to live a lifestyle free from substance abuse. Provides free residential, treatment, education, and prevention services to people over the age of 18.

Center for AIDS Prevention Studies

http://www.caps.ucsf.edu/capsweb

Conducts epidemiological and behavioral studies in the primary prevention and early intervention of HIV disease. Carries out these research activities locally, nationally, and internationally. Also conducts ethical studies and policy analyses of AIDS-related issues, and provides a program of technology transfer and exchange with community-based organizations.

CGS Biomedical Information Service

http://www.eskimo.com/~cgs/

Information research company searching major databases, libraries, and other resources, specializing in biomedicine, biotechnology, health care marketing, and legal aspects of any biomedical topic.

The CHATBACK Trust

http://www.tcns.co.uk/chatback/

Serves as a place where children who have disabilities can have their own dialogue. Functions primarily as an e-mail exchange through a related listserv. Provides information about this service.

The Chiropractic Page

http://www.mbnet.mb.ca/~jwiens/chiro.html

Primarily serves as a pointer to health-related subjects, focusing on information for chiropractors, students, other health care practitioners, and interested laypersons. Offers many sites and links.

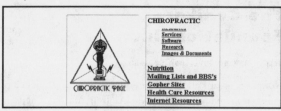

Code Four Medical

http://web.idirect.com/~cfm

A Public Health & Safety company that provides training, consulting, and supplies.

The Complete Guide to Psychology-Related Sites on the Net

http://pegasus.acs.ttu.edu/~civelek/thanatos.html

Indexes psychology-related sites on the net. Includes universities, journals, and conferences across the Web.

Conscious Choice

http://www.consciouschoice.com/

Online bi-monthly midwestern magazine that reports on environmental issues and natural alternatives in health care, food, and nutrition.

Cyber-Psych

http://www.charm.net/~pandora/psych.html

Offers psychological information and relevant links for mental health information and resources.

Cyberspace Hospital

http://ch.nus.sg

Provides one-stop access to medical Web servers around the world. Organizes the links into medical specialty departments using a virtual hospital setting.

Deaf World Web

http://deafworldweb.org/deafworld/

Lists some information in German and French, as well as English, and is fairly international in scope. Provides information on deaf studies, deaf culture, useful services, and more.

Department of Neurosurgery at New York University

http://mcns10.med.nyu.edu/

Serves as a resource center for patients, families, and health care professionals on a broad range of neurosurgical issues. Also describes the surgical specialties and research of the staff of the Department of Neurosurgery at the New York University Medical Center.

Department of Otolaryngology at Baylor College of Medicine

http://www.bcm.tmc.edu/oto/page.html

Provides information from the Department of Otolaryngology, including faculty and resident directory, residency and fellowship information, audiology program information, grand rounds archives, subscription information for the OTOHNS-Online Otolaryngology discussion group, and links to other otolaryngology resources.

The Digital Anatomist Program

http://www1.biostr.washington.edu/DigitalAnatomist.html

Contains an interactive atlas of the brain and heart (in 2-D and 3-D).

Doody Publishing Health Science Book Reviews

http://www.doody.com/

Targets people interested in newly published health sciences books—professionals, students, librarians, bookstore staff, and publishers in the health sciences. Offers access to a book reviews database that consists of bibliographic and descriptive information on 5,000 titles with original reviews of 3,000 of them (by paid subscription), but offers a one-day free trial.

Dr. Bower's Complementary Medicine Home Page

http://galen.med.virginia.edu/~pjb3s/
ComplementaryHomePage.html

Attempts to catalog and assist in the research being carried out world-wide in complementary medicine. Offers links to other health-related sites.

Dr. Bower's Complementary Medicine Home Page

This Home Page is intended to catalog and assist in the research being carried out worldwide in Complementary Medicine. No endorsement is implied by the presence of any particular topic or practitioner linked from this list. Likewise, any material you may wish to contribute or URL of interest that you don't already find here, please email the information too : Peter J. Bower, M.D.

Dragon Herbarium

http://www.teleport.com/~seahorse/dragon/

Online herbal store. Offers many herbs, spices, essential oils, tinctures, potions, lotions, and more. Features an online catalog and price list.

E-Zee Vision Prescription Eyeglasses

http://www.eyeglass.com

Offers prescription eyeglasses, factory-direct. Features high-resolution color images and sound.

FHP Health Care

http://www.fhp.com

Targets anyone who wants to assess their own health or learn more about HMOs.

Fischer Pharmaceuticals Laboratories

http://www.dr-fischer.com

Researches, develops, and manufactures dermatology preparations, skincare lines, sunscreen protection, and eye and cosmetic products.

Fitness

http://www.fanzine.se/fitness/

Presents *Fitness*, online. Serves as your guide to beauty, health, diet, and fashion. Lets you check your fitness profile (some parts only in Swedish).

Fleming's Healthy Life Products

http://www.ibp.com/pit/fleming

Provides information on how to stay healthy, support the immune system, and aid in overcoming illness and disease through natural means. Includes a product list. Offers an income opportunity for caring individuals.

Formula One

http://www.wondernet.com/alliance/formula1.html

Advocates use of Formula One as part of your daily plan to supplement your overall health, follow a weight management program, or build your body to its maximum level of performance.

Galaxy's Nutrition-Medicine

http://galaxy.einet.net/galaxy/Medicine/Nutrition.html

Includes hundreds of different topics within the nutrition, medicine, and biology sciences.

General Complementary Medicine

http://www.forthrt.com/~chronicl/archiv.htm#5

Offers links to other health and medicinal home pages.

Global Health Network

http://info.pitt.edu/HOME/GHNet/GHNet.html

Focuses on networking everyone engaged in public health and prevention world-wide. Lists agencies and contacts in public health and provides information about diseases and health care.

The Global Health Network

The Good Health Web

http://www.social.com/health/index.html

Provides daily health news (and an archive), a library of health articles, discussions, and lists of FAQs, newsgroups, and mailing lists.

The Green Page—Natural Health/Nutrition

http://www.nmia.com/~sethguy/herbgreen.html

Discusses high-tech natural nutrition and weight management methods.

Hair Loss Handbook and Support Group Network

http://www.mcny.com/hairloss

Targets the countless number of men and women who want to learn more about hair loss.

HANS—The Health Action Network Society

http://www.hans.org/

Involves current issues at hand, such as acupuncture, chiropractice, disease, fluoride, food, government, pesticides, vitamins, and water. Offers films, books, and videos for sale.

Harvard Biological Laboratories' Biosciences-Medicine

http://golgi.harvard.edu/biopages/medicine.html

Provides information about what many colleges offer in their health/medicine field, as well as search units to find key topics about health questions, such as pharmacy, epidemiology, and even veterinary medicine.

Health and Longevity

http://www.sims.net/organizations/naturopath/naturopath.html

Includes information on naturopathy, herbology, nutrition, and homeopathy. Derives information from their monthly newsletter.

The Health Connection

http://www.deltanet.com/BeverlyHills/HealthConnect

Offers health and nutrition news (updated monthly) and a wide variety of unique and hard-to-find natural health products.

Health Resource

http://www.coolware.com/health/joel/health.html

Provides information about health, stress, sexuality, and many other problems that people can encounter.

Heart Mind Body Institute

http://www.power.net/hbm/hbm1.html

Explains new approaches in the prevention and reversal of coronary heart disease without open heart surgery. Seeks to help you free yourself from any kind of heart disease using this new approach.

Herb'n Outfitters

http://204.213.234.53/

An online herbal store that provides information and photos.

Welcome to Herb'n Outfitters...

Herb'n Outfitters

A Network of Herbal Resources

Herbal Hall

http://www.crl.com/~robbee/herbal.html

Focuses on all things herbs. Includes a list of resources, books, schools, and herbalists. Also features pictures and text.

High Techsplantations, Inc.

http://www.ht.com

Develops physically based virtual environment software applied primarily in the area of surgery simulation. Focuses on revolutionary virtual reality (VR) surgical simulations technologies broadly applicable to improving medical training and practice.

Hospital Web

http://dem0nmac.mgh.harvard.edu/hospitalweb.html

Offers a list of hospitals that have Web servers to which you can jump, as well as a list of medical schools on the Web.

Institute of Psychiatry

http://www.iop.bpmf.ac.uk/

Postgraduate school of the University of London, recognized by the World Health Organization as a collaborating center for research and training in mental health. Seeks to promote excellence in the research, development, and teaching of psychiatry and its allied subjects and to apply and disseminate knowledge through the development of treatment for the relief of suffering. Contains information and research on mental health, psychiatry, and neuroscience.

The Interactive Patient

http://medicus.marshall.edu/medicus.htm

Presents a program that allows you to simulate an actual patient encounter, intended as a teaching tool for physicians, residents, and medical students.

The Internal Capsule

http://www.voicenet.com/1/voicenet/homepages/levinson/index.html

Provides resources and information on physical therapy.

International Health News

http://www.perspective.com/health/index.html

Presents a monthly electronic newsletter and discussion group for people who want to gain a better understanding of news and research on the relationship between health, nutrition, and lifestyle.

The Internet Medical Products Guide

http://www.medicom.com/medicom/home.html

Provides a database of medical product sales and technical information for health care providers.

An Introduction to Vision Correcting Procedures by Med-Source, Inc.

http://www.ozarksol.com/medsource/

Informs the public about vision correcting procedures, including radial keratotomy (RK) for nearsightedness, astigmatic keratotomy (AK) for astigmatism, automated lamellar keratoplasty (ALK) for farsightedness, and the soon-to-be FDA approved photorefractive keratectomy (PRK) for nearsightedness.

Lifelines Health Page

http://www.rain.org/idsolute/

Covers many aspects of health, medicine, and nutrition. Offers a newletter, a shopping site for vitamins and other healthy foods, and instructional audio and video tapes. Offers Spanish and English versions.

Lifestyles' Natural Health Foods

http://www.inforamp.net/electracity/Lifestyles/LifestylesHome.html

Includes many pictures of health foods sold, such as vitamins, shakes, cookies, and cakes.

Marquette University Program in Physical Therapy

http://www.mu.edu/dept/pt

Includes information about the Master's in Physical Therapy Program at Marquette University and about the profession of physical therapy. Offers many links to other physical therapy and health-related topics.

MDB Information Network

http://mdbinfonet.com

Provides objective information for health care decision makers. Helps health care providers reduce risk, contain costs, and increase efficiencies by providing reliable data, strategic analysis, and counsel. Delivers services through three divisions: MDB Technology Services, MDB Information Services, and MDB Financial Network.

The Medical Education Page

http://www.primenet.com/~gwa/med.ed/

Targets premed and medical students. Lists medical schools in the United States, offers links to medical reference materials and ftp sites, and provides lists of specialists, and more.

Medicine Online

http://meds.com

Serves as a commercial online medical information service. Provides health care professionals and consumers a convenient place to obtain medical information. Serves as a gateway to access other health information services on the Internet. Currently focuses on cancer information.

MedLink International

http://www.medlink.com

Links physicians with practice opportunities around the world. Assists physicians seeking employment opportunities as well as medical organizations recruiting qualified doctors.

Medscrip Windows Prescription Writer for Physicians

http://www.rust.net/~skindell/medscrip.html

Offers a Windows prescription writer program for physicians, written by physicians for physicans. Reduces the workload and decreases the probability of errors.

Missouri Institute of Mental Health

http://www.missouri.edu/~mimhmj

Highlights the research, education, and multimedia efforts in which the Missouri Institute of Mental Health currently is involved.

Mom's Advice

http://www.cts.com/browse/crossink/online/Mom

Offers fruits and vegetables in capsules.

MSU Athletic Training

http://vax1.mankato.msus.edu/~k061252/MSUATC.html

Provides information for people interested in the athletic training profession. Provides information about MSU as a curriculum program and information concerning it. Also offers a number of other athletic training or related links, such as program information, alumni information, history, athletic training listserver discussion directory, and staff.

MANKATO STATE UNIVERSITY

Athletic Training Home Page

My Life International

http://www.cashflow.com/mylife

Markets organically sourced health products, including BioGen Plus.

National Alliance for the Mentally Ill Home Page

http://www.cais.com/vikings/nami/index.html

Focuses on improving the lives of people who have severe mental illness and their families.

National Health Video

http://www.frp.com/healthvid

Provides information on dieting, diabetes, and weight management. Offers many educational health videos.

The Natural Health and Nutrition Shop

http://cyber-hawaii.com/health/

Provides information about nutritional supplements.

Nature's Medicine

http://www.halcyon.com/jerryga/welcome.html

Provides natural alternatives to Western medicine. Specializes in targeted nutritionals for better health. Offers more than 200 products.

Navigator's Health and Nutrition Page

http://www.nav.com/home/hnpage.html

Includes jumps to a wide range of health and medicine sources from around the country. Serves as a starting for any health-related search.

New England Medical Center

http://www.nemc.org

Provides information about the tradition and history of the prestigious New England Medical Center. Offers comprehensive inpatient and outpatient care for adults and children.

Noah's Ark Home Page

http://www.rain.org/~sals/my.html

Provides information about organic farming and the kind of insects that the organic farmer should use rather than pesticides.

Northridge Family Practice Residency Program Home Page

http://www.w2.com/docs2/n/nfp/index.html

Targets applicants and those interested in family practice.

Northwestern University Department of Radiology

http://pubweb.acns.nwu.edu/~dbk675/nwu_radiology.html

Offers links to current radiologic information and case presentations, as well as a description of services provided, staff, residency, and fellowship programs.

The Osteopathic Source

http://www.primenet.com/~pulse/thesource.html

Targets osteopathic medical students, osteopathic physicians, the allopathic medical community, and people considering medicine as a career.

Parkinson's Web

http://neuro-chief-e.mgh.harvard.edu/parkinsonsweb/Main/PDmain.html

Serves as a resource directory, pointing you to sources of information on Parkinson's disease.

Pediatric Rheumatology Home Page

http://www.wp.com/pedsrheum

Provides information for children and young adults who have arthritis and other rheumatic diseases of childhood, their families, and the physicians who care for them.

The People's Place

http://peopleplace.com

Provides information and resource listings for health, personal growth, alternative medicine and therapies, healthy eating, fitness, yoga, vegetarianism, macrobiotics, and ayurveda. Also lists resorts, retreats, and related workshops and events.

PhRMA Home Page

http://www.phrma.org

Provides overview of PhRMA, which represents more than 100 United States pharmaceutical research companies. Also provides answers to frequently asked questions about pharmaceuticals, latest news, health guide series, and an interactive stroke survey.

The Physical Therapy WWW Page

http://www.mindspring.com/~wbrock/pt.html

Provides general information about physical therapy.

Physician Finder Online™

http://msa2.medsearch.com

Presents a tool you can use to search for your next physician, surgeon, or dentist. Provides information on participating physicians who have e-mail links for an initial consultation.

PhytoZyme

http://www.wondernet.com/alliance/pzyme.html

Explains about PhytoZyme, which aids in balancing the digestive process for proper nutrient utilization.

PLink—The Plastic Surgery Link

http://www.IAEhv.nl/users/ivheij/plink.html

Offers a collection of plastic-surgery–related links. Targets physicians and interested lay readers. Includes hospital Web pages, journals, books, and general information.

PPS OnLine®

http://www2.pps.ca/pps.html

Online pharmaceutical product ordering and information service. Targets health care professionals. Presents the PPS Online® Pharma-Response™ System, a pharmaceutical information system developed for consumers.

Preview the Heart

http://sln.fi.edu/tfi/preview/heartpreview.html

Takes you on a complete tour of the human heart, courtesy of the Franklin Institute. Includes many pictures.

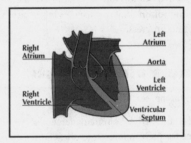

Psychiatry and Psychotherapy

http://www-leland.stanford.edu/~corelli/

Offers links to mental health information and resources. Provides information on psychiatric diagnosis and on personality disorders and other areas of psychological interest. Offers links to information on psychotherapy and psychopharmacology. Includes a personal reading list in areas of psychiatry, psychotherapy, and Jungian psychology.

Psyrix Help-Net and High Performance Consultants

http://www.ottawa.net/~helpnet

Connects you with highly trained and experienced professionals in clinical and performance psychology. Offers to provide you with advice from experienced psychotherapists from a variety of specialties, including drugs and alcohol, sex and relationships, sleep, anxiety and depression, child and family counseling, medication, and general psychology. Serves as an information resource. Includes trained and registered psychotherapists, psychologists, and other professionals.

Rehabilitation Learning Center

http://weber.u.washington.edu/~rlc/

Seeks to create a computer-based multimedia rehabilitation environment designed to educate and train individuals with acute or chronic spinal cord injuries so they can successfully leave the in-patient rehabilitation environment and function in society. Provides information about their plans and progress.

Roxane Pain Institute

http://www.Roxane.com

Offers cancer and AIDS pain management services. Serves as a resource for pain sufferers and clinicians. Offers educational materials, including newsletters, clinical articles, presentation slides on cancer pain management, and a schedule of upcoming pain management seminars.

Rusty Chambers Insurance Agent—Life, DI, Disability, Health

http://www.intellinet.com/~rusty

Includes a brief list of insurance products and services. Also offers quotes for any type of insurance.

The Safer Sex Page

http://www.cmpharm.ucsf.edu/~troyer/safesex.html

Provides safer sex information. Offers short brochures about safer sex, HIV transmission, and condoms, as well as resources for health educators and counselors. Lets you get on a Web Chat, an interactive forum for people who have questions about certain sex subjects.

Society for Medical Decision Making

http://www.nemc.org/SMDM

Focuses on promoting rational and systematic approaches to decisions about health policy and the clinical care of patients. Includes decision analysis, applications of quantitative methods in clinical settings and medical research, studies of human cognition and the psychology of clinical reasoning, medical ethics, medical informatics and decision making, artificial intelligence, evaluation of medical practices, and cost-effectiveness or cost-benefit assessments.

Springboard Health and Nutrition Products

http://www.springbeech.com/springboard

Offers health and nutrition products.

Sudden Infant Death Syndrome (SIDS) Information Home Page

http://q.continuum.net/~sidsnet/

Provides information about Sudden Infant Death Syndrome. "This page will grow and evolve as we progress up the learning curve together. Your patience, understanding, and contributions to this page will make it grow into a true network of people and information dedicated to stopping SIDS, the number one killer of infants between the ages of one month and one year." — Chuck Mihalko, President, SIDS Network

Swan Medical, Inc.

http://www.vnet.net/swanmed/

Provides information about the latest in minimally invasive

surgical equipment and instrumentation. Also distributes CooperSurgical, and EuroMed, in North Carolina and South Carolina.

Tapestry Books— Adoption/ Infertility Book Catalog

http://www.webcom.com/~tapestry

Serves as a source for adoption and infertility books and information. Offers the *Adoption Book Catalog*, which contains more than 275 books on adoption, infertility, and parenting challenges.

Telemedicine Information Exchange—TIE

http://tie.telemed.org/

Nonprofit research organization. Provides the Telemedicine Information Exchange (TIE), a database of information on telemedicine.

Three-Dimensional Medical Reconstruction

http://www.ge.com/crd/ivl/three_dim_medical.html

Provides 3-D Mpeg format movies of the human body, brain, skull, colon, heart, torso, and heart arteries.

To Your Health

http://www.vitamin.com/

Offers nutrition and weight loss tips.

UBC (University of British Columbia) MultiCentre Research Network

http://unixg.ubc.ca:780/~emerg_vh/ubc_multicentre.html

Emergency medicine research consortium made up of the emergency medicine research divisions of three teaching hospitals, the Royal Columbian Hospital, St. Paul's Hospital and the Vancouver Hospital. Outlines information about the network's current and recent research activities. Also outlines recent publications, abstracts, presentations, and textbook chapters. Functions as a "bulletin board" type service, whereby members can post intra-network messages using a password-controlled link. Also offers links to a faculty-wide e-mail directory.

United States Public Health Services

http://phs.os.dhhs.gov/phs/

Provides information from the United States government about agencies, programs, health information, news and public affairs, and other health-related sites.

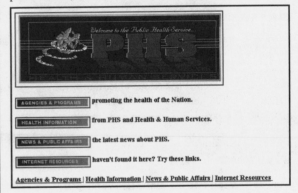

Universal Healthcare Distributors

http://www.magicnet.net/UHCD

Distributes pharmaceutical, surgical, and medical supplies. Also provides Universal Plus, a clinical pharmacy service.

University of Vermont Department of Neurology

http://salus.uvm.edu/Neurology.html

Offers residency training in neurology. Focuses on neuro-muscular and neurodegenerative diseases. Offers many links to neuroscience- and biotechnology-related sites.

Virtual Environments and Real-time Deformations for Surgery Simulation

http://www.cc.gatech.edu/gvu/medical_informatics/research/surg_sim.html

Focuses on simulating the perceived environment that a surgeon encounters during endoscopic surgery. Offers a large downloadable Mpeg movie.

Vision Impairments: A Guide for the Perplexed

http://www.wimsey.com/~jlyon/index.html

Provides contact information about agencies, consumer groups, Internet resources, and vendors of adaptive technology for persons with vision impairments. Covers international resources and resources local to British Columbia and Western Canada. Also carries discussions that cover the experience of vision impairment.

Vitamin Plus

http://cybersight.com/cgi-bin/vits/s?main.gmml

Offers a wide range of vitamins, minerals, herbs, and many other supplements for sale. *Warning:* The site suggests that you e-mail your order with your credit card information. Don't do that, it's not safe. Call them at the number listed if you want to order.

Welcome to Acupuncture

http://www.acupuncture.com/acupuncture/

Contains information on acupuncture, Oriental and Chinese medicine, herbology, Qi Gong (a.k.a. Chi Kung,

Chi Gong, Qi Kung), a practitioner referral list, and a list of accredited schools for Chinese medicine. Also provides state laws regarding acupuncture.

A Word on Health

http://www.webcom.com/~revista/

Focuses on a few topics, such as vitamins and medicine. Changes every three months.

World Health Net

http://world-health.net/

Covers research therapies such as Longevity Institute International, American Acedemy of Anti-Aging Medicine, and National Academy of Sports Medicine.

The World Health Organization Press Releases

http://www.who.ch/press/WHOPressReleases.html

Provides information about diseases, natural disasters, and other world catastrophies from the official World Health Organization.

World Wide Drugs

http://community.net/~neils/new.html

Lists medical and pharmaceutical hospitals and sites.

WorldWide Wellness

http://www.doubleclickd.com/wwellness.html

Provides a database of alternative and holistic health information and resources. Lists events and expos going on in the Maryland area.

ABZU

http://www-oi.uchicago.edu/OI/DEPT/RA/ABZU/ABZU.HTML

Provides information concerning the ancient Near East, including information and pictures about specific sites, museum exhibits, journals, and so forth. Provides plenty of resources to ancient Egypt and Mesopotamia, including reconstructions of sites and texts.

Alexandria, Egypt

http://ce.ecn.purdue.edu/~ashmawy/ALEX

Provides information on the ancient Egyptian city of Alexandria. Includes history, maps, and visitor information.

American and British History Resources

http://info.rutgers.edu/rulib/artshum/amhist.html

Provides a large archive of links to material concerning American and British history. Offers online books and essays by such people as Francis Bacon, Samuel Johnson, John Locke, William Penn, Thomas Paine, Benjamin Franklin, and Thomas Jefferson.

American Civilization Internet Resources

http://www.georgetown.edu/departments/amer_studies/internet.html

Provides a compilation of topics and links concerning American studies.

American Classical League Home Page

http://www.umich.edu/~knudsvig/ACL.html

Provides information about the organization and access to its gopher site, as well as numerous links to other classically related sites, publications, architecture pages, museums, teaching resources, other organizations, and professional resources.

American Memory

http://lcweb2.loc.gov/amhome.html

Highlights of collections planned for the 1995–1996 season include exhibits of African-American pamphlets published between Reconstruction and the First World War, photographic panoramas, and materials from the turn-of-the-century American variety stage. Other collections featured include paper print films of the Westinghouse Factory in 1904 and sound files of ethnic folk music from northern California.

American Revolution and the Struggle for Independence, The

http://grid.let.rug.nl/~welling/usa/revolution.html

Presents American history, from the colonial period until World War I. Contains many images and accompanying historical descriptions.

American Studies Web

http://minerva.cis.yale.edu/~davidp/amstud.html

Provides links to every known topic concerning American studies (seriously, this is quite possible). Includes literature, art, history, ethnicity, religion, and so on.

Ancient City of Athens

http://www.indiana.edu/~kglowack/Athens/Athens.html

Includes many images of the historical sites of Athens, Greece. Offers links to other sites concerning Greek history and architecture.

The Ancient City of Athens

Ancient World Web: Main Index, The

http://atlantic.evsc.virginia.edu/julia/AncientWorld.html

Offers many links to sites that focus on ancient history. Includes archaeology, literature, arts, mythology, law, architecture, and more.

Anti-Imperialism in the United States, 1898–1935

http://web.syr.edu/~fjzwick/ail98-35.html

Focuses on presenting information and literature about the anti-imperialist movement in the United States. Focuses on the period 1898–1935 and provides numerous links to texts by people and organizations active at that time in the movement. Provides backgrounds for different pieces.

Archaeological Survey in the Eastern Desert of Egypt

http://rome.classics.lsa.umich.edu/projects/coptos/desert.html

Contains information about the transdesert trade routes between the Nile Valley and the Red Sea, which linked early Mediterranean civilizations with those of the Indian Ocean between 300 B.C. and A.D. 400.

Archaeology

http://spirit.lib.uconn.edu/archaeology.html

Provides links to various museum Web pages. Offers a clickable map that provides you with a list of archeological data servers worldwide. Also offers links to various university departments to learn about their course offerings and research programs.

Archive of Materials on Bulgarian Jewry During World War II

http://ASUdesign.eas.asu.edu/places/Bulgaria/Jewish/

Provides an archive of material regarding the rescue of Bulgarian Jews during World War II. Offers links to various documents and other sites pertaining to the Holocaust and related Jewish topics. Also provides a short bibliography.

ArchNet: Main Menu

http://spirit.lib.uconn.edu/archnet/archnet.html

Provides links to and information regarding archaeology on the Internet. Includes the following subject areas: archeometry, ceramics, educational materials, ethnohistory, ethnoarchaeology, geo-archaeology, and more.

Armenian Research Center Home Page

http://www.umd.umich.edu:80/dept/armenian/

Provides Armenian culture and history, as well as information on the Armenian genocide. Offers a link to the Society for Armenian Studies.

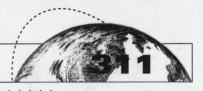

Berlin Wall Falls Project

http://192.253.114.31/Berlin/Introduction/Berlin.html

Presents the collaborative Web project, the "Berlin Wall Falls: Perspectives from 5 Years Down the Road." Involves students and researchers around the globe.

BUBL Information Service Web Server

http://www.bubl.bath.ac.uk/BUBL/History.html

Offers links to various history sites on the Net. Includes many topics other than history. Contains links to Russian, Vietnam War, United States, French and Indian War, Viking, medieval, and Civil War historical sites.

Castles on the Web

http://fox.nstn.ca/~tmonk/castle/castle.html

Provides a collection of sites that offer information and pictures of castles from around the world.

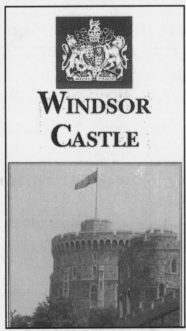

WINDSOR CASTLE

CHELP Home Page

http://128.253.68.14/CHELP.HTM

Describes the Cornell Halai East Lokris Project.

Classics and Mediterranean Archaeology Home Page

http://rome.classics.lsa.umich.edu/welcome.html

Focuses on Mediterranean and classical archaeology, but also provides access to all sorts of archaeological links, including articles, journals, projects, exhibits, images, related academics, museums, geographic information, other Internet resources, and more.

Cybrary of the Holocaust

http://www.best.com/~mddunn/cybrary/

Provides information on the Holocaust. Offers details on the rise of Nazism in Germany and its subsequent effects on the Jews. Includes pictures, eyewitness descriptions of concentration camps, and historical perspectives.

D-Day

http://192.253.114.31/D-Day/Table_of_contents.html

Provides Army and Navy news reels, past issues of the *Stars & Stripes* newspaper, famous speeches from the National Archives, and a collection of maps and battle plans from the Center for Military History.

Didaskalia: Home Page

http://www.warwick.ac.uk./didaskalia/

Provides information on ancient dance, drama, and music. Also provides access to *Didaskalia* itself (a journal on the Greek and Roman theater) and other related Internet sites.

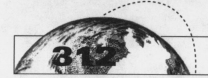

Excavations at Catalhoyuk

http://club.eng.cam.ac.uk/~vsb1001/catal.html

Covers the excavations of the Neolithic Catalhoyuk. Includes summary of research, interpretation, and reconstructions of the ancient site.

Fair Play

http://rmii.com/~jkelin/fp.html

Online magazine. Focuses on giving Lee Harvey Oswald a fair shake. Presents articles concerning various views on the JFK assassination.

George Rarey's Journals of the 379th Fighter Squadron

http://www.nbn.com/home/rareybird/index.html

Provides the journal of a young cartoonist who was drafted into the Army Air Corps in World War II. Documents his various drawings throughout the war. Provides images and accompanying text.

Germany—Database of German Nobility

http://faui80.informatik.uni-erlangen.de/html/WW-Person-Engl.html

Targets historians and geneologians. Features a database of biographies and portraits of German nobility.

GIS and Remote Sensing for Archaeology: Burgundy, France

http://deathstar.rutgers.edu/projects/france/france.html

Sums up most of the major modern technological techniques for excavating and sensing underground.

Gopher and WWW Servers

http://hpb1.hwc.ca:10002/irg-servers.html#arch

Describes what you can find on Web servers dedicated to archaelogy. Offers links to gophers, FAQs, or servers.

Graduate Institute of International Studies, The

http://heiwww.unige.ch/iuhei/int-history-politics/

Presents a variety of historical and political resources. Provides information about the Institute's programs, admission requirements, and mission statement.

Gulf War Photo Gallery

http://www2.msstate.edu/~rah2/gulf-war.html

Presents a Gulf War photo gallery, compiled by Ronald A. Hoskinson. Displays images taken primarily from the personal collection of Norman Jarvis. Offers a few links to other Gulf War sites.

Historical Text Archive, The

http://www.msstate.edu/Archives/History/index.html

Archives historical texts from various countries and periods. Includes a large collection from the United States. Offers many links to other historical resources.

History Computerization Project

http://www.directnet.com/history/

Provides a large collection of links to history sites.

History of Astronomy

http://aibn55.astro.uni-bonn.de:8000/~pbrosche/astoria.html

Focuses on the history of astronomy and in general, on science. Contains links to biographies of important people, images from observatories around the world and other archives, museums, and astronomy exhibits on the Net.

History of Space Exploration

http://www.c3.lanl.gov/~cjhamil/SolarSystem/history.html

Provides information on the history of space exploration. Includes images of spacecraft and planets.

History Pages

http://ux1.cso.uiuc.edu/~kundert/josh/../history/history.html

Focuses on Celtic history. Plans to add pages on Saxon and Frankish history. Provides information on the Celts, including maps and links to other Celtic sites.

Images of My War

http://www.ionet.net/~uheller/vnbktoc.shtml

Contains Ulf R. Heller's account of his Vietnam experience. Includes jungle training in Panama, impressions of the Vietnamese people, battles, discipline and moral, and his return home.

Index of /expo/

http://sunsite.unc.edu/expo

Provides an index to exhibits that include the Library of Congress' "Scrolls of the Dead Sea," "The 'Palace' of Diocletian at Split," and exhibits of paleontology, the Soviet Union, the Vatican, and more. Offers a list of terms relating to Middle Eastern and classical terms. Includes downloadable Jpeg and GIF files.

India

http://grafton.dartmouth.edu:8001/lrc/culture/asia/india.html

Offers links under the Cities and Regions topic that provide information on the history and culture of India. Provides in-line images.

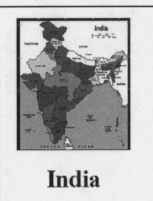

India

Indiana Historical Society

http://www.spcc.com/ihsw/ihs.html

Nonprofit membership organization. Collects, preserves, and promotes the history of Indiana. Features information on the Society's collections, exhibitions, publications, and numerous other activities.

Institute for Human Sciences—Vienna

http://www.ping.at/iwm/iwmhome.htm

Provides information on an independent, interdisciplinary institute for advanced study that offers in-residence fellowships for scholars in the humanities, and that operates a number of long-term policy projects in the nations of the former Eastern bloc. Encourages both senior and junior scholars with similar research interests to explore this site.

Institute of Egyptian Art and Archaeology, The

http://www.memst.edu/egypt/main.html

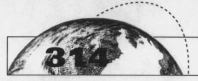

Presents exhibits online that include mummies and other artifacts. Offers the chance to see the relics of old or take a Web tour of Egypt.

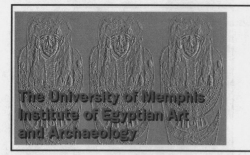

Intentional Communities

http://www.well.com/user/cmty/index.html

Seeks to be an inclusive title for information on ecovillages, cohousing, residential land trusts, communes, student co-ops, urban housing cooperatives, and other related projects and dreams.

James B. Ross' Home Page

http://134.129.87.200/jrhome.htm

Serves as a starting point for exploring history sites on the Internet. Offer many links.

Kelsey Museum Educational and Outreach Program

http://classics.lsa.umich.edu/Kelsey/Outreach.html

Exhibits a variety of objects from the ancient meccas of culture, from Greece to Rome to Egypt. Also provides coverage of the Karanis excavations in Egypt and maps of the ancient world.

Labyrinth WWW Home Page

http://www.georgetown.edu/labyrinth/labyrinth-home.html

Provides complete information about medieval studies on the Web. Also provides search capabilities.

Latino Connection, The

http://www.webspace.com/~pedro/index.html

Simplifies the search for information on Latin/Hispanic countries. Offers individual country pages with links to history, travel, education, food, culture, maps, arts, and countries.

Leonardo Internet Home Page

http://www.leonardo.net/

Provides services to the Internet community. Features the View the Museum link, which takes you to an online exhibit about the life and works of Leonardo da Vinci.

Leptiminus Archaeological Project

http://rome.classics.lsa.umich.edu/projects/lepti/lepti.html

Represents a cooperative effort between the University of Michigan and the Institute National du Patrimoine of Tunisia. Provides information about the fieldwork conducted from 1990–1993, as well as images of the site.

LGBT History

http://www.cyberzine.org/html/GLAIDS/History/historypage.html

Offers links to sites that contain information about gay history, plus more. Also serves as a site for gays and friends to gather and discuss common issues.

Life Histories—American Memory Project

http://lcweb2.loc.gov/wpaintro/wpahome.html

Presents a collection of life histories sponsored by the Manuscript Division of the Library of Congress and written for the United States Works Progress Administration's Federal Writer's Project between 1936 and 1940. Includes 2,900 documents that represent the work of more than 300 writers from 24 states. Lets you access these documents by various search means, including by region or state.

Maritime History Virtual Archives, The

http://pc-78-120.udac.se:8001/WWW/Nautica/Nautica.html

Includes an archive on maritime history, organized under topics such as ships, shipbuilding, rigging, health of seamen, and seamanship. Also includes images of various vessels and links to other maritime sites. Provides versions in Swedish and English.

Mary Rose Virtual Maritime Museum

http://www.synergy.net/homeport.html

Offers you an opportunity to learn more about this Tudor-period warship that sank in 1545.

The Mary Rose Virtual Maritime Museum

The Mary Rose was a four masted warship, built on the orders of Henry VIII between 1510 and 1511. After a long and successful period of service she sank accidentally during an engagement with the French fleet in the Solent in 1545. Her rediscovery and raising were one of the seminal events in the history of nautical archaeology. The ship was raised by and is being cared for by the Mary Rose Trust.

Maya

http://www.realtime.net/maya/

Includes history, geography, geology, astronomy, archaeology, anthropology, and art forms related to the Americas before Christopher Columbus's discovery. Includes information on Mayans, Aztecs, and Native Americans.

Maya Astronomy Page, The

http://www.astro.uva.nl/michielb/maya/astro.html

Focuses on Mayan civilization. Presents the Mayan creation story. Provides information about Mayan astronomy, mathematics, and their calendar. Offers links to other Mayan sites.

Michael C. Carlos Online Exhibit

http://www.cc.emory.edu/CARLOS/carlos.html

Contains a permanent collection of more than 13,000 artifacts representing 9,000 years of history. Presents images of some of these artifacts.

Mithraism

http://www.io.org/~hermes3/Mithras.html#int

Presents a look at Mithraism, a religion of the pre-Christian Roman Empire, for those interested in the roots of Western religion.

Musei

http://www.christusrex.org/www1/vaticano/0-Musei.html

Provides around 600 images of holdings of the Vatican museums. Also offers links to hundreds of images of the Sistine Chapel and the Raphael Stanze.

Museum Professional, The

http://www.sirius.com/~robinson/musprof

Serves as a starting point for accessing online resources in the museum field. Includes links to museum Web site lists, virtual museums, and specialization resources.

NASA Astronautics History

http://www.hq.nasa.gov/office/pao/History/astronautics.html

Provides key historical documents on NASA space flight, human space flight, planetary probes, lunar probes, and more.

NEH Archaeology Projects Online

http://www.neh.fed.us/documents/rkpubs.html

Presents currently ongoing projects, including histories and images of archaeology projects sponsored by the National Endowment for the Humanities. Includes images in the reports.

Newstead Project

http://www.brad.ac.uk/acad/archsci/field_proj/newstead/newstead.html

Focuses on the archeological exploration of settlements surrounding a Roman fort, called Trimontium, in southern Scotland.

Ohio State University Excavations at Isthmia, The

http://www.acs.ohio-state.edu/history/isthmia/isthmia.html

Covers the excavations at The Sanctuary of Poseidon at Isthmia (Greece). Examines the work and describes several points of interest in the area.

Online Archaeology— An Electronic Journal of Archaeological Theory

http://avebury.arch.soton.ac.uk/Journal/journal.html

Focuses on "promoting rapid dissemination of speculative ideas about archaeology." Covers various thoughts about archaeology.

Operation Desert Storm Debriefing Book

http://www.nd.edu/~aleyden/contents.html

Provides information concerning military and political aspects of the Gulf War. Includes backgrounds on politicians, descriptions of military hardware, statistics, and links to other Gulf War sites.

Oregon—World War II Farming

http://arcweb.sos.state.or.us/osuhomepage.html

Exhibits "Fighters on the Farm Front: Oregon's Emergency Farm Labor Service, 1943–1947," which includes more than 60 images and printed documents.

Oriental Institute

http://www-oi.uchicago.edu

Provides information about the University of Chicago's Oriental Institute museum and philology projects. Includes information and visual images on ancient Near East regions. Also includes a new bibliographic reference, "Women in the Ancient Near East."

The Oriental Institute
The University of Chicago

THE ORIENTAL INSTITUTE - The University of Chicago

Oriental Institute Archaeology

http://www-oi.uchicago.edu/OI/PROJ/OI_Archaeology.html

Covers many ongoing excavations and other archaeological projects by the Oriental Institute at the University of Chicago. Offers links to many different projects.

OWAN

http://www.wesleyan.edu/classics/OWAN.html

The *Old World Archaeology Newsletter* (OWAN) covers the conferences, research, and publications concerning archaeology. Includes editorials and announcements.

Papyrology Home Page

http://www.umich.edu/~jmucci/papyrology/home.html

Provides access to papyrology collections worldwide, literature from and concerning the collections, and images of papyri, including fragments from the *Book of the Dead*.

Paris Museums

http://www.paris.org/Musees/

Contains images and information for more than 20 museums in Paris, including the Louvre, Centre Pompidou, L'Orangerie, Auguste Rodin, and la Cite des Sciences et de l'Industrie.

Perseus Project Home Page

http://medusa.perseus.tufts.edu/

Presents an interactive multimedia database on ancient Greece. Includes ancient texts and information about sites and artifacts. Includes a searchable database for finding coins, vases, and more.

Pompeii

http://www.tulane.edu/pompeii/text/pompeii.html

Sports images and a brief history of Pompeii.

Pompeii Forum

http://jefferson.village.virginia.edu/pompeii/page-1.html

Includes maps and pictures. Also serves as a forum.

Remembering Nagasaki

http://www.exploratorium.edu/nagasaki/

Observes the 50th anniversary of the dropping of atomic bombs on Hiroshima and Nagasaki. Includes photographs taken by Yosuki Yamahata of Nagasaki the day after, which create a backdrop for discussion and reflection on issues concerning the atomic age. Lets you share your views and read those of others.

Romarch List Home Page

http://www.umich.edu/~pfoss/ROMARCH.html

Provides a "crossroads for Web resources on the art and archaeology of Italy and the Roman provinces, from ca. 1000 B.C. to A.D. 600." Offers many links to sites that contain images of Roman art and architecture.

Salzburg 1945–1955: Introduction

http://www.image.co.at/image/salzburg/

Presents Austrians and American G.I.'s sharing remembrances of the "Era of Occupation" of Salzburg, Austria, subsequent to the defeat of Nazi Germany in 1945. Includes links to images and text interviews.

Shikhin

http://www.colby.edu/rel/Shikhin.html

Serves to help find and identify the lost city of Shikhin. Presents the story of Shikhin, its pottery, pictures, and maps.

Shore Line Trolley Museum

http://www.panix.com/~christos/TrolleyPage.html

Exhibits the Shore Line Trolley museum of East Haven, Connecticut. Provides information about museum operations, including hours and directions, as well as a tour of some streetcars in Shore Line's collection.

Soviet Archives: Entrance Room

http://sunsite.unc.edu/expo/soviet.exhibit/entrance.html

Provides the Library of Congress Soviet Exhibit, divided into two categories: The Internal Workings of the Soviet System and The Soviet Union and the United States.

U-Boat War 1939–1945, The

http://rvik.ismennt.is/~gummihe/Uboats/u-boats.htm

Provides an archive of facts and statistics concerning German U-boats during World War II.

United States Presidents: Welcome Page, The

http://chestnut.lis.utk.edu/~presidnt/USPres1.html

Covers some of the highlights of each president's administration, including notes in their own words. Also describes some of the problems with which each president struggled during his term. Additionally, it presents images of each president's signature.

United States—History

gopher://wiretap.spies.com/11/Gov/US-History

Contains texts of historically significant United States documents, including the Declaration of Independence, Emancipation Proclamation, Monroe Doctrine, WWII surrenders of Germany and Japan, Tonkin Gulf Resolution, and more.

Vietnam Veterans Home Page

http://www.vietvet.org/

Focuses on Vietnam veterans from both sides of the conflict. Provides a forum for exchange of information, stories, poems, songs, art, pictures, and experiences.

Vikings Home Page

http://control.chalmers.se/vikings/viking.html

Provides information about Viking cults, the Vikings of Russia, and Vikings of today. Also features a Swedish-Viking-English dictionary and offer links to other Viking-related Web servers.

Voice of the Shuttle Home Page

http://humanitas.ucsb.edu/

Covers literature, art, theory, women's studies, politics and government, and more. Also offers many links.

War from a Parlor: Stereoscopic Images of the Philippine-American War and Soldiers' Letters Home, The

http://web.syr.edu/~fjzwick/stereo/

Juxtaposes the visual (stereoscopic images) with excerpts from letters written by United States soldiers during the Philippine-American War.

WWW Medieval Resources

`http://ebbs.english.vt.edu/medieval/medieval.ebbs.html`

Offers links to different resources relating to medieval times.

WWW Medieval Resources

WWWVL History of Science, Technology, and Medicine— Overview

`http://coombs.anu.edu.au/SpecialProj/ASAP/WWWVL-HSTM.html`

Keeps track of information facilities in the field of the history of science, technology, and medicine. Also offers links to organizations, biographies, institutions, museums, and electronic journals.

A-Ball Plumbing Supply

http://a-ball.govivo.com/

Contains a comprehensive list of plumbing supplies. Also provides information about restoration and preservation and a tour of European plumbing crafters.

ALLDATA Corporation

http://199.4.107.1/0c:/alldroot.htm¦/

Provides automotive repair information. Contains information about recall notices, technical service bulletins, and locations of ALLDATA repair shops.

Amboan & Badinia Furniture of Spain

http://www.servtech.com/public/amboan/

Offers an online catalog of classic, hand-finished furniture. Also provides a directory of sales representatives worldwide.

Welcome to...

Amboan and Badinia are two of the worlds highest quality manufactures for classic, hand-finished furniture. Our popularity throughout Europe and the Orient has never been greater. Within the past year we have opened our first United States sales office which is presently servicing both the US. and Canada. It has never been more convenient and cost effective for Retailers and Distributors throughout the US. and Canada to begin carrying these two extraordinary lines of furniture.

The American Society of Home Inspectors

http://csbh.mhv.net/~dfriedman/ashihome.htm

The national professional and certifying organization of home inspectors in the United States and Canada. Contains information for home buyers, owners, and inspectors. Also offers links to other related organizations.

AmeriSpec

http://www.io.org/~amrspec/

Provides information on property maintenance assessments, partial and relocation inspections, termite, radon, carbon monoxide, and lead-based paint inspections. Also contains an area of frequently asked questions about home inspections.

Auto Repair Hotline

http://www.deltanet.com/allstar/autorepr.htm

Advertises the services of a 1-900 telephone number that provides how-to information on various auto repair topics.

Bayviewer Chair Company

http://www.xmission.com:80/~gastown/balaam/bayview.htm

Provides advertising and ordering information for the Bayviewer Chair Company.

Blue Canyon Woodworks

http://www.rt66.com/blue/

Advertises Blue Canyon Woodworks, makers of New Mexican furniture. Offers several images of products and provides ordering information.

Bombay Company

http://www.pathfinder.com/@@hb0GchBdkwEAQO4U/Catalog1/Bombay.index.html

Provides advertising information on the products of the Bombay Company, including furniture, wall decor, and gift items.

Builders Graphics

http://www.homeplan.com/homeplan/

Contains builders graphics, information on CAD (computer aided drafting), tips for homeowners, construction

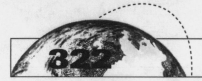

terminology, links to housing-related WWW sites, and a style gallery. Also offers ready-to-build house plans for sale or to teach you how to create your own plans.

Carole Boleman: Landscape Architect

http://WWW.in.net/cboleman/

Advertises Boleman's landscaping design services, but also provides interesting information on her residential and subdivision entry designs and how she uses computer-aided design.

Carpet Connection of America

http://www.carpets.com/

Gives examples of colors, textures, fibers, and styles of carpet. Also provides a cost and information guide on buying hardwood and vinyl flooring and links to carpet manufacturers.

Carpeteria's Home Page

http://www.fishnet.net:80/~carpets/

Offers valuable information on carpet styles and textures, lifestyle ratings for various types of carpets, and links to other carpet manufacturers.

The Centre for Landscape Research (CLR)

http://www.clr.toronto.edu:1080/

Provides a collaborative environment for the exploration of ideas related to the design, planning, and policies of the environment. Focuses primarily on developing and utilizing electronic media to foster more informed decision-making.

Chrysler Power Magazine

http://www.enews.com:80/magazines/chrysler_power/

Provides up-to-date features on Chrysler Corporation offerings (past and future), in-depth technical explanations for restoration buffs, parts sources and advertisers with almost any new or old part for Chrysler's entire production history, and a showtime section that lists more than 100 Chrysler/Plymouth/Dodge specific shows each year.

Colton Inc.

http://www.cc.utah.edu/~jc3908/colton.htm

Advertises the products of Colton Inc., a drapery manufacturing company in Salt Lake City, Utah.

Cottage Furniture

http://www.olworld.com:80/olworld/mall/mall_us/c_gifts/
m_cotage/index.html

Advertises products of Cottage Furniture, makers of handmade furniture. Also provides a history of Cottage Furniture and some images of various pieces.

Crazy Creek Products

http://www.sccsi.com/CrazyCreek/home.html

Advertises products offered by Crazy Creek, including the original Crazy Creek chair and the ThermaLounger. Also provides various accessory and ordering information.

Dalton Carpet Outlets

http://www.hickory.nc.us:80/ncnetworks/carpets.html

Provides a listing of carpet dealers in Dalton, Georgia, home of more than 100 carpet outlets and dealers.

Dan Friedman's Home Page

http://csbh.mhv.net/~dfriedman/welcome.htm

Provides information about specific topics relating to electrical wiring, plumbing, the environment, structural foundations, heating systems, and chimneys and flues.

Department of the Interior Materials and Engineering and Research Laboratory

http://donews.do.usbr.gov/merl/reprhome.html

Provides information about the research of new materials and methods for concrete maintenance, repair, and preservation. Also presents publications documenting results of technical studies on conventional and new repair methods and materials; concrete, cultural and historical facilities repair; and new materials and methods for durable, long-lasting grouts.

Domestic Dream—Finely Crafted Decorative Shelves Made in Montana

http://www.libby.org/millwork/millwork.html

Describes their versatile, handcrafted shelving system, made using carefully selected quality pine grown in the Great Northwest, which allows you to combine different pieces and lengths to create many different arrangements.

DSS Digital Satellite System

http://www.viper.net/clients/RCADATV/

Advertises and describes the new technology of digital satellite systems.

Faucet Outlet Online

http://www.faucet.com/

Contains selections of faucets. Provides information about installing, choosing, and selecting a faucet.

Final Touch Bath Shop

http://bathshop.finaltouch.com/

Advertises products and offers an online shopping guide and catalog. Invites users to help locate hard-to-find bath items.

Floor Coverings International

http://kaos.deepcove.com/carpet/

Advertises products offered by Floor Coverings International. Also provides information on carpet terminology, types of carpet styles and fibers, carpet cleaning, and answers to frequently asked questions (FAQs) related to carpets.

Furniture, Furniture, Furniture

http://www.hickory.nc.us:80/ncnetworks/furnitur.html

Offers a collection of links to various furniture manufacturers near Hickory and High Point, North Carolina.

Hill's Plumbing Page

http://www.halcyon.com/hill/hill.html

Features frequently asked questions about plumbing, an area in which you can ask the plumber a question, and plumbing links, as well as some plumbing fun.

Home Builder's Utopia

http://www.dfw.net/~custmbld/utopia.html

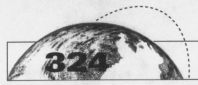

Serves as a guide to links to professional homebuilders on the Internet. Also lists building associations and products and services.

Home Repair Hotline

http://www.deltanet.com/allstar/homerepr.htm

Provides information about a 1-900 number that gives instructions related to the following topics: plumbing improvements, electricity, small and large appliances, heating and cooling units, and home improvement projects ($2.49 per minute).

The Home Team

http://www.hometeam.com/

Contains information about intelligent home design, lighting controls, standards, security systems, communication systems, and more. Involves many industries and numerous members, from manufacturing to service providers, all dedicated to spreading the word about the latest technologies for homes, and primarily directed by trade associations. Does not sell any of the products described, other than a few educational products. Provides information and remains neutral and unbiased to the industry.

Indiana Business Directory Home Care/Repair

http://www.iquest.net/~ariel/ibd/label10.html

Offers links to the following Indiana businesses: contractors/builders and related services; heating/air conditioning and related services; electrical contractors and related services; plumbing contractors and related services; landscaping and related services.

InfoVid Outlet

http://rare-teas.com/infovid/c320.html

Contains videos for sale at InfoVid, the educational and how-to video warehouse. Offers a variety of home improvement videos, such as attic conversion, basic carpentry, plumbing, and so on.

Lock Info Worldwide

http://boss.cpcnet.com/gpla/gplalink.html

Contains links to various professional security and lock providers.

Mana Electronics Online

http://www.magic.mb.ca/~icis/mana/mana.html

Contains a mail-order catalog for consumer electronic products.

Master Lock Company Home Page

http://www.masterlock.com/cgi-bin/c?master+idx

Advertises the products of Master Lock. Also contains home and commercial security tips and a news and views section.

Milestone: The Chimney Doctor

http://greenlie.terranet.com/docs/cdoctor/cdoctor.html

Provides information on services offered by the Chimney Doctor. Also contains useful information on safety tips,

preventing chimney fires, chimney cleaning, masonry, weatherproofing, screens, and pest removal.

National Consumer Alert Hotline

`http://www.deltanet.com/allstar/conalert.htm`

Provides information on recalls and product warnings. Provides information on many types of appliances, as well as service providers, such as motels, dentists, and carpet cleaners.

OAK Repository

`ftp://oak.oakland.edu/SimTel/msdos/database/handy120.zip`

Offers downloadable software that calculates estimates for home repair material costs.

Oasis Interactive

`http://www.wavenet.com/~prntlock/`

Advertises products by Oasis Interactive. Lists only the personal property identification system.

Quality Woodwork and Supply, Inc.

`http://www.tach.net/public/quality.html`

Carries a wide variety of woods, from the common to the exotic, as well as an array of other woodworking supplies. Offers an online price lookup system that allows you to enter the type and amount of wood you need and gives a price for the wood.

The Quiltery of Allentown, Pennsylvania

`http://mmink.com/mmink/dossiers/quilt/quilt.html`

Serves as an online shopping guide for The Quiltery, a cottage industry that represents three dozen women from all over the United States. Also contains images of various types of quilts.

Security Plus

`http://www.iwc.com/lock/lock.html`

Advertises Security Plus, makers of the portable door alarm.

Sudberry House

`http://connix.com/~dbeers/sudhome.htm`

Displays fine wood accessories used for mounting needle-work and crafts, as well as an online color catalog, a factory tour, and many needlework designs.

Swahili Furniture

`http://www.mmrcorp.com/corporate/lamu/`

Advertises products made by Lamu Industries, makers of Swahili furniture, which they derive from old beds and door carvings still used on the island of Lamu. Also displays images of various pieces of the furniture.

Symbol Talk

`http://www.teleport.com:80/~symbol/index.html`

Advertises meditation pillows made by Symbol Talk. Provides information on the various types and styles of pillows, both color, and how to order.

UBC Vancouver School of Architecture Home Page

`http://arch-d3.architecture.ubc.ca/icarus/icarus.htm`

Contains sections concerning design and architecture: a section on design and machines, a virtual design studio that contains many images, electronic design tutorials, and electronic media courses.

The Woodworking Catalog

http://www.woodworking.com/

Contains useful information on lumber, hardware, power tools, finishing supplies, books and plans, woodworking schools, workshops, and stores, accessories, hand tools, wooden products, and machinery. Also contains a collection of links to other woodworking-related sites. Offers a downloadable DOS program called Woodpro (a lumber database and wood selection expert system).

5 Top Internet Marketing Successes of 1994

http://arganet.tenagra.com/Tenagra/awards94.html

Provides information on the top 5 Internet marketing success stories of 1994. Includes information regarding Pizza Hut, Doom!, and other successes.

A1 Index of Commercial WWW URL Submission and Search Sites

http://www.vir.com/~wyatt/index_commercial.html

Indexes hyperlinks to numerous commercial sites where you can gain exposure for your Web page by submitting your Web page or URL address to searchable online malls, business directories, and databases.

The aaabook

http://yarrow.wt.com.au/~rudra/aaabook/

The Annotated Australian Address Book. Offers a collection of Australian Web sites.

About Web/Genera

http://gdbdoc.gdb.org/letovsky/genera/genera.html

Provides Web/Genera, a software package for integrating Sybase databases into the Web. Offers downloadable alpha mode (pretesting) software.

Aether Madness

http://www.aether.com/Aether/

Provides online version of the book, *Aether Madness: An Offbeat Guide to the On-line World*. Lets you click on things that sound interesting and quickly transfers you. Includes many tours.

All-Internet Shopping Directory

http://www.webcom.com/~tbrown/

Serves as an easy-to-use, fast-loading central hot link to products, services, malls, and stores on the Web.

The Almost Complete HTML Reference

http://www.well.com/user/olcom

Presents a guide to HTML.

Andy's MetaSearch System (AMeSS)

http://www.cs.princeton.edu/~acmyers/form.html

A simple metasearch tool for the Web. Searches InfoSeek, Yahoo, Lycos, and Webcrawler's databases, and returns the combined results.

Ansible's Web Page Design Services

http://www.cyberenet.net/~ansible/

Provides Web page design and HTML coding services. Offers to help any company construct a Web presence based on their marketing literature, product catalog, newsletters, press releases, print ads, proposal boilerplate, and so on.

Argotech Business Systems Networking Solutions Provider

http://www.argonet.net

A Novell, NetWare, Microsoft, and Unix networking company that specializes in connectivity solutions for southern California.

Argus/University of Michigan Clearinghouse

http://www.lib.umich.edu/chhome.html

Serves as a clearinghouse for subject-oriented Internet resources guides. Lets you submit your own guides or obtain guides written by people on various Internet-related topics.

Aspen Systems Corporation

http://www.aspensys.com

Provides complete Internet services. Offers requirements and needs analysis, Internet publishing services, systems support, and customer support. Specializes in professionally designing home pages to get noticed.

Aspen Systems Corporation Web server

Association of Internet Users

http://beach.com/welcome/aiu.html

Provides information about the association and the benefits of membership (one benefit of joining is that you can register your domain name for free).

Association of University Technology Managers

http://autm.rice.edu/autm/

Features resources for the technology transfer professional. Offers links to other resources. Also includes information about AUTM (publications, membership, events), job postings, and a way to search lists of technologies you can license from more than 20 different university, government, and organizational sites in one query (via a harvest gatherer).

Astoria Software

http://stepupsoft.com

Provides the ZipLock Payment System, a secure, automatic credit card processing system for Internet electronic commerce.

Autopilot

http://www.netgen.com/~mkgray/autopilot.html

Utilizes Netscape version 1.1 and connects you to a different Web site every 12 seconds. Lets you find totally random sites with little effort. Also lets you change the amount of time between connections.

Autorama

http://www.hooked.net/users/1auto

Provides information, software, and links related to Web-authoring and automated cybernetic delivery. Offers a download site for Web hot spots, an image map editor, and the Cyberspace Shuttle Loading Kit (a toolkit for creating single-step Web smart Zip files).

Babbs's Bookmarks

http://www.aquila.com/babbs.bookmarks/

Monthly column featured in *Boardwatch Magazine*. Focuses on Web sites that help you make the most of the amazing resources available on the Web.

Banana Report Easy Visual Basic Tips

http://www.infohaus.com/access/by-seller/
BananaReport_Visual_Basic_Tips/i.free.html

Provides a way for Visual Basic programmers to get quick tips and techniques that solve common Visual Basic programming problems.

The Bare Bones Guide to HTML

`http://www.access.digex.net/~werbach/barebone.html`

Lists every HTML 2.0 tag and most of the 3.0 tags, with a special section on the Netscape extensions.

A Beginner's Guide to Effective E-mail

`http://www.webfoot.com/advice/email.top.html?Yahoo`

Presents a beginner's guide to effective e-mail. Talks about the ways to express intonation and gestures thru e-mail. Gives information on page layouts and format of e-mail as well.

A Beginner's Guide to HTML

`http://www.ncsa.uiuc.edu/General/Internet/WWW/HTMLPrimer.html`

Presents a beginner's guide to HTML. Talks about linking to other documents, troubleshooting, and creating forms.

Beverly Hills Internet

`http://www.bhi90210.com`

Award-winning Internet presence provider based in Beverly Hills, California. Contains hundreds of free home pages, organized into neighborhoods reflecting various sites, such as WallStreet or Hollywood. Presents a thriving community, including in these bustling GeoCities live video feeds from all over as well as the freshest hotlists.

Building Internet Servers

`http://www.charm.net/~cyber/`

Provides a collection of information and links to information on how to create an Internet server. Covers a very wide range of PC-based operating systems. Includes a tutorial.

The Business of the Internet

`http://www.rtd.com/people/rawn/business.html`

Introduces the Internet for Commercial Organizations. Offers information about the structure of the Internet, how the Internet can help business, and how to connect your business to the Internet.

c|net: the computer network

`http://www.cnet.com/`

c | net: the computer network, creators of c | net online and the television series c | net central, is an on-air and online interactive showcase for computers, multimedia, and digital technologies.

Canada Net Pages

`http://www.visions.com/netpages`

Provides a place for businesses to become part of the Web. Registers clients in search engines such as What's New and Yahoo. Also provides links for various pages, such as Canada Net Financial Pages and Canada Net Business Directory.

The Canadian Internet Handbook/Advantage Home Page

`http://www.csi.nb.ca/handbook/`

Presents guides to Internet access in Canada. Lets you add your Canadian Internet address to the handbook, find out

more about their publications, send the authors e-mail, and more.

Carter & Associates WEB Studios

http://www.klos.com/~jonathan

Specializes in Web page construction for individuals and companies who want to advertise on a personal or corporate scale on the Internet. Offers to create and maintain an established business presence for you on the Internet. Creates a look and feel that is customized to the personal tastes of our clients.

The Categorical Catapult

http://www.clark.net/pub/cargui/links.html

Offers a database of more than 1,000 links, organized hierarchically.

Censorship and the Internet

http://dis.strath.ac.uk/people/paul/Control.html

Offers a collection of links about censorship and associated issues on the Internet. Offers resources on the legal and ethical issues of running a Web service.

Cerebral Systems Development—Home of Webber™

http://www.csdcorp.com/Welcome.html

Offers Webber™, a fast, friendly, and flexible HTML editor for Windows. Provides full-featured help, including HTML tag descriptions and an easy-to-use validation system to help you create valid HTML documents. Lets you download Webber as shareware (this version supports the HTML 2.0 dtd). Also offers a registered version that supports the draft HTML 3.0 dtd and Netscape Extensions.

Charm Net Personal IP Page

http://www.charm.net/pip.html

Provides information on how to connect your computer directly to Internet. Includes information for users of Macs, Windows, Windows NT, and OS/2.

Chats

http://sunsite/unc.edu/dbarber/chats.html

Provides information about IRC (Internet Relay Chat). Offers recorded dialogues from various disasters (the Oklahoma bombing, assorted California earthquakes, and so forth).

Cnet—Canada

http://cnet.unb.ca/cnet/

Provides information specific to Canada. Lets you search the database by clicking on the geographical regions on a map or by using standard keywords.

College and University Home Pages

http://www.mit.edu:8001/people/cdemello/univ.html

Provides links to the Web pages of more than 750 colleges and universities around the world. Provides information on schools. Lets you search alphabetically or just browse.

ColorEditor for Windows

http://www.bbsinc.com/colorEditor_FAQ.html

Provides a stand-alone MS Windows shareware to assist the Web page author develop a HTML page color scheme using extensions to the HTML 3.0 specification. Provides a Style Box that enables users to edit, save, and retrieve color schemes. Runs on Windows 3.1, Windows 3.1 for Workgroups, and Windows NT 3.5.

Columbines Grow Here, Apparently

`http://phoebe.cair.du.edu/~bcole/colorado.html`

Serves as a guide to Colorado Web sites and links about government, law, business, media, sports, the outdoors, and entertainment.

Comics 'n' Stuff!

`http://www.phlab.missouri.edu/~c617145/comix.html`

Contains links to more than 50 different comic strips (some daily) on the Web. Includes popular ones, such as Dilbert, and others less known, like Buzz the Fly.

COMMA Hotlist Database

`http://arachnid.cm.cf.ac.uk/htbin/AndrewW/Hotlist/hot_list_search.csh`

Provides a graphical searchable database. Lets you choose your search criteria from their list and then searches and gives you an output list.

Commerce Place

`http://www.virtualynx.com/commerce/`

Contains hundreds of stores through which you can surf. Offers VirtuaLynx, which can help out your company by linking or setting up a storefront for your business in Commerce Place.

Commercial Services on the Net

`http://www.directory.net/`

Provides a collection of links to commercial Web sites on the Internet. Lets you search by a word or name of a company.

Common Internet File Formats

`http://www.matisse.net/files/formats.html`

Provides information on the different file types and formats on the Internet. Each blurb about a specific file type also gives links to obtaining readers for that type.

Comprehensive Listing of Law Enforcement Sites on the Web

`http://bmt.cent.com/users/iwilsker/ira.html`

Possibly the most comprehensive list of law enforcement-related sites on the Web.

Connect, Inc.—Audio Innovations

`http://www.tc.net/connect`

Harnesses the power of audio on the Internet. Provides applications that let you instantly update your Web page(s) or e-mail applications by simply picking up your telephone and calling a fully automated system. It also qualifies as an authorized AT&T 900 service bureau, so it can set up and run any 900 or 800 voice or data application.

Cool Science Site of the Day

`http://www.geopages.com/WallStreet/1304`

Offers a collection of science-related Web sites, selected for content and design.

Cool Site of the Day

http://www.infi.net/cool.html

Connects you to the cool site of the day on the Internet, determined by the moderator. Works better than a random site connector because the sites are more likely to be pretty cool.

CRAYON—CReAte Your Own Newspaper

http://www.eg.bucknell.edu/~boulter/crayon/

Serves as an interactive news agent. Lets you choose from sections such as News, Sports, Entertainment, and others to find the best periodical information on the Internet. Lets you organize it into your own personal newspaper—you might never read a print publication again.

Creative Web Co-op

http://www.mojoski.com/~writan/cwc.html

A group of experienced Internet professionals who provide Net access to the world. Features a team of HTML architects, researchers, writers, systems administrators, and graphic artists who can design, construct, and maintain Web sites. Includes offices in Canada, the United States, and Australia.

CSUSM Windows World

http://coyote.csusm.edu/cwis/winworld/winworld.html

Provides virtually any shareware Windows software. Lets you search the entries by keyword.

Current Weather Maps/ Movies

http://rs560.cl.msu.edu/weather/

Offers a complete collection of weather images, compiled from a variety of satellites and sources.

Cyber Trek Technologies Home Page

http://www.cais.com/cybertrek/phpl.cgi?index.html

Offers connections to various sources, such as sports information, news, weather, and so on. Features a link to a site that gives the most recent news from ABC using the RealAudio tool.

CyberCentral

http://www.scsn.net/~musex/cyber/central.html

Offers many links to some major (and not so major) search sites. Serves as a place to go for starting queries for specific, possibly rare, information.

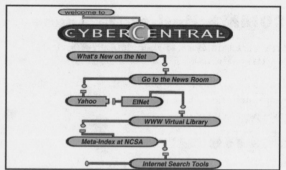

Cybergate Systems, Inc.

http://cybergsi.com

Provides Internet solutions, home pages, programming, graphics, and scanning services. Also sponsors the USA Football Center Online, which gives scores and updates to college and pro and features a pregame show.

The Cyberspace Connection

http://www.main.com/~kirton/index.html

Offers a variety of resources, from search engines to personal and commercial Web links.

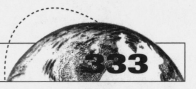
Cyberspace Today ISP Index

http://www.cybertoday.com/cybertoday/ISPs/ispinfo.html

Presents a database on Internet Service Providers (ISPs) around the United States. Lets you search by area code, alphabetically, and by services.

CypherSite

http://www.geopages.com/CapitolHill/1148

Provides information on personal privacy, including links to personal privacy and cryptography information and resources.

Database Demos

http://bristol.onramp.net/

Shows how you can set up your Oracle-based database management system (DBMS) for access via the Web. Good for creating your own search engine or providing Web access to large bodies of information.

Dave's Netscape Tricks

http://home.ptd.net/~dkt/trick/tricks.htm

Includes a collection of interesting and funny Netscape v1.1+ tricks.

David B. Martin's VRML Page

http://www.kfu.com/~dbmartin/vrml.html

Provides a decent page of VRML links, describes what VRML is, and offers a little bit about its inventors.

DCI's Internet Expo

http://www.ocm.com/dci/internet/default.htm

Provides information on the Expo that happens in Toronto in September and then again in Boston in November. Offers information about the more than 100 conference sessions and advice online from Internet business experts.

Dr. Jim's Virtual Veterinary Clinic

http://rampages.onramp.net/~drjim

Focuses on common behavior and health-related questions asked by pet owners.

Dunn & Edwards Services

http://www.iwc.com/des/index.html

Provides a variety of services and resources for development of sophisticated home pages for use on the Web.

Dynamic Diagrams Home Page

http://dynamicDiagrams.com/

Focuses on the organization and presentation of information in print and electronic forms, interactive publication and prototype design, SGML applications, Web servers, and computer kiosks for museums.

The E-Minder Free Reminder-By-E-Mail Service

http://www.netmind.com/e-minder/e-minder.html

Offers to send you automatically-generated reminder messages for any event or occasion for which you register. Requires an e-mail address, but otherwise is completely anonymous. Lets you specify the number of days in advance you want a reminder. Provides a simple e-mail interface that you can use to list or delete reminders.

Easy Mosaic and Introductory Web Surfing

http://www.lm.com/~lmann/docs/easymosaic.html

Serves as a basic primer on using the Mosaic Web browser. Provides a history of how information was disseminated before the Web.

Economic FAQs about the Internet

http://gopher.econ.lsa.umich.edu/FAQs/FAQs.html

Presents a collection of FAQs about the economics behind the Internet. Discusses the technology behind the Internet, the NSF backbone.

Economics and the Internet

http://gopher.econ.lsa.umich.edu/EconInternet.html

Provides a collection of documents related to the economics behind the Internet. Includes high resolution slides.

Economics of Networks Internet Site

http://edgar.stern.nyu.edu/networks/

Provides information and links to the economics behind all networks. Includes downloadable papers on topics ranging from network compatibility to financial networks.

EFF's (Extended) Guide to the Internet

http://www.eff.org/papers/bdgtti/eegtti.html

Features a list of Internet providers by state, and describes e-mail, usenet groups, ftp, telnet, and BBS.

EFFweb—The Electronic Frontier Foundation

http://www.eff.org/

Nonprofit civil liberties organization. Promotes privacy and free expression. Includes many online resources and references. Contains *EFFector Online*, its publication.

EINet Galaxy

http://www.einet.net

Serves as a search site. Includes general topics and sublists under each of these. Also offers a list of job opportunities.

Enterprise Internet Services

http://www.enterprise.net

Acts as a major provider of Internet Services based in the Isle of Man, British Isles. Also specializes in providing Web-based applications that utilize a secure Netscape Commerce Server. Offers a diverse and extensive Web server for all applications.

Entry Level

http://www.mecklerweb.com/webguide/entry.htm

Presents a guide to entry-level Internet information. Gives advice on searching the Internet, offers style tips for newsgroups, and provides information concerning how to use encryption.

EPage Classifieds

http://ep.com

Popular classified advertising forum. Free for the Internet community. Lets you view all classifieds by region or subject; all classifieds can be anonymous for your safety. Contains some regional newspaper classifieds that you cannot find elsewhere on the Internet.

The Executive Guide to Marketing on the New Internet

http://www.industry.net/guide.html

Online paper. Focuses on the effect of the Internet on business. Talks about the changing role between the Internet and the marketing executive. Speculates on the future on the Internet.

Explorer

http://www.rtis.com/explorer/

Serves as a search site for finding resources for the Internet. Arranges areas by subject.

Exploring the Internet

`http://www.cen.uiuc.edu/exploring.html#BlindSpin`

Introduces you to *blindspinning*, spinning around and then going in a random direction. So, provides all sorts of random links.

The Film and Broadcasting Page

`http://www.io.org/~proeser/`

Lists various resources in the film and broadcasting media, including various broadcasters, regulators, associations, equipment manufacturers and suppliers, freelancers, and so on.

FLFSoft, Inc. Home Page

`http://www.execpc.com/~flfsoft/`

Develops Windows-based utilities and Internet software and services. Features Web Spinner, a Windows-based HTML editor.

Fountainhead Internet Systems

`http://www.fountainhead.com/`

Full-service Internet presence provider based in Los Angeles, California. Provides Internet hookups, consulting, Web page design, and training. Also publishes the *Los Angeles Superstation*.

Free Internet Encyclopedia

`http://www.cs.uh.edu/~clifton/encyclopedia.html`

Presents an encyclopedia composed of information available on the Internet. A MacroReference contains references to large areas of knowledge. A MicroReference contains information and references about a specific subject.

Free Range Media, Inc.

`http://www.freerange.com`

Specializes in keeping track of the newest tools. Produces a wide variety of Web-related products. Also shares many tips and techniques.

FreedomPAGE!

`http://homepage.seas.upenn.edu/~dmelczer/FreedomPAGE.html`

Offers links to information and sources that might offend some people. Helps you peruse the darker side of the Internet. Offers links to sites on how to improve your sex life, how to make bombs, and so forth.

FutureNet:.net1, Dec '94— Easy Internet—Introduction

`http://www.futurenet.co.uk/netmag/Issue1/Easy/index.html`

Serves as a complete and in-depth beginner's Internet guide. Provides information on how to hook up your machine, how to use information to your advantage, and more. Also provides a history of the Internet.

FutureTel, Inc.

`http://www.ftelinc.com`

Possesses leading technology in both compression and telecommunications, so is uniquely positioned to serve the needs of the digital video publishing and distribution markets. Provides the most complete solution to the challenges of distributing and publishing digital video both on CDs, and wired and wireless networks. The company's digital video publishing product line includes PrimeView, a family of real-time PC-based Mpeg encoders, and MPEGWORKS, a comprehensive encoding control software package for human assisted or pass-through compression.

Get the Hell Out of Dodge

`http://www.fn.net/~roundman/jwz/rand/ran.html`

Presents a collection of Web sites, but differs from other random Web link pages in that the maintainers of "Dodge" must approve the links on this page. Serves as a random linker, but excludes some of the really boring Web sites you

find on other random linkers. Also lets you choose your area by topic and go from there rather than randomizing.

Glass Wings: All That Is Fun Wise and Wonderful

http://www.aus.xanadu.com/GlassWings/welcome/html

Provides a collection of links and a search site for only fun and nonbusiness-oriented stuff. Includes an online mall where you can buy things, links to humorous sites, and more.

Global Institute for Interactive Multimedia

http://www.thegiim.org/

Provides information and guides for teaching people how to create a home page. Divides the information according to the audience: for example, provides teachers a different tutorial than for business owners.

Global Network Navigator Home Page

http://gnn.com/gnn/gnn.html

Presents GNN, the creaters of the Web browser Mosaic. Provides information on Mosaic and GNN's net Internet access service. Includes their Whole Internet Catalog and offers perusable online publications on virtually every topic.

Glossary of Internet Terms

http://www.matisse.net/files/glossary.html

Lists Internet and computer-related acronyms.

GTLug ISP Index

http://www.gtlug.org/isp/

Lists Internet service providers (ISP). Lets you you find ISPs by clicking on a map of the United States.

Guide to Mapping the Internet

http://www.uvc.com/gbell/promo.html

Presents Gordon Bell, one of the pioneers of the Internet, discussing his views on the direction in which the Internet now should proceed. Discusses his proposal for ending the problems with limited bandwidth and the increased traffic on the Internet. Includes a slide show and sound bites with the presentation.

Guided Web Tours

http://www.netgen.com/tour.html

Presents guided tours of the Web.

A Handy Guide

http://www.ahandyguide.com/

Serves as a complete guide to thousands of sites on the Internet and Web. Lets you search by category or company name. Also offers learning American Sign Language as an option.

The Hermes Project

http://www.umich.edu/~sgupta/hermes

Presents an ongoing research project that is trying to determine the commercial uses of the Web. Offers an online consumer survey from people on the Web.

Hideki's Home Page: How to Use Japanese on the Internet

http://www.jweb.com/~hirayama/

Provides information about how to use Japanese on the Internet. Offers many links to Japanese resources, including information on Netscape's Japanese Capable WWW Browser. Also provides many links on Japan.

The High-Tech Investor

http://www.interlog.com/~mathewi/invest.htm

Discusses investment-related resources on the Web and offers a collection of links to some of those resources.

Hippermedia

http://www.io.org/~farellc/hipper.html

Specializes in getting businesses and organizations on the Web as simply and as inexpensively as possible.

Hole in the Wall Gang Camp Wish List

http://www.tiac.net/users/oline/camp

Contains a camp established by Paul Newman for children with life-threatening illnesses.

Home Space Builder

http://www.paragraph.com/whatsnew/homespce.htm

A 3D Web authoring tool that enables you to create a 3D home space using a standard Windows personal computer. Offers beta 1 for free.

Home Page Cards

http://www.futuris.net/touch/homecard.htm

Creates a special greeting card with your home page on the cover and URL inside. Also offers to arrange to mail the cards as a turn-key service.

Hot Topic: Internet 25th Anniversary

http://www.amdhal.com/internet/events/inet25.html

Celebrates the Internet's 25th anniversary from September 1st to December 31st of 1995. Provides information about how the Internet was born, links to information sources on things like the history of the Internet, the Internet timeline, and more. Also provides information about the Unix 25th anniversary and the Charles Babbage Institute online.

How to Search a WAIS Database

http://town.hall.org/util/wais_help.html

Provides information on how to begin and structure a WAIS search. Describes how to use Boolean operators, wild cards, relevance ranking, and so on. Offers a tutorial on using a WAIS search engine.

How to Select an Internet Service Provider

http://web.cnam.fr/Network/Internet-access/how_to_select.html

Describes what you should look for when you set out to purchase an Internet connection. Includes information on network topology, network link speeds, technical staff, and more.

HTML Hot List

http://www.ohiou.edu/~jvannest/info/

Lists HTML-related information. Encourages you to add links to other informational pages. Includes links to CGI, forms, image maps, tables, and lists. Includes information on the latest developments in these areas.

IBC: Internet Timeline

http://tig.com/IBC/Timeline.html

Presents Hobbes' Internet Timeline. Covers events related to the creation of the Internet, such as Sputnik's launch in 1956.

ICC: Internet Seminar Series

http://www.icons.com/seminar.html

Provides information for businesses concerning security, firewalls, and server design and implementation.

ICL ProSystems AB

http://www.pro.icl.se

Provides the Internet e-mail product, EMBLA.

The Iconovex Corporation Server

http://www.iconovex.com

Produces Indexicon, indexing software for word processors, and AnchorPage, indexing software for Web servers. Offers full information on Iconovex Corporation's product line, as well as demonstrations of their products.

Image Alchemy Digital Imaging

http://www.alchemy.com.au/

Presents a gallery of digital art and photography, traditional art, and photography. Offers services such as photo retouching and manipulation. Also designs Web sites.

Image Compression for Publishing Online

http://www.jgc.com

Provides information about Johnson-Grace company, a multimedia software development that has developed an image compression format called ART. Suggests that using ART enables image compression three times more efficient than when you use Jpeg or GIF. Targets online service providers and publishers. Says that using the ART format enables you to download quality images in one-third the time.

ImageFX—Computer Graphics and Animation

http://www.supernet.net/~jbraatz

Specializes in 3D graphics and animation for corporate logos, broadcast work, multimedia, Web page design, and VRML creation. Also offers video digitizing services. Includes samples of their work that you can view and download from our pages.

INFO Online

http://www.pona.com

Focuses on oncology and specifically provides information for physicians dealing with networks, integration, and pharmaceutical companies. Also provides information for people involved with oncology, including patients.

INFOMINE

http://lib-www.ucr.edu/

The library at the University of California. Aims to make resources available to UCR students and staff, but is open to the public. Offers many online card catalogs and articles.

Inter-Links

http://www.nova.edu/Inter-Links/start.html

Serves as site for browsing the Internet and locating specific resources. Features Internet resources, guides and tutorials, news and weather, library resources, fun and

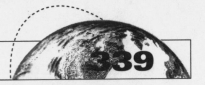

games, a reference shelf, and a miscellaneous section. Includes several original search engines, as well.

International Business Resources on the WWW

http://ciber.bus.msu.edu/busres.htm

Serves as an index of business, economics, trade, marketing, and government sites with an international focus.

Internet Access Providers around the World

http://www.best.be/iap.html

Offers a list of Internet access providers.

The Internet Advertising Resource Guide

http://www.missouri.edu/Internet-advertising-guide.html

Offers many links to information about advertising on the Internet. Offers links to Web tracking services, advertising law, and its role on the Internet and a list of best Internet stores.

Internet Bookshelf

http://www.mecklerweb.com/mags/iw/books/books.htm

Contains book reviews, ordering information, and more on books that relate to the Internet.

Internet Business Center

http://www.tig.com/IBC/index.html

Provides information about conducting business on the Internet. Includes Internet statistics, maps, and charts. Also lists hot sites and services.

Internet Business Connection

http://www.intbc.com/

Offers home page development and marketing services to any business seeking an Internet presence.

The Internet Companion

http://www.obs-us.com/obs/english/books/editinc/obsxxx.htm

An online version of the *Internet Companion*, 2nd Edition. Provides book review and answers such questions as "Who runs the Internet?"

Internet Conference '96 Home Page

http://www.niagara.com/~netcon/

Provides information on the Internet Conference '96, to be held at Niagara Falls, Canada, in February, 1996. Includes the itinerary, registration information, and hotel and airline accommodations. The purpose of the conference is to showcase new Internet products and services.

Internet Conference Calendar

http://www.automatrix.com/conferences/

Lists upcoming conferences, symposia, conferences, and workshops related to the Internet. Lets you use the submission form to add your own events to the calendar. Also lets you list upcoming events geographically. Provides links to separate pages for each event listed, if available.

Internet Connection for Windows

http://www.issc1.ibm.com/pcdirect/p22h6021.htm

Provides information about IBM's Internet access package for Windows. Includes product features, requirements, and pricing information.

Internet Connections

http://tbone.biol.scarolina.edu/~dean/kit/kit.html/

Provides links to various Internet software packages. Provides information on all the different packages you can

use to access the Internet. Lists the standards and some lesser-known ones as well.

Internet FL Group

http://www.compass.net/~sunny

Provides Internet consulting to get you connected with a service provider and up and running on the Internet. Specializes in home page authoring and design in the south Florida area.

Internet Info Store Directory

http://www.openmarket.com/stores/walsh@internetinfo.com/
store/StoreFront.html

Tracks commercial activity on the Internet. Offers special reports online about financial service firms, public software companies, and venture capital firms on the Internet.

Internet Learning Center

http://oeonline.com/~emoryd

Offers tutorial columns, as well as "where to go" columns. Also includes links to Unix Reference Center, Hypertext Guide, Rinaldi's Netiquette, Odd de Presno's Online World book, and other Internet resources.

Internet Marketing Resource: A How To

http://edit.cprost.sfu.ca/~sigma6/

Serves as an Internet marketing resource site. Offers some commonly asked questions and answers for prospective Internet businesses.

The Internet Pearls Index

http://www.execpc.com/~wmhogg

Features collections of the best of the Internet. Includes sections for beginners as well as comprehensive coverage of topics such as business, medicine, jobs, cinema, shareware, astronomy, futuristic technologies, fun, cartoons, comics, virtual reality, and more.

Internet Phone

http://www.vocaltec.com/

One of the most talked about applications of the Internet. Lets you use the software at this site (and a PC that has a sound card) to talk to people anywhere in the world for free. Provides downloadable information about the program.

"Talk For Free Over the Internet"

Internet Relay Chat Games

http://calypso.cs.uregina.ca/Games/

Offers information and history on the most popular games played on the IRC network. Offers information on Risky Business, Chaos, Boggle, and Acrophobia.

Internet Resources

http://www.brandonu.ca/~ennsnr/Resources/

Contains pointers to more than 100 guides, lists, and indices of documents that help you learn how to use the Internet. Includes pointers to The December and Yanoff Lists, Patrick Crispen's Internet Roadmap (in HTML), The Awesome List, and many others.

Internet Resources Newsletter

http://www.hw.ac.uk/libWWW/irn/irn.html

Free monthly Web newsletter. Focuses on higher education and the Internet. Features lists of new Internet resources, plus other items of interest.

Internet Servers for the Mac OS

http://www.freedonioa.com/ism/

Contains many links to Macintosh-specific software packages for running a Mac-based server. Topics include mail servers, mail gateways, ftp servers, telnet servers, and so on.

The Internet Sleuth

http://www.charm.net/~ibc/sleuth/

Offers a collection of more than 500 searchable databases on a wide variety of subjects. Offers links to a search form or page that lists a number of related searchable databases. Also lets you search by keyword or browse alphabetically or by category.

For Those Quick Keyword Searches on Hundreds of Databases

Internet Tour

http://www.globalcenter.net/gcweb/tour.html

Overviews the Internet. Incorporates many graphics and a laid-back attitude. Shows you how to send birthday flowers.

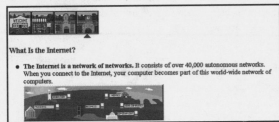

What Is the Internet?

- **The Internet is a network of networks.** It consists of over 40,000 autonomous networks. When you connect to the Internet, your computer becomes part of this world-wide network of computers.

Introduction to HTML: Table of Contents

http://www.cwru.edu/help/introHTML/toc.html

Presents a guide to authoring Web pages. Divides sections by different images, lists, and anchors. Gives information on how to take advantage of Netscape functions.

Introduction to the Internet

http://www.sils.umich.edu/~fperfect/inet/

Offers links to a variety of Internet resources. Offers many links and provides information on different Internet programs.

Introduction to the Internet II

http://uu-gna.mit.edu:8001/uu-gna/text/internet/index.html

Provides information about a class to introduce users to various resources available on the Internet.

The IRC Gallery

http://www.powertech.no/IRCGallery/

Serves as a place where people using IRC can put up images of themselves. Lets you search by country or name.

The IRC Poker Channels Home Page

http://maelstrom.cc.mcgill.ca/poker/poker.html

Offers everything you need to know to play IRC poker. Lets you play poker with people anywhere in the world in real time.

The Japan Yellow Pages

http://www.csj.co.jp/J/Yellowpage-j/yp/html

Offers links to information pertinent to and/or located in Japan (in Japanese).

Joel's Hierarchical Subject Index

http://www.cen.uiuc.edu/~jj9544/index.html

A lesser-known but fairly thorough search site.

Kevin's Internet Encyclopedia

http://duke.usask.ca/~lowey/encyclopedia/index.html

An online encyclopedia (incomplete). Provides an abstract and then lists resources for the topic (for the subjects that it contains so far).

Kids on Campus (Cornell Theory Center)

http://www.tc.cornell.edu/Kids.on.Campus

The Cornell Theory Center sponsors Kids On Campus as part of our celebration of National Science and Technology Week. The purpose of this event is to increase computer awareness and scientific interest among Ithaca-area third, fourth, and fifth grade students. We want to introduce computing to children in ways they can enjoy and understand. Hands-on computer activities, innovative videos, and exciting demonstrations help the children develop interest and excitement in computers and science.

A List of Virtual Libraries on the Web

http://www.w3.org/hypertext/DataSources/bySubject/Virtual_libraries/Overview.html

Offers links to collections of information, based on the subject matter of those sites.

List of WWW Archie Services

http://pubweb.nexor.co.uk/public/archie/servers.html

Offers a list of hypertext links to Archie (Archive) servers. Helps you find files anywhere on the Internet. Lists archie servers that use forms and others that don't.

LookUp!

http://www.lookup.com/

Offers a directory service that provides easy-to-use Name to e-mail address mapping.

The Lycos Home Page: Hunting WWW Information

http://lycos.cs.cmu.edu/

Provides a Web search engine. Contains more than 5.5 million Web pages in its database. Provides context for evaluating whether a document or page is relevant to your search.

MagicURL Mystery Trip

http://www.netcreations.com/magicurl/index.html

Focuses on providing things from hippies, including such things as lava lamps. Offers links that are screened by moderators before being added to the database, ensuring that they are, well, cool.

Making Money on the Internet

http://cism.bus.utexas.edu/ravi/making_money.html

Offers information on electronic publishing, Internet economics, education, and other areas.

Map of GNN Sites Worldwide

http://gnn.digital.com/gnn/wel/sitesmap.html

Provides a graphical interface that shows the locations of all the GNN sites around the world.

The Maserati Pages

http://www.america.com/~spdracer/maserati.html

Targets not only Maserati enthusiasts, but all fans of high performance automobiles. Includes graphics images of Maseratis as well as pictures of other fine Italian automobiles. Includes links to other interesting automotive sites and clubs. Includes an advertisers section for people who want to buy, trade, or sell and a tech section.

Media Connection of New York—Links Page

http://www.mcny.com/linkspage/

Offers a collection of links to Web resources in or about New York City.

Media Logic's Index of Economic and Financial Resources

http://www.mlinet.com/mle/

This index of resources is provided by Media Logic as a service for the Internet community. It provides a searchable index of data, news, and services that are of interest to investors, researchers, and other members of the financial community. Unlike many other Internet indices, all entries here are subject to editorial review to ensure that they are useful, relevant, and current.

Medius Communications, Inc.

http://www.medius.com

Medius Communications, Inc. provides Corporate Internet access and presence services, enabling organizations to plan, build, implement, and promote complete online information and application services.

The Meeting Place

http://www.nis.net/meet/

Serves as a way to meet adults who share similar interests anywhere over the Internet. Lets you input your interests and then lists people who report the same interests.

MeGALiTH's Sensational Visual IRC Beta Home Page

http://apollo3.com/~acable/virc.html

Visual IRC is the first of a 'new generation' of IRC clients for Windows, incorporating state-of-the-art file transfer, audio, and advanced IRC features. Features channel surf and other great features. Grab the latest beta (0.41c) from this page.

Meta-list of What's New Pages

http://homepage.seas.upenn.edu/~mengwong/
whatsnew.list.html

Offers a collection of links to all of the different Internet What's New sites for Web.

The Mother-of-all BBS

http://www.cs.colorado.edu/homes/mcbryan/public_html/bb/
summary.html

Seeks to collect all Web addresses of all companies, universities, research centers, government agencies, research projects, and hardware and software announcements, into one searchable.

Motorcycle Shopper Online

http://www.mshopper.eurografix.com

Motorcycle Shopper Online is the electronic version of the printed magazine. You can read and place classified ads online, read motorcycling news and articles, download databases, visit the 'Vendors' section, and more!

MultiMedia Dimensions— New Horizons in Sight and Sound

http://www.cybercomm.net/~mediaman/mmdimen.html

MultiMedia Dimensions is a full-service interactive multimedia and Web Page design and consulting company helping people find the right business solutions for their needs and budget.

The Multimedia Help Page

http://www.sdcs.k12.ca.us/people/schumsky/greg.html

Provides quick access to sources of multimedia tools and tips on the Web. Also provides links and tips for video production, search engines, and production tools for the Apple Newton.

The NET Compass

http://home.cc.umanitoba.ca/~umwittma

Serves as a meta-index for searching the Web by subject or by keyword, and for searching ftp software by file name or by file description.

The Net: User Guidelines and Netiquette, by Arlene Rinaldi

http://www.fau.edu/rinaldi/net/index.html

Offers a collection of user guidelines and *netiquette* for the Internet. Discusses legal and ethical issues involved.

NETCOM Online Communications Services, Inc.

http://www.netcom.com

Contains information about NETCOM, one of the nation's largest Internet Providers. Offers local access numbers online for subscribers on the go. Subscription information available online.

Netscape Tutorial

http://w3.ag.uiuc.edu/AIM/Discovery/Net/www/netscape/index.html

Gives a step-by-step tutorial on using Netscape. Can be very in-depth. Allows for different levels of expertise.

Netscape: J.P. Morgan's Equities Research

http://www.jpmorgan.com/MarketDataInd/Research/WebReport/TOC.html

A rather large report by JP Morgan associates on the impact the World Wide Web has and will have on business. Tables and Appendices are useful.

NetView Press Release 17 July 1995

http://www.newview.com/

Information about NetGuardian, a program that allows parents to monitor what a child sees on the World Wide Web. Gives product and ordering information.

NetWatchers Legal Cyberzine

http://www.ionet.net/~mdyer/netwatch.shtml

A monthly e-zine that reports on legal developments in cyberspace and the online world.

Network Hardware Suppliers List

http://www.ua.com/hardware/hardware.html

Look here to find a list of recommended used telecommunications and hardware dealers. These dealers have been recommended by various people all over the net.

The NetWorXs of California

http://www.garlic.com/~andersen

Offers a full range of Web home page authoring and design services. Also offers full turn-key systems, including training in-house personnel so that you can enhance your Web server as your services or products change.

New Riders' Official World Wide Web Yellow Pages

http://www.mcp.com/nrp/wwwyp/

The online version of this book. Searchable by keyword. Obviously the most complete and useful search site available.

The New User Directory

http://fas-www.harvard.edu/~calvarez/ndir.html

Presents a large collection of links to information. Offers tips for specific kinds of computers (MAC, IBM, Unix, and so forth), links to search engines, and more. Also provides information on how to create Web pages and download software.

new3, Inc.

http://www.new3.com/

new3, Inc. is a leading edge website architectural and development firm. With high-level technical knowledge of programming plus a creative focus, new3, Inc. has played a role in bringing some of the best sites to the Web. Their

specialty is areas of development considered too complex for many developers.

Newton Online

http://www.newtonline.com

Newton Online provides business consulting for companies who want to complement marketing and communications strategies by using the Internet. Web page and Web site outsourcing.

NickNet

http://www.pinc.com/nburger/home.html

More than 3,200 links to dazzle and amaze you! If websurfing were any more fun they would have to ban it! Everything you could ever want is here and categorized so it is all easy to find. Webaddicts beware!

NlightN: Finding What You Want To Know...Now

http://www.nlightn.com

With a single query, the NlightN Universal Index searches the Web, World News, Online Databases and traditional reference sources.

Nothin' But Net A–B Sample

http://www.xmission.com/~vothcom/ltompkins/index.html

Nothin But Net (NBN) is a complete Internet Encyclopedia covering more than 200+ categories packed with 2,500+ non-commercial, resourceful Internet sites. Provides a sample excerpt from the A-B categories as well as full ordering information.

Omega West

http://www.cs.ubc.ca/spider/hoppe/

A site with something for everyone. Well-organized into a hierarchical structure, everything from business resources and financial tips to a broad spectrum of entertainment and Web developer resources. Omega West, an international

distribution and services company, will soon have an "intelligent interface" that is capable of adapting to users' actions. This, of course, will mean that return visits and continued interaction will provide users with a personalized interface.

The Online World Resources Handbook

http://login.eunet.no/~presno/

Provides practical advice on using the Internet to get information or programs. Breaks topics down into various topics, such as how to get free expert assistance, how to read your electronic daily news, and more.

Overall Knowledge Company, Inc.

http://www.okc.com

Overall Knowledge Company, Inc. is a general Web presence provider with an emphasis on the film and television trades, as well as the arts and entertainment industries. We also publish several industry-specific directories on the World Wide Web.

Patrick Crispen's Internet Roadmap

http://www.brandonu.ca/~ennsnr/Resources/Roadmap/Welcome.html

This is the Internet Roadmap online training course, available in HTML. This is a well-written tutorial, and very user-friendly. A must for any school Internet coordinator's bookmark list!

The Personal Home Page of Bob Hunter

http://www.awinc.com/users/bhunter/

Focuses on testing HTML coding examples and pushing the limits of hypertext markup language and all of its extensions.

Photo Exhibitions and Archives

http://math.liu.se:80/~behal/photo/exhibits.html

Provides a collection of links to photography-related sites. Attempts to divide up the links into categories. Also offers many links to photo images on the Internet.

PICC Home Page

http://www.openmarket.com/picc/picc.html

Partners for Identifying Content in Cyberspace. Seeks to control access to the Internet by indexing various resources. Offers online information about its proposal. Offers a list of frequently asked questions.

Planet Earth Home Page

http://www.nosc.mil/planet_earth/info.html

Search site on the Internet, organized like a library. Offers a library floorplan that you can use to browse the sites in its database. Also lets you search the database by keyword.

Point Survey and Escort

http://www.pointcom.com

Provides a large collection of reviews of Web sites. Rates sites for content, presentation, and experience. Includes more than 1,000 reviews across many categories. Helps you get started on the Web with answers to common questions and guided tours of browsing software and sites.

The Postcard Store

http://postcards.www.media.mit.edu/Postcards/

Lets you choose a virtual postcard from the rack (which mainly consists of famous paintings) and then you can attach a message and then send it to someone.

Presence—An Information Design Studio

http://www.presence.com/

Focuses on providing innovative and effective marketing solutions through the Internet.

A Primer for Creating Web Resources

http://www-slis.lib.indiana.edu/Internet/
programmer-page.html

Offers a list of links to HTML resources. Also offers links to Perl and CGI languages for creating top-of-the-line Web pages.

The Professional Photographers Web Page

http://rampages.onramp.net:80/~blitz/

Lets professional photographers research locations; get weather reports, hotels, and airfare, Photoshop and Corel-DRAW! tips, and links to Kodak and other related sites.

Prospero's Global Stage

http://www2.prospero.com

Focuses on adding live interaction to the Web. Lets you download the software for free here and offers discussion areas.

Publicize Your Home Page

http://www.ntg-campus.com/ntg/public.htm

Provides a collection of links to various search engines. Focuses on connecting you to the part of these search engines that allows you to register and add your own home page.

PVEP

http://www.indirect.com/www/ceridgac/index.html

Serves as a starting point for resources associated with commercial nuclear power and emergency preparedness for commercial nuclear power generation facilities. Also includes an index of Internet-related resources for generalized information.

Q-D Software Development

http://www.intac.com/~dversch/

Presents the creators of WebForms; the Web forms generator; and WinBrowse, the multiple PC database utility.

RAMWORKS

http://www.ramworks.com/ramworks/

Provides cutting edge technology blended with award-winning traditional design to offer Interactive Multimedia services, Internet presences, and Web pages, CD-ROM and CD-I authoring, interactive touch-screen kiosks, and corporate communications.

RealAudio Home Page

http://www.realaudio.com/

Provides RealAudio, software you can use to both record and play your own sounds. Many Web sites use RealAudio on the Internet to provide audio.

Real-World Research Home Page

http://mp.cs.niu.edu:8000/~z946880

Provides the answers to everything your mother warned you about. Also provides a business link for people interested in research on any topic. Also contains links to Web search engines and databases.

Recondite Reference Desk

http://www.unt.edu/~ns0003/

Serves as a starting place for Web searches. Features an online form that is linked to the search forms of major data sites.

Rob's Multimedia Lab

http://www.acm.uiuc.edu/rml

Provides many images, sounds, and movies.

Sample Form

http://www.uni.edu/~wells27/samform.html

Presents a form for no other purpose than to provide examples of how you can create various objects on a Web page. Teaches you how to make check boxes and buttons.

Search, Find—Internet Resource Locators

http://ananse.irv.uit.no/law/nav/find.html

Provides a graphically oriented set of links to search engines on the Internet, such as Open Text Web Index, InfoSeek Search, and others.

SearchAmerica

http://www.serachamerica.com/

Lets you access databases that contain information about millions of people. Helps you find addresses all across the United States. The computerized equivalent of Directory Assistance, but without the bother. Also offers pricing information.

Searching the Web

http://union.ncsa.uiuc.edu/HyperNews/get/www/searching.html

Provides information and links to searching for information on the Web. Offers links to searching services, searching software, and searching references.

Setting Up Shop

http://www.netrex.com/business.html

Provides information regarding commercial use strategies, including dos and don'ts of online marketing.

Sibylla—General Description

http://www.cib.unibo.it/guests/ariadne/sibylla/sibyllaeng.html

Provides information on Sibylla, a development kit geared towards creating Web software with the purpose of providing access to information sources (such as company databases) through the Web. Also provides pricing information on the software.

SpectraFAX Corp. Home Page

http://naples.com/spectrafax/

Describes fax broadcast and fax on demand technology. Also compares costs for reaching United States markets via fax and via postal service from locations outside the United States. Introduces the SpectraFAX Service Bureau and lets you use an online form to arrange for fax services.

Spinning the Web: WWW Servers

http://scholar.lib.vt.edy/reports/Servers-web.html

Gives information on how to create a Web Server. Offers an accompanying slide show that provides hardware specifics needed to make a Web Server.

Stannet WWW Designing and Publishing Company

http://www.webcom.com/~stannet

Focuses on authoring, designing, and publishing Web pages for businesses and individuals. Performs custom graphics work. Maintains and upgrades customers' sites as needed. Offers to meet customers in the greater New York City area in their offices.

Starting Point (Add to Your Hotlist)

http://www.stpt.com/

Provides a starting site for finding information on the Web. Offers many links.

SuraNet's Archie Guide

http://www.sura.net/archie/Archie-Usage.html

Provides information on how to use archive servers (Archie). Provides formats for simple and complex searches.

Surf the Net with PacketWorks

http://www.packet.net

Provides full Internet access in the Clearwater, Sarasota, Tampa, and Ft. Myers calling areas. Offers PPP dialup and dedicated connections at speeds ranging from 28.8 V.34 via modem to 115.2kbps via ISDN. Carries a full Usenet newsfeed and maintains high availability by keeping the user-to-line ratio at less than 10:1. Provides details on pricing and a map of the exchanges.

Surfin' the Net

http://www.shore.net/~adfx/video

Introduces the Internet.

SurfWatch Home Page

http://www.surfwatch.com/

Presents SurfWatch, a program for reducing the risk of children uncovering sexually explicit material on the Internet. Talks about its agreements with AOL and offers an online product demonstration.

Welcome to the SurfWatch Software's World Wide Web site!

SWITCH—Swiss Academic and Research Network

http://www.switch.ch/

Presents SWITCH, an Internet service provider that interconnects all Swiss universities, many libraries and research labs, as well as other Swiss and international organizations.

Table of Top-Level Internet Domains

http://www.isoc.org/domains.html

Offers a listing of all the top-level Internet domains.

Teach Yourself the Internet Support Page

http://watarts.uwaterloo.ca/ENGL/nrandall/tyi.html

Provides a structured tutorial to teaching yourself how to use the Internet and all of its tools in 21 days. Targets beginners, but serves as a good tutorial overall. Spends one week teaching the basic Internet tools, then other weeks focus on the personal and professional uses of the Internet.

Telefilm-South.Com

http://www.telefilm-south.com

Provides information about the American South's burgeoning film and video industry.

That Place

www.hooked.net/users/bacchus/

Offers a unique rating system to make choosing from the available links much simpler, updated at least weekly, and usually more often.

This Is the Worst

http://mirsky.turnpike.net/wow/Worst.html

Provides an alternative to the many sites that serve up a "cool" site of the day or point you to "great" places. Offers links to sites that exemplify why some people shouldn't be allowed to make their own Web sites.

A Thousand Points of Sites

http://inls.ucsd.edu/y/OhBoy/randomjump1.html

Generates random Web site links. Sends you to a Web site randomly selected from its listings when you access.

ThreadTreader's WWW Contests Guide®

http://www.4cyte.com/ThreadTreader/

Presents ThreadTreader's WWW Contests Guide®, a complete, current compilation of contests on the Web. Provides easy ways to browse through an extensive index of online contests, drawings, raffles, sweepstakes, and other prize-oriented promotions. Even lets you add your own contest to the ThreadTreader's Guide.

Timothy W. Amey Resource Links

http://www.acti.com/tamey/

Offers a collection of resource links and information regarding OS/2 resources, OS/2 advocacy, Lotus resources, Intel alternatives, religion, Ford advocacy, and IT/IS resources.

tkHTML Editor Information

http://www.ssc.com/~roland/tkHTML/tkHTML.html

Presents tkHTML, a simple HTML editor based on the Tcl script language and the tk toolkit for X11 that enables you to quickly compose and edit HTML-format documents, as well as rapidly convert text documents to the HTML format.

The Today Page

http://www.vossnet.co.uk/local/today/index.html

Offers a collection of links to sites that change daily; for example, includes links to news, your horoscope, and weather photos.

The Transformer WWW Pages

http://www.canit.se/~optimus/tf.html

Offers links to all other transformer resources and provides a small picture archive of its own.

UK Index Beginner's Guide to the Net

http://www.ukindex.co.uk/begin0.html

Serves as a beginner's guide to using the Internet and includes pointers to more resources.

Understanding the Internet

http://www.screen.com/start

Provides a large collection of links to many resources on the Internet. Gives sources for browsers, software, page development, and more.

UnderWorld Links

http://www.nd.edu/StudentLinks/jkeating/links.html

Offers some of the more offbeat links. Provides Star Wars information, audio and video clips from movies, weather maps, and more.

The University of Toledo Instrumentation Center in Arts & Sciences

http://www.icenter.utoledo.edu

Provides information about resources and activities available at the center for the research communities in the University of Toledo and northwest Ohio.

The Unusual or Deep Site of the Day

http://vvv.com/adsint/freehand/deepsite/

Offers links to sites that provide some sort of intellectually stimulating purpose.

The URL-Minder: Your Own Personal Web Robot

http://www.netmind.com/URL-minder/URL-minder.html

Presents the URL-Minder, your own personal Web robot, which retrieves your registered URLs regularly and reports back to you by e-mail when they change. The URL-Minder also runs searches on Web databases regularly and lets you know when anything new that matches your search shows up. It also keeps track of the places you've been, so you can spend your time (and money) doing new things on the Web.

Valiquet Lamothe, Inc.

http://www.vli.ca

Offers access to Internet. Provides information on links to French and English sites. Also provides information on tourism, aboriginal, and levels of government.

Vannevar New Media

http://www.vannevar.com

An Internet publishing and applications company that puts business on the Web.

Virtual Realty Showcase

http://www.homexchange.com/vrs

Serves as a meeting place for Realtors and buyers world-wide. Provides an electronic listing of participating brokers and a selection of their properties by geographic areas.

Virtual Software Library

http://vsl.cnet.com/

Offers a tool for searching for shareware and freeware on the Internet.

The Virtual Tourist

http://wings.buffalo.edu/world/europe.html

Provides a graphical map interface that you can click on to find and then jump to Web servers operating in many countries around the world.

The Virtual Town
City Limits

http://www.cs.ucsdavis.edu/virt-town/welcome.html

Contains many links to stores, public offices, and other things you might find in a real town. Lets you manuever around it the way you do around a real town.

VSL Front Desk at the OAK
Repository

http://www.acs.oakland.edu/cgi-bin/shase

Lets you enter a keyword and the engine searches the major Internet shareware archives for the program you want.

WAIS Access Through
the Web

http://www.ai.mit.edu/the-net/wais.html

Provides information about WAIS, a system that allows you to retrieve documents from databases via full-text searches. Allows you to search by name or by topic.

WAIS, Inc.

http://www.wais.com/

Serves as the home of WAIS software and publishing. Provides information on WAISserver, and anything to do with the WAIS search engine.

Washington University Data Archive

http://wuarchive.wustl.edu

Provides information on the Washington University file transmission protocol (ftp) site. Contains more than 45 gigabytes of software available to the general public.

Washington Web

http://www.washweb.net/

Presents an online guide of Internet resources for the greater Washington, D.C., area.

WaterWeb™

http://www.waterweb.com

Provides a collection of water-related information on the Internet, including water treatment equipment and chemicals, water testing equipment and services, consultants and engineers, water conservation technologies, trade journals, trade associations, research databases, government agencies, upcoming events, and more.

Wavelinx Multimedia Publishing

http://www.wavelinx.com

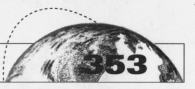
Focuses on Web presence and multimedia design, creating illustrations, 3D graphics, animations, kiosks, interactive marketing presentations, and brochures.

Web Authoring Tools, Images, and Resources

`http://www.smscorp.com/webtools`

Offers a collection of Web authoring tools, images, and resources.

Web KNX Connects the Web

`http://www.webknx.com/webknx.shtml`

Deals with business page hosting, home page hosting, HTML creation Web consulting, PC consulting in Milwaukee and surrounding areas, and PC Support.

The Web Letter, a Guide to HTML/Web Publishing

`http://www.writething.com/`

Serves as an HTML resource. Includes a newsletter, video, and training books, as well as numerous links to help you build your own Web.

Web Marketing— Beyond Boundaries

`http://www.prgone.com/beyond/`

Helps business expand in the new Internet culture. Provides information about Internet marketing and displays the talents of Beyond Boundaries' creative staff. Explains how Beyond Boundaries helps companies survive their ride on the Information Superhighway.

Web Publishing Australia

`http://AusWeb.com.au/`

Introduces you to a professional Web publishing and promotion company based in Queensland, Australia.

A Web Resource Site

`http://www.wwwa.com/resource.html`

Serves as a complete Web resource site with HTML commands, software for publishing, searches, libraries, and high-speed Web host connections for your company or home page.

Web Weavers: A Listing of Resources for Aspiring Web Authors

`http://www.nas.nasa.gov/NAS/WebWeavers/`

Provides a comprehensive listing of Web tools and techniques for aspiring Web authors.

Webants™ Home Page

`http://thule.mt.cs.cmu.edu:8001/webants/`

Provides information about project Webants, to develop an information retrieval system for the Web using cooperative agents. Offers information about their approach and current progress reports.

The Webcatcher

`http://plum.tuc.noao.edu/webcatcher/webcatcher.html`

Monitors the Web for new sites and e-mails you regular updates according to the topics you select.

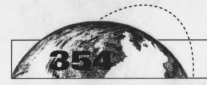

Webchat: WebStation Transport Services

http://www.acme.web.com/webchat/webstation.html

Serves as the main location of a relatively new way of talking to people over the Web, called WebChat, a graphical version of the old Internet Relay Chat system.

WebDesigns

http://www.execpc.com/~jeffo/webdes/

Web page creation service. Focuses on posting and maintenance, logo and graphic design, photography (including improvement of existing photographs), image maps, online newsletters, and getting your page listed in directories like this one, among others.

WEBula

http://www.eg.bucknell.edu/cgi-bin/webula/index.html

Lets you search the site to find links to all sorts of random things.

Welcome to Netscape

http://home.mcom.com/

Offers information about the new security measures being built into HTML, offers a downloadable version of Netscape for Windows 95. Also offers technical support.

Welcome to the First Virtual InfoHaus!

http://www.infohaus.com/

A public-access information mall. Lets you sell information products (books, newsletters, software, and so forth). Enables user to search by seller, type, keyword, or date.

Welcome to Worlds Chat

http://www.worlds.net/wc/welcome.html

Provides a 3D multiuser chatting system. Lets you utilize images and sound while you chat with others.

What's New in Japan

http://www.ntt.jp/WHATSNEW/index.html

Provides information on recent happenings or recent changes in the Web in Japan. Offers a Japanese langauge version of the site.

The Whole Internet Catalog

http://gnn.com/wic/newrescat.toc.html

Presents the Whole Internet Catalog, one of the most complete search sites for the Internet. Lets you browse information by category or search by keyword for specific information.

WIC Top 50

http://gnn.com/gnn/wic/top.toc.html

Offers the Whole Internet Catalog's Top 50 sites.

Windows 95 InterNetworking Headquarters

`http://www.mwci.net/win95/`

Offers Windows 95 shareware, Internet setup information, networking across the Internet, and more.

Winfield Design Group

`http://www.gate.net/~winfield/index.html`

Internet site developers and Internet providers. Offers CGI scripting, C++, perl, and programs.

Winsock Connections

`http://sage.cc.purdue.edu/~xniu/winsock.html`

Explains both the hardware and software issues concerning setting up your Windows PC to access the Internet. Explains where to get the software you need and how to configure it. Also provides information on creating HTML documents.

The World-Wide Web Initiative: The Project

`http://www.w3.org/`

Offers information about the upcoming WWW International Conference. Also offers a wealth of information on various Web issues, such as security, HTTP, and graphics standards.

World-Wide Web: Origins and Beyond, The

`http://homepage.seas.upenn.edu/~lzeltser/WWW/`

Provides the origins of the Web and also talks about some of the other uses of hypertext, such as the Xanadu project. Also discusses some disadvantages of the Web.

WorldTel Global Marketplace

`http://www.worldtel.com/home.html`

Lists businesses and individuals offering products, services, and/or opportunities to the world market.

WorldWide Information and Netcasting Services

`http://www.corcom.com/wins/wins.html`

A full-service Internet company. Offers services ranging from anonymous ftp, data storage, to Mpeg and multimedia and graphic design. Offers to travel to meet a company's needs.

Writing the Information Superhighway

`http://www.umich.edu/~wbutler/UC153Syl.html`

Offers information regarding how to write literature for the Internet (originally an online class at University of Michigan). Lets you direct questions at the professors who originally taught the class. Also includes a linked bibliography of other sites.

WWW Page Design Pointers

`http://www.infonet.net/showcase/nwc-iowa/html/perl.html`

Offers a set of pointers to material concerning the design and implementation of Web page design. Includes pointers to material using HTML, perl, forms, and general Web page considerations.

WWWW—World Wide Web Worm

`http://www.cs.colorado.edu/home/mcbryan/WWW.html`

Best Navigational Aid on the Web in 1994. Lets you give the Worm database some search criteria, and it searches other search sites for those criteria. Claims to have 3 million URLs in its databse.

Yahoo

http://www.yahoo.com

Probably the most popular search site on the Web. It is considered to be the place to go for anything, as long as it isn't too technically oriented. Only offers links to sources, which is different from something like Lycos that also searches directories and files themselves.

Youth Quake

http://emall.com/yq/home.html

Serves as a destination for computer-literate youth. Plans to cater to education all around the world.

Zen and the Art of the Internet—Table of Contents

http://www.cs.indiana.edu/docproject/zen/
zen-1.0_toc.html

Serves as a beginner's guide to the Internet. Offers information on the search engines available. Even offers a section on how to create a newsgroup.

101 KUFO Portland

http://www.europa.com/kufo/

A rock site on the Web. Includes audio clips of the most-played songs.

3-D Zone

http://leonardo.net/3dzone/

Provides information available on publishing 3-D comic books. Also lets you purchase comic books online.

95.7 WQMF 105.9

http://iglou.com/wqmf/

Includes concert information (around the country) and the joke of the week.

99.5 KISS Rocks San Antonio

http://www.txdirect.net/kiss/

Rock station on the Web. Features a virtual tour of the station.

A. C. Nielsen Home Page

http://www.nielsen.com/home/index.html

Tells you all about the ratings system that television and radio stations use to choose programs. Provides information about the services the A. C. Nielsen broadcasting market research firm provides. Includes a virtual store and other information for the busy network executive.

Access ET

http://www.telegraph.co.uk/

Online version of the *Electronic Telegraphy*, a United Kingdom newspaper. Presents European and international stories. Offers information that has a different slant.

Acoustic Musician Magazine

http://www.netinterior.com:80/acoustic/

Online edition of the *Acoustic Musician* magazine. Covers all aspects of acoustic music for the folk musician. Features a few articles, a music festival guide, the table of contents for the forthcoming issue, and a place to submit letters to the editor. Also presents covers of back issues.

Adventurous Traveler Bookstore

http://www.gorp.com/atbook.htm

Provides many helpful books and maps to plan fun and safe trips around the world.

Advertising Age

http://www.adage.com/header.cgi

Online magazine. Presents images for viewing. Contains archives, ad market information, and a daily top story. Lets you join the AdAge mailing list.

AE Magazine

http://www.io.org/~hideout/ae/ae.html

AE Magazine's site of new movie reviews. Also provides actor biographies and the like.

American Country Collectibles

http://rivendell.com/antiques/pubs/gcr/country/

Provides jumps to descriptions and subscription information for GCR Publishing Group, Inc.'s magazines: *American Country Collectibles*, *Collectibles Flea Market Finds*, and *Victorian Decorating and Lifestyle* magazine. Contains an editorial profile and a guide to where to buy each magazine, as well as a table of contents for the current month's issues.

American Wine

http://www.2way.com:80/food/wine/

American Wine magazine online. Focuses on American vineyards and their products. Features in-depth listings of wine and wine-related links. Also includes the complete text of the magazine.

Anton's FreeHand Page

http://www.euro.net/ecompany/afpindex.html

Focuses on the illustration program FreeHand. Includes tips and tricks for enhancing Freehand, samples of work, and listservs and discussion groups about FreeHand.

APT Data Group Plc— Home Page

http://power.globalnews.com/

Includes a host of computer-related publications and magazines.

Aquanaut

http://bighorn.terra.net/aquanaut/

Online magazine. Focuses on scuba diving. Includes classified ads, maps, destination, reviews of products, and lists of training agencies.

Architronic Home Page

http://arcrs4.saed.kent.edu/Architronic/

Architectural magazine online. Includes archives of past issues and subscription information.

Asia, Inc. Online

http://www.asia-inc.com/

Business magazine from Asia online. Includes financial news, the *Asia Report*, and other information for Asian businesspeople and their followers.

Associated Press

http://www1.trib.com/NEWS/APwire.html

The Associated Press online. Requires free login, but then provides full access to the AP news wires.

The Association of America's Public Television Stations (APTS)

http://universe.digex.net:80/~apts/

Contains information about public television, including FAQs, subscriber information, station lists, and programming information. Also offers a repository for news articles that relate to public television.

Association of American University Presses

http://aaup.pupress.princeton.edu/

Features an index of university presses and includes a searchable index of books.

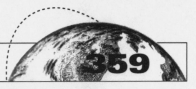

Astrology et al Bookstore

http://www.wolfe.net/~astroetl/index.html

Search the online catalog and place orders online.

The Astronomer Magazine

http://www.demon.co.uk/astronomer/

A British publication online. Targets the advanced amateur but still contains items for beginners. Contains information on comets, asteroids, supernovae, and a variety of other topics that pertain to astronomy.

Atomic Books "Literary Finds for Mutated Minds"

http://www.clark.net/pub/atomicbk/home.html

Alternative bookstore online. Features comics, alternative fiction, magazines, and more. Includes online ordering.

The Audiobook Source

http://www.ambook.org/bookstore/audiobook/

Audiobooks online. Lets you search the catalog and place orders for more than 7,000 titles.

AW's Home Page

http://www.aw.com/

Addison-Wesley Publishing online. Includes sites of Addison-Wesley's many divisions and companies. Searchable.

Barnes & Noble Direct

http://www.shopping2000.com/shopping2000/barnes/

Barnes & Noble bookstore online. Presents selected summaries of titles. Doesn't offer online ordering.

basilisk

http://swerve.basilisk.com/

Online quarterly journal of film, architecture, philosophy, literature, music, and perception.

BDD: Home Page

http://www.bdd.com/

Bantam Doubleday Dell online. Features intimate visits with authors, information about new books, and a daily horoscope.

Blakslee Publishing Home Page

http://www.iii.net/users/Blakslee_Publishing.html

Hypertext Science fiction online. Publishes e-zine serials.

Boardwatch Magazine

http://www.boardwatch.com/

Boardwatch magazine online. Focuses on BBSs and the Internet. Provides subscription information (offers the entire publication free online), and enables you to contact the specific departments or editors of the magazine.

Book Stacks—Home Page

http://www.books.com/

Online bookstore. Includes the Book Cafe, a virtual coffee shop in which literary discussion occurs.

BookWire—The First Place To Look for Book Information

http://www.bookwire.com/

Focuses on books and publishing on the Web. Includes indices of book and publishing-related sites, a reading room, the comic of the day, bestseller lists, and book reviews.

BookZone

http://ttx.com/bookzone

BookZone, "the Internet source for extraordinary books," enables you to learn more about and order books directly from publishers. Includes works from small, medium-size, and alternative publishers whose works you don't always find in the typical bookstore.

Borders Books and Music

http://www.borders.com/borders/

Enables you to search for books and then order them from Borders' large selection of books and magazines. Also provides a list of store locations and lets you browse in person.

BradyGAMES Home Page

http://www.mcp.com/brady/

Includes a combination of strategies, how-to information, game background, editorial content, valuable "inside" information, interviews with game creators, and more.

Broadcasting Services

http://www.wkar.msu.edu/

Includes information about the broadcast stations at Michigan State.

BRP Publications, Inc.

http://brpinc.com/

Provides access to selected articles from more than 20 newsletters that cover the fields of telecommunications, multimedia, data networking, technology, and human resources.

Campus Newspapers on the Internet

http://beacon-www.asa.utk.edu/resources/papers.html

Lists student newspapers available on the Internet. Includes listings for dailies, weeklies, and less frequent publications.

Canadian Broadcasting Centre Virtual Tour

http://www.cbc.ca/aboutcbc/tbc/tour/tour.html

Provides a linear tour of the CBC facilities. Offers background on CBC and photos of the buildings.

Car Collector Home Page

http://205.133.124.2/carcoll/

Car Collector magazine online. Features back issues, advertising information, subscription information, and automotive news.

Catalogue Index

http://www.firmware.com.au/cgi-bin/mediacat.cgi

Offers multimedia developer books and resources for purchase.

CBS Television Home Page

http://www.cbs.com:80/index.html

Features information about current and future CBS programming, CBS news, and "behind the scenes" information about CBS.

Chicago Moving Image Scene

http://www.rtvf.nwu.edu:80/Omnibus/Chicagoindex.html/

Serves as a resource for media people in Chicago and around the world. Includes links, phone numbers, and information about media production.

The Christian Broadcasting Network

http://the700club.org/

The 700 Club online. Offers press releases, viewer guides, fact sheets, information on prayer lines, and links to recommended Web sites.

Christian Warehouse

http://www.christwh.com/cw/index.html

Christian bookstore online. Includes bestselling Christian books and online ordering.

chronicle.merit.edu

gopher://chronicle.merit.edu/

Chronicle of Higher Education's gopher site. Includes archives of back issues as well as current issues.

CineMedia/Multimedia Sites

http://www.gu.edu.au/gwis/cinemedia/CineMedia.multimedia.html

Index of sites related to multimedia production.

CineMedia/Television Sites

http://www.gu.edu.au/gwis/cinemedia/CineMedia.tv.html

Complete index of television sites online. Includes most networks and stations that are online. Also offers a host of other sites related to media and television.

CLiCK—July 1995—Cover

http://www.click.com.au/

CLiCK, an interactive magazine. Enables you to read the magazine online or just find out about events in the interactive media world.

Cocoon

http://leonardo.net/cocoon

Online book. Focuses on dissolving depression.

Cody's Books Home Page

http://www.parentsplace.com/shopping/codys/index.cgi

Provides books on parenting. Features information about parenting and children's books. Includes online ordering.

Commercial Multimedia Producers

http://www.mcli.dist.maricopa.edu/authoring/comm.html

Online index to companies online that produce multimedia.

Commercial Publications

http://www.spub.ksu.edu/other/journlist/commercial.html

List of commercial magazines that are on the Internet.

Computer Manuals Online Bookstore

http://www.easynet.co.uk/compman.htm

Online bookstore in the United Kingdom. Offers a searchable index of 4,500 titles. Presents reviews of books and lets you make purchases online.

Condé Nast Traveler

http://www.cntraveler.com/

Condé Nast Traveler online. Previews the current issue on the newsstands, and provides articles for travelers who want to save money.

Croatian Radio Television

http://www.hrt.com.hr/eng/index.html

Radio-free Croatia. Includes information about program schedules and frequencies. Mirrored in Croatian language.

Cyber Cyclist

http://hyperlink.com:9000/bike

Web magazine for bicyclists. Includes information about bikes, product reviews, current cycling events, and other news.

cyberSPOKESMAN

http://tecnet2.jcte.jcs.mil:8000/cybrspke/cybrspke.html

The Air Force online in the form of a magazine. Interesting for military personnel and buffs. Provides information about news and events in the Air Force.

Cyberwest Magazine

http://www.netway.net:80/cyberwest/

The magazine of the American West online. Features articles and offers links about the West.

The Daily Tar Heel

http://www.unc.edu/dth/

Provides access to news wires online.

Derek R. Spencer's Independent Comic Page

http://www.primenet.com/~drs/

Presents comic books by artists who don't have a contract with a mainstream distributor. Offers these hard-to-find, independently produced comics for purchase online.

designOnline

http://www.dol.com/

Features information about the design aspects of desktop publishing. Includes forums for the discussion of issues, files, contact information, and sample information.

Desktop Publishing/ Printing GS Home Page

http://degaulle.hil.unb.ca/UNB_G_Services/ GSHomePage.html

Focuses on desktop publishing. Contains an image bank, a font and software bank, and links to more resources, as well as information about UNB's products.

Deutsche Welle Radio & TV—English Home Page

http://www.dwelle.de/english/

Provides online program schedules and news and other reports.

Dial-A-Book, Inc.

http://dab.psi.net/DialABook/

Bookstore online. Enables visitors to read the first chapters of available books, including the *Bible*.

Director Web

http://hakatai.mcli.dist.maricopa.edu/director/ index.html

Features links and information relating to the multimedia software, Macromind Director. Includes tips and XObjects.

Directory of /pub/info/ pagemakr

ftp://ftp.dopig.uab.edu/pub/info/pagemakr/

Contains hundreds of plugins and filters for Aldus PageMaker.

dirhome.html

http://www.portal.com/~dwalker/dirhome.html

Presents Director Viewer, the authoring tool. Provides information on the program and its applications.

Dirty Linen

http://kiwi.futuris.net/linen/

Abridged edition of top American magazine for folk, electric folk, Celtic, and world music. Features a selection

of articles, reviews, interviews, and letters to the editor from the current issue. Also includes a guide to concerts and festivals.

Discover Magazine

http://www.enews.com:80/magazines/discover/

Discover magazine online. Includes text of issues, photos, links related to articles, and a subscription service.

Drama Book Publishers

http://www.interport.net/~dramapub/

Focuses on books dedicated to the performing arts. Provides a 1995 catalog for your perusal, in which each entry contains a picture of the book, a synopsis, and book vitals. No ordering online.

DreamLight WebSite

http://www.shore.net/~dreamlt/

Provides information about multimedia production. Features a virtual demo-reel that explains how each project was done.

Welcome to the DreamLight WebSite!

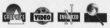

DTP Internet Jumplist

http://www.cs.purdue.edu/homes/gwp/dtp/dtp.html

Features links to fonts and clip art on the Net, a desktop publishing FAQ, and other desktop publishing resources on the Internet.

East View Publications, Inc. Home Page

http://www.eastview.com/

Offers books, magazines, and newpapers published in Central Europe, the CIS, and the former Soviet Union. Offers online delivery of newspapers.

Eastman Kodak Company

http://www.kodak.com/

Contains a digital image bank for multimedia, a chat forum, and information about products.

Editor & Publisher/ Contents

http://www.mediainfo.com/edpub/ep/index.htm

Editor & Publisher magazine online. Offers selected articles from the printed version of the magazine, as well as Web-only content. Offers comprehensive coverage of new media news and trends affecting the newspaper industry.

Electronic Green Journal

http://www.lib.uidaho.edu:70/docs/egj.html

Environmental journal online. Contains information about environmental issues. Also lists the contents of the recent issues of the journal.

Electronic Newsstand

http://internet.com/

Offers sample articles and subscription information for more than 300 magazines.

Elsevier Science— Home Page

http://www.elsevier.nl/

Contains extensive information about publishing. Includes books about writing and publishing.

Esperfonto System for Will-Harris House

http://www.will-harris.com/esp1.htm

Focuses on desktop publishing. Helps visitors choose the best font for a job. Interactive.

Esselte Online

http://www.letraset.com/

Letraset, Dymo, ITC, DeskTop, and Esselte online. Offers free fonts and demos of products from these publishers.

Experimental Service, TeX Information

http://curia.ucc.ie/info/Tex/menu.html

Offers archives, typefaces, and add-ons for TeX and LaTeX publishing programs.

Family World Home Page

http://family.com/homepage.html

Offers selections from more than 40 monthy publications on parenting. Offers links to Internet resources for parents, children, and schools.

FCC Welcome Page

http://www.fcc.gov/

Federal Communications Commission online. Serves as a forum for public discussion concerning FCC issues (including broadcasting). Contains current legislation, full text of relevant speeches, agenda, and the FCC daily digest. Also lists e-mail addresses to which to send comments and concerns about television.

The Felix Culpa Home Page

http://cq-pan.cqu.edu.au/felix-culpa/felix-culpa.html

Australian student magazine. Provides in-depth content.

FH: Canada Travel Home Page

http://www.fleethouse.com/fhcanada/fhc_expl.htm

Canada Travel magazine online. Provides information about travel to Canada. Offers information you should have if you want to plan a trip to Canada.

Financial Times Group

http://www.nsa.ft.com/

Offers highlights from *Financial Times*, news, and stock indices, updated daily.

Firehorse

http://firehorse.com/

Online magazine for multimedia designers.

FiX—Funkier Than Blown Vinyl

http://www.easynet.co.uk/fix/fix.htm

Exemplifies twenty-somethings on the net. Resembles a coffee shop, somewhat pretentious and smoke-filled, frequently raunchy—but interesting nonetheless.

Flinn Broadcasting— Sports 56 WHBQ

http://memphis.accessus.net/~flinn/56.html

Presents all sports, all the time. Includes information about this Memphis station and many sports-related Internet links.

Flinn Broadcasting— Unforgettable 1430

http://memphis.accessus.net/~flinn/1430.html

Features *senior links*—links to the Frank Sinatra home page—and the Senior Computer Informaton Project.

Folk Roots Home Page

http://www.cityscape.co.uk/froots/

Condensed, electronic version of *Folk Roots*. Features their guide to folk and world music events in Britain and Europe, CD reviews, charts and lists of best selling music, a playlist from Folk Routes radio program on the BBC World Service, a complete table of contents from the current issue, and much more.

Fortran Journal

http://www.fortran.com/fortran/fug_fj.html

Fortran Journal online. Includes a simple form to order the magazine and an in-depth description of the magazine.

FOX Broadcasting

http://www.eden.com/users/my-html/fox.html

Focuses on the FOX television network. Includes contact information, program information, links to other sites that relate to FOX programming, and other information related to the fourth network.

Fractal Design Corporation

http://www.fractal.com/

Contains information on Fractal Design Corporation's products, technical support, and examples.

Free Range: Home Page

http://www.freerange.com/

Features a tips and hints section.

Fréquence Banane WWW Server

http://fbwww.epfl.ch/english/

Swiss station on the Net. Also presents French and English language version, but the sound files are in French.

Future Fantasy Bookstore— Home Page

http://futfan.com/

Fantasy and science fiction bookstore online. Enables you to search the inventory, order online (pay offline), check

out some cover graphics, and read the newsletter. Offers jumps to books that have home pages.

FutureNet:.net—Index

http://www.futurenet.co.uk/netmag/net.html

.net magazine online. Covers Internet-related topics. Features their news page. Provides an Internet tutorial, job listings, and back issues. Also provides articles online that don't appear in the published magazine.

fX

http://www.delphi.com/fx/fxtop.html

fX, "the world's first living network," presents its Web presence. Offers programming information, information about the fX apartment, host interaction, and Usenet discussion groups.

Gazeta Wyborcza

http://info.fuw.edu.pl/gw/0/gazeta.html

Presents *Gazette Online*, an electronic version of Poland's largest daily newspaper, *Gazeta Wyborcza*.

GIFs Directory

http://www.acm.uiuc.edu/rml/Gifs/

Contains an archive of GIF photos, sorted by date or alphabetically (according to category).

Glass Wings: Sensual Celebrations

http://www.aus.xanadu.com/GlassWings/sexual/celebrations.html

Online magazine. Focuses on the sensual side of humanity.

Golf Channel

http://www.gdol.com/golfchannel/

The Golf channel online. Features program schedules and other golf information.

Good Medicine Magazine

http://none.coolware.com/health/good_med/ThisIssue.html

Good Medicine Magazine online. Provides stories and information, such as guided imagery, holistic skin and body care, Reiki (energy healing), and network chiropractic. Proposes that holistic and traditional Western medicine should be combined and considered together as "medicine."

Graphic Design (General Products and Services)

http://doradus.einet.net/galaxy/Business-and-Commerce/General-Products-and-Services/Graphic-Design.html

Contains links and information about all aspects of graphic design—articles, software, businesses, and more.

Graphics and Desktop Publishing

http://www.awa.com/nct/software/graplead.html

Online magazine. Reviews products and systems that relate to desktop publishing.

Grass Roots Magazine

http://www.bendtech.com/library/grassroots/

Grass Roots magazine online. Includes feature articles, text of speeches, and links to other environmental sites.

Great Lakes Skier Magazine

http://www.iquest.com/michweb/glskier/

Skiing magazine online. Includes articles and contact information for a subscription. Includes a few skiing links.

HAYWOOD + SULLIVAN

http://www.hsdesign.com/new/welcome.html

Provides information about the company, and the clients, as well as sections on scanning tips and design tips.

Hampton's Travel Book & Travel Guide Summary

http://www.dynapro.com/dynamic/travel.books.summary.html

Offers extensive references to travel books and resources. Includes online ordering.

HarperCollins Publishers Home Page

http://www.delphi.com/harpercollins/

HarperCollins online. Includes information about Best Sellers, New Releases, and an online bookstore.

Harvard Advocate Home Page

http://hcs.harvard.edu/~advocate/

Venerable literary site on the Net from Harvard. Offers many links to other online literary resources.

Hayden Books

http://www.mcp.com/adobe/

Hayden Books online. Publishes Adobe Press Books as well as books that focus on Macintosh computers and Macintosh programs. Features a Macintosh tip of the day.

High Country News Home Page

http://www.infosphere.com:80/clients/HCNArchive/

High Country News online. Reports bi-weekly on the West's natural resources, public lands, and changing communities.

Home Page of the Corporation for Public Broadcasting

http://www.cpb.org/

Provides information about the CPB. Includes press releases, contact information, WWW listings of interest to the CPB, and news articles about the CPB.

home.htm

http://www.shens.com/home.htm

Focuses on children's books. Encompasses a wide variety of themes and subject areas for children of all cultural backgrounds.

Houghton Mifflin Company

http://www.hmco.com/

Houghton Mifflin Company online. Publishes educational books and materials. Includes links to subsidiaries.

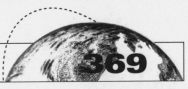
HTML-SimTel

http://ubu.hahnemann.edu/SimTel/deskpub.html

Provides a collection of shareware programs and utilities for the desktop publisher. Includes clip art collections.

Humber College Radio Broadcasting

http://humnet.humberc.on.ca/radio.htm

Offers a collection of links related to college radio and low power radio stations. Includes course outlines for the Humber College radio program.

IMS: Radio France International

http://town.hall.org/travel/france/rfi.html

Provides users with information about French radio. Includes French audio with translation and daily news reports in French.

Index of InteractiveArt

http://porsche.boltz.cs.cmu.edu:8001/InteractiveArt

Contains an index and repository of interactive art and screen shots.

Index to Multimedia Information Sources

http://viswiz.gmd.de/MultimediaInfo/

Serves as an index to multimedia information of all types, including current events in multimedia, guides, media archives, bibliographies, digital galleries, and commercial services.

index.html

http://iww.org/~monkeywrench/index.html

Monkeywrench Press online. Caters to the anarchist in all of us. Features information about authors and current books.

InfoCafé

http://www.infocafe.com/

Combines a coffee shop and a bookstore. Includes searchable and orderable books and indices. Audio books are also available.

infoMCI

http://www.fyionline.com/infoMCI/

Provides news summaries about businesses, sports, and headlines. Features industry spotlights for the business surfer.

Information Superlibrary

http://www.mcp.com/

Macmillan Publishing presents this site as a resource to the many computer books it publishes. Provides information on books published by Que, SAMS, New Riders, Brady, and Hayden, and lets you review sample chapters of the latest computer book and order that book online. Enables you to subscribe to *The SuperLibrary Newsletter*, a monthly newsletter that offers a wide variety of articles and features. Contains hundreds of Macmillan programs and software packages.

INFOSEARCH—Broadcasting Links

`http://www.xmission.com/~insearch/links.html`

Lists hundreds of broadcasting links alphabetically. Includes equipment, stations, networks, lobbying groups, and entertainment.

INFOSEARCH—PrintNet

`http://www.xmission.com/~insearch/printnet.html`

Lists publishing sites on the Net.

InfoVid Outlet: Art & Graphic Design

`http://rare-teas.com/infovid/c303.html`

Offers a descriptive price list of educational videos about art and graphic design. Offers online ordering.

Inquisitor Mediarama

`http://www.echonyc.com/~xixax/Mediarama/`

Exemplifies the twenty-something cyberculture on the Web.

Interactive Age Home Page

`http://techweb.cmp.com:80/techweb/ia/current`

Interactive Age Magazine online. Focuses on tracking electronic commerce. Enables you to contact the magazine staff, find out the 100 best business Web sites, use their hot link section, or look at their traffic analysis of the most-visited Internet sites. Also features daily articles online for registered users.

Interactive Graphics Generation Page

`http://www.eece.ksu.edu/IGR/`

Presents an interactive graphics rendering engine.

The Interactive Group

`http://www.igroup.com/igroup.html`

Produces interactive products.

InterActive8

`http://www.interactive8.com/`

Presents a page from a company that produces interactive multimedia. Provides the company's portfolio.

International Pages

`http://www.omroep.nl/international.html`

The Dutch public broadcasting system's Web site. Includes program information and other information about the Netherlands.

Internet Disaster Information Center

`http://www.disaster.net/`

Offers information about ongoing disasters, historical information about disasters, and links to other disaster sites on the Net.

Internet Resources—Cable Television

http://www.cablelabs.com/NR/cable_tv.html

Presents an index of Web sites relating to cable television and the cable TV industry. Features listings of stations, legal issues, and technical issues, and provides content information.

Internet Writer Resource Guide, The

http://www.math.uio.no/faq/writing/resources.html

Provides a guide to writing on the Internet. Includes a list of who accepts e-mail submissions, a FAQ, and tips on how to improve your writing.

InterText: The Online Fiction Magazine

http://ftp.etext.org/Zines/InterText/intertext.html

Monthy online fiction magazine. Contains short stories. Features five authors whose work has been published in this magazine and who have won awards.

Iowa State Daily Home Page II

http://www.daily.iastate.edu/

Iowa State's newspaper online. Includes up-to-date versions of the paper as well as valuable supplemental information. Features a section entitled, "How to Put a Newspaper on the Web."

IPL Books

http://ipl.sils.umich.edu/ref/RR/ENT/Books-rr.html

An Internet library, complete with information about books and authors in specific genres. Concentrates on children's literature, comics, horror, nonfiction, and romance.

iWORLD Home Page

http://www.mecklerweb.com/

Meckler Media online. Offers many links and provides information. Includes a newsand.

JAZZ FM98 KiFM, San Diego

http://www.kifm.com/

Contemporary jazz online. Includes program listings, station information, and many other jazz-related links.

JEST Home Page

http://www.math.byu.edu/~roc/jest.html

JEST (*Journal of Extraneous Scientific Topics*) online. Includes humorous looks at science.

JOIN US

http://techweb.cmp.com/

Offers links to 16 computer-related magazines on the Net. Includes *Communications Week, Windows Magazine, Electronic Buyer's News, Electronic Engineering Times, Net Guide, Home PC, Computer Reseller News, Computer Retail Week, Informatiques Magazine, VarBusiness, OEM Magazine, Network Computing, InfomationWeek,* to name a few of them. Also includes a virtual tour.

The Journal of Online Law

http://www.law.cornell.edu/jol/jol.table.html

Discusses the legal issues raised by the Internet.

K102 Radio

http://www.k102.com/

Offers country music on the Web. Includes program guides, concert reviews, and other information for the country and western fan.

Kai's Power Tips and Tricks for Photoshop

http://the-tech.mit.edu/KPT/KPT.html

Focuses on desktop publishing, particularly on KPT and Photoshop. Also features stock photos and other items. Includes the 23 KPT tips directly from Kai.

KGTV Home Page

http://www.kgtv.com/

One of the few ABC affiliates on the Net. Provides information about the San Diego area. Includes the executive news summary, a listing of daily news headlines, and more.

KKLI Lite 106.3 FM

http://kkli.com/kkli/

Focuses on lite music. Includes music and information about this station from Colorado.

KLON'S JazzAvenue Jazz Information Service

http://www.klon.org/~jazzave/

Features include a biography of a featured artist (updated daily), a weekly top 20, CD covers and track listings, and weekly playlists. Also provides local concert information, and a list of Los Angeles area jazz venues.

Knowledge Industry Publications, Inc.

http://www.KIPInet.com/

Offers links to Knowledge Industry's magazines: *AV Video*, *Multimedia Producer*, and *Tape/Disc Business*. Also offers links to companies in the audio visual and multimedia fields.

Koinonia House

http://www.khouse.org/khouse/

Christian book publisher online. Includes information about books and magazines and offers links to other Christian sites on the Internet.

The KPT Backgrounds Archive

http://the-tech.mit.edu/KPT/bgs.html

Contains an archive of backgrounds for your desktop. Also includes a tutorial for creating your own backgrounds.

KROCK 101.5 The Rock of N.E. Kansas

http://codrus.mmedia.com/KROCK/html/home.html

Lets you request music and then (if possible) listen to it later. Also contains links to other music sites and a list of regional concerts.

KZSU Radio

http://kzsu.stanford.edu/index.html

Stanford University radio station. Includes lists of other noncommercial stations around the country and in the Bay area. Features information about current programs and airplay charts.

Language and Literature

http://phenom.physics.wisc.edu/~shalizi/hyper-weird/language.htm

Contains links to pages and information on genres, particular authors, bookstores, and publishers.

Latin American Bookstore

http://199.170.0.83/lab/labld.html

Latin American bookstore online. Carries a wide variety of academic publications from Latin America and Spain. Includes a link to the University of Guadlajara and offers links to United States centers for Latin American study.

libraries.americas

ftp://ftp.ping.at/pub/info/internet/libraries/libraries.americas

Provides information on information retrieval from online libraries.

LIFE Photo Home Page

http://www.pathfinder.com/@@egQ6VwAAAAAAIMR/Life/lifehome.html

The magazine that pioneered photojournalism has reimagined itself for cyberspace. Visually stunning site. Includes many images.

List of Animation Houses

http://www.xmission.com/~grue/animate/houses.html

Contains a list of animation houses. Includes addresses and phone numbers.

List of Lists

http://www.matterform.com/mf/indices/indexlist.html

Matterform Media, a software and design company, online. Presents examples of work, links to other pages, and an introduction to graphic design.

Little, Brown & Company

http://www.pathfinder.com/@@9B66QQAAAAAAIcR/twep/Little_Brown/Little_Brown.html

Little, Brown & Company publishing company online. Features reviews and summaries of current books.

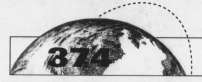

Living Poets, EJournal Home Page

http://dougal.derby.ac.uk/lpoets/

Online magazine. Presents new poetry on the Web.

The Logical Alternative— Front Door

http://shell.conknet.com/fusion/

Online magazine. Targets multimedia authors. Contains reviews, tips, and other information.

Low Power Broadcasting FAQ

http://www.math.uio.no/faq/radio/broadcasting/low-power-faq.html

Provides information about starting your own low power radio station.

MacNet Journal

http://www.dgr.com/web_mnj/

Contains *MacNet Journal*. Lets you suggest ideas for improving the Macintosh operating system, peruse a free help wanted page, obtain guidelines for submitting articles, and search past issues. Also lets you browse the current issue or subscribe (it's free).

Macworld Online Web Server

http://www.macworld.com/

MacWorld online. Lets you search past issues and read articles. Also provides Internet tips.

Make Your Scanner a Great Design and Production Tool

http://www.hsdesign.com/scanning/

Contains information about a book all multimedia beginners might want to check out, a book that provides detailed information on the best way to scan objects and use art in graphic design.

MC's ftp Stuff

ftp://magna.com.au/pub/users/mark_carolan/HeadsOff.html

Focuses on Macromedia Director. Offers a downloadable collection of XObjects (add-in programs), authoring tips, shareware, and examples of work created using Director.

McGraw Hill

http://www.cityscape.co.uk/bookshop/mccat.html

Online bookstore. Enables you to browse through McGraw Hill titles.

Mercury Center Home Page

http://www.sjmercury.com/

The San Jose Mercury online. Offers in-depth coverage of news events and utilizes hypertext links within stories.

The Millennium Whole Earth Catalog

http://www.well.net/mwec/home.html

A limited edition of Howard Rheingold's *Whole Earth Catalog* online. Provides many online excerpts from the catalog book.

MMWIRE WEB

`http://www.mmwire.com/`

Electronic magazine. Focuses on multimedia and design. Provides much information.

Mobilia Magazine

`http://www.mobilia.com/`

Mobilia magazine online. Focuses on the worlds of motoring and collecting. Lets you read it online and offers subscription information.

The MoJo Wire

`http://www.mojones.com/`

Mother Jones (magazine) online. Provides insightful information with a Mother Jones slant.

Money & Investing Update—Welcome

`http://update.wsj.com/`

The Wall Street Journal online. A free subscription lets business surfers access daily *The Wall Street Journal*.

Monitor Radio

`http://town.hall.org/radio/Monitor/`

The Christian Science Monitor Radio Program online. Includes program information and a behind-the-scenes look at Monitor Radio.

Moon Travel Home Page

`http://www.moon.com/`

Combines travel information with interactivity (pictures, sound) training to give prospective travelers to Hawaii a preview of what awaits them. Includes online ordering of other travel books, plus information about travel to foreign destinations.

Motorcycle Online

`http://www.motorcycle.com/motorcycle.html`

Online magazine. Covers all aspects of motorcycles. Includes reviews, pictures, and tours.

mtv.com

`http://www.mtv.com/`

Music Television Network online. Provides information about current MTV programs, including images, sounds, and movie clips.

Multimedia Authoring Web

`http://www.mcli.dist.maricopa.edu/authoring/`

Provides a collection of links and information about multimedia authoring.

Multimedia Information

`http://sunsite.sut.ac.jp/multimed/multimed.html`

The Sunsite Multimedia Information page. Features links to multimedia information on the Net, images, sounds, and movies relating to multimedia development.

Multimedia Newsstand Home Page

`http://mmnewsstand.com/index.html`

Offers a collection of subscription information and forms for more than 500 magazines, books, and videos. Also contains a number of different contests sponsored by the various magazines.

Multimedia Page

`http://www.mcli.dist.maricopa.edu/authoring/mm.html`

Lists sites relating to all aspects of multimedia production.

Muse Magazine

`http://www.val.net/VillageSounds/Muse/index.html`

Online magazine. Focuses on women in music. Features CD reviews, book reviews, and the full text of the magazine.

My Local Home Page

`http://www.neosoft.com/neopolis/onestop/default.html`

Online digital service bureau. Offers to print or make negatives of your digital file. Offers downloadable services and price list.

NAB Home Page

`http://www.nab.org/`

National Association of Broadcasters. Contains information about the NAB's activities, including legislative and regulatory information, information about the NAB conventions, a resource library, and more.

National Student Television Association

`http://www.cs.bham.ac.uk/~amw/nasta/`

Offers links all over the world for student broadcasting.

Natural History Book Service—Home Page

`http://www.nhbs.co.uk/`

British online bookstore. Focuses on natural history, environmental issues, and science. Provides information in English, Spanish, Italian, and German.

NCS Career Magazine

`http://www.careermag.com/careermag/index.html`

Career online. Offers listings of available jobs and employers contact information. Includes a search engine.

Net Traveler

`http://www.primenet.com/~ntravel/`

Contains Net Traveler magazine. Provides information about their list of sites and tools. Offers links to new things to hit the Internet. Includes a collection of links to sites of importance, as well as a files archive.

Netsurfer Digest Home Page

`http://www.netsurf.com/nsd/`

Provides current information about the newest and coolest sites on the Net.

New Riders

http://mcp.com/newriders/

New Riders concentrates on staying current and delivering the necessary depth and breadth of computer-related information—all in a timely fashion. So stay ahead of the game, and check out our Web site for the latest information on the hottest computer topics—from networking and AutoCAD to communications/Internet and multimedia/graphics.

NewsLink Menu

http://www.newslink.org/menu.html

Offers a free service that provides access to many online newspapers, periodicals, and so on around the world every day.

Newspaper/Diario LA NACION—San Jose, Costa Rica

http://www.nacion.co.cr/

Presents news in Spanish. *La Nacion*, the largest newspaper in Costa Rica, provides news and information about Central America and the world.

Newspaper Internet Services

http://www.nyc.pipeline.com/edpub/e-papers.links.html

Provides you with a means for determining whether your local newspaper offers links to the Internet, and if so, for accessing them.

Newsshare Corporation

http://www.crocker.com/~densmore/

Supplies interactive media products to newspapers, broadcasters, and the public.

NHK Home Page

http://www.nhk.or.jp/

Provides information about the NHK (Japanese Broadcasting Company) Broadcasting Center, the Science and Technical Research Labs, and the Broadcasting Culture Research Institute. Offers a Japanese language version.

NHK International TV Broadcasting

http://www.ntt.jp/japan/NHK/TV/

Provides the program guide and listing for the International TV Broadcasting Section of NHK. Includes satellite transponder numbers. Also offers a Japanese language version.

Nightclub and Bar Magazine

http://www.inst.com:80/ncb/Welcome.html

Contains helpful information about starting your own bar. Also provides information if you own or currently run one. Includes bar links.

NJ Online Weather

http://www.nj.com/weather/

The Old Farmers Almanac online. Includes weather forecasts for the United States, helpful tips, and other information—just like the hard copy.

Norwegian Bookshop Home Page

http://www.oslonett.no/home/paul/nw.html

Norwegian bookshop online. Provides Norwegian books or books about Norway. Also includes information about Norwegian language and education.

NOS TeleTekst

http://teletext.iaehv.nl/teletext/nos/index.en.html

Dutch Broadcasting Service. Provides a clickable interface to news and other information from the Dutch wire services. Includes English menus but provides the articles in Dutch.

NPR Online

http://www.npr.org/

National Public Radio online. Provides information about NPR and other topics. Includes audio version of daily noon newscasts, transcripts of other programs, and in-depth looks at current events.

O'Reilly Home Page

http://gnn.digital.com/gnn/bus/ora/

Acts as a source for computer books about topics such as Unix, TCP/IP, and the Internet.

Oceanography— The Magazine

http://www.tos.org/tos/tos_magazine_menu.html

Does not contain full text versions of the articles but does list the table of contents and biography information about editors of the magazine.

The Oklahoma Daily Online

http://www.uoknor.edu/okdaily/

Independent student paper from Oklahoma. Provides up-to-date information during the school year.

Old Time Radio (OTR) WWW Page

http://www.crl.com/~lgenco/otr.html

Focuses on radio programs from "radio's golden age." Contains pointers to many entertaining and educational areas for fans of nostalgic radio shows.

The Omnivore

http://ukanaix.cc.ukans.edu/carrie/news_main.html

Provides a free daily news service designed to quickly and concisely deliver coverage of events around the world as they happen (uncensored news, straight from the source and original point of view). Provides many links to other news services.

Online Access Web Edition

http://www.oamag.com/online/access.html

Contains *Online Access* magazine. Serves as a guide to online services, bulletin boards, and the Internet. Offers an online events catalog of events happening in cyberspace, a

list of the magazines links, and a monthly column devoted to ground-breaking shareware software. Also offers subscription information.

The Online Books Page

http://www.cs.cmu.edu/Web/books.html

Offers full text versions of hundreds of books. Also includes links related to English literature.

Online Center for Continuous Improvement

http://www.europa.com/productivity/press.html

Offers information about books, newsletters, consulting, and training that supports continuous improvement. Features include free excerpts from leading management books, an information search capability, testimonials, authors' biographies, and an online catalog.

Online Educator

http://www.cris.com/~felixg/OE/OEWELCOME.html

Offers lesson plans, sample articles from the *Online Educator* magazine, and many other resources. Offers the magazine itself for subscription in both print and electronic forms.

The Online Islamic Bookstore—Home Page

http://www.sharaaz.com/

Online bookstore. Features Islamic books, music, and CD-ROMs. Offers online ordering.

Other Change of Hobbit Bookstore—Home Page

http://www.dnai.com/~ochobbit/

Science fiction and fantasy bookstore online. Features new releases, online ordering, and other information.

OutNOW!

http://www.zoom.com/outnow/

Weekly paper for the gay community. Presents news and information.

Outside Online

http://web2.starwave.com:80/outside/online/

Offers sections on news, locations, activities, and gear for the outdoor enthusiast.

Page de France

http://gplc.u-bourgogne.fr:8080/pdf/Welcome.html

French bookstore online (bilingual: French and English). Features books about France and books in French.

Pan Asian Publications Home Page

http://www.panap.com/

The source for Asian Publications online. Provides searching and online ordering.

Penthouse on the Internet

http://www.penthousemag.com/

Penthouse online. Features an Internet edition of the magazine and contains many images. Also includes an erotic toy store.

People

http://www.dol.com/Root/people/people.html

Indexes organizations, conferences, and people involved in design.

Personal Technology Home Page

http://ptech.wsj.com/

Features the personal technology section from *The Wall Street Journal.* Provides information related to technology and contains archival data.

Perspective

http://hcs.harvard.edu/~perspy/

Monthly liberal magazine from Harvard University. Recent issues have focused on the Web.

pgrmli.txt

http://www.library.nwu.edu:80/media/resources/pgrmli.txt

Burrelle's Transcripts, a leading transcription company for more than 20 years, provides transcripts and, where indicated, videotapes, of more than 75 news, public affairs, health, and talk shows.

Phoenix Home & Garden Magazine

http://www.enews.com:80/magazines/phoenix_hg/

Phoenix Home & Garden's online magazine. Serves as a resource for gardening, travel, and the unique history of the region. Sponsors successful gardening, furniture, and lifestyle shows.

Playboy Home Page—Open Your Mind

http://www.playboy.com/

Playboy magazine online. Includes interviews, reviews, and a Playboy forum. Very few images.

Playboy TV

http://www.playboy.com/PlayboyTV/PlayboyTV.html

Playboy Channel's Web site. Includes program information and previews of upcoming shows. No images.

The PM Zone

http://popularmechanics.com/

Popular Mechanics online. Provides movies, pictures, and information about new and useful products and technology.

POLLSTAR Online

http://www.pollstar.com/

Focuses on the concert industry. Features listings of current tours and other information.

Polonia Bookstore, Chicago

http://www.wtinet.com/wti/polonia.htm

Polish-American bookstore online. Provides information about books in Polish, books about Poland in English, and more. Includes Polish video and music titles. Also offers links to other Polish sites.

Popular Science Magazine

`http://www.enews.com:80/magazines/popsci/`

Electronic version of *Popular Science* magazine. Aims to be the most timely and authoritative source of enlightened and practical information about what's new in science and technology.

PowerPC News

`http://power.globalnews.com/ppchome.htm`

Online bi-weekly magazine. Features current news about major companies that produce PowerPC microprocessors, software that runs on the PowerPC chip, and products that incorporate the chip. Lets you sign up for an e-mail version of the magazine.

Prentice Hall Home Page

`http://www.prenhall.com/`

Publishes college textbooks and technical books. Offers Prentice Hall's online catalog of books and information, as well as links to their gopher site and to fun Internet sites, including other Viacom sites.

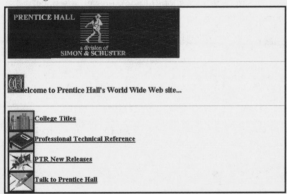

Publishers' Catalogues Home Page

`http://northern.lights.com:80/publisher/`

Provides a listing of publishers from all over the world and their home pages, indexed by country.

Putnam Berkley Online

`http://www.mca.com/putnam/`

Features a virtual environment in which you can examine the books and explore the "cafe."

Que's Home Page

`http://www.mcp.com/que/`

Que publishes books on every major category of personal computer technology, from end-user applications to programming languages, from the Internet to new hardware and software technologies. The home page provides information about the technology you've come to depend on, and explains how you can gain access to Que computer books.

The QVC Local

`http://www.qvc.com/`

Home Shopping on the Net. Enables you to meet the hosts, sample the current products, and see what is coming up.

Radio Centro

`http://www.internet.com.mx/empresas/radiocen/index.html`

Contains listings and information about Spanish language radio stations.

Radio HK

`http://hkweb.com/radio/`

Hong Kong Radio. Broadcasts exclusively into the Internet, real-time and non-stop. Provides information in addition to the real-time radio broadcasts.

Radio JAPAN

http://www.ntt.jp/japan/NHK/

Provides information about Japanese radio. Includes transmission maps and program schedules.

Radio Prague

http://town.hall.org/Archives/radio/Mirrors/Prague/

Radio Prague provides information about radio programming and offers audio broadcasts of radio programs.

RadioActivo 98.5 FM

http://nayarit.info.udg.mx/~dochoa/raindex.html

Mexico City Radio online. Focuses on hard rock radio. Presents site in Spanish.

RadioSpace Home Page

http://www.radiospace.com/welcome.html

Serves as a resource for radio station programming and news staffs. Provides ready-for-broadcast sound bites, news, and programming.

RadioWorld Europe

http://www.vhc.se/radio.html

Includes a listing of radio stations in Europe that are online. Also includes a listing of radio networks in Europe.

Random House

http://www.randomhouse.com/

Features a smattering of information, but includes the Del Rey Books (science fiction and fantasy) home page and the Knopf Publishing Group's home page.

RealAudio: ABC News

http://www.realaudio.com/contentp/abc.html

Offers ABC Radio news, available with the RealAudio player. Lets you download audio files of daily news broadcasts.

Rob's Multimedia Lab (RML)

http://www.acm.uiuc.edu/rml/

Offers multimedia in the loosest, or perhaps strictest, sense. Includes links to sites about movies, images, interface, sounds, and much more.

ROCK104

http://www.jou.ufl.edu/about/stations/rock104/

Includes album and concert reviews. Offers many rock-related links.

Roswell

http://www.nstn.ns.ca/cybermall/roswell/roswell.html

Online book store and publisher. Specializes in computer books. Offers more than 8,000 books for purchase online.

RTE To Everywhere Home Page

http://www.bess.tcd.ie/ireland/rte.htm

Provides audio files of news stories from Irish Public Radio. Provides alternative information about Ireland.

RTHK on Internet Home Page

http://www.cuhk.hk/rthk/

Radio Television Hong Kong provides program schedule information and content information.

SAMS Home Page

http://www.mcp.com/sams/

SAMS Publishing online. Produces professional references on computer topics. Specializes in programming books. Also features recent titles on emerging technologies.

The Satellite TV Page

http://itre.uncecs.edu/misc/sat.html

Provides information about satellite television, including lists of equipment suppliers, networks, and other information.

The Satellite TV (and Radio) Page

Sci-Fi Channel: The Dominion

http://www.scifi.com/

Features a real-time program guide, in-depth information about the programs, an interactive television experiment, and a programming grid.

Science Fiction Resource Guide

http://sundry.hsc.usc.edu/hazel/www/sfrg/sf-resource.guide.html

Serves as a guide to all science fiction resources on the Net. Covers fiction, role-playing games, publishing, conventions, and more.

Scripps Howard Home Page

http://www.scripps.com/

Presents the media giant on the Web. Scripps Howard owns eighteen daily newspapers and nine TV stations and a host of other stuff you might want to check out.

Sea Frontiers

http://www.rsmas.miami.edu/sea-frontiers/sea-frontiers.html

Oceanography journal online. Contains full text versions of articles from recent editions.

seaside

gopher://gopher.nstn.ca:70/11/e-mall/Bookstores/seaside

Provides information about stamps and stamp books.

Serif: The Magazine of Type & Typography

http://www.quixote.com/serif/

Online magazine. Targets the desktop publisher. Features sample articles, subscription information, and desktop publishing links on the Internet.

Shogakukan Home Page

http://www.toppan.co.jp/bookshop/

Shogakukan publishes magazines for children, comic magazines, weeklies, dictionaries, encyclopedias, and art books. Features Japanese links, books, and magazines. Provides English and Japanese language versions.

Shortwave/Radio Catalog (Page 1)

http://itre.uncecs.edu/radio/

Provides shortwave and radio hobbyists informative and timely links to services and information related to shortwave listening (SWL), satellite radio, and other topics on or about radio.

Small Media and Large

http://smallmedia.com/

Independent publisher of gay and lesbian books. Also features feminist books. Offers online ordering.

Software Net Product Menu

http://software.net/automenu.htm/1521/
SK:kfbfkoafbmahjacj

Lets you order desktop publishing and graphics software online.

South African Broadcasting Corporation Welcome Page

http://www.sabc.co.za/

South African Broadcasting online. Provides many phone numbers and other information. Includes sports scores and news services.

The St. Petersburg Press Home Page

http://www.spb.su/sppress/

English language weekly newpaper from St. Petersburg, Russia. Covers news, business news, commentary, culture, and classifieds.

The Stanford Daily Home Page

http://www-daily.stanford.edu/

Provides a good example of daily newspapers available on the Internet. Contains news and information.

Stellar Business: Worldwide Edition

http://corp.tig.com/stellar/global/index.html

Contains articles about business and the Net.

Strangelove Internet Enterprises

http://www.phoenix.ca/sie/

Internet business publishing, consulting, and training organization. Includes information on their book *How to*

Advertise on the Internet, and on their publication, *The Internet Business Journal*.

. . . .
StrataWelcome

http://www.strata3d.com/

Software company whose programs are used to create 3-D models and animations. Provides information on products, technical support, and online ordering.

. . . .
The Tech

http://the-tech.mit.edu/

MIT bi-weekly student newspaper. Provides articles, including national news wires.

. . . .
Tharunka Home

http://www.real.com.au/magazines/tharunka/

Australian university student magazine. Offers a different angle on the news (that is often funny).

. . . .
Thistle and Shamrock Stations List at the Ceolas Archive

http://celtic.stanford.edu/pmurphy/thistle.html

Provides a list of stations arranged alphabetically by state and city. Broadcasts a popular Celtic music radio program on National Public Radio. Includes broadcast times.

. . . .
Time Daily News Summary

http://www.pathfinder.com/@@fHsKBwAAAAAAAH4Q/time/daily/time/1995/latest.html

Provides one paragraph summaries of current stories and provides a searching engine you can use for a more in-depth look.

. . . .
Time Life Explorer

http://www.timelife.com/

Contains a visual database of all the Time-Life products. Lets you browse and order products.

. . . .
Tokyo Journal

http://www.iac.co.jp/tj/

English magazine from Japan.

. . . .
The Tolkien Timeline

http://www.lights.com/tolkien/timeline.html

Offers a chronological list of important events relating to Tolkien's life, career, and scholarly pursuits, and attempts to provide a clearer picture of this astounding man.

. . . .
TOR SF and Fantasy

http://www.tor.com/

TOR online. Publishes science fiction and fantasy books. Includes links to other science fiction and fantasy sites on the Web, offers a browsable database of books, and allows online ordering.

Travel Weekly

http://www.novalink.com/travel/

Travel Weekly online. Serves the travel agency community. Includes feature articles. Also offers hundreds of links to sites associated with hotels, airlines, railroads, and tour operators.

TravelASSIST Magazine

http://travelassist.com/mag/mag_home.html

Online magazine. Contains articles on travel and travel spots around the United States and the world. Includes back issues for online reading.

TV Net

http://tvnet.com/TVnet.html

Contains a television index.

TV1 HOME

http://tv1.com/

Provides what's on tonight. Lets you view programs by time, channel, or grid format.

TV2 / DANMARKs ugeprogrammer

http://www.dknet.dk/tv/tv2/

TV2/Denmark (schedules, in Danish).

Typofile Magazine—Home Page

http://www.will-harris.com/type.html

Online magazine. Focuses on type and its uses. Includes articles and links to other type and desktop publishing sites.

United Paramount Network

http://www.cdsnet.net/vidiot/UPN/upn.html

United Paramount Network's unofficial home page. Includes background information about the fledgling network and offers information and links to pages of its more popular programs. Also provides you the chance to meet the executives of the UPN.

The Unofficial Place to Find Out All the Scoop on UPN

United States Local TV

http://tvnet.com/TV/localtv.html

Provides easy access to local television stations. Lets you click on your state to see which local stations are on the Net.

Unix News International

http://apt.usa.globalnews.com/UNI/

Contains the current issue of *Unix News International*, a monthly publication about Unix systems.

Urban: The Latino Magazine

http://www.computel.com/~urban/

Lets you browse back issues and read the current issue of *Urban: The Latino Magazine*. Serves as a good resource online. Offers subscriptions.

USIA International Broadcasting

http://www.usia.gov/usiahome/bbureau.html

The United States Information Agency. Provides information about Voice of America and other programs.

UT Science Bytes

http://loki.ur.utk.edu/ut2kids/science.html

Online hypertext magazine. Focuses on UT scientists' research projects. Describes the projects at a level appropriate for elementary school students and links any unfamiliar words or concepts to a definition or explanation.

Videomaker's Camcorder & Desktop Video Site

http://www.videomaker.com/

Videomaker magazine online. Includes a product search engine, back issues, and other information about camcorders and video.

Virtual Pathways

http://edge.edge.net/~jhbryan/pathways/toc.html

Backpacking magazine online. Includes reviews of trails and locations around the United States.

Vocal Point

http://bvsd.k12.co.us/cent/Newspaper/Newspaper.html

High school newspaper online. Offers monthly news from a teen's perspective.

Voice of the Shuttle: English Literature Page

http://humanitas.ucsb.edu/shuttle/english.html

Serves as a guide to English literature, both British and American. Covers many genres and time periods, in addition to literary theory and minority literature. Also furnishes a search engine.

Voyager

http://www.voyagerco.com/interface/gallery.cgi

Voyager online. Produces books on CD-ROM. Includes an online catalog.

The Wall Street Journal Link

http://journal.link.wsj.com/

Provides an online advertising directory of *The Wall Street Journal*. Contains links to advertiser Web sites and e-mail addresses.

Walls and Ceilings Magazine

http://www.wco.org/wac.html

Contains the official publication of the walls and ceilings industry: *Walls & Ceilings Magazine*. Serves contractors, suppliers, and distributors. Contains a virtual library of features on specialty subjects and offers links to an online bookstore and virtual library.

Warning! Abandon hope, all ye who enter here

http://www.comcentral.com/

A zany Web site from the folks at Comedy Central. Provides information about Comedy Central's programs.

Wave~Length Paddling Network

http://interchange.idc.uvic.ca/~wavenet/magazine.html

Kayaking and Paddling magazine online. Includes archives of past articles and current issues with pictures.

Weather Watch Magazine

http://northshore.shore.net/~wxcentrl/

Weather Watch magazine online. Provides information about the magazine and offers current weather information.

Web Review Cover- August 1* 1995

http://www-e1c.gnn.com/wr/

Online magazine. Focuses on the Web and all its parts.

WebWeek Home Page

http://www.mecklerweb.com/mags/ww/

Contains *WebWeek Magazine.* Targets Web developers. Offers an online-only column every Monday. Also previews the printed issues and lets you read some of the articles.

Welcome

http://ericir.syr.edu/Discovery/

The Discovery Channel online in conjunction with The Learning Channel. Serves as an educational supplement to their programming. Provides members with supplemental information about the programs that air on each network.

Welcome KDFC

http://www.tbo.com/kdfc/index.html

Classical music online. Offers links to other classical music sites around the Internet.

Welcome to Amazon.com Books

http://www.amazon.com/exec/obidos/subst/index2.html/
9165-5202824-522726

Offers more than one million books online and ready for purchase. Features the Personal Notification Service—if you're waiting for a title to come out in paperback, they'll send you mail when it does.

Welcome to BBC Radio

http://www.bbcnc.org.uk/radio/index.html

BBC Radio online. Contains information about program schedules and information about specific programs carried on the BBC radio network.

Welcome to BBC Television

http://www.bbcnc.org.uk/tv/index.html

BBC online. Includes information about program schedules and information about specific programs, divided by program type.

Welcome to Carbon 14

http://www.rsabbs.com/carbon14/

Online magazine. Focuses on underground music in all its forms. Features interactive graphics and samples from currently featured albums.

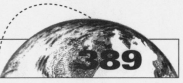
Welcome to Computer Shopper

http://www.zdnet.com/~cshopper/

Provides an online edition of the current *Computer Shopper* magazine. Lets you search through the advertisers for the lowest prices on computer components, or browse through current and past articles.

Welcome to Corel

http://WWW.corel.ca/

Corporate home page for Corel Corporation. Contains information about the company and its line of graphics and home software. Offers links to Corel's FTP site, press releases, and the Corel knowledge base of techical support information.

Welcome to Corel Corporation's Home Page

Welcome to CorelNet

http://www.corelnet.com

Focuses on Corel Products such as CorelDRAW! and CorelVentura. Lets you chat with users and authors who have written about Corel products; download software patches, shareware, and utilities; and learn the latest tips and tricks.

Welcome to HotWired!

http://www.hotwired.com/

Wired! online. Includes information not found in the paper version of the magazine. Offers many links.

Welcome to I-Channel

http://www.I-channel.com/cgi-bin/bf.w3?welcome.shtml

International Channel provides multilanguage programming featuring more than 20 different languages from Asia, Europe, and the Middle East.

Welcome to Infobahn Magazine

http://www.postmodern.com/

Contains *Infobahn* magazine, a publication devoted to covering the Internet from a cultural point of view. Lets you sign up for a free trial issue, contact the editors, get advertising information and prices, and find out how to submit articles.

Welcome to Macromedia

http://www.macromedia.com/

Contains information and support files for Macromedia's line of graphics and multimedia authoring tools. Also focuses on information, news, and resources for the graphics arts community.

Welcome to NandO.net

http://www.nando.net/

Provides in-depth news coverage and up-to-date information.

Welcome to Pathfinder

http://www.pathfinder.com/@@5NGfxQAAAAAwIIQ/pathfinder/welcome.html

Time Warner's site. Offers links to *Time* online, *Sports Illustrated* online, *Money Magazine* online, and more.

Welcome to PBS

http://www.pbs.org/

The Public Broadcasting Service Web site provides access to information about PBS, national programming, learning services, local PBS stations, and the PBS store, at which you can buy videos.

Welcome to the Internet Book Shop

http://www.bookshop.co.uk/

Claims to be the largest bookstore online.

Welcome to the Internet World Home Page

http://www.mecklerweb.com/mags/iw/iwhome.htm

Contains *Internet World* magazine. Lets you view some of the articles of the current newsstand issue, search back issues, get subscription information, and find out about advertisers. Also features a weekly online collection of news.

Welcome to USA Today

http://www.usatoday.com/web1.htm

USA Today online. Features headlines, subscription information, and daily news reports.

Welcome to ZD Net

http://www.ziff.com/

Ziff-Davis publishes many computer magazines. Provides articles and information about computers, as well as links to other Ziff-Davis publications, including *PC Magazine*, *PC Week*, *Mac Week*, *Mac User*, *Computer Life*, and more.

West Publishing

http://www.westpub.com/

West Publishing online, a legal and educational publisher. Includes information on their products. Lets you use West's Legal Directory to find a lawyer, law firm, or corporate or governmental lawyer located in the United States or Canada.

Where the Buffalo Roam

http://internet-plaza.net/wtbr/

Presents a cartoon published weekly on the Web. Provides cartoons published in the last five weeks. Tells fans about ordering books and T-shirts.

White House Press Release Summaries Home Page

http://eos.esusda.gov/wh/whsum.html

Presents news from the White House. Lets you read the same press releases from the president that the network reporters do.

Wild West Revival Mercantile

http://www.wildwest.com/wwrm/

Online Christian bookstore. Sells books, music, clothing, jewelry, artworks, and software. Features an online catalog. Also offers links to other Christian organizations and sites.

Wood Radio Limited Partnership

http://www.woodradio.com/cgibin/var/wood/home.htm

Wood Radio, out of West Michigan, provides information about the station and the region.

World Traveler Books and Maps

http://www.explore.com/wtbm/wtbm.html

Features travel books online, organized by geographic region. Also offers a selection of maps. Includes links to many travel-related resources.

The World-Wide Web Virtual Library: Broadcasters

http://www.comlab.ox.ac.uk/archive/publishers/broadcast.html

Provides a list of international broadcasting sites. Focuses mainly on radio and TV, but includes other information, too.

WTAW News/Sports/Talk 1150 AM

http://www.rtis.com/reg/bcs/com/wtaw/

Includes an image of Rush Limbaugh and advertisers' prices.

WWW Multimedia Law

http://www.batnet.com/oikoumene/

Contains information on multimedia law. Offers links to multimedia law firms and publications, as well as information on recent court decisions affecting the multimedia world.

WWW VL: Literature/IBIC Virtual Review of Books

http://sunsite.unc.edu/ibic/IVRB.html

Provides an index of book reviews on the Internet, including general and specialized subjects.

WXRT Home Page

http://www.wxrt.com/

Radio station online. Includes Chicago community information, staff biographies, and other information.

YLE ohjelmatiedot

http://www.freenet.hut.fi/ohjelmatiedot/index.html

Finland radio and television. Provides *YLE ohjelmatiedot* (TV and radio schedules, in Finnish).

Z Central 950805

http://www.everyday.se/hem/zcentral/

Swedish online magazine.

Zarahemla Book Shoppe

http://www.xmission.com/~zarahmla/

Online bookstore. Provides Mormon books. Lets you browse the CD-ROM offerings. Offers links to Mormon-related sites.

29th Montreux Jazz Festival Official Site

http://www.mhm.fr/festival/montreux/

Covers an international jazz festival held in Montreux, Switzerland, every year. Contains general festival information, programs, artists' photos and bios, band lineups, a catalog of festival merchandise, and more.

Abayudaya Jews in Uganda: Music

http://www.intac.com/PubService/uganda/music.html

Documents the songs of the Abayudaya people of Uganda, who converted to Judaism in the 1920's. Contains several audio files of songs, most of which are versions of American-Jewish songs. Also offers more information on the Abayudaya people.

AC/DC Live Wire, The

http://www.sdstate.edu/~cc92/http/acdc.html

Serves the AC/DC fan. Includes a history of the band members, lyrics and pictures from every album, and a frequently asked questions file. Also offers a page of links to other AC/DC sites on the Net.

Accordiana

http://www.cs.cmu.edu/afs/cs/user/phoebe/mosaic/accordion.html

Provides information on accordions and all free reed instruments. Includes where to purchase instruments, where to study, and where to get accordion music. Also includes a bibliography of books about accordions.

Addicted to Noise

http://www.addict.com/ATN/

Includes interviews with major artists like R.E.M., Veruca Salt, and Primus. Features groups like the MC5, Oasis, Wilco, and Elastica. Provides columns by rock critics, including Dave Marsh and Greil Marcus. Offers daily rock news reports. Serves as a guide to rock spots on the web. Also offers album reviews with sound bytes, movie reviews, rock book reviews, and music and technology columns.

African Music: Music from Africa and the African Diaspora

http://matisse.net/~jal/afrcanmx.htm

Contains information on African and African-influenced music and musicians from all over the world, including South America and the Caribbean. Includes articles, artist profiles, and sound samples. Also offers links to the home pages of the various countries. Provides text in English and Spanish.

Afropop Worldwide

http://majorca.npr.org/programs/afropop/

Presents the popular African/world music program on National Public Radio online. Provides information on African music in general. Features a station guide and program listings, as well as concert schedules, suggested disc lists, artist photos, and even recipes.

Agnetha, Benny, Björn & Anni-Frid's Home Page

http://phymat.bham.ac.uk/ABBA/

Serves as a source for all the ABBA lyrics. Also includes pictures and links to other ABBA pages on the Web.

Ain't Whistlin' Dixie

http://mothra.nts.uci.edu/~dhwalker/dixie/

Offers a collection of Irish, Scottish, and English traditional tunes played on the pennywhistle and ocarina. Provides a sample audio file that gives you a few seconds of the tune.

aljazz.html

http://www.the-matrix.com/jazz/aljazz.html

Alabama Jazz Hall of Fame. Contains information about the organization whose stated mission is "to foster, encourage, educate, and cultivate a general appreciation of the medium of jazz music. . . ." Includes information on jazz events and on their museum.

Also Broken Home Page, The

http://wanda.pond.com/~karlbey/broken.htm

Presents a new band from Philadelphia who have just released their debut album, Division of Grace. Contains band bios, photos, sound bytes, and club dates. If you like Rush, King's X, and Living Colour, you'll like Also Broken.

American Music Center

http://www.amc.net/amc

Nonprofit contemporary music information and resource center. Provides lists of scores, opportunities for composers and performers, information on grants, and more.

Amy Grant Site in College Park, MD

http://www.wam.umd.edu/~xiaoqin/ag.html

Provides information on Amy Grant, including a page of technical merit and the CDLink Voyager page, which lets you play your CDs in a whole new way.

Ari Davidow's Klezmer Page

http://www.well.com/user/ari/klez/

Focuses on a blend of traditional Jewish folk music and jazz. Contains articles on Klezmer, artist profiles, CD reviews, concert and festival information, a guide to radio programs, contact information for Klezmer musicians, links to locations where you can purchase Klezmer CDs, and record company addresses.

Arizona Jazz, Rhythm and Blues Festival

http://www.infomagic.com/~azjazz/index.html

Offers complete schedules and ticket information for this fairly new jazz and blues event held in Flagstaff and brought to you by the organizers of the famous Telluride Jazz Festival. Also provides information on travel and accommodations.

Arto Wikla's Music Page

http://userwww.cs.helsinki.fi/~wikla/music.html

Provides information for lute players and early music enthusiasts. Includes articles on lute playing, transcriptions of lute pieces, photos of lutes, and links to many other early music sites.

Australian Folk Songs

http://www.wise.mq.edu.au/WWWise/MarkG/songNet/intro.html

Presents a collection of more than 100 Australian folk songs. Includes sheet music, sound samples, lyrics, and annotations about each song. Contains an alphabetical title index, a glossary of terms, and a chronological list of songbooks.

Autoharp Page, The

http://www.realtime.net:80/~fmouse/harppage.html

Provides information about the autoharp, including publications, recordings, concert and festival schedules, and how to buy and get started playing an autoharp.

B-52's WWW Pages, The

http://www.york.ac.uk/~dwe101/b52s/

Contains lyrics, photos, and more from the band. Includes a complete band biography and a list of B-52 related quotations.

Bali & Beyond Home Page

http://www.kaiwan.com/~gamelan/balihome.html

Contains information on Gamelan music in general (a form of Indonesian orchestral music characterized by gongs, chimes, and percussion), and Balinese and Javanese Gamelan in particular. Also offers some technical information on musical scales and structure and a glossary of Indonesian music terms.

Banjo Tablature Archive

http://www.vuw.ac.nz/~gnat/banjo/tab/

Contains banjo tablatures in a variety of musical styles, including classical, bluegrass, and jazz.

Banjo Tabs

http://www.wsnet.com/~phil/banjo.html

Contains a collection of banjo tablatures and a variety of other banjo and bluegrass-related information. Also includes banjo jokes and cartoons, as well as tour and festival dates.

Batish Institute of Indian Music and Fine Arts, The

http://hypatia.ucsc.edu:70/1/RELATED/Batish

Provides information about this Indian Music Institute in California and about "Sitar Power," a popular hybrid of Indian classical music and rock.

Bay Area Celtic Music Calendar

http://www.cygnus.com/misc/celtfolk.html

Offers a calendar that serves as a guide to concerts, festivals, and events, for local residents and visitors to the area.

Be Happy or Die!

http://www.emba.uvm.edu/~jross/aonhome.html

Focuses on the techno group Art of Noise. Includes a complete discography with covers of each album above the track titles. Also includes a summary of all information from the liner notes in each album.

Beastie Boys—Grand Royal

http://www.nando.net/BeastieBoys/

Contains all conceivable data regarding the 80s hard-rock band, along with more that you probably haven't conceived of.

Bhangra Page

http://yucc.yorku.ca/home/sanraj/bhangra.html

Focuses on this unique style of dance music from the Punjab region of Northern India and Pakistan. Provides information on concerts, new CD releases, and radio and TV shows. Also offers several audio excerpts.

Billy Joel Info Pages

http://yallara.cs.rmit.EDU.AU/~s9407312/billy.html

Offers many links to plenty of information. Provides album information, lyrics, bootleg information, concert information, a photo album, a sound library, and more. Also includes a downloadable Billy Joel Program for Windows.

Björk's—Web Sense

http://www.centrum.is/bjork/

Presents the Web site "of the six senses, where sight, hearing, smell, taste, touch, and intuition" serve as the focus.

Blue Highway, The

http://www.umn.edu/nlhome/m161/schn0170/index.html

Offers a tour through delta blues country, introducing the blues immortals along the way. Includes photos and biographies accompanied by a road map of the route you take. Also lets you enter comments and read those of others who have traveled the blues highway.

Bluegrass Music Page, The

http://www.best.com/~kquick/bg.html

Consists mainly of extensive links to other bluegrass and related (and a few not-so-related) Web sites, as well as ftp sites and newsgroups.

Bluegrass Unlimited Reviews—Table of Contents

http://www.clark.net/pub/warnock/WWW/review_toc.html

Offers reviews of bluegrass-related recordings by Archie Warnock III, originally published in *Bluegrass Unlimited Magazine*.

Bluenote

http://www.cis.ohio-state.edu/hypertext/faq/usenet/music/bluenote/top.html

Contains the FAQs from two Usenet newsgroups. Contains basic information on these musical styles.

BluesNet Home Page

http://dragon.acadiau.ca/~rob/blues/blues.html

Contains biographies of musicians, an archive of photos (many previously unpublished), a feature on teachers, and many informative articles. Lets you leave your comments in the guest book. Offers links to other major blues sites.

BMG Goes Online

http://www.bmg.de/

Lets you explore the universe of music and download sound samples, pictures, and videos of various artists. Also offers links to the hottest music related Web sites.

Bodhran Page, The

http://www.panix.com/~mittle/bodhran.html

Features Celtic ornamental designs. Focuses on the goat-skin drum, the *bodhran*. Includes everything from making or buying one and learning how to play, to information on bodhran players, recordings, and concerts.

Bolivian Music Page, The

http://cc.usu.edu/~slcpc/bmp/Main-E.html

Serves as a source for Andean music in general and Bolivian music specifically. Provides information about the bands and their recordings. Includes full track listings.

The Bolivian Music Page.

Boston Chamber Ensemble

http://www.mit.edu:8001/people/jcb/BCE/bce.html

Presents productions with a historical range from the Renaissance to the present day, with a special commitment to supporting contemporary composers. Holds a nation-wide composition competition in an effort to expand its interaction with American composers. Provides more information about BCE and this competition.

Bottom Line Archive, The

http://syy.oulu.fi/tbl.html

Electronic version of this magazine for bassists. Features articles for the practicing bassist and electric bass players. Contains all back issues. Also offers photos of musicians and links to various bassists' home pages.

Boy George Home Page, The

http://www.umich.edu/~geena/boygeorge.html

Presents the works of Boy George. Includes a discography with all lyrics and pop chart information from the United States, United Kingdom, Japan, Sweden, and Italy.

Bryan Adams Home Page, The

http://www.glue.umd.edu/~xiaoqin/music/adams.html

Offers lyrics, reviews, pictures, and more. Also provides charts and statistics from around the world.

Building a Library: A Collector's Guide

http://www.ncsa.uiuc.edu/SDG/People/marca/barker-beethoven.html

Serves as a guide to classical record collecting. Delineates the general principles and reviews specific well-known works.

carnatic.html

http://tam2000.tamu.edu/~vrd4958/carnatic.html

Focuses on Carnatic, or South Indian, classical music. Provides an introductory essay about Carnatic music, as well as information on the different Raga forms, musical instruments, and musicians, including photos.

Cascade Blues Association

http://www.teleport.com/~boydroid/blues/cba.htm

Nonprofit organization. Promotes blues and jazz in Oregon, offers photos of blues legends, and provides concert schedules and information about the organization.

Celtic Music Index Page

http://www.execpc.com/~danb/celtic.html

Focuses on Irish music. Contains sheet music for traditional tunes, reviews of recent CDs, audio excerpts, and more.

Ceolas Celtic Music Archive

http://celtic.stanford.edu/ceolas.html

Provides a guide to Celtic music resources, artist profiles, discographies, reviews, sound samples, concert and festival schedules, a guide to musical instruments, tune indexes, music software, and links to countless other sites.

Chamber Music

http://www.ultranet.com/~cwholl/cmc/cmc.html

Provides a guide to chamber music conferences for amateur musicians and students. Contains information, schedules, fees, and application forms for about a dozen conferences.

Chicago Concert Search

http://student-www.uchicago.edu/users/achatche/music/concerts.html

Features a searchable database that contains classical music concert schedules, including festivals, for the Chicago area. Lets you search by time period, performer, composer, or work.

Chinese Music Page

http://vizlab.rutgers.edu/~jaray/sounds/chinese_music/chinese_music.html

Presents an archive of Chinese music. Contains many audio samples of traditional classical instrumental and vocal music, folk music, ceremonial music, and more.

Christian Music Online

http://www.cmo.com/cmo/index.html

Contains Word records and Star song records. Provides up-to-date information on the latest release of the respective companies' artist.

Clannad WWW Home Page, The

http://www.empire.net/~whatmoug/clanhome.htm

Features a discography, lyrics, images, and information about the Irish band, Clannad.

Clash Page

http://www.idiscover.co.uk/paul/rob/clash.html

Features a complete discography of all Clash albums and the lyrics to every track. Also offers a chart history of all the hits that made it big.

Classical MIDI Archives

http://www.hk.net/~prs/midi.html

Provides archives of classical music audio files in MIDI format.

Classical Music Home Page

http://www.webcom.com/~music/

Provides information on classical and early music. Includes a guide to building a basic CD collection, a buying guide for the serious collector, lists of more than 1,850 recommended CDs, and informative composer profiles. Searchable.

Classical Music Home Page: N.S.Sundar

http://www.cis.ohio-state.edu/~sundar/

Provides information on North and South Indian classical music, Indian classical dance forms, a FAQ for rec.music.indian.classical, and an eclectic gallery of photos from musicians to Hindu deities to Mahatma Gandhi. Also includes databases of song lyrics and great personalities of Carnatic (South Indian) music.

Classical Music in Italy

http://www.fastnet.it/cultura/music_en.htm

Serves as a guide to classical music in Italy. Provides information on festivals and concerts, theaters, orchestras, music associations, music competitions, the music press, music education, and musical groups.

 Classical Music in Italy

Classical Music Reviews

http://www.ncsa.uiuc.edu/SDG/People/marca/music-reviews.html

Provides reviews of recent recordings, a basic repertoire CD list (by period) for the beginning collector, and a series of exhaustive lists of recommended CDs (also by period) that includes track listings and musician credits. Covers medieval through modern periods.

Cleveland Concert Search

http://student-www.uchicago.edu/users/achatche/music/Cleveland/concerts.html

Provides a searchable database that contains comprehensive classical music concert schedules, including festivals, for the Cleveland area. Lets you search by time period, performer, composer, or work.

Club ZigZag

http://www.interverse.com/clubzigzag/

Features jazz, "new swing," and anything else that grooves—the Cyberspace equivalent of a '30s night club.

Welcome. . .

to the first 24 hour performance venue in cyberspace

Concertina!

http://funnelweb.utcc.utk.edu/~tkoosman/boxlinks.html

Contains links to Web sites for the concertina or would-be concertina player. Includes concertina playing, and associated music forms, such as Irish and Morris Dance music, as well as links to tunebooks.

Counting Crows

http://hammers.wwa.com/hammers/crows/crows.html

Provides Counting Crows information. Offers a complete discography, pictures, and an extensive FAQs file. Tells you who "Mr. Jones" really is.

Cuban Music

http://itre.uncecs.edu/music/cuban-music.html

Provides music samples, Spanish lyrics, and English translations of a wide variety of Cuban songs.

Current Opera Website

http://www.webcom.com/~redwards/

Focuses on live opera. Features *Current Opera Digest*, a "daily gleaning of highlights from opera discussions on the Net," an article about an opera "conspiracy," and links to other opera resources on the Net.

Cybergrass—The Internet Bluegrass Magazine

http://www.info.net/BG/

Features everything you'd expect in a magazine, including article, artist profiles, and events calendar. Includes reader comments and bluegrass want ads. Also includes a guide to magazines and newsletters and offers links to other bluegrass sites.

Cyberspace Opera

http://www.en.utexas.edu/~slatin/opera/

Presents an ongoing collaborative effort in which Net surfers can join. Provides the basic story line, characters, acts, and music, and asks you to help supply the libretto.

Dan Cox's Flamenco Page

http://clever.net/flamenco/index1.htm

Offers a history of flamenco, sound clips of songs, and many links to other flamenco music sites, newsgroups, and a flamenco bulletin board.

Dave Matthews Band Home Page, The

http://liberty.uc.wlu.edu/~ajacob/dmb/

Guides you to information about the DMB. Offers biographies, lyrics, and tour dates.

David Bowie File, The

http://liber.stanford.edu/~torrie/Bowie/BowieFile.html

Chronicles the life of David Bowie. Provides information about all his albums, movies, and videos.

Dawn's Basket Full of Country

http://www.hcc.cc.fl.us/services/staff/dawn/basketc.htm

Offers a personal collection of country-related sites for country western music fans and cowboys. Also provides fanclub information and a pen pal list.

DC Blues Home Page

http://www.intelus.com/dcblues/

Provides information on concerts, events, and venues in the Washington, D.C. area. Lets musicians submit information regarding their own concerts to include in the schedule. Features sounds, pictures, and reviews of D.C. area musicians. Also provides information on the DC Blues Society.

Depeche Mode Home Page, The

http://www.cis.ufl.edu/~sag/dm/

Focuses on the eclectic alternative band. Includes dozens of pictures and several links to other Depeche Mode resources. Also provides information on how to subscribe to their mailing list.

Diana Ross Fan Club

http://www.knoware.nl/music/diana/ross1.htm

Focuses on Diana Ross. Includes plenty of reminiscence about the Supremes. Also tells you out how to get *ROSS*, the official Diana Ross fan club magazine.

Didjeridu W3 Server, The

http://www.nd.edu/~sborman/didjeridu/

Focuses on didjeridu players around the world. Contains myths, legends, and literature related to this Australian aboriginal instrument, audio samples, CD reviews, cover photos, information on building and repairing didjeridus, lessons and tips on playing, and a didjeridu player's resource guide.

Digeridoo Page, The

http://www.well.com/user/nhunter/didj/index.html

Provides information about modern musicians who use the digeridoo (sic), an Australian aboriginal instrument, in their music. Contains artist biographies, discographies, and record labels.

Digital Tradition Folk Song Full Text Search

http://web2.xerox.com/digitrad

Consists of a searchable database that contains the lyrics and music to thousands of traditional folk songs. Offers full text searching. Also offers keyword, title, and tune lists.

Discographies (and More) at Nibble's

http://www.swcp.com/~lazlo/Discographies.html

Indexes many varied discographies of many bands, like Erasure, Falco, Devo, and Men Without Hats (and many more).

Disgraceland

http://www.wmin.ac.uk/%7Etjdec/welcome2.html

Provides information about Belinda Carlisle and the Go-Gos. Includes a large image bank.

Doc Hamilton's Bluegrass Home Page

http://ccwf.cc.utexas.edu/~docham/

Presents a photo gallery of bluegrass greats.

Doc Watson

http://sunsite.unc.edu/doug/DocWat/DocWat.html

Contains a brief biography, a discography, a concert schedule, and a performance by Doc Watson accompanied by his son Merle. Includes links to pages on other bluegrass greats, such as Bill Monroe.

Doors, The

http://www.vis.colostate.edu/~user1209/doors/

Presents information about this historic band. Includes lyrics, pictures, and bootleg information. Also includes plenty of other Net resources.

Drums and Percussion Page, The

http://www.cse.ogi.edu/Drum/

Targets the active drummer or percussionist in all genres of music. Offers transcriptions of drum and percussion pieces, a searchable list of percussionists on the Net, a directory of drum and percussion-related organizations, assorted articles and bibliographies, FAQs, jokes, and links to other drum sites.

Electric Gallery: The Jazz and Blues Wing, The

http://www.egallery.com/egallery/jazz.html

Features paintings and sound samples of blues and jazz greats.

Electronic Early Music

http://www.hike.te.chiba-u.ac.jp/eem/

Features several dozen audio files, primarily of Renaissance dance music played on various MIDI instruments.

ELP—Emerson, Lake & Palmer

http://bliss.berkeley.edu/elp/

Provides Emerson, Lake & Palmer (ELP) information. Includes online back issues of the ELP digest.

Elvis Costello

http://east.isx.com/~schnitzi/elvis.html

Focuses on Elvis Costello. Includes mailing lists, concert reviews, lyrics, guitar tablatures, and a complete discography online. Also features a page of closely related artists whom you might also like.

Elvis Home Page

http://sunsite.unc.edu/elvis/elvishom.html

Focuses on Elvis. Reports recent sightings and lets you download some pictures and sounds. Brings Graceland to the Net. Also lets you make an Elvis connection and find an Elvis pen pal on the Net.

Enigma

http://www.hsr.no/~joarg/Enigma.html

Provides information on Enigma. Provides a discography of the band and its founding father Michael Cretu. Also provides mailing list information, a picture gallery, and reviews of Enigma.

Entrance to Northwest Jazz Page

http://www.speakeasy.org/nwjazz/

Contains a potpourri of jazz information, pertaining to the northwestern United States (mostly Washington). Includes area artists and their recordings, concert and festival schedules, jazz publications, and visual art.

Enya—Unofficial Home Page

http://www.bath.ac.uk/%7Eccsdra/enya/

Provides pictures, sounds, translations of the Irish lyrics, the popular Enya Pages, and transcripts of interviews with Enya.

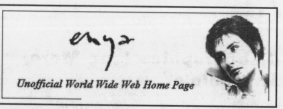
Unofficial World Wide Web Home Page

Excess of INXS, An

http://www.columbia.edu/~nak6/inxs.html

Includes INXS biographies, discographies, lyrics, pictures, guitar tabs, digital songs, and more.

Falco

ftp://ftp.swcp.com/pub/users/lazlo/discographies/falco

Provides a complete discography of Falco.

FAQ: rec.music.classical

http://www.cis.ohio-state.edu/hypertext/faq/usenet/
music/classical-faq/faq.html

Contains information for the beginner. Answers questions on how to select recordings, which books to read to learn more, how to identify a piece heard on the radio, TV, or in a movie, what distinguishes different genres of music, and more.

Fasola Home Page

http://martinique.umhc.umn.edu:8001/Docs/.www/
fasola_homepage.html

Provides information resources for Sacred Harp (a form of early American three- and four-part a cappella folk music that traces its roots back to Reformation and Renaissance England) and other American Shape Note traditions of singing.

Flamenco Home Page

http://solea.quim.ucm.es/flamenco.html

Focuses on the flamenco scene in Madrid, containing useful information for the would-be tourist and flamenco aficionado about where to see live flamenco. Provides some information in Spanish.

Folk DJ List

http://www.hidwater.com/folkdj/folkdj.html

Provides information on folk and bluegrass music on the radio, submitted by the programs' disk jockeys. Contains station lists, show profiles, and playlists.

Folk Music Home Page

http://www.eit.com/web/folk/folkhome.html

Covers every aspect of folk music: artists, albums, commercial resources, concerts, and folk music on the radio. Also contains information on ftp sites, mailing lists, and usenet newsgroups, as well as links to many other folk music sites.

Folk Stuff

http://www.lm.com/~dshu/folkstuff.html

Presents a directory of information for folk musicians and people designing and building folk and experimental musical instruments. Covers catalogs, books, and periodicals, for a wide variety of instruments, including hammered dulcimers, folk flutes, and many others.

Folkbook: An Online Acoustic Music Establishment

http://www.cgrg.ohio-state.edu/folkbook/

Contains all sorts of information about folk music and folk musicians. Provides information on venues, festivals, and concerts, artist profiles, discographies, record labels and distributors, song lyrics, tablatures, and more. Also contains links to Usenet newsgroups of interest.

Fractal Music Project, The

http://www-ks.rus.uni-stuttgart.de:80/people/schulz/
fmusic/

Provides information about anything related to fractal music. Provides online paper abstracts, sound bites, means to getting on the mailing list, and downloadable software.

Frank Sinatra WWW Page, The

`http://www.io.org/~buff/sinatra.html`

Provides up-to-date concert reviews, books, newspaper articles, and a complete filmography and discography. Also includes information on how to join the Frank Sinatra fan club.

Frankie Say No More—FGTH Fan Pages

`http://www.cs.rulimburg.nl/~antal/fgth/fgth-home.html`

Presents Frankie Goes to Hollywood, the band, online. Provides FGTH resources.

Future Love Paradise WWW Site; Dedicated to Seal, The

`http://minerva.cis.yale.edu/~ariedels/seal.html`

Includes an image oasis, the Seal FAQ file, a lyric library, and more. Includes transcriptions of online conferences with Seal.

FutureNet: Classic CD

`http://www.futurenet.co.uk/music/classiccd.html`

Contains articles and reviews, a CD finder, and subscription information. Provides a beginner's guide that includes features on classical music in the media, and a history of classical music, plus a classical CD top 100 and an at-a-glance guide to the composers, A–Z.

Gaia: Olivia Newton-John Home Page

`http://www-leland.stanford.edu/~clem/`

Provides information about Olivia. Offers links to SoulKiss, the ONJ Internet Mailing list, movie information, videos, and a photo collection. Also offers information on how to join the fan clubs.

Gallery of the Unusual and Absurd

`http://serv2.fwi.com/~gordong`

Serves fans of music groups Heart, Kansas, Uriah Heep, and Elton John, among others. Also contains links to thousands of games and other sites.

GEMM Home Page

`http://gemm.com`

Focuses on music. Enables you to search for information about artists, albums, and companies. Lets you register to be notified when a particular item you want is mentioned elsewhere in the marketplace.

Get Crued

`http://www.aquila.com:80/motley.crue/`

Focuses on the heavy metal band Motley Crue. Includes information about the IRC channel and a full discography. Also provides information on each individual band member.

Gloria Estefan Home Page

`http://nyx10.cs.du.edu:8001/~lwright/`

Focuses on Gloria. Includes links to many pictures, sounds, and animations, as well as an easy fill-out form for subscribing to a Gloria Estefan mailing list.

GMO—African Archive (Music)

`http://www.iuma.com/GMO/africa.html`

Online forum for African musicians to market self-produced CDs. Offers users the opportunity to provide information about, sample, and purchase music they might otherwise never know about.

Granger's Fiddle Tunes for Guitar

http://www.msen.com/johng/ag/gft.html

Presents a collection of more than 500 fiddle tunes in guitar tablature. Contains sample tablatures, as well as an index and several appendixes from the book. Also offers a couple reviews.

Grateful Dead, The

http://www.cs.cmu.edu/afs/cs.cmu.edu/user/mleone/web/dead.html

Contains an exhaustive tribute to the Grateful Dead. Includes everything, from lyrics, pictures, and sounds to tour dates, rumors, and Dead icons for the Macintosh. Also offers links to Jerry Garcia memorial pages.

Green Day

http://www.cs.caltech.edu/~adam/greenday.html

Focuses on the band Green Day. Also offers links to plenty of other Green Day Net resources and links to other bands that sport a similar sound.

Gregorian Chant Home Page

http://www.music.princeton.edu/chant_html/

Supports advanced research on Gregorian chant. Contains an informative essay on the state of Gregorian chant studies, sound files (coming soon), and links to other chant research Web sites, as well as lists and links to resources on related topics.

Guinness Temple Bar Blues Festival

http://www.eeng.dcu.ie/~stdcu/blues/

Mammoth three-day blues festival in Ireland. Features 200 hours of live music. Virtually all events are free. Provides program and other festival information.

Guns n' Roses Home Page

http://www.teleport.com/~boerio/gnr-home.html

Focuses on Axel and Slash. Includes a complete discography, lyrics, and tour information. Also includes guitar tabs and interviews with the band.

Guns n' Roses Home Page

HACK1: InSoc

http://www.webcom.com/~ricochet/insoc/

Information Society online. Offers many sound samples and lyric sheets.

Hammered Dulcimer

http://tfnet.ils.unc.edu/~gotwals/hd/dulcimer.html

Provides information on hammered dulcimers, including workshops, festivals, publications, photos, sound samples, musicians, and information on building or buying an instrument.

Hanspeter Niederstrasser's Def Leppard Page

http://www.princeton.edu/~nieder/defleppard/def.html

Focuses on this eighties band who defined modern metal. Provides all you might need to complete your collection. Includes complete lyrics, band history, images, and sounds. Also presents a guest book and survey to fill out so you can express your opinion about the band.

Hard Bop Cafe™ Jazz Home Page

http://www.mbnet.mb.ca/~mcgonig/hardbop.html

Serves as a complete guide to jazz in Canada. Includes concert and festival information, jazz on the radio, jazz publications, CD reviews, and more.

Harmonica World

http://www.bekkoame.or.jp/~mshige/

Provides harmonic photos and sounds, information on harmonica players, CDs, concerts, even a harmonica festival. Represents all styles of music, although blues and classical predominate.

Harmony Ridge Music

http://www.rahul.net/hrmusic/

Provides information about female singer-songwriters and musicians. Includes everything from avant-garde to world music. Includes a photo gallery of artists.

Harp Page, The

http://www.tns.lcs.mit.edu/harp/harp.html

Targets the harp or folk harp enthusiast. Includes information on harp societies, publications, and events, as well as links to various harpists' home pages.

High Lonesome, The

http://www.io.com/~thl/high_lonesome

Focuses on the band The High Lonesome. Features bios, history, lyrics, photos, sound, ordering information, upcoming gigs, and more.

Hindi Movie Songs

http://www.cs.wisc.edu/~navin/india/songs/index.html

Focuses on Indian movie songs in the Hindi language. Contains song information and full lyrics. Includes categorized indexes of singers, music directors, lyricists, films, actors/actresses, as well as a searchable song title index.

Historical Harp Society Page

http://www.tns.lcs.mit.edu/harp/HHS/

Promotes the appreciation and use of historical harps (i.e. non-modern, folk, and art music harps). Contains details about its history, purpose, membership, and of special interest to historical harp enthusiasts, their Annual Historical Harp Conference and Workshop.

HMV Toronto Superstore

http://www.hmv.ca/

Contains new releases, charts, and reviews on CDs, video, laserdiscs, CD-ROMs, and video games. Also contains a Canadian Indie Music Archive and a scrapbook of the stars that pass through our doors.

Hole in the Web Phish Phorum, The

http://cinti.cent.com/dfessel/phish.html

Includes a growing collection on the band Phish. Offers a trading area where you can get together with other Phishheads to exchange records over e-mail.

Home Page for Elton John Fans

http://itchy.hrfs.uiuc.edu/elton.html

Includes information about the Elton John AIDS Foundation. Also offers plenty of album information, pictures, and a discography. Also provides tour information.

Home Page of MT&C Music Club

http://violet.berkeley.edu/~gsyu/

Contains information about the music and recent CD releases, as well as an opportunity to browse and shop online. Contains full track listings and pictures of all CDs.

Hootie & the Blowfish Home Page

http://www.stcloud.msus.edu/~pullit01/music/hootie/hootie.html

Provides information about the band. Includes a who's who list of the band, additional external links, and tour dates. Also includes a growing lyric database.

House of Blues Online— Summer Preview

http://underground.net/HOB

Offers QuickTime virtual reality scenes. Includes concert schedules, music and video samples, blues bios, and more.

Huey Lewis and the News Homepage, The

http://www.nmt.edu/~nguyenm/huey.html

Includes a detailed history of Huey's (born Hugh Cregg) life and times, and full details on every album since "Four chords and seven years ago."

Hype! Music Store & CD Reviews

http://www.hype.com/music/home.htm

Provides a searchable database of classical and rock CD reviews. Allows you to submit your own review of a CD for inclusion in the database.

Hyper Idol—The Billy Idol Home Page

http://minerva.cis.yale.edu/~markl/billy-idol/

Represents every album as a separate page with images and lyrics to every song. Contains a growing collection of images besides those found on the albums.

IDRS WWW

http://idrs.colorado.edu/

International Double Reed Society online. Provides information for double reed players (oboists, bassoonists). Contains information on the society, its conference, and membership. Also offers online editions of their two publications, the *Double Reed* and the *Journal of the International Double Reed Society*, which contain many articles of interest to practicing musicians, from current and back issues.

Index of Bulgaria Sounds

http://pisa.rockefeller.edu:8080/Bulgaria/sounds/

Provides audio samples of folk music from Bulgaria. Represents all the major regional styles. Includes scenic photos of Bulgaria.

Indian Classical Music

http://www.vt.edu:10021/org/malhaar/music.html

Features an introduction to Indian classical music, excellent biographies of master musicians, and some detailed information about the different ragas and styles of music. Also offers a number of links to online catalogs of Indian CDs and to other Indian music sites.

Indian Music: Recordings and Instruments

http://www.winternet.com/~khazana/cd1.html

Serves as an online source for CDs of Indian music. Claims to be able to get anything in print. Also offers a gallery of Indian musicians, featuring photos, bios, and audio selections, and offers a gallery of music instruments, featuring illustrations, descriptive material, and sound samples.

Indiana University School of Music

http://www.music.indiana.edu/

Presents the school of music at Indiana University, Bloomington, online. Offers a resource page that can help you find nearly anything. Provides detailed information about the school. Also includes an index of music resources on the Internet.

Indigo Girls Main Page

http://www.tezcat.com/~mtp/IG//HTML/ig-page.html

Focuses on the Indigo Girls. Includes up-to-the-minute tour information and a frequently asked questions page.

Indonesian Music

http://www.umanitoba.ca/indonesian/music.html

Features information on various types of Indonesian music and instruments, including Gamelan and Angklung (bamboo instruments). Also offers Indonesian song lyrics and links to pages on Gamelan groups in the United States.

InterJazz Home Page

http://www.webcom.com/~ijazz/welcome.html

Presents a jazz bulletin board where venues and record labels can announce schedules, new releases, and booking agencies; where show promoters can communicate with prospects for business; where individuals can search for a business or add their own with a personal "business card," and musicians can make items available, communicate with other musicians and fans, or post a schedule.

Internet Music Monolith, The

http://203.1.75.10/~mcontact/monolith

Serves as a guide to the Australian Music industry for fans, musicians, students, and all other industry participants. Includes a directory to industry resources, media, software, Australian artists, charts, musicians contact service, video, and more.

Irish Folk Songs

http://www.cs.hut.fi/%7Ezaphod/search/

Provides a searchable database that contains the lyrics to more than 300 Irish folk songs. Also contains an alphabetic index for easy browsing.

Irish Music on the Net

http://orathost.cfa.ilstu.edu/public/OratClasses/
ORAT389.88Seminar/Exhibits/PeterJuvinall/0home.html

Presents an exhibit that attempts to "capture much of the allure" of traditional Irish music. Includes works of medieval Irish art, album covers, and landscape photos; a theater that features some video clips of musicians playing; and a recording studio that features audio excerpts of music on different Irish traditional instruments.

Iron Maiden Page

http://www.cs.tufts.edu/~stratton/maiden/maiden.html

Offers a collection of album covers and a running commentary on the meaning and value of each album. Includes many pictures.

Jane's Addiction and Porno for Pyros

http://raptor.swarthmore.edu/jahall/JA/

Contains all the latest facts on the bands. Provides detailed discographies, pictures, and sound samples from both Jane's Addiction and Porno for Pyros. Also contains links to many other Web pages (like Woodstock '94) and ftp sites.

Janet Jackson Homepage

http://web.mit.edu/afs/athena/user/a/g/agoyo1/www/
janet2.html

Focuses on Janet. Includes the latest news, tour information, sounds, lyrics, and more.

Jazz Improvisation

http://gopher.adp.wisc.edu/jazz/

Presents a series of articles for a course on jazz improvisation, taught at the University of Wisconsin. Serves as an introduction to the subject. Includes many images of musical notation and photos of jazz musicians.

Jazz in France

http://www.erb.com/cdeus/jazzfr.htm

Surveys the entire French jazz scene, including festivals, magazines, jazz on radio and TV, and jazz awards.

Jazz Music Stores Around the World

http://www.acns.nwu.edu/jazz/lists/stores.html

Serves as a guide to jazz record stores world-wide, arranged alphabetically by location. Includes useful information on shops' strengths in terms of formats and new/used, bargains, and more.

Jazz Net

http://www.dnai.com/~lmcohen/index.html

Provides jazz and blues information pertaining mostly to the West Coast. Covers publications, CDs, photography, concerts, and festivals.

Jazz Roots Homepage

http://poe.acc.virginia.edu/~tm4q/next/JazzRoots/
Introduction.html

Provides information on the early jazz masters, such as Fats Waller and Benny Goodman. Includes photos, bios, band members, discographies, and other information on the artists' careers.

Jethro Tull Music Archive

http://remus.rutgers.edu/JethroTull/

Focuses on the band Jethro Tull. Provides information about the band and its whereabouts. Includes lyrics to all the band's songs and a connection to an FTP server that provides pictures, articles, and even a few MIDI sequences.

Jewish Music Home Page, The

http://www.jewishmusic.com/tara/

Offers a wide variety of Jewish music selections. Provides an online catalog, sound clips, and jumps to other Jewish music links.

Jimi Hendrix Server

http://www.parks.tas.gov.au/jimi/jimi.html

Provides many Jimi goodies. Includes pictures, a discography, and sounds.

Jimmy Buffett Web Page

http://www.homecom.com/buffett/

Includes resources for finding Jimmy Buffett on the Net. Offers pictures and sound bytes.

Joe's Aerosmith Tribute

http://coos.dartmouth.edu/~joeh/

Focuses on Aerosmith. Includes pictures of the band and downloadable sound bytes. Provides tour dates and other recent Aerosmith news. Also offers chord charts.

Justin's Early Music Web

http://www.sirius.com/~justinr/em2.html

Provides information about early music and instruments.

Kerrville Folk Festival, The

http://monsterbit.com/kerrville.html

Provides information about the Kerrville Folk Festival, a major United States folk festival that takes place for two and a half weeks every Spring. Contains performance schedules, ticket and camping information, a photo gallery of participating artists, and more.

King Biscuit Time

http://www.island.net/~blues/

Online blues magazine. Offers news, CD reviews, a great selection of audio files, photos, extensive biographies of musicians, articles, links to other blues sites, and more.

Kinks, The

http://hobbes.it.rit.edu/kinks/kinks.html

Includes everything from pictures, sounds, and videos to a complete discography and lyric database.

KISS Network— Los Angeles, CA, The

http://www.galcit.caltech.edu/~aure/strwys.html

Focuses on the musical group KISS and contains information about collectibles, band history, discography, and more. Also offers downloadable sound files.

Kraftwerk Unofficial Infobahn

http://wwwtdb.cs.umu.se/~dvlawm/kraftwerk.html

Includes pictures, sounds, and videos, and a collection of Kraftwerk MIDI sequences. Lets you add your name to the list of all the Kraftwerk fans in the world.

Lark in the Morning

http://www.mhs.mendocino.k12.ca.us/MenComNet/Business/Retail/Larknet/larkhp.html

Provides information on music instruments for the performance of all types of acoustic music. Provides a wide selection of instruments, books, recordings, and videos. Also contains various informative articles.

Larry Aronson Home Page

http://www.interport.net/~laronson/WorldBeat.html

Contains a variety of information on Afro-pop music, particularly Soukous, the pan-African dance music that originated in Zaire and the Congo. Features recommendations on bands, CDs, and other useful information.

Le Nozze di Figaro

http://server.music.vt.edu/lenozze/lenozzehome.html

Contains information on the opera, The Marriage of Figaro. Offers sections on the composer (Mozart), music, and dramatis personae.

Led Zeppelin Home Page

http://www.cs.virginia.edu/~jsw2y/zeppelin/zeppelin.html

Focuses on Led Zeppelin. Includes links to the Digital Graffiti mailing list, plenty of pictures, a discography, lyrics, and guitar tabs. Also offers a link to a Zeppelin page written in French.

Leland's Andean and Flamenco Page Index

http://lvande.us.net/

Contains a wealth of information on Andean and Flamenco music. Includes a guide to Flamenco guitar and dance teachers and a searchable music database.

Live Blues and Blues Radio, Steamin' Stan Ruffo

http://www.primenet.com/~steamin

Introduces Steamin' Stan Ruffo to the Internet community as a singer, songwriter, blusician, world-renowned harmonicator, as well as producer and host of the blues radio show, Blues On Tap, on Visalia's K100 99.7FM. Also offers links to other music and nonmusic related sites.

Lloyd Robbins' Moody Blues Page

http://www.ids.net/~lrobbins/moodys.html

Serves as a site for people who believe that all the best music was written 25 years ago. Offers links to information about the Moody Blues, including pictures and a discography. Also contains links to Alan Parsons Project information.

Lollapalooza Information (Unofficial)

http://nimitz.mcs.kent.edu/~cstone/lolla.html

Focuses on what Lollapalooza was and is. Includes details about the multiband festival for every year since 1991. Includes links to the individual home pages of featured bands.

Lou Reed's Web Home

http://charlotte.acns.nwu.edu/charm/html/lou/

Provides information about Lou Reed and more. Includes a bootleg gallery, a couple of guitar tabs, and plenty more.

Madonna Home Page, The

http://www.mit.edu:8001/people/jwb/Madonna.html

Serves as a means to finding any of a myriad of pages about Madonna on the Web. Includes a link to the Madonna Lyrics Archive, a complete discography, and Madonna's Top 10 List from the infamous Letterman episode. Also includes many pictures.

Mammoth Music Meta-List @ VIBE, The

http://www.pathfinder.com/@@DSzPaQAAAAAANkP/vibe/mmm/

Contains a directory of music-oriented Web sites. Includes folk, bluegrass, blues, jazz, world, classical, rock, and other styles of music.

Mandolin Pages, The

http://www.execpc.com/~danb/mandolin.html

Focuses on mandolins and related instruments (citterns, octave mandolins, bouzoukis, and more). Features a couple instrument guides, historical information, and images of mandolins.

Mary Chapin Carpenter

http://www.sony.com/Music/ArtistInfo/
MaryChapinCarpenter.html

Provides all the latest and most accurate information about what's coming up. Includes a biography, discography, and tour information.

Mazzy Star Home Page

http://www.acs.appstate.edu/~kj7341/mazzy.html

Focuses on Mazzy Star. Includes an "unofficial" discography and an ever-growing picture page. Also includes a video clip from the Jesus & Mary Chain.

Meat Puppets Home Page

http://www.nando.net/music/gm/puppets/index.html

Offers information on the band Meat Puppets, including tour and release dates, band art, discography, and merchandise information.

WELCOME TO THE MEAT PUPPETS HOME PAGE

BOX 110
TEMPE, AZ 85281

Men Without Hats: The (Unofficial) Home Page

http://www.mit.edu:8001/people/tobye/mwh/mwh.html

Offers all the latest discoveries about this '80s band. Includes a complete discography and a few pictures.

Merger

http://www.wp.com/Merger/home.htm

Presents Merger, an original rock and roll band in the Los Angeles, California, area.

Metallica Compilation

http://freeabel.geom.umn.edu:8000/metallica/
metallica.html

Focuses on Metallica. Includes lyrics and selected digitized songs from every album. Also includes pictures of all the album covers (even the completely black one).

Metro One

http://dostoevsky.ucr.edu/rms/

Online rest stop for the small Christian alternative record label, Metro One. Contains product information on new releases.

Mike Markowski's Beatles Page

http://www.eecis.udel.edu/~markowsk/beatles/

Includes a metaindex of other Beatles resources. Provides all the information you need about the Fab Four, including sounds, pictures, lyrics, and more.

Mike Oldfield

http://www.ensica.fr/~campedel/oldfield/

Presents a guy who can play any instrument you hand him. Provides information about the man behind the intriguing album Tubular Bells.

MIZIK

http://www.unik.no/~robert/mizik/mizik.html

Presents an eclectic collection of world music information and links. Includes discographies, sound samples, reviews, and more.

Moroccan Auditorium, The

http://www.dsg.ki.se/~v95-mel/Music/music.html

Contains excerpts of Moroccan music in a variety of styles, in several audio formats. Includes classical Andalusian music, Gnoua music, Berber music, and more.

Muscle Music, Inc.

http://www.hiwaay.net/mm

Contains information about music, video, and Web services and previews of artists and bios of Alabama music achievers.

Musi-Cal Performer Index

http://www.automatrix.com/cgi-bin/list-performers

Provides a concert calendar for folk, bluegrass, blues, and world music performers, organized alphabetically by artist.

Music Hall

http://www.ncsa.uiuc.edu/SDG/Experimental/
vatican.exhibit/exhibit/e-music/Music.html

Presents the music area of the Vatican Exhibit at the Library of Congress online. Contains four "rooms" of art treasures, primarily pages from Medieval and Renaissance illuminated music manuscripts. Provides notes with all the art works.

Music Home Page

http://www.cs.utk.edu/~basoglu/music.html

Contains a Turkish music archive that features musical excerpts of all styles and genres of Turkish music. Includes many photos of musicians and their instruments.

Music Resources on the Internet

http://www.music.indiana.edu/misc/music_resources.html

Contains resources in the form of audio clips, video clips, links, and files to just about every type of music. Also offers a collection of links to other music sites.

Music Under Soviet Rule

http://www.webcom.com/~beatlebk/musov/musov.html

Offers a collection of documents related to the classical music of the former Soviet Union. Documents the relationship between music and politics.

MuteWeb

http://www.nvg.unit.no:80/~optimus/devo/index.html

Focuses on the eighties eclectic band, Devo. Provides information about what's new with these different sort of fellas. Includes an image gallery and offers many external links to other devotees.

MWS—Discography/Lyrics

http://www.cs.rose-hulman.edu/~hochstrb/mws/

Focuses on contemporary Christian/Pop artist Michael W. Smith. Contains a complete discography and lyrics to every track. Also includes information on contacting the fan club in Nashville.

National Folk Festival

http://www.adfa.oz.au/NFF/NFF.html

Presents the Australian folk festival. Provides information on the festival, including schedules and how to become a performer at the festival.

Netcentral

http://www.netcentral.net/

Contains several Christian record companies, such as Benson, Sparrow, and the Gospel Music Association. Serves as a good jumping off point to different Christian entertainment companies.

New England Folk Concert Calendar

http://theory.lcs.mit.edu/~wald/calendar.html

Offers a calendar of concerts, festivals, and events, organized by month, for folk fans in the New England area. Also contains a guide to other print and electronic folk calendars.

New Orleans Jazz and Heritage Festival

http://yatcom.com/neworl/jfest/jfesttop.html

Provides a press release, complete performance schedules, notes on the different musical styles, accommodation information, and a decade of festival posters.

Nicks Fix (JK's Home Page), The

http://www.iadfw.net/jkinney/index.htm

Features Stevie Nicks, former lead singer of Fleetwood Mac. Contains Stevie news, album information, song lyrics, and more. Also includes several links to other Stevie-related pages.

Northern Journey: Canadian Folk Music Website

http://www.io.org/~njo/

Northern Journey: A Guide to Canadian Folk Music, the online edition. Claims to be "the definitive guide" to Canadian folk music. Overviews excerpts from the book, contains information about Canadian folk artists and folk festivals, and reviews some new and recent Canadian folk CDs.

Obvious Gossip Home Page

http://www.infohouse.com/obviousgossip/home.html

Presents the official k.d. lang fan club. Lets you investigate the purchase of various k.d. lang paraphernalia and provides the latest album and concert information.

OffBeat Magazine

http://www.NeoSoft.com/~offbeat/

Online edition of the print magazine, "New Orleans' and Louisiana's only music and entertainment magazine." Features interviews, articles, reviews, polls, and more on the New Orleans jazz scene, as well as club, concert, and festival information, and classified ads.

Old Time Music Bulletin Board

http://140.190.128.190/oldtime/oldtime.html

Enables readers to exchange and sell instruments and discuss banjo playing, fiddling, songs and lyrics, reviews, and anything else regarding old time music. Lets you post messages, including HTML tags that will be fully functional.

OM Kalthoum

http://ce.ecn.purdue.edu/~ashmawy/ok.html

Offers photos, a biography, and a detailed song listing. Contains information on songs, lyrics, and audio clips. Offers links to other pertinent sites.

Opera Schedule Server, The

http://www.fsz.bme.hu/opera/main.html

Offers a searchable database that contains the schedules of opera companies around the world. Also contains basic information on major opera houses world-wide.

opera-l_home_page

http://www.physics.su.oz.au/~neilb/operah.html

Includes a guide to recorded opera, an A–Z guide to composers, an A–Z guide to operas, synopses of operas, photos of opera stars, and links to other opera sites.

Original Mariah Carey Home Page, The

http://biogopher.wustl.edu/audio/mariah.html

Targets the Mariah Carey fan. Includes many pictures and many links to other Mariah pages. Also provides fan club information.

Oz-jazz Worldwide

http://magna.com.au/~georgeh/

Presents Australian musicians, concerts, festivals, organizations, radio programs, CDs, and jazz record shops. Also includes audio clips and a directory of Aussie jazz musicians overseas.

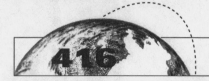

Pat Metheny Home Page, The

http://www.cecam.fr/~lensink/metheny.html

Provides a Metheny discography, concert reviews, tour dates, and more. Also offers downloadable pictures of every album cover. Includes links to related sites.

Pet Shop Boys USA

http://www.airworld.com:80/psb/

Provides pictures. Also includes sample audio sources and concert information. Includes links to a few other Pet Shop Boys pages on the Net.

Pete Lambie's Bruce Springsteen Page

http://www.gla.ac.uk/~gkrx11/Bruce/

Provides many pictures, lyrics, and more. Suggests a way to bring your bootlegs to life by making your own covers.

Peter Gabriel

http://www.horus.com/rec/music/gabriel/

Offers a collection of goodies about Peter Gabriel. Includes lyrics, pictures, and sound bytes. Also includes links to other pages on Peter and related bands.

Pink Floyd Home Page, The

http://humper.student.princeton.edu/floyd/

Includes many pictures, lyrics, a discography, and more. Also offers transcribed interviews with band members and a downloadable Pink Floyd screen saver.

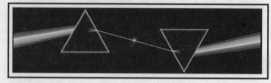

Planet Music

http://www.execpc.com/planet

Specializes in hard-to-find CDs. Offers thousands of different CDs. Also sells video tapes and music T-shirts.

PolkaNet

http://www.cyberenet.net/~szymczak/

Calls itself "the complete guide to contemporary polka music." Features a history of modern polka music, news on concerts, radio programs, and events, a message board, and an archive of sound clips of polka music, as well as information about where to buy recordings. Also includes a list of bands and their schedules.

Prince / O(+>

http://www.winternet.com/~charbone/prince.html

Includes all sorts of links concerning the rock star formerly known as Prince. Includes pictures and lyrics to all the major albums and singles. Also includes links to other related music.

Proximity—Led Zeppelin Collector's Journal

http://www.dnaco.net:80/~buckeye/prox/

Online edition of the fan magazine.

PunkRock Web

http://www.eden.com/punk

Focuses on Austin, Texas punk bands, cybercafes, video games, and virtual reality.

Queen

http://www.sognhs.no/egne/queen/queen.htm

Includes pictures, lyrics, sound samples, and guitar tabs.

R.E.M. Home Page

http://www.halcyon.com/rem/index.html

Includes notes on the R.E.M. tour, all about Mike Mills, and a Frequently Asked Questions sheet. Offers a discography, lyrics, and guitar chord sheets. Also includes a photo archive.

RADISH Home Page

http://www.rockhouse.com/radish/

Presents RADISH, an original rock band from Greenville, Texas (just east of Dallas), that plays original rock music as well as other classic rock. Introduces RADISH band members, Ben Kweller, Ryan Green, and John David Kent.

Random '80s Lyrics

http://itg-pc1.acns.nwu.edu/cgi-bin/lyric

Generates random '80s lyrics. Presents you with lyrics from a famous 1980s song when you connect to this page.

Random Band Name

http://ugweb.cs.ualberta.ca/~aaron/get_line.cgi

Helps you find a name for that band you're starting. Serves entertainment purposes, and generates names that actually come close to some current bands.

Reba McEntire

http://ruby.ph.utexas.edu/RebaWWW/Reba.html

Provides a wealth of Reba resources. Tells you how to join Reba's International Fan Club. Offers a schedule of appearances, Reba's Special Events, and more. Also lets you add your favorite Reba pictures.

Renaissance Consort

http://www.hike.te.chiba-u.ac.jp/cons1/

Lets you see and hear the instruments that make up a typical Renaissance consort. Provides photographs (accompanied by audio clips) of recorders, crumhorns, flutes, viols, and more.

Richard Robinson's Tunebook

http://www.leeds.ac.uk/music/Info/RRTuneBk/tunebook.html

Offers a collection of sheet music of traditional tunes, primarily from the Celtic lands and Scandinavia. Lets you access them by title, country, or type (jig, reel, waltz, and so on).

Rock the Strip

http://www1.digiplanet.com/VIM

Features sound and video samples from relatively new bands. Features an interactive trivia show hosted by ex-MTV jock Nina Blackwood and LA Radio KLOS host Kenny Sargent. Gives away a grand prize every month.

Rockmine Archives

http://www.wintermute.co.uk/rockmine

Provides a collection of information about British rock and roll.

Rolling Stones Web Site, The

http://www.stones.com/

Contains a vast collection of sounds and pictures. Includes a few pages especially for the new HotJava browser by Sun Systems™.

Roots/World Music FAQ

http://www.acns.nwu.edu/WNUR/drift/faq/

Offers definitions for the terms *world music* and *roots music*. Provides some basic information from a wide geographical area on musical styles, notable artists, musical instruments, and more.

RootsWorld: Music on the Net

http://www.rootsworld.com/rw/rw1.html

Offers news, CD reviews, articles, and special features, including a great guide to the music and musicians of Finland.

Rounder Records Group

http://harp.rounder.com:70/1/

Presents a catalog for the major independent bluegrass and folk label. Features sound samples from recordings of several of their most popular artists. Also features artist profiles and discographies.

Roxette: Home Page

http://www.ccsf.caltech.edu/~dmz/roxette/roxette.html

Offers information about concert dates, an interactive discography, and many pictures. Also includes information on soloists Marie Fredriksson, Per Gessle, and Gyllene Tider.

Russian Music

http://mars.uthscsa.edu/Russia/Music/

Contains an archive of Russian singers and their songs. Includes photos, discographies, song lyrics, and audio and video clips. Also offers recommended recordings and where to buy them. Includes folk and pop music.

Samba in Sweden

http://www.algonet.se/~johanw/

Focuses on the Brazilian music scene in Sweden. Provides information about the current groups and samples of some of their music. Offers links to Samba sites.

Samba Music

http://sunpath.stanford.edu:3007/music/Samba/Samba.html

Enables you to sample some full-length samba sound clips.

Sami's Urdu/Hindi Film Music Page

http://www.lehigh.edu/sm0e/public/www-data/sami.html

Serves fans of Urdu and Hindi film music. Offers articles on various singers, musical directors, and lyricists, lists of songs by singers, music directors, and so on, as well as notes and chords of songs and more. Also presents many photos.

Sarah Page

http://www.nettwerk.com/sarpg.html

Focuses on the music and activities of Sarah McLachlan. Includes a biography of Sarah, tour dates, and information on joining the fan club (and more).

SCA Music and Dance Home Page

http://fermi.clas.virginia.edu/~gl8f/
music_and_dance.html

Society for Creative Anachronism, online. Focuses on Renaissance dance and dance music. Includes dance "cheat sheets," a discography of Renaissance dance music, a collection of articles taken from the society's newsletter on Renaissance dance, articles on troubadours and bardic songs, and many links to other Early music and dance sites.

Sheena Easton

http://www.metronet.com/~bmeier/sheena.html

Provides information on when and where you can see Sheena in concert next. Also includes plenty of pictures, lyrics, a discography, and a videography of the artist's work.

Shona Music

http://www.teleport.com/~dbullock/shona_music.html

Provides information about Shona Music from Zimbabwe, and its typical mix of mbira, marimba, and other indigenous instruments. Contains a directory of Shona musicians and a Shona music bulletin board, and offers many links to other sites with information on Zimbabwe and on African music in general.

Similarities Engine™, The

http://www.webcom.com/~se/

Lets you enter your five favorite artists and albums, then e-mails you a list of other bands or artists in which you might also be interested.

Simon and Garfunkel Home Page

http://www.dur.ac.uk/~d213ga/

Offers Simon & Garfunkel and some Paul Simon solo stuff containing many tabs and some information on the duo. Contains a picture gallery, lyrics, and many guitar tabs.

Simple Minds—Good News From the Web

http://matahari.cv.com/people/Simon.Cornwell/
simple_minds/

Contains information about the '80s band Simple Minds. Includes a full discography, lyrics, and a FAQ file. Also includes many links to other Simple Minds resources on the Net.

Sinead O'Connor Home Page, The

http://www.engr.ukans.edu/~jrussell/music/sinead/
sinead.html

Contains an official discography, a biography of Sinead, pictures, quotations, and additional Sinead information. Serves as a master index to all sorts of goodies.

Some Peruvian Music...

http://www.rcp.net.pe/snd/snd_ingles.html

Contains sound files of Andean flute music from Peru.

Soul Pages, The

http://www.ot.com/sting/

Focuses on Sting. Provides information, lyrics, images, and sounds.

Southern Folklife Collection HomePage

http://ils.unc.edu/barba/sfc.html

Contains archives of Southeastern American tradition-derived music. Includes numerous photographs, interviews, oral histories, video and film documentaries, books, and periodicals. Contains pages on music and musicians in the following categories: early country music, old-time string bands, gospel and spiritual songs, and southeastern blues traditions, all illustrated with photos.

Station, The

http://www.marshall.edu/~bennett7/hstation.html

Provides barbershop harmony and a cappella information. Offers links to International Quartet Champions and other a cappella Web sites. Includes information about SPEBSQSA, Inc., and the MBNA Collegiate Quartet Contest.

Stiff as Toys and Tall as Men

http://miso.wwa.com/~anaconda/cure2.html

Focuses on The Cure. Includes fan club information, lyrics, images, and more. Also includes a few sound bites.

Stirrings Folk Mag

http://www.cityscape.co.uk/users/ah98/

Online edition of British folk music magazine. Features CD, book, and concert reviews, interviews, concert and festival schedules, the latest news, and more.

Stranglehold—Ted Nugent Page

http://thunder.indstate.edu/h5/jngonzo/.nuge.html

Provides information about the Nuge. Includes a complete discography, pictures, lyrics, and information on the fan club.

Susan Ashton

http://rendall.notis.com/ashton/ashton.html

Serves as a resource page for contemporary Christian singer Susan Ashton. Includes the expected Net resources, as well as many meta-links that point to other Christian music resources.

T. M. McComb: Music Home Page

http://www.best.com:80/~mccomb/music/

Provides one music writer's recommendations of classical, early music, and world music CDs. Contains informative notes on the different styles of music.

Talking Heads

http://129.237.17.3/Heads/Talking_Heads.html

Provides Talking Heads information. Spares nothing—includes digitized songs, images, and more. Also includes information on signing up for the Talking Heads mailing list.

Tango Dance Notation Argentina Argentine

http://litsun.epfl.ch/tango/index.html

Contains a calendar of events, a world-wide geographical listing of where to dance, lyrics to songs, history of the tango, biographies of teachers, musicians, and dancers, audio files, discographies, videos, book information, photos, and more.

TMBG WWW Home Page, The

http://www.dnai.com/~obo/tmbg/index.html

Focuses on They Might be Giants. Now lets you dial-a-song online and get previously unreleased material from TMBG.

Tom Morgan's Home Page

http://poe.acc.virginia.edu/~tm4q/

Presents Tom Morgan, alternative radio station director and freelance writer. Features profiles of important early jazz figures, such as W. C. Handy, from his book *From Cakewalks to Concert Halls: An Illustrated History of African-American Popular Music 1895–1930*, as well as several other articles and columns on blues and jazz.

Tori Amos Home Page, The

http://www.mit.edu:8001/people/nocturne/tori.html

Includes a special link to *Really Deep Thoughts*, a mailing list digest about the music of Tori Amos. Also includes many pictures and sounds. Also offers a few QuickTime videos.

Traditional Jazz (Dixieland)

http://www.best.com/~kquick/dixie.html

Focuses on Dixieland music. Provides information on the bands, festivals, publications, societies, and places to hear Dixieland on the radio all over North America. Offers many links to newsgroups, mailing lists, and other jazz Web sites.

TuneWeb

http://www.ece.ucdavis.edu/~darsie/tunebook.html

Provides an archive of traditional tunes of mostly Celtic (Irish, Scottish, Breton), American, and English origin. Provides complete sheet music for all the tunes, with audio excerpts for many. Categorizes by tune type (jig, reel, hornpipe, and so on).

Turkish Music Home Page, The

http://vizlab.rutgers.edu/~jaray/sounds/turkish/turkish.html

Presents a Turkish music archive and index to other Turkish music sites. Includes articles on Turkish music genres, audio files, discographies, and more. Includes classical, folk, religious, and other styles of music from Turkey and Cyprus.

Turmoil's Seattle Music Web

http://www.blarg.com/~turmoil

Focuses on alternative and underground music in Seattle. Contains many .WAV clips and whole songs. Also furnishes a Seattle music calendar and related art.

Two Dozen Canadian Folk Festivals

http://www.interlog.com/~ufojoe/

Provides information and schedules for Canadian folk music festivals. Highlights the Mariposa Festival in Toronto (an institution now, after 35 years) and dozens of others. Also features a festival discussion group and links to other festival information.

Ultimate Band List, The

http://american.recordings.com/wwwofmusic/ubl/ubl.shtml

Offers links to information about any genre or style of music. Includes information not only on Web pages, but on newsgroups, mailing lists, and more.

Unofficial Nine Inch Nails Home Page, The

http://ibms15.scri.fsu.edu/~patters/nin.html

Targets the intense fan. Provides photos, lyrics, frequently asked questions, and more. Also includes a questionnaire so you can tell the world what you like best about them.

Unofficial Strawberry Music Festival Web Pages, The

http://www.hooked.net/users/jimcrust/strawbryz.html

Contains an eclectic variety of music and the presents the "Strawberry Way" to produce "the finest festival of its type, anywhere."

Vangelis WWW Page, The

http://bau2.uibk.ac.at/perki/Vangelis.html

Provides information about the man and his music and movies (*Bladerunner* being the most popular so far). Contains an array of pictures, sounds, and digitized film sequences, as well as a page of all the Vangelis fans in the world.

VH1 Music First

http://here.viacom.com/vh1

VH1 online. Features the latest information on various artists, from biographies and videographies, to news updates and special features such as downloadable files. Also spotlights the videos and specials playing on VH1. Provides special coverage of events in music culture.

W.A.M.S. Home Page

http://www.teleport.com/~rfrederi/

Presents the Wolverine Antique Music Society. Focuses on the preservation of music originally recorded for 78 rpm records. Offers much to the 78 collector and early jazz aficionado. Contains many articles on the music, collecting, and all sorts of technical and resource information pertaining to antique audio. Also contains information on the early record labels, 78 album cover art, and sound clips.

Wayne's Home Page with Lute Stuff!

http://www.cs.dartmouth.edu/~wbc/

Offers a collection of lute information. Includes a gallery of old lute art works and photos of new lutes, as well as additional photos of various harps and bagpipes.

Welcome to HIStory!

http://www.music.sony.com/Music/ArtistInfo/MichaelJackson.html

Serves as the official Sony page for Michael Jackson. Includes graphics and considerable information and depth of thought.

Welcome to Planet Bluegrass

http://www.csn.net:80/planet/

Blue Planet Music, organizers of the legendary Telluride Bluegrass Festival, online. Contains festival schedule and

information, as well as information about Blue Planet recordings and their mail order operation.

Welcome to the GUITAR.NET Preview!

http://www.netcentral.net/guitar/index.html

Offers instruction via the guitar chord of the week (including sound clip) for those learning guitar. Lets you ask Abe Wechter questions. Also provides access to many files from the Online Guitar Archives.

Will Clifton, Double Basses and Some Other Things

http://www.gonix.com/wgcabp

Offers some music links and some information on the double bass.

William Ransom Hogan Archive of New Orleans Jazz

http://www.tulane.edu/~lmiller/JazzHome.html

Contains oral history interviews, recorded music, photographic collections and film, sheet music and orchestrations, and numerous files containing manuscript materials, clippings, and bibliographic references. Contains information about the archive, photos, sound clips, and a complete index to the oral history interviews.

WNUR-FM JazzWeb

http://www.acns.nwu.edu/jazz/

Contains information on jazz. Includes essays on the different styles of jazz (accessible from a unique hypermap that reveals their interrelationships), artist bios, discographies, and reviews. Also offers information on festivals, venues, regional concerts, instruments, jazz in the media

(radio, television, press), jazz art, and various jazz resources.

WOMEX—Worldwide Music Expo

http://www.eunet.fi/gmc/womex/womex.html

Advertises this event—"a Summorldwide of World, Roots, Folk, Ethnic and Traditional Music," which is a combination conference, trade fair, and musical showcase. Provides the complete history of WOMEX, a conference schedule, and registration information.

World Music/Boston

http://www.hsdesign.com/wm.www/wmhome.html

Provides schedules and ticket information for world music concerts and festivals happening in Boston. Provides short but informative biographies of the performers.

Zar's Paula Abdul

http://www2.csn.net/~danzirin/paula.html

Lionizes Paula Abdul, complete with sound bytes, QuickTime videos, and plenty of pictures. Also includes personal information about Paula.

A.R.E.

http://www.ip.net/are

The Association for Research and Enlightenment, Inc., a nonprofit organization that sponsors activities, services, and outreach throughout the world, serves as the international headquarters of the work of Edgar Cayce, an oft-documented psychic. Seeks to preserve, research, and make available insights from Cayce's information.

Aesclepian Chronicles

http://www.forthrt.com/~chronicl/homepage.html

A monthly journal, online version. Takes a fresh look at complementary medicine and its relationship to conventional medicine. Includes articles and ongoing columns about what's new in the mind-body approach.

AESCLEPIAN CHRONICLES
Synergistic Medicine Center - Chapel Hill, North Carolina

Almitra Tapes

http://www.neosoft.com/~clayton/AlmitraTapes.html

Offers a series of self-help audio cassette tapes of meditations and contemplations. Offers guidance and insight into topics of concern to everyone on the path, including self-help, spiritual guidance, healing relationships, or the next step in recovery; whether you're in pain and crisis or just looking for answers to life's questions. Provides primarily in English, incluses some Spanish and some French.

The Aquarian Age

http://granite.sentex.net:80/~aquarius/

Focuses on astrology and new age studies. Includes a directory of online astrologers, a section on astrological lore, and a section on divination techniques. Rounds out the site with an informational area for vistors and a romance area.

Astral Projection Home Page

http://www.lava.net/~goodin/astral.html

Offers links to other resources dealing with astral projection, out-of-body experiences, and lucid dreams. Provides many different resources, including newsgroups, articles, books, organizations, and institutions. Annotates some of the resources.

Astrology

http://www.dgsys.com/~star/

Offers astrological profile reports, including charts and interpretations for lovers, past lives, career-minded adults, adult/children birth potentials, relocation possibilities, and daily forecasting reports.

Cosmic Web

http://www.sirius.com/~cosmic/welcome.html

Presents a "cosmic forum" concerned with the well-being and evolution of planet earth. Provides a daily meditation section, an events section, the *Cosmic Web Journal*, and the Cosmic Love Link. Includes the Cosmic Online Bookstore, which offers new age books, audiotapes, and videos.

The Goddess Shoppe Online

http://www.primenet.com/~goddess

Online bookstore. Offers a wide range of items, such as altars, bumper stickers, ceramics, and more.

The Home Page of Summum

http://www.summum.org/Summum

Nonprofit organization that promotes the Summum philosophy, based on the "principles of creation" that underlie all existence.

How To Talk New Age

http://www.well.com/user/mick/newagept.html

Contains definitions of various new age terms. Each letter of the alphabet lists one to three terms (such as K, for Karma). Provides cartoons for some terms.

Interlude: An Internet Retreat

http://www.teleport.com/~interlud/

Focuses on meditation. Includes meditation archives, prayers, poetry, and bibliography. Offers links to other related sites.

Moksha Foundation

http://nbn.nbn.com/home/moksha/

Includes information about Cohen and his teachings, as well as places to obtain his works.

The Movement of Spiritual Inner Awareness

http://www.msia.com/

Contains the teachings of John-Roger. Focuses on becoming aware of oneself as one with God and as a soul. Includes excerpts from books, information on teachings, and some actual teachings. Also features a catalog of products.

Neutopia

http://twain.oit.umass.edu/~neutopia/

Focuses on Gaia, the planetary superorganism. Includes all the information you need to understand the Neutopian movement. Also offers links to other Neutopia sites.

New Age Web Works

http://www.newageinfo.com/

Offers links to new age bookstores and vendors. Also contains articles, book reviews, and poetry. Offers online tarot and I Ching readings. Includes a master list of new age topic links.

NewHeaven NewEarth

http://www.well.com/user/nhne

Targets people who believe that a "divine plan" is "unfolding" on Earth. Provides information about changes in the earth so you can better understand and prepare for these changes. Also offers some other major and minor links.

The Oracle Home Page

http://idirect.com/oracle/oracle.html

Focuses on metaphysics, the new age movement, and "the unknown in human spirituality, religion, and consciousness." Offers Oracle mailing lists, news, and the Oracle library.

Paper Ships Books & Crystals

http://www.nbn.com/jacob/ship.html

Celebrates diversity leading to unity. Offers specialty books and products covering areas of spiritual, metaphysical, extra terrestial, angels, sacred geometry, sacred spaces, goddesses, Native Americans, and books for personal and global healing.

Path of Discoveries

http://www.infohwy.com/community/lahala/

Presents a Web vehicle for the Paths of Discoveries organization, which hopes to deal with modern problems through ancient wisdom (using Dusty Lobb, who they claim channels the Light of God). Provides information about this group and offers videotapes for sale.

Pepper Press—Alexander Material

http://www.otisnet.com/alexander

Focuses on the new age teachings of Alexander, translated by his human host, Ramon Stevens. Includes excerpts from some of his works. Offers a list of works and online ordering.

The Rosicrucian Fellowship

http://www.cts.com/~rosfshp/index.html

Provides information on the Rosicrucian order in California. Includes an HTML library, an ftp library, and online magazine archives. Provides information concerning Rosicrucian study, courses, and book ordering.

The Rosicrucian Emblem

Salem New Age Center

http://www1.usa1.com/~salemctr/

Contains information on the best new age books, meditation, healing, and alternative medicine. Also covers updates on new conferences and events in the New England area. Offers inspirational pieces, poetry, quotes, and links to other new age sites.

Silicon Phoenix—Return to Earth

http://sunacm.swan.ac.uk:80/~erulian/

Targets people who want to know more about new age. Provides information concerning what the new age movement is all about.

Spirit of the Wind

http://www.nbn.com/jacob/spirit.html

Targets people looking for inner peace through Native American rituals and ceremonies. Promotes natural living. Provides information about the organization's purpose and its purification ceremony.

Spirit-WWW

http://spirit.satelnet.org/Spirit.html

Includes informative sections about channeling, lightwork, UFO phenomena, and healing methods. Offers links to other sites with information on journals, magazines, and new age. Also offers images, movies, reviews, sound clips, and a bibliography.

Sun Angel

http://www.sun-angel.com/

Focuses on spiritual growth. Offers audio tapes, incense, School of Wisdom publications, and other items. Features a numerology reading and a metaphysical random quote service, and lets you ask the Angel Fortune a question.

White Mountain Education Association

http://www.primenet.com/~wtmtn/

Offers teachings based on a collection of ancient wisdom from the past. Draws upon various religions, philosophies, and teachers. Provides information on the group's teachings, publications, suggested readings, and connections to other sites.

Zodiacal Zepher

http://metro.turnpike.net/S/SRozhon/index.html

Provides astrological information. Includes articles on
astrology, charts, book catalogs, and astrological societies,
among other items. Offers links to other astrology sites.

American Philosophical Association

http://www.oxy.edu/apa/apa.html

Provides information on how to join APA and offers links to APA's Proceedings and Electronic Bulletin Board. Also offers links to other Web resources for philosophers. Includes information on upcoming events sponsored by APA and/or of interest to philosophers.

ANALYSIS Home Page

http://www.shef.ac.uk/uni/academic/N-Q/phil/analysis/homepage.html

Provides information about the philosophy journal *ANALYSIS* and its monthly e-mail supplement *ANALYST*. Provides information on how to subscribe to both *ANALYSIS* and *ANALYST*. Includes recent and current contents of *ANALYSIS*, as well as links to the *ANALYST* ftp archive.

APA Electronic Bulletin Board

gopher://apa.oxy.edu:70/1

Provides information about the American Philosophical Association (APA). Includes information on grants, fellowships, academic positions, bibliographies, software, summer institutes, and calls for papers.

Arisbe: A Home for Charles S. Peirce Studies

http://204.119.173.21/peirce/

Contains hypertext versions of Charles Peirce's papers and information on various subjects relating to Peirce.

Augustine

http://ccat.sas.upenn.edu/jod/augustine.html

Contains translations and texts of Augustine. Also includes other research materials and reference aids. Also contains papers from an online seminar and images.

Australasian Philosophy Network: Home Page

http://www.arts.su.edu.au/Arts/departs/philos/APS/APS.home.html

Focuses on philosophy in Australian and New Zealand. Contains information on AP Net, Australasian philosophers, departments, conferences, and job postings.

BEARS on Moral and Political Philosophy

http://www.netspace.org/bears/

Brown Electronic Article Review Service on Moral and Political Philosophy. Contains short reviews of articles that have appeared in the last six months. Provides information on contributors and a list of reviews.

Cybernetics and Systems Theory

http://pespmc1.vub.ac.be/CYBSYSTH.html

Contains information gathered through the Principia Cybernetica Project. Contains general information and background material on cybernetics and systems theory.

Department of Philosophy

http://www.csv.warwick.ac.uk:80/WWW/faculties/
social_studies/Philosophy/

Presents the University of Warwick department of philosophy. Contains information about the department's faculty, courses, and programs. Provides information on their new graduate program in the Philosophy and Ethics of Mental Health. Also contains information about upcoming conferences sponsored by the university.

Department of Philosophy, University of California, Riverside

http://www.ucr.edu/philosophy/phil.html

Provides information about the University of California of Riverside Department of Philosophy. Also offers a departmental newsletter. Provides up-to-date information on several university-sponsored colloquia throughout the year and others of interest.

The Electronic Journal of Analytic Philosophy

http://www.phil.indiana.edu/ejap/ejap.html

Includes three issues in hypertext, simple text, or PostScript; provides analytical philosophy articles. Provides information on how to subscribe to the journal via a listserv. Includes topics for upcoming issues, and invites submissions. Also contains links to other philosophy sites.

Environmental Ethics

http://www.cep.unt.edu/

Provides information on environmental ethics. Focuses on environmental ethics resources. Provides book reviews and site summaries and links of interest to environmental philosophy.

This World Wide Web server is dedicated to providing access to Internet resources throughout the world which pertain to or focus on environmental ethics and environmental philosophy

CENTER FOR ENVIRONMENTAL PHILOSOPHY

- About the Center for Environmental Philosophy
- Environmental Ethics
- Environmental Ethics Books
- Graduate Program – University of North Texas
- Postdoctoral – Professional Development Opportunities at North Texas
- News from Here and There

FU-Berlin Philosophy Web

http://pollux.zedat.fu-berlin.de/~aporia/philos.html

Provides lecture timetables and news about the FU-Berlin Philosophy Department. Includes German and English versions. Also provides links to other European and North American Philosophy servers.

Index Page—McGill Philosophy

http://godel.philo.mcgill.ca/

Provides information about McGill University's philosophy department. Contains annotated descriptions of site links.

Indiana University Philosophy Department

http://www.phil.indiana.edu/

Provides standard information about faculty, programs and courses. Contains links to local features, including schedules of local seminars; Paul Vincent Spade's Mediaeval Logic and Philosophy Home Page; Raymundo Morado's

5,000+ Bibliography of Belief Revision and Nonmonotonic Logics; David Chalmers's 1,600+ annotated Bibliography of Contemporary Philosophy of Mind; and *The Electronic Journal of Analytic Philosophy*, a peer-reviewed hypertext journal of philosophy.

The International Philosophical Preprint Exchange

`http://phil-preprints.1.chiba-u.ac.jp/IPPE.html`

Part of an international working group coordinating access to philosophy preprints. Provides information in a visual index, as well as a textual one. Includes subject access, submissions, and directory links.

IUS Philosophy Department

`http://149.160.3.48/IUSPhilosophy.html`

The Web server for the Indiana University Southeast Department of Philosophy. Contains basic information about courses, programs, and faculty. Also contains the *Collaborative Bibliography of Women in Philosophy*. Lets you collaborate in the construction of a first-rate and continuously updated bibliography of works in philosophy published by women.

Kierkegaard

`gopher://babel.its.utas.edu.au:70/11/Publications/Kierkegaard`

Contains bibliographies on Kierkegaard, as well as other documents.

Mechanosphere

`http://www.scsn.net/~efolley/`

Provides an index of links to resources relating to the French philosophers Gilles Deleuze and Felix Guattari.

The Nietzsche Page at USC

`http://www.usc.edu/dept/annenberg/thomas/nietzsche.html`

Provides information on all aspects of study. Contains the complete text of Nietzsche's *Thus Spoke Zarathustra*, information on the available e-mail lists for Nietzsche studies, assorted mixed opinions and maxims from Nietzsche, and many other documents and links.

Philosophy, Utrecht University

`http://www.phil.ruu.nl/`

Features a list of the Logic Group preprints; a Web version of the (Dutch!) newsletter for CKI students, the *Cognitio*; an ftp server that contains an electronic archive of the logic preprint series; information on FAB ("Feminist Approaches to Bio-ethics"; and information on cogpsy (about Cognitive Psychology and Connectionism).

Philosophy and Religion

`gopher://marvel.loc.gov/11/global/phil`

Presents the Library of Congress' gopher guide to philosophy and religion. Contains links and documents relating to philosophy from all over the world.

Philosophy at UMass

`http://www.umassd.edu/1Academic/CArtsandSciences/Philosophy/Philosophyhomepage.html`

Provides information about the philosophy faculty and programs. Maintains an Internet listserv in undergraduate philosophy, available through a link at this site.

Philosophy at UT Martin

`http://unix1.utm.edu/departments/phil/phil.html`

Provides course descriptions, faculty information, and program requirements. Also contains The Hume Archives,

a repository of electronic texts by and about 18th-century Scottish philosopher David Hume, as well as the Philosophy Forum, a student philosophy club.

Philosophy in Cyberspace— Home Page

http://www.monash.edu.au/cc/staff/phi/dey/WWW/phil.html

Provides an annotated guide to philosophy resources and tools available over the Internet. Includes information a novice needs and offers links even the most experienced user can use.

Philosophy Resources

gopher://gopher.liv.ac.uk/11/phil

Contains a list of all the philosophy departments in the United Kingdom, their addresses, contact information, and their head. Also provides information on conferences, workshops, and calls for papers.

PSYCHE: An Interdisciplinary Journal of Research and Consciousness

http://psyche.cs.monash.edu.au/

Provides direct access to PSYCHE's archives. Also contains a FAQ associated with the journal that covers the following topics: general introduction; notes for authors; book reviews; subscriptions to the electronic version of PSYCHE; subscriptions to the MIT Press version of PSYCHE; the discussion list Psyche-D; archival information; the executive editor, associate editors, and editorial board.

School of Philosophy, University of Sydney: Home Page

http://www.arts.su.edu.au/Arts/departs/philos/
philosophy.home.html

Provides general background about the University of Sydney's philosophy department. Also contains research reports that contain information on book chapters, conferences, and theses; and many other types of scholarly information.

Stanford University Department of Philosophy

http://csli-www.stanford.edu/philosophy/philosophy.html

Contains information on courses, faculty, and upcoming colloquia. Offers a few links to philosophy resources, and if you root around in the pages you can find some Stanford content available to anyone.

The Tech Classics Archive

http://the-tech.mit.edu/Classics

Contains full text documents by many philosophers spanning the ages. Includes a full text copy of Candide (English).

University of Chicago Philosophy Project

http://csmaclab-www.uchicago.edu/philosophyProject/
philos.html

Serves as a forum for electronically mediated scholarly discussion of philosophical works. Contains several moderated philosophical discussions between small groups of participants.

UT Philosophy Department Home Page

http://www.dla.utexas.edu/depts/philosophy/main.html

Contains the standard information about courses, faculty, and programs for the University of Texas philosophy department. Offers a jump to philosophy resources on the

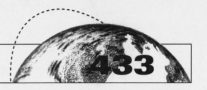
Net, from which you can access information on philoso-
phers, philosophies, journals, electronic texts, projects and
organizations, and newsgroups.

UW Department of Philosophy

http://watarts.uwaterloo.ca/PHIL/cpshelle/
philosophy.html

Contains course, faculty, and program information about
the University of Waterloo. Also, contains a Philosopher's
Gallery, which offers images in JPEG and GIF formats,
categorized for easy access.

White Mountain Education— A Source for the Ageless Wisdom

http://www.primenet.com/~wtmtn

Provides articles, lectures, the online publication *Meditation
Monthly International*, esoteric astrology, and psychology.

Alden Yacht Brokerage

http://www.webcom.com/~orb/Alden/

Specializes in serving the yachtsman, ranging from designing and building a boat to insuring it, arranging charters, providing winter storage and service, and even selling it.

The Alfa Romeo Spider Home Page

http://pages.prodigy.com/CA/krfh19b/AlfaRomeo.html

Dedicated to the owners and lovers of the Alfa Romeo Spider.

The Alfa Romeo Spider Home Page

America's 4×4 4U Video Magazine

http://www.4x44u.com/pub/k2/am4x44u/4x4.html

Online magazine. Contains four-wheeling information, live reports from trail rides, shows, competitions, and events from around the world. Includes product installations and reviews. Offers hundreds of pages and more than a million archived digital images.

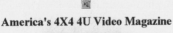

America's 4X4 4U Video Magazine

| Trails | Truck Tech | Events & Clubs | Truck Stop |

American Horticultural Society

http://eMall.com/ahs/ahs.html

Provides articles from the *American Horticulturist* magazine and information on joining the society.

Arizona Bassin' Home Page

http://www.primenet.com/~pic

Highlights the great bass fishing of Arizona lakes and rivers using weekly lake reports, fishing and tackle tips, reports on Arizona tournaments, and other Arizona fishing-related topics.

Arthur's Pub Guide

http://www.londonmall.co.uk/pubguide

Presents an interactive guide to London pubs. Allows readers to add their own pubs, or add comments to current descriptions.

Auctions Online

http://www.auctions-on-line.com/

Provides free access to auction catalogs, sales information, and fine art reference guides. Includes auction lists for antiques, books, maps, collectibles, coins, arms, armor, wine (and more).

Australia's National Parks

http://www.colossus.net/vortex/toot/parks/

Lists all of Australia's National Parks. Provides information on how to get to each park, flora and fauna, photos, and more.

The Beavis and Butt-Head Episode Guide

http://www.cen.uiuc.edu/~dcpiii/bnbguide.html

Presents the Netscape-enhanced version of the *Beavis & Butt-Head* episode guide. Also includes descriptions of various episodes.

Beethoven Karaoke

http://twws1.vub.ac.be/studs/tw15120/karaoke.htm

Offers songs in English, Dutch, French, Spanish, Italian, Philipino, and Chinese.

Big Red Scuba Divers

http://www.intersource.com:80/·deepvis/bigred/

Offers professional diving sales and service to the Midwest. Also provides links for information on Open Water certifications, specialty classes, Nitrox, and upcoming travel tips, as well as to other scuba web sites.

The Birmingham Zoo

http://www.bhm.tis.net/zoo/

Takes you on tour of The Birmingham Zoo. Displays many photographs and describes the zoo animals. Also features the zoo's 1994 safari to Kenya with Director Jerry Wallace.

 Tigers

White Bengal Tiger Panthera tigris tigris

Siberian Tiger

These largest of all cats are well-equipped hunters. Their heavily muscled bodies give them great strength. Creeping close, the tiger pounces, toppling large victims to the ground. The cat then grabs them in a suffocating throat hold. Smaller animals are dispatched with a single killing bite. Only about one in ten of a tiger's hunting trips is successful.

Bonsai Home Page

http://www.pass.wayne.edu/~dan/bonsai.html

Contains a collection of bonsai materials, including a dictionary, club newsletter, and materials created by individuals. Also presents the "Online Bonsai Icon Collection."

Bruce's Paddling Page

http://ssnet.com/~bef/BrucesPaddlingPage.html

Provides resources for whitewater paddling and sea kayaking in the Delaware/Chesapeake region. Also provides information on current events, tips for the best boating areas, and even tide level details for avid paddlers and kayakers.

Buckingham Palace on the London Mall

http://www.londonmall.co.uk/palace

Serves as the official London residence of Her Majesty The Queen, whose personal standard flies when Her Majesty is in residence.

Burton's Coins & Cards

http://www.wwcd.com/burton/burton.html

Offers products in the collectibles industry.

Camp Unalayee

http://www.reed.edu/~bsalzber/unalayee1.html

Nonprofit, coed wilderness camp for kids 10–17. Seeks young people from different racial and economic backgrounds. Values differences among campers; each camper's input helps create the camp community.

Canadian Orchid Congress

http://www.ccn.cs.dal.ca/Recreation/OrchidSNS/coc.html

Contains a series of pages that deal with the Canadian Orchid Congress, the association for orchid societies from across Canada. Provides information on orchid growing and offers links to other orchid-related sites.

Casio Watches at Wholesale Prices

http://www.emi.net/boynton/casio/casio1.html

Authorized Casio distributor. Displays the entire Casio Watch current line. Ships worldwide.

Cast Your Vote

http://pages.prodigy.com/CA/lenz/vote.html

Features a new football topic for users to vote on every Sunday.

Chris Smolinski's Radio Page

http://www.access.digex.net/~cps/radio.html

Provides information (and links to other pages with similar information) about shortwave and amateur radio.

City Farmer's Urban Agriculture Notes

http://unixg.ubc.ca:780/~cityfarm/urbagnotes1.html

Contains articles on being an urban farmer. Includes articles on growing food, setting up a community garden, and technical information.

Classic China, Inc.

http://www.cyserv.com/cchina/index.html

Offers fine china, crystal, flatware, wedding gifts, wedding and personalized invitations, executive gifts, and gourmet gift baskets. Includes a Bridal Registry.

The Classifieds

http://www.wwcd.com/classified/classified.html

Serves as a buy-sell-trade classified and collectibles stop. Also includes employment opportunities.

Continuously Refreshing Fish Cam Image

http://www1.netscape.com/fishcam/fish_refresh.html

Demonstrates Web functionality, serving as a virtual fish tank.

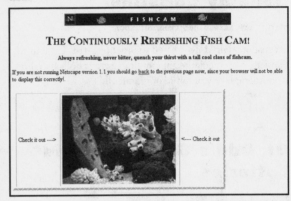

Darkstorm Comics and Collectibles

http://infoweb.magi.com/~gethings/darkstorm.html

Serves as a source for Comics, Japanese Animation, and Models. Provides information on new comics, video rental, and graphic novels. Offers links to comic Web sites.

Deep Space Nine Novels

http://www.bradley.edu/campusorg/psiphi/ds9/books.html

Includes information about each novel in the Star Trek: Deep Space Nine series, as well as other DS9 books. Presents separate subpages for each book, including information about writers, publication dates, and cross-references between episodes.

Deep Visions Scuba Artwork

http://www.intersource.com:80/~deepvis/dv/

Offers professional art for professional divers. Includes scuba-related clip art for Macintosh or PC.

Deeter's Stamps

http://www.compassnet.com/~jws/gkmain.htm

Provides information on bulk paper stamp mixtures.

Dolls by Christine

http://www.imsweb.net/cweb/dollsbc/

Offers porcelain dolls created to order by artist Christine Sanders, who specializes in creating portrait dolls based on a photograph of your child or grandchild.

Dr. Odd's Guide to World Lotteries

http://www.londonmall.co.uk/drodd/

Acts as a guide to world lotteries and introduces the new London Mall lottery.

Dream-Land Dollies

http://www.mind.net/chrystal/dolls.html

Serves as an online shop for antique porcelain dolls.

East Burke, Vermont

http://www.pbpub.com/vermont/eburke.htm

A town 3 ½ hours from Boston and 2 ½ hours from Montreal. Offers year-round vacation opportunities. Includes skiing at Burke Mountain, windsurfing on Lake Willoughby and Lake Seymour, dining in European-style restaurants, and staying in inns. Also offers mountain and road biking and rents bikes.

EROS

http://www.infobahnos.com/united/eros.html

Sells EROS, an all-natural, safe, and guaranteed combination of extensively studied ingredients that have been used for centuries to effectively stimulate arousal, sexual appetite, sensuality, and to improve performance for both men and women during intimacy.

EWACARS—Automobilia

http://www.ewacars.com/ewacars

Acts as a United States resource for automobile books, scale models, videos, and magazines. Includes more than 15,000 items. Offers links to hundreds of race and classic car pages around the world.

Florida's Suncoast Outdoors Online

http://www.desktopadv.com/soo/

Online magazine. Specializes in outdoors activities along Florida's western coastal regions. Includes sections on sport-fishing, diving, boating, wildlife, watersports, and suncoast weather.

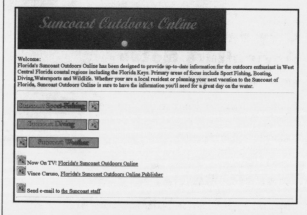

Friends of Acadia

http://www.acadia.net/w95007

Nonprofit organization that works in partnership with Acadia National Park; the National Park Service; local, state, and federal governments; Maine residents; and park visitors to ensure the preservation and protection of Acadia and Mount Desert Island.

GardenNet: A Resource Center for Garden Enthusiasts

http://www.olympus.net/gardens/welcome.html

Provides virtual tours of gardens, information on gardens around the country, book reviews, online catalogs, and a link to *GardenNet* magazine articles. Also offers links to other Internet resources.

The Global Yacht Connection on the Internet

http://www.waterviews.com

Features many topics of general interest to boaters and the cruising community. Provides textual and photographic forums for listing all types of vessels for sale or charter. Includes forums for new vessels, vessels available for re-sale, and many marine-related businesses.

The Gold Prospecting Page for California

http://www.primenet.com/~miner/gold.html

Focuses on defining gold, finding gold, and using the right equipment. Covers prospecting in Southern California, but much of the information applies to any place you find gold. Offers links to other gold sites (professional and nonprofessional), as well as to sites related to coins, metal detecting, and mining.

GORP—Great Outdoor Recreation Pages

http://www.gorp.com/

Describes most United States national parks, forests, and wilderness areas, as well as many national monuments and wildlife refuges. Provides information on hiking, biking, fishing, paddlesports, climbing, wildlife viewing, skiing, caving, and so on. Arranges location pages by state and country to point to Internet resources, including outdoor recreation and travel-related information. Also includes pages for books and magazines, trips, gear, food, health, and nonprofit organizations dealing with outdoor recreation and travel.

Gunnison, Colorado

http://www.gunnison.com/

Provides information about the local area mountain sports, current events, Gunnison country facts, and mountain living in both the summer and winter months, as well as travel information for Colorado visitors.

Hardy Palm FAQ

http://www.mindspring.com/~maia/c12.html

Contains information on growing hardy palms in areas in which palms don't usually grow, including on the west coast of Canada, in England, and on Cape Cod. Lists mail-order resources and provides information on the International Palm Society, and the Pacific Northwest Palm and Exotic Plant Society.

Hedges Cellars

http://www.hedgescellars.com/welcome.html

Fine wine producer. Enables you to place an order for wine, check out the distributor list, or simply browse the wine list.

Welcome to Hedges Cellars

HorseWeb

http://www.horseweb.com

Use the HorseWeb page (a hypertext document with Web technologies) to sell your horse, or advertise your stallion services, horse facilities, or training services using unlimited text and color photos. Supports video capabilities as well. Also provides the opportunity to shop for a horse or horses.

Welcome to the HorseWeb Pages!

Interactive Model Railroad

http://rr-vs.informatik.uni-ulm.de/rr/

Enables you to operate a model railroad and watch it in real time. Provides interactive video to the Web. Demonstrates inline video using standard Web servers and clients. Also offers links to other model railroad servers.

Internet Anagram Server

http://www.wordsmith.org/awad-cgibin/anagram

Carries an anagram engine, Anagram Hall of Fame, and other interesting tidbits about anagrams.

Italia Online WEB Chat

http://www1.iol.it/chat/chate.htm

Offers many real-time interactive argument-oriented rooms: Free Chat, Music, Politics, Sex, and so forth (English and Italian versions available).

Jeep Journal

http://www.4x44u.com/pub/k2/jeep/jeep.htm

Online magazine. Provides information for the jeep enthusiast, technical tips, offroad performance upgrades, jeep parts, and accessories. Includes sections on jeep owners clubs, trail rides, jamborees, jeep history, and new models.

Joyous Guard

http://www.deltanet.com/users/roy/home.html

Contains many links to a variety of places, including a movie hall, a music chamber, a philosophy tower, a science fiction domain, and an adult galleria.

Kayaking in Washington (Pacific Northwest)

http://www.olympus.net/biz/kayakpt/kayakpt.htm

Advertises sea kayaking at its best in the Pacific Northwest. Offers ecotours, combo mountain biking and kayaking tours, and trips to Baja and Venezuela.

Kipper's Mail Art Gallery

http://www.enterprise.net/kiphome.html

Offers insight into the creativity of rubber stamping. Displays 12 different stamped cards and provides information on the cards and how they were produced, along with credits and techniques used. Also includes references to rubber stamping magazines and available literature, how to get started, and a list of other stampers who have organized theme exchanges.

Limestone Zoological Park and Exotic Wildlife Refuge

http://iquest.com/~wildside

Dedicated to protecting endangered/unwanted/injured animals.

Little Man Cartoons

http://www.CityHall.Com/lm/

Presents Little Man Cartoons, about the little man who lives and works in the author's computer. Offers information on how Little Man relaxes and presents his adventure of the week.

The London Mall Lottery

http://www.londonmall.co.uk/mainlot/default.html

Provides a free lottery and demonstrates WebTcl—the advanced embedded HTML programming language developed by Micro Media Services Limited.

Enter The London Mall Lottery

Lou Bignami's Fine Fishing Internet Magazine

http://www.finefishing.com

Online magazine. Contains feature articles with regional, topical, editorial and how-to sections, updated weekly.

Mahone Bay Kayak Adventures

http://fox.nstn.ca/~seakayak

Serves as full-service kayak shop. Offers kayaking instruction, rentals, and tours. Sources all kayak operators in Atlantic Canada. Also profiles family-oriented activities along Nova Scotia's south shore.

The Marine Corner

http://www.helix.net/marine

Offers only marine-related goods and services, including fishing, tackle, boat brokers, marina, and charter boats, as well as electronics, and more.

Marinemart

http://www.marinemart.com/users/marine/mart.html

Advertises, lists, and displays marine goods and services of all types from the various manufacturers, dealers, marinas, boat brokers, charter services, and the like.

Marinemart

A mall dedicated exclusively to the purpose of advertising, listing, and displaying pleasure boat marine goods and services of all types from the various manufacturers, dealers, marinas, boat yards, boat brokers, charter services, and the like.

Methow Valley Pride

http://www.ncw.net/beerinabag

Features the Premier Mini-Brewery, a product that enables you to make own fresh beer at home.

MN Four-Wheel Drive Association

http://www.primenet.com/~ben_b/mn4x4.html

Promotes responsible four-wheeling in Minnesota.

Molson Canadian's 'I Am Online'

http://www.molson.com/canadian

Offers the functionality of a free online service (mail, chat, discussion groups, user profiles, and so on) along with content relating to everything Canadian (music, sports, Canadian culture). Entertains, informs, and breaks ground in the realm of interactive community-building.

Montgomery—The Covered Bridge Town

http://www.pbpub.com/vermont/montgom.htm

Promotes little town buried deep in Vermont's Green Mountains, close to the Canadian border, at the foot of Jay Peak, a big alpine ski area, as a vacation site. Highlights the town's five covered bridges, Zack's restaurant, a general

store that has an original soda fountain (and a piano player on weekends), and inns and B&Bs. Also highlights a long hiking trail and biking.

Mooncrow's NW Naturist Pages

http://www.halcyon.com/mooncrow/naturist.htm

Provides information about naturist/nudist clubs and activities in the Pacific Northwest and offers links to naturist information around the world.

Musicmaker's Kits, Inc.— Home Page

http://www.primenet.com/~musikit/

Displays online catalog of instruments, providing descriptions and sound samples with each image.

National Park Outdoor Activities Center

http://www.acadia.net/w95008

Offers rental equipment, guides, tours, and outdoor activities in and around Acadia National Park, Mount Desert Island, and Downeast Maine.

Nintendo

http://www.nintendo.com

Provides information about Nintendo's latest products.

Numancia, la Ciudad Virtual en Español

http://www.laeff.esa.es/~crb/

Acts as a virtual city in which anyone can become a citizen and incorporate World Wide Web pages as a part of the city (in Spanish).

NW Windsurfing Network

http://www.eskimo.com/~billwind

Public service site provided by several Washington State windsurfing clubs. Includes links to NW weather; windsurfing information such as current events, club home pages, shareware programs useful to windsurfers; and more.

Once upon a Breeze Kiteshop

http://www.webcom.com/~mrkites/

Offers online catalog and links to other kiting activities.

Online Animal Catalog

http://www.wolfe.net/~critter

Presents online animal catalog that advertises both exotic and domestic pets. Also contains links to zoos, gifts, pictures, services, and other related subjects. Invites visitors to leave related URLs for consideration as additions to this page.

Orchid Society of Nova Scotia Home Page

http://www.ccn.cs.dal.ca/Recreation/OrchidSNS/orchid.html

Contains a series of pages dealing with the Orchid Society of Nova Scotia and orchid growing. Provides contact information, growing information, and links to other orchid-related sites.

Oregon Rockhounds Online—Rock and Mineral Collecting in Oregon

http://www.teleport.com/~tfish/ore_rock.htm

Serves as an online information guide to rock, mineral, and fossil collecting in Oregon and Washington. Includes directions and pictures of sites and rough and finished agate, jasper, obsidian, minerals, and fossils.

The Original Sting-Ray Bicycle Site

http://www.webresponse.com/sting-ray/

Provides information for collectors of muscle bikes.

Oxbow Benelux Home Page

http://www.euronet.nl/users/ub150/oxbow.html

Offers information (in Dutch) for the French sportswear brand Oxbow. Also offers a catalog and addresses of the nearest dealers.

Parrots: IAS Table of Contents

http://www.mecca.org/~rporter/PARROTS/iastoc.html

Dedicated to the care of exotic birds and funding avian research and conservation.

Parrots: IAS Table of Contents

Dedicated to the Birds of the World!

Perfect Image Sportscards and Memorabilia

http://www.wwcd.com/pimage/image.html

A collectibles stop. Offers sportscards and other collectible memorabilia.

The Positive Planet

http://www.ppmedia.com/planet

Presents *Positive Planet* magazine and dateline. Features many personal ads from around the world. Also includes a technosexual dating magazine.

Pro and Fantasy Football

http://pages.prodigy.com/CA/lenz/football.html

Offers draft help, injury information, stats, and more.

Proventricular Dilitation Syndrome in Parrots

http://www.mecca.org/~rporter/PARROTS/pds.html

Nonprofit organization dedicated to the welfare of parrots and exotic birds in the wild and in captivity. Seeks to educate and inform the public of the Proventricular Dilitation Syndrome and how it affects birds.

RA Cores—Custom Computer Foam Wing Cutting

http://world.std.com/~racores/index.html

Manufactures custom computer cut foam wing cores for use in R/C model airplanes. Includes current contest information and newsletters.

Rainbow Card Company

http://www.wwcd.com/rainbow/rainbow.html

Carries a complete line of trading cards.

Redwood Empire Group Industries

http://www.sonic.net/~rod/

Consists of several small companies and nonprofit organizations in Sonoma and Marin counties, California. Provides photography, computer consulting, Web resources, antique swords and knives, and a stock photo image bank.

Rock 100 WDIZ

http://innet.com/~ispace/WDIZ

Emphasizes current rock and roll.

Rubber Stamping Page

http://www.xmission.com/~jmabunga/stamp.htm

Provides information on rubber stamping. Includes resources, e-mail addresses of other stampers, convention information, and links to other related pages.

The SakAtak Web View

http://www.magicnet.net/~sakatak/index.html

Offers a jumping off point onto the Web that you can use to search for anything you want to find on the Web.

The Samling at Dovenest

http://www.quay.co.uk/samling/

Advertises exclusive hideaway used as a conference center, executive retreat, or as a private resort for entertaining.

San Diego 30+/40+ Singles Dances

http://www.sirius.com/~jg2525/dgdir/

Presents weekly dance parties especially for singles in their mid-30s, 40s, and early 50s at San Diego/La Jolla locations.

San Diego Model Railroad Museum

http://www.globalinfo.com/noncomm/SDMRM/sdmrm.html

Offers four scale model layouts.

Scenes of Vermont

http://www.pbpub.com/vermont/

Professional journalists and photographers examine Vermont regions. Offers editorials about specific areas of the state. Provides information about Quechee, Woodstock, and the Valley area in Central Vermont. Also covers Vermont's forgotten Northeast Kingdom. Includes information about biking, hiking, windsurfing, skiing, as well as listings of real estate, B&Bs, inns, and restaurants.

Shipyard Quarters Marina

http://www.marinemart.com/users/marine/shipyard.html

Displays view of Boston Harbor with dockage for 350 boats up to 200 feet in length. Offers seasonal, year-round, and transient slip accomodations. Provides easy access to downtown Boston, Logan International Airport, and historic sites.

SkiClub Central

http://www.netwave.net/skiclubs/ski.htm

Provides information from ski clubs in your area or around the world.

Sports, Collectibles, and Money

http://www.primenet.com/~collect

Offers a sports collectible program. Combines making money with sportscards and building a collection, and creating valuable contacts.

The Swap Meet

http://www.mm.com/swapmeet

Offers classic cars and motorcycles for sale. Includes auction news, restoration vendor advertising, free want ads, links to automotive pages and other auto market information.

Thirteenth Floor Cyber Headshop

http://www.microweb.com/mrhemp/13thmer.html

Carries many unique and handmade items (strives to carry as many as possible). Features Bruce Britton Sculpture pipes, sculptures, and candle and incense holders; Gilligan's bamboo waterpipes and handpipes; and several unique T-shirt designs.

The Total Yellowstone Page

http://acs1.byu.edu/~uhlerjw/yellowstone.html

Provides information about Yellowstone. Aims to discuss and display any and every piece of information affiliated with Yellowstone National Park, ranging from a historical review of Yellowstone to current activities.

The Tree Doctor

http://205.139.129.111/t/treedoc/default.htm

Introduces Mauget micro-injection, an environmentally friendly way to treat tree diseases and pests. Explains what you can do to help preserve urban forests and argues why you should do so. Offers organic biostimulants and tree care suggestions as well.

VE2DM's Internet Amateur Radio Connections

http://www.cam.org/~dino/ham.html

Contains links to various amateur radio internet resources. Hosts the complete text of the Canadian Amateur Rules and Regulations from Industry Canada as well as the examination requirements for new prospective radio amateurs. Also includes newsgroups, vendors, databases, lists, and ftp archives.

The Virtual Garden

http://www.pathfinder.com/@@JFQQ8gAAAAAAHgJ/vg/Welcome/welcome.html

Offers an interactive plant encyclopedia, book excerpts, links to botanical gardens, house plant directory, and garden how-to project instructions.

The Virtual Saab Museum

http://darkwing.uoregon.edu/~dennisw/saab/saab.html

Presents a virtual walkthrough of the Saab museum in Trollhattan, Sweden. Offers many pictures, facts, and Saab trivia.

Wah Kel

http://twws1.vub.ac.be/studs/tw15120/wahkel.htm

Advertises Wah Kel, a Chinese restaurant in Belgium, in Antwerp's red light district, just across from the famous dance club Café d'Anvers and close to the Red & Blue club.

Webville and Hypertext Railroad Company

http://www.he.tdl.com/~colemanc/webville.html

Archives historical and informational documents and binaries concerning railroads, railfanning, and model railroading.

The Weimaraner Homepage

http://www.eskimo.com/~chipper/weim.html

Provides information about the Weimaraner breed of pointing dog. Includes standards, addresses of clubs, history, rescue dogs, and more.

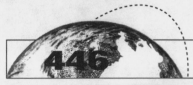

The Weimaraner Breed!

🐕 History of the Weimaraner (Current as of: 07/06/95)

🐕 The Official Standard of the Weimaraner (Current as of: 07/06/95)

🐕 Canis Major's The gray ghost of field and family room

🐕 Books about the Weimaraner (reviews) (Current as of: 07/06/95)

🐕 List of Local Weimaraner Clubs (Current as of: 07/17/95)

West View Designs

http://www.islandnet.com/~arogers/needlework.html

Offers to create custom stitchery charts from your photograph or picture.

Wilderness Furnishings Outdoor Catalog

http://www.sccsi.com/Wilderness/wilderness.html

Offers a catalog of outdoor items ranging from tents to swingsets, from water gear to cooking gear (which you can order online).

Wildflower Menu

http://rampages.onramp.net/~garylipe/index.htm

Provides several resources on wildflowers, including a database of wildflower common names and Latin names, and a listing by state of wildflower gardens.

William Booth

http://www.infoweb.com.au/wbooth

Supplies mail-order collectors' stamps from all countries, which you can order directly.

World Wide Quilting Page

http://quilt.com/quilt.html

Offers quilting essentials, including the following: basic quilting techniques; diagrams and directions for many traditional quilt blocks; a collection of foundations for paper piecing; a place for users to post questions, hints, and other info; a brief history of quilting around the world; quilt stores where you can find fabric and supplies in your area; a design board where you can see what fellow quilters are doing; quilt shows; quilt exhibitions and museums; quilt book reviews; the latest fabric offerings; computer software for quilt designing; quilted clothing; artists and teachers, the people who have turned quilting into an art form and carry on the traditions; frequently asked questions about quilting; quilting guilds you can join in your area; information on the tools of the trade; catalogs online from which you can order quilting and other supplies online; miscellaneous quilting topics; quilt-related mailing lists; and a place for finding quilters with whom to exchange fabric and blocks.

World-Wide Collectors' Digest

http://www.wwcd.com

Lists dealers and manufacturers of trading cards, memorabilia, figurines, trade shows, classifieds, and more.

World's Most Precious Baby Book—A World Wide Mall™

http://www.olworld.com/olworld/mall/mall_us/c_toys/m_worlds/index.html

Presents means to view and order directly personalized gifts.

YMCA of Seattle Camping Services

http://www.pacificrim.net/~orkila

Provides information about the year-round program and employment opportunities at YMCA of Seattle Camping Services. Features YMCA Camp Orkila and YMCA Camp Colman.

The A–Z of Jewish & Israel Related Resources

http://www.ort.org/anjy/resource/a-z.htm

Introduces a wide variety of Jewish topics, organizations, and resources available on the net. Offers alphabetical indexes of sites.

Access to Insight

http://world.std.com/~metta/

Focuses on supporting and deepening Buddhist meditation practice. Emphasizes teachings from the Theravada Buddhist tradition, but represents other Buddhist traditions as well.

Aish Ha Torah Discovery

http://j51.com:80/~jrsflw

Presents a Jewish adult-education seminar. Provides information ranging from basics of Judaism to the latest research by mathematicians and computer specialists on the hidden codes in the *Bible*.

Discovery
The World's Most Popular Jewish Adult Education Seminar.

The Amish—The Plain People

http://www.epix.net/homepage/Amish/amish.html

Provides a good, concise explanation of the Amish people. Also includes an online question and answer session.

Anglicans Online

http://infomatch.com/~haibeck/anglican.html

Provides information about the Anglican church. Includes Anglican news, links to the church in Canada, the United States, and the world. Offers other links that cover resources, Synod news, schools, newsgroups, and mailing lists.

Answers in Action Home Page

http://www.power.net/users/aia/

Seeks to be "a dynamic nonprofit religious organization training Christians to adopt and promote a Christian world view in every area of their lives." Features book reviews, information on contempory issues, the *Bible*, Christian apologetics, and more.

APOLOGIA—To Offer a Reason

http://diakonos.hum.utah.edu/philosophy/religion/apologia/

Focuses on a reasoned defense of the Christian faith and ethics. Presents a positive Christian world view.

B'nai B'rith

http://unixg.ubc.ca:780/~steinbok/bbyo/BBYO.html

Provides information about this international Jewish youth organization.

Bahá'í Resources on the Internet

http://www.bcca.org/srb/resources.html

Provides information on Bahá'í; points you in the right direction with links to Bahá'í related resources that include introductory material, Bahá'í texts, and organizations.

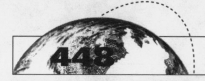

Baker Bookhouse Company

http://www.bakerbooks.com/ccc/

Christian book publisher. Offers information and special offers on their books. Presents a Christian Internet directory, a list of many jumps to Christian information sources, as well as jumps to many sites devoted to different Christian denominations.

The Baptist Faith and Message

http://www.utm.edu/martinarea/fbc/bfm.html

Contains statement of faith adopted by the Southern Baptist convention.

Believers Information Network

http://minotaur.marques.co.za/duke/index.htm

Presents a pan-religious approach to modern life.

The Bhagavad Gita

http://www.cc.gatech.edu/gvu/people/Phd/Rakesh.Mullick/gita/gita.html

Offers the *Bhagvad Gita* in Sanskrit (requires a PostScript viewer, such as Ghostscript). Also offers an English translation.

Sanskrit Verses

BrotherMark's Christian Material

http://www.tit.fi/~mark/Christian/

Provides a collection of links to Christian sites and resources. Offers a diversity of links that include humor, magazines, history, Christian organizations, Christian home pages, and theology. Provides some material in Finnish, but most in English.

Buddhist Scripture Information Retrieval

http://www.mahidol.ac.th/budsir/budsir-main.html

Promotes a software package (BUDSIR) that searches the Pali cannon for the information you want.

Canada Toronto East Mission

http://www.goodnet.com/~rob

The Church of Jesus Christ of Latter Day Saints. Provides former missionary e-mail addresses, information about upcoming reunions, mission history and experiences, and access to Toronto resources.

Catholic Online

http://www.catholic.org/catholic/index.html

Provides message centers, forums, and research materials.

Chabad Lubavitch in Cyberspace

http://www.chabad.org

Offers information on Chabad. Includes children's links, multimedia, listserv, and gopher resources. Seeks to bring information about the Jewish heritage to the Internet.

Christian Articles Archive

http://www.garlic.com/rfwilson/archive/

Contains articles for Christian newsletters, religious periodicals, brochures, and sermon illustrations. Also provides information about using Internet e-mail conferencing for Christian teaching and discipleship.

Christian Book Connection

http://www.xmission.com/~seer/Christian-Book/index.html

Online bookstore. Offers a selection of materials from which you can choose.

Christian Classics Ethereal Library

http://www.cs.pitt.edu/~planting/books/

Focuses on classic Christian literature. Contains works from St. Augustine to Wesley.

Christian Computing Magazine

http://www.website.net/~ccmag/

Online editon of *Christian Computing Magazine*. Contains current as well as back issues of the printed magazine. Provides subscription information and links to Christian resources and literature as well.

Christian Connections

http://tcm.nbs.net/~cc/cchome.html

Aims to inspire and educate the Christian community in online resourcing and communication. Offers reference materials, Web page storage/training, and direct dial-in for the western side of Washington. Offers many indexed Christian reference lists and a Christian index of all major denomination Websites. Specializes in online communication, resource sharing, and publishing.

Christian Poetry

http://www.pennet.net/resident/hoffman/crossway.html

Publishes works of Christian poets who want to share the gospel of Jesus Christ through the medium of poetry.

The Christian Recovery Connection

http://www.fileshop.com/personal/iugm/

Enables you to participate in a 12-step recovery program for abuse, addiction, or grief by offering links to different Christian recovery programs on the Web that can offer support from a Christian point of view.

The Christian Resource Network

http://www.cresnet.org

Hundreds of documents on Christianity, cults, missions, evangelism, pastors' sermon notes, and so on. Also features a wide selection of Christian shareware including electronic *Bibles*, church management software, an online *Bible*, Christian educational software and games.

Christian Singles Online

http://www.netrunner.net/~gigimia/singles/index.html

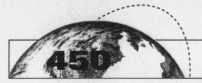
A Christian dating service online. Offers a six month membership that entitles you to at least 10 matches with a compatible Christian single (for a fee).

The Church of St. Joseph

http://www.gti.net/bahamas/stjoe.html

Lets you access parish information, events, latest news of the church, and a mass schedule.

The Community

http://www.seas.smu.edu/~jackson/Chrysalis/chrys.html

Provides information on the Emmaus and Chrysalis weekends led by lay people and clergy. Also provides information on Kairos weekends—a similar program that focuses on prison inmates.

CyberMuslim Information Collective

http://www.uoknor.edu:80/cybermuslim/

Provides information and resources. Offers links to the HyperQur'aan project. Includes information on Islamic culture, schools, computing services, bookstores, and digital activism.

Cyberspace Church of Christ Home Page

http://www.sky.net/~nragan/cyber1.html

Lists Church of Christ sites on the Web. Also offers numerous jumps to information on missions, Usenet groups, directories, and online *Bible* study.

DEFA Home Page

http://sunsite.unc.edu/dharma/defa.html

DharmaNet Electronic Files Archive. Contains the online Buddhist libraries maintained by DharmaNet International. Offers links to the Dharma Newsstand, Buddhist Info Web, BBS listings, and more.

Dictionaries of Buddhist Terms and Classical Chinese Characters

http://www2.gol.com/users/acmuller/index.html

Provides information in the area of East Asian Buddhist studies and classical Chinese philosophy/religion. Features two extensive dictionaries: one a dictionary of Chinese, Korean, and Japanese Buddhist terms, the other a Chinese character dictionary that emphasizes ancient/classical ideographs (both dictionaries provide romanized pronunciations in Wade-Giles, Pinyin, Korean, and Japanese).

Dictionary of the Bible

http://www.cs.colorado.edu/homes/mcbryan/public_html/bb/27/38/summary.html

Contains a dictionary of biblical terms.

Duke University Catholic Student Center

http://www.duke.edu/~rlm4/csc.html

Publicizes events and schedules of Duke's Catholic Student Center. Also offers links to other Roman Catholic Web pages.

East 7th Street Baptist Ministry—Graffiti

http://soho.ios.com/~dwna/grafhome.html

Aims to foster faith, hope, and love in the Lower East Side of Manhattan, New York, through ministries to help meet the spiritual, social, educational, and economic development needs of the community.

The ECOLE Institute

http://www.evansville.edu/~ecoleweb/

Seeks to create a hypertext encyclopedia of the works of early Christian church authors.

Electronic Book of Common Prayer

http://listserv.american.edu/anglican/bcp

Contains the *Electronic Book of Common Prayer*.

The Evangelical Free Church of America

http://www.halycon.com/churchse/cefc/efca.html

Contains the basis of faith of this church and offers links to individual church bodies that have a Web presence.

Evangelical Lutheran Church in America Home Page

http://www.elca.org/

Contains news and pointers to areas of the church's interest. Provides much information.

Family Research Council

http://www.townhall.com/townhall/FRC/

Seeks to reaffirm and promote the traditional family unit and the Judeo-Christian value system.

Famous Unitarian Universalists

http://www.execpc.com/~biblogic/cvuufamo.html

Provides a list of well-known contemporary and historical figures who have been involved with the Unitarian Universalist movement and offers links to sites that provide information about these people.

Fasting & Prayer '95

http://www.mdalink.com/fasting-prayer/

Promotes three day event that took place November 16–18, 1995, in which top Christian leaders from all over the nation joined thousands of other Christians in Los Angeles, California, to fast and pray for revival in the United States. Also presents reasons for fasting, as well as tips for safe and effective fasting.

Fort: Panth Khalsa

http://www.community.net/~khalsa/

Provides a glimpse into the culture of the Sikh Nation. Posts Hukam-Namah (daily verses from the Sikh Scriptures) in native Gurmukhi format. Contains information about Sikh history and current events relevant to the Sikh people.

[Click on any Image to Enter]

FORT : PANTH KHALSA
INFORMATION ON THE SIKH NATION

Free Daism

http://www.he.tdl.com/~fdac/

Presents Free Daism, the "ancient, eternal, and always new religion of self-transcending God-Realization," based on the teaching of Adi Da.

Friends of Osho

http://earth.path.net/osho/

Presents the unfolding work of Osho, whose discourses have been published in more than 650 volumes, including translations into more than 30 languages.

Global Hindu Electronic Network

http://rbhatnagar.csm.uc.edu:8080/hindu_universe.html

Offers Hindu-related links. Contains the alt.hindu newsgroup and offers scripture, information on publications, Hindu festivals, and links to Jain, Buddha, and Sikh dharmas.

Gospel Communications Network

http://www.gospelcom/net

This is a great jumping off point to things like Legionnaire ministries-InterVarsity Press-The *Bible* Gateway and more.

Gospel Films, Inc.

http://www.gospelcom.net/gf/

Distributes Christian videos in a range of subjects, from children's tapes to historical/biblical and true life stories. Also features Christian games, articles, and news.

Grace Chapel Youth Ministry (Tucson, AZ)

http://east.pima.edu/~rmcmurray/gcym.html

Presents a transdenominational youth outreach ministry that serves southern Arizona. Also features links to other Christian Web sites.

Greater Grace World Outreach

http://www.smart.net/~ggwo

International Ministry with links to its associated ministries including: The Grace Hour International Radio Show, Missions, Churches, Schools, Books & Tapes, *Bible* Resources. Plus a whole lot more.

The Green Pages

http://www.mindspring.com/~greenman/index.html

Serves as an information clearinghouse for pagan information. Includes many links to related pages, essays, periodicals, and a calendar of pagan events.

The GROKNet—Comedyatre and Resources

http://www.ozemail.com.au/~grok/

Presents an Australian Christian two-man comedy theatrical team. Includes information on GROK's performance history, reviews, and schedules.

Haqqani Foundation Home Page

http://www.best.com/~informe/mateen/Sufi/Haqqani_Foundation.html

Offers a look into the teachings and precepts of Sufism. Offers many pages of information, pictures, and links intended to spread Sufi teachings of the brotherhood of man.

The Hare Krishna Home Page

http://www.webcom.com/~ara/

Provides an insight into one's spiritual identity by establishing a distinction between matter and spirit. Also guides serious inquisitors in attaining unlimited spiritual happiness.

Harvest Online

http://www.harvest.org/

Includes dates for upcoming events of Harvest, along with information about the "A New Beginning with Greg Laurie" broadcasts.

Hawaii Bahá'í Youth Page

http://aloha.net/hol/home/lizhm/bahaiyou.htm

Provides a resource of links and graphics about the Bahá'í faith.

The Hinduism Today Home Page

http://www.HinduismToday.kauai.hi.us/ashram/htoday.html

A Hindu family newspaper online. Provides an index of issues, along with subscription information.

The Holy Bible—King James Version

http://www.iadfw.net/webchap/kjvb/

A complete text of the King James Version of the *Bible* in HTML 3.0 format. Each chapter is a separate HTML file providing quick access to any verse in the Bible. Verses are referenceable by the URL of the file followed by a # and the verse number. There is also a 13,857 word concordance that is hyperlinked to the Bible.

Ibrahim Shafi's Page in Islam

http://www.wam.umd.edu/~ibrahim/

Provides links focusing on the many facets of Islamic religious life. Offers many links to Muslim organizations, texts, ftp, gopher sites, newsgroups, and other resources. Also offers links to Muslim countries.

ICMC Home Page

http://www.xc.org/icmc/

Provides an electronic magazine you can use to browse a member directory. Maintains a list of links to resources for Christians.

In the Footsteps of the Lord

http://www.xensei.com/users/Angel/Home/CR.html

Offers many Christian links. Contains a few loose categories.

Institute for Christian Leadership

http://iclnet93.iclnet.org

Serves as a Web gateway for the Institute for Christian Leadership's BBS (ICLBBS). Contains many resources, from readings to setting up discussion groups.

International Meditation Centres (in the Tradition of Sayagyi U Ba Khin)

http://www.webcom.com/~imcuk/welcome.html

Offers information on 10-day Vipassana meditation courses as well as a newsletter, Theravada Buddhist publications, and images of pagodas.

International Research Institute for Zen Buddhism

http://www.iijnet.or.jp/iriz/irizhtml/irizhome.htm

Focuses on Zen. Presents a knowledge base on Zen along with a searchable database of Zen centers around the world.

International Union of Gospel Missions

http://www.iugm.org/iugm/main.html

Offers information about rescue missions and other organizations. Focuses on homeless, urban youth, and general inner city life.

InterVarsity Christian Fellowship

http://www.gospelcom.net/iv/

Sports links to the InterVarsity Press. Also offers online ordering for books and more.

Islam

http://www-leland.stanford.edu/~yusufali/islam/index.html

Provides information about Islam. Includes the Shi'a encyclopedia and information about the Ahlul Bayt. Features a daily verse from the *Qu'ran* and a daily saying that represents Islamic principles.

Islamic Resources

http://latig.com/welcome.html

Provides information about Islamic beliefs, resources, community events, businesses, and organizations.

Islamic Society of Wichita

http://www.southwind.net/~masjid

Offers links to hundreds of Muslim Web sites. Provides information on *Qu'ran*, Hadith, Prayer timings, and much more.

The Israelite Handbook

http://www.interport.net/~barzel

Serves as the base of operations on the Internet for blacks and Latinos who want to forge a new cultural and religious identity as Hebrew Israelites. Discusses such topics as Islam, Christianity, atheism, Afrocentricity, drugs, and slavery.

Jain Studies

http://www.dmu.ac.uk/~pka/guides/jain.html

Provides a starting point for people looking for resources on Jainism on the Internet. Offers many links to resources.

Jain World Wide Web Page

http://www.wavefront.com/~raphael/jain/jain.html

Overviews Jain resources on the Web. Offers links to gopher sites, ftp sites, Web sites, organizations, books, and periodicals.

The Jerusalem One WWW Network

http://www.jer1.co.il/

Offers numerous links to Aliya information, Torah and Judaic studies, a Jewish calendar of events, current news and views from Israel and the world's largest Jewish software, and a clip art library.

The Jesus Army

http://www.tecc.co.uk/jesusa/

Contains an electronic magazine and many pictures.

Jesus Fellowship Home Page

http://www.fiu.edu/~wgreen01/jf.html

A family church, a Christian teaching center, a covenant community, a worldwide outreach center, a campus ministry, a neighborhood *Bible* fellowship, and much more.

Jesus Fellowship - Miami, Florida

The Jesus Film Project

http://www.mdalink.com/JESUSproject/index.html

Presents the Campus Crusade for Christ's Jesus Film project. Includes well-designed graphics pages. Offers links to other Campus Crusade for Christ sites in the United States and abroad.

The Jewish Theological Seminary

http://www.jtsa.edu/

Represents this conservative seminary online. Includes links to other schools. Provides a wealth of resources.

Jewishnet

http://jewishnet.net/

Offers a list of Jewish-related sites. Offers links to gopher sites, home pages, libraries, ftp sites, and information on newsgroups and mailing lists.

Jews for Jesus Home Page

http://www.jews-for-jesus.org/index.html

Serves as a means to finding Jewish Christians. Contains documents on Jewish Christianity and information on how to contact them, along with a music and concert schedule and a fun quiz.

Journal of Buddhist Ethics

http://www.cac.psu.edu/jbe/jbe.html

The Journal of Buddhist Ethics, an online publication that promotes academic research in Buddhist ethics. Offers current and back issues. Includes a number of articles in Adobe Acrobat format.

The Life and Faith Network

http://www.telos.ca/lf/index.html

Provides a group of conferences for people interested in discussing their faith and how it affects their life.

Logictarian Christian Home Page

http://www.geopages.com/CapitolHill/1205

Focuses on the quest for the meaning of life. Offers a blend of Christianity, Shintoism, martial arts, and science. Also serves as a division of the UFG/ECD, Inc., a Canada-based nonprofit research body.

Logos Research Systems

http://islander.whidbey.net/~logos/welcome.html

Electronic publishing firm. Offers CD-ROMs of biblical translations, from King James to Revised Standard Version. Also includes many other titles.

Lutheran Marriage Encounter

http://www.pic.net/~speed/lme.html

Focuses on providing married couples the opportunity to examine their lives together.

Menorah Ministries

http://www.rmii.com/~menorah

International Messianic missionary ministry of the Gospel to both Jews and Gentiles. Offers information and articles regarding the Messiah, Biblical Jewish roots of Christianity, and Israel. Also serves as a resource-help forum.

SHALOM!

Menorah Ministries

Minister's Reference Center

http://www.rr-mrc.com/

Serves as a subscription site from which you can download other ministers' messages for a fee each month. Offers a free trial period as well as a discount for lay members and students.

Muslim Educational Trust Home Page

http://www.teleport.com/~metpdx/

Serves the interest of the Muslim Community in the Portland, Oregon Metropolitan Area, through education, a weekend Muslim school, and a speaker's bureau.

The New Crusades

http://www.geopages.com/Hollywood/1414/index.html

Offers many links to Christian, science fiction, and fantasy sites.

The New Crusades

From Rob Huston of Barrie, Ontario, Canada.

- World Wide Web Directories
- Christian World Wide Web Sites
- Science Fiction and Fantasy Sites
- Other Cool and Interesting Sites
- The Local Barrie Area Internet Scene

New Kadampa Tradition

http://www.webcom.com/~nkt/

A Mahayana Buddhist organization. Aims to preserve and promote the essence of Buddha's teachings in a form suited to the Western mind and way of life. Offers information on books, meditation programs, and a directory of NKT centers.

New Media Communications

http://www.iac.net/~dlature

Seeks to gather together resources to enable seminaries and theological organizations to bring theological education to all who seek it.

Nichiren Shoshu Buddhism

http://www.primenet.com/~martman/ns.html

Offers a look into this school of Buddhism. Includes a list of temples and articles from the *The Nichiren Shoshu Monthly*.

The Online Islamic Bookstore

http://www.sharaaz.com

Provides information about books, tapes, and software. Offers links to Islamic sites and book reviews of important books.

The Orthodox Christian Page

http://www.ocf.org/OrthodoxPage/

Contains an introduction to Greek Orthodox Christianity. Provides links to European and American Orthodox sites, jumps to scriptures and liturgy, icons, prayers, readings, and other resources.

Orthodox Ministry ACCESS

http://www.maceast.com/usr/om/home_page

Provides information about Orthodox Christianity; the Greek Orthodox Archdiocese; the Orthodox Ministry ACCESS Bulletin Board System (accessible via the Internet); Orthodox Christian resources; Orthodox Christian organizations; and more.

Our Daily Bread

http://www.gospelcom.net/rbc/odb/

Presents a short, daily devotional guide for Christians. Includes an archive page for access to previous months' devotions.

The Pagan Pages

http://www.eor.com/pages

Provides free advertising, announcements, and networking for pagan and pagan-friendly people and their businesses in hopes of strengthening community ties.

Panth Khalsa

http://odin.community.net:80/~khalsa/

Focuses on the Sikh Nation. Also offers a look into the Sikh code of conduct and the spirit of Sikhism.

Presbyterian Church (U.S.A.)

http://pcusa.org/

Serves as the online presence of the Presbyterian church. Contains a vast array of Presbyterian news, as well as links to research sites, resources, and referrals.

The Project Genesis Home Page

http://israel.nysernet.org:80/genesis/

Presents the Project Genesis, an active initiative to utilize the Internet to teach college students about their Jewish roots. Also offers Jewish educational materials online.

Project Wittenberg

http://www.iclnet.org/pub/resources/text/wittenberg/
wittenberg-home.html

Provides the writings of Martin Luther online. Plans to accumulate Luther's work, along with that of other theologians.

The Religious Society of Friends WWW Site

http://www.quaker.org/

Offers a list of links about Quakers on the Web. Includes links to sites focusing on Quaker schools, journals, The American Friends Service Committee, genealogy, Quaker history, newsgroups, and more.

Revival Theology Resources Home Page

http://www.xmission.com/~gastown/revival/

Provides a forum for the advancement of Christian Revival Theology and Moral Government Theology. Offers links to newsletters, articles, and ministries.

Saint Mary's Press

http://wwwsmp.smumn.edu/

Features their online catalog. Offers some links to other Christian publishers.

Salaam Ailaikum

http://www.wco.com/~altaf/altaf.html

Contains Islamic and social justice poetry, articles, links, and stories. Also contains several articles by the Islamic author, the late Dr. Ali Shariati.

San Francesco di Paola

http://www.diemme.it/paola/francesco.html

Focuses on the life and works of Saint Francis of Paola, the patron saint of sailors.

Scrolls from the Dead Sea

http://sunsite.unc.edu/expo/deadsea.scrolls.exhibit/
intro.html

This exhibit from the Library of Congress is a great scholastic site. The published text of the Quamran scrolls, commonly known as the Dead Sea Scrolls. These works have been extensively studied by *Bible* scholars. The site offers a link to the Expo Bookstore where a printed copy of the exhibition catalog can be purchased.

SDANet

http://www.sdanet.org/

This is the site for the Seventh Day Adventist (SDA) WWW server. Links to gopher sites, SDA institutions, and *Bible* Study forums can be found here.

Serious Developments— Christian Software Catalog

http://www.viper.net/clients/serious/

A good source for Christian software, featuring hundreds of products, including *Bible* Study software, clip art, games, and religious studies. You can select from a choice of free software, just for visiting this Web page. There are also links to other Christian sites from this page.

Shamash

http://shamash.nysernet.org

Offers links to various Jewish religious organizations from Hillel to the world Zionist organization.

Shin Buddhism Network

http://www.aloha.net/~rtbloom/shinran

Contains English and Japanese articles on Shin Buddhism, as well as a list of links to Buddhist resources.

Shin Buddhist Resource Center

http://www.well.com/user/shinshu/SBRC/

Includes an online library of text and a bookstore.

Shtetl, Yiddish Language and Culture Home Page

http://sunsite.unc.edu/yiddish/shtetl.html

Provides information on Yiddish culture. Provides resources that point toward a wide range of links, from books to read to kosher recipes.

Sikhism: Religion of the Sikh People

http://www.io.org/~sandeep/sikhism.htm

Provides information about Sikhism, which preaches a message of love of one God, truthful living, and the equality of mankind, through the teachings of its Gurus enshrined in the Sri Guru Granth Sahib, the Sikh Holy Book, and Eternal Guru.

Society Hill Synagogue of Philadelphia

http://www-leland.stanford.edu/~nadav/shs.html

Presents an independent, conservative, egalitarian synagogue, and offers numerous programs in all aspects of religious and cultural life. Includes detailed descriptions, a brochure, a monthly newsletter, and some nice graphics.

St. Louis Life News

http://uptown.turnpike.net/S/sllife/index.html

Presents pro-life news and information, including opinion pieces and links to pro-life and pro-abortion sites.

Stanford University Zoroastrian Group

http://www-leland.stanford.edu:80/group/zoroastrians/

Zoroastrianism online. Offers information about this individual group, but also offers many links to information on this religion.

Symbol Talk

http://www.teleport.com/~symbol/

Serves as a Web resource for meditation pillows.

Taoism Information Page

http://www.cnu.edu/~patrick/taoism.html

Offers a look into the Taoist tradition. Provides Sun Tzu's *The Art of War*, and the *I Ching*.

This Week in Bible Prophecy

http://www.niagara.com:80/~twibp/

This Web site supplements a television program on *Bible* prophecy that is aired over the Trinity Broadcasting network in the United States, and over Vision TV in Canada. You can receive transcripts of recently aired programs through this site, as well as read magazine articles and select videos and books.

Tien Dao Christian Media

http://www.webcom.com/~tiendao/tiendao.html

Focuses on Chinese Christianity. Offers software and an online bookstore (includes text in both Chinese and English).

Tiger Team Buddhist Information Network

http://www.newciv.org/TigerTeam/

Offers online files, conferencing, and shopping. Includes links to Buddhist resources and to the table of contents for the CyberSangha.

The United Church of Christ

http://www.apk.net/ucc

Provides information and demographics concerning The United Church of Christ.

The United Pentecostal Church International

http://www.prairienet.org/community/religion/fire/upc.html

Serves as an unofficial page for the The United Pentecostal Church International. Contains a moderate amount of information about the church on both a regional and general level.

The University of Delaware Wesley Foundation

http://triton.cms.udel.edu/~keiner/wesley.html

Provides information about upcoming events related to Methodist Church activities at this and other selected college campuses.

University of Michigan Interfaith Student Council

http://www.umich.edu/~umisc/

Serves as a resource site for people interested in religious events near or on the Ann Arbor campus of the University of Michigan. Also serves as a place to publicize global religious efforts/affiliations.

University of St. Michael's College—Faculty of Theology

http://www.utoronto.ca/stmikes/index.html

Provides theological education in programs of an academic and professsional nature and promotes research in these areas. Includes information on an Internet research project entitled, "The Impact of the Internet on Theological and Religious Studies." Also contains additional annotated resources for theological and religious studies.

UNIVERSITY OF ST. MICHAEL'S COLLEGE

Faculty of Theology

Welcome to the *unofficial* home page for the Faculty of Theology at the University of St. Michael's College, Toronto, Canada.

WAMY IslamNet (World Assembly of Muslim Youth)

http://www.cais.com/islamic/index.html

Offers a page of links relating to this organization. Includes sounds, magazines, and the Fiqeh database online, among other resources.

Web Chapel—A Mission to Cyberspace

http://www.iadfw.net/webchap/

Web Chapel is a mission to cyberspace, providing World Wide Web access to Christian writings and sermons, an on-line *Bible* study and devotional material, information on how to become a Christian, and prayer requests.

Western Region Jewish Committee on Scouting

http://www.emf.net/~troop24/

Offers boy scouting opportunities for Jewish youth. Also offers information on scouting and links to other Jewish youth resources.

The Wire

http://www.roehampton.ac.uk/link/wire/

Presents an ecumenical Christian communications periodical, published electronically using the Acrobat PDF format. Includes issues of interest to Christian computer users.

The World ORT Union

http://www.ort.org/

Serves as a host site to ANJY (A Network for Jewish Youth), *The Jewish Quarterly*, and other Jewish resources. Exhibits on this server are of special interest to young people, including a tour of the Diaspora Museum, a prototype software system for teachers.

The World Wide Study Bible

http://www.cs.pitt.edu/~planting/books/wwsb/

The World Wide Study *Bible* was conceived as a means of organizing all of the Bible-related resources on the World Wide Web according to scripture reference. Invites user contributions.

The WWW Bible Gateway

http://www.calvin.edu/cgi-bin/bible

Provides a search form for the *Bible*, and handles many common translations. Lets you conduct searches and

output verses in French, German, Swedish, Tagalog, Latin, or English.

Yaohushua, the Genuine Messiah

`http://metro.turnpike.net/Y/yaohush/index.html`

Explains about the original, archaic Hebrew name of the Creator and His unique Messiah: Yaohushua. Also includes files on scriptural doctrines of faith, salvation, health, wealth, love, family, marriage, success, and deliverance.

Zen Buddhist Texts

`http://oac11.hsc.uth.tmc.edu/zen/index.html`

Offers hypertext versions of classic Zen literature, as well as a large assortment of Zen-related links.

The Zen Garden

`http://www.nomius.com/~zenyard/zenyard.htm`

Presents Zen stories, koans, images, and sounds.

Zen Mountain Monastery

`http://the.quickpages.com/dharma`

Focuses on Zen. Features questions for Cybermonk, dharma communications, Buddhist resources, a list of worldwide affiliates, Zen art, a Zen environmental studies center, meditation, and a journal.

Zen@SunSITE

`http://sunsite.unc.edu/zen`

Focuses on Zen. Presents koans from the gateless gate and links to other Zen sites, including links to the Zen Hospice Project and to Zen and Taoist texts.

1990 United States Census LOOKUP

http://cedr.lbl.gov/cdrom/doc/lookup_doc.html

Provides information about localities nationwide. Requires a WWW client with forms capability.

A.J. Automation Home Page

http://www.cris.com/~rmac/ac.html

Contains MathMadness Screen Savers. Also offers fractal puzzles online.

Accelerator Physics at SLAC

http://beam.slac.stanford.edu/

Describes accelerator physics at the Stanford Linear Accelerator Center. Includes links to most accelerator physics and resources on the Web, including almost all accelerator labs in the world, lab-specific and general news and job-listing sites, physics societies and organizations, texts, and more.

ACT Meters Ltd.

http://www.u-net.com/~compsec/act.html

Introduces Checkmate 2 from ACT Meters Ltd., a new radio-linked meter that combines radio, audio, and digital meter to enable a single engineer to perform remote circuit testing and troubleshooting effortlessly.

The AECOM/MMC Department of Radiation Oncology Department Home Page

http://www.ca.aecom.yu.edu/~franklin/radonc.html

Describes the radiation oncology department of The Albert Einstein College of Medicine, and the Montefiore Medical Center. Includes links to cancer resources for patients and doctors. Also offers links to radiation oncology resources.

Agriculture Online

http://www.agriculture.com/

Contains current news of interest to the agricultural community. Also offers links to sites on the Internet related to agriculture issues.

AgriGator: Agricultural Conferences

http://gnv.ifas.ufl.edu/www/agator/htm/agmeeting.htm

Offers links to information about agricultural conferences.

AgriGator: Commercial Agriculture Sites

http://www.ifas.ufl.edu/WWW/AGATOR/HTM/AGCOMMERCIAL.HTM

Contains links to businesses on the Internet related to agriculture.

AgriWeather

http://www.agriweather.com/~agwx

Presents an online catalog of weather instruments and related products. Also offers a customized weather forecast service that provides separate weather forecasts for agricultural, business, and corporate needs.

The Air Affair

http://www.airaffair.com/

Focuses on all manner of flying machines. Includes a calendar of flying shows, aviation fuel prices, and an aviation library.

Air Force Maui Optical Station (AMOS)

http://ulua.mhpcc.edu/amos.html

Provides information about the Air Force Maui Optical Station (AMOS), located in Hawaii, and operated by the Phillips Laboratory. Describes telescopes and sensors at

AMOS, as well as how visiting experimenters can request use of the facilities.

Airship: The Home Page for Lighter-Than-Air Craft

`http://spot.colorado.edu/~dziadeck/airship.html`

Offers links for finding information about lighter-than-air craft. Includes information on these craft in fiction, models, and pictures; a bibliography; and links to Internet resources and discussion groups.

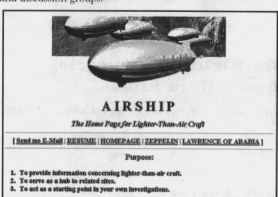

Alden Electronics

`http://www.alden.com/`

Provides weather data systems, marine electronics, and specialized imaging products and papers. Offers software, hardware, and customized data products.

All Electrical Engineering Academic Programs (Almost)

`http://www.eee.umr.edu/schools/ee_programs.html`

Contains a complete listing of electrical engineering academic programs, organized by country.

AlpacaNet

`http://www.webcom.com/~odyssey1/alpaca/alpaca.html`

Serves a resource for Alpaca ranchers, breeders, weavers, spinners, investors, and anyone who wants more information about alpacas.

Althausen's WWW Wonderland

`http://www.stpt.usf.edu/~johnalt/index.html`

Provides information and links to the wonderful world of geography, concentrating on the fields of remote sensing and geographic information systems. Also provides links to pages that deal with the topic. Althausen tosses in pages for his favorite professional teams and musicians as well. Offers links to numerous government agencies.

AMATH, Inc.

`http://www.smartpages.com/amath/`

A pre-algebra course for students who have trouble learning math. Provides a preview and ordering information.

American Astronomical Society

`http://blackhole.aas.org/AAS-homepage.html`

Provides general astronomy information of interest to professionals and amateur enthusiasts. Maintains links to other astronomy resources on the Net.

American Electronics Association

`http://www.aeanet.org`

Provides information on AEA and its activities and services, including an events calendar, a directory of services, and a membership roster. Provides instant links to more than 100 high-tech firms.

American Institute of Chemical Engineers

http://www.che.ufl.edu/WWW-CHE/aiche/

Provides information on the group's mission, the upcoming world conference, and its programs. Also offers membership information.

American Institute of Physics

http://aip.org/

Provides general information on physics. Contains lists of other Web sites as well as services such as online journals and software archives. Offers information varying from news about what is happening in the field of physics, presented at a newspaper reading level, to listings of job openings in the field of physics.

The American Nuclear Society

http://neutrino.nuc.berkeley.edu/ans/ANS.html

Provides information on membership, upcoming conferences, links to student chapters, and links to other WWW resources.

The American Physical Society

http://aps.org/

Publishes a variety of journals and offers several services both of a professional and educational nature.

Anatomy Images

ftp://grind.isca.uiowa.edu/image/gif/anatomy/

Contains directory of anatomy images.

Anderson's Timesaving Comparative Guide

http://www.atcg.com/atcg/

Serves as reference for molecular biologists, providing the world's most comprehensive listing of restriction enzymes, modifying enzymes, commercial DNA libraries, and more.

Applied Anthropology Computer Network (ANTHAP)

http://www.acs.oakland.edu/~dow/anthap.html

Offers information to practicing anthropologists and to the public interested in applied anthropology. Applied anthropology is a growing branch of the anthropological sciences devoted to applying anthropological knowledge to the solution of human problems. Applied anthropologists solve problems in the areas of business, education, law, medicine, historical preservation, and others.

The Art of Renaissance Science: Galileo and Perspective

http://bang.lanl.gov/video/stv/arshtml/lanlarstitle.html

Features the life of Galileo, including many images from the period; based on a videotape entitled "The Art of Renaissance Science: Galileo and Perspective."

(Art)^n Fractal Gallery

`http://www.artn.nwu.edu/fractal.html`

Contains a collection of high-resolution fractal images.

ASLO Home Page

`http://www.ngdc.noaa.gov/paleo/aslo/aslo.html`

"The purposes of ASLO are to promote the interests of limnology, oceanography and related sciences, to foster the exchange of information across the range of aquatic science, and to further investigations dealing with these subjects." Contains general information about the organization as well as information on careers and job listings.

ASM International Home Page

`http://www.asm-intl.org/`

Provides information about ASM, the Materials Information Society. Provides a searchable collection of web sites, a calendar of events, and a collection of materials producers of interest to materials engineers.

ASSET Welcome Page

`http://source.asset.com/`

Contains links to various resources on software engineering. Provides information about available courseware and STARS reports and offers a collection of related links.

Association of Academic Physiatrists

`http://a1.com/aap`

Physiatrists are physicians who specialize in physical medicine and rehabilitation, a medical specialty that deals with the evaluation and treatment of patients whose functional abilities have been impaired.

Astro!Info

`http://ezinfo.ethz.ch/ezinfo/astro/astro.html`

Aims to provide general information about a variety of astronomical events (large portion written in German, but some parts written in English).

Astronomical Data Center

`http://nssdc.gsfc.nasa.gov/adc/adc.html`

Element of the National Space Science Data Center (NSSDC) / A World Data Center for Rockets and Satellites (WDC-A-R&S). Part of an international federation of astronomical data centers. Acquires, verifies, formats, documents, and distributes files that contain astronomical data in computer-readable form. Also develops and maintains software tools to access these data.

Astronomical Museum in Bologna

`http://boas3.bo.astro.it/dip/Museum/MuseumHome.html`

Provides background on the history of astronomy and the instruments at this museum.

Astronomical Resources on the Internet

`http://mesis.esrin.esa.it/html/astro-resources.html`

Contains list of sites broken down into gopher, telnet, ftp, and WWW resources. Offers many links as well.

Astronomy HyperText Book

`http://zebu.uoregon.edu/text.html`

A hypertextual astronomy textbook written at the college level. Contains interactive information about astronomy. Also offers links to sites that offer astronomy assistance.

Astronomy-Related Web Sites

`http://www.skypub.com/links/astroweb.html`

Offers listing of astronomy-related Web sites and includes brief descriptions.

AstroWeb: Astronomy/ Astrophysics on the Internet

`http://msowww.anu.edu.au/~anton/astroweb/`

Provides a searchable index of information about astronomy and astrophysics that you can find on the Internet. Contains a keyword or string search option.

Atlantic Tropical Weather Center

`http://www.neosoft.com/citylink/blake/tropical.html`

Provides the latest hurricane information and other weather information dealing with tropical cyclones.

Auditory Perception

`http://www.music.mcgill.ca/~welch/auditory/Auditory.html`

Offers a multimedia document about auditory perception, including demonstrations, discussions, and experiments,

Automated Weather Source—Nationwide School Weather Network

`http://www.aws.com/index.html`

Provides national weather information from images to textual data. Also presents a photo gallery of severe weather by storm chasers throughout the country.

Aviation Enthusiast Corner

`http://omni.brooklyn.cuny.edu/rec/air/air.html`

Provides many resources, including picture libraries, airshow information, and aircraft locators.

Aviation Image Archives

`http://acro.harvard.edu/GA/image_archives.html`

Contains links to many aviation images and movies, including aircraft, aerobatics, combat, hang gliding, and logos from around the world.

Aerobatics Images

Last Update: Tuesday, 15-Aug-95 16:51:19 EDT

Aviation Weather

`gopher://geograf1.sbs.ohio-state.edu./1/wxascii/aviation/airways`

Provides up-to-date information on North American weather in the aviation meteorological code. Also includes severe weather warnings for pilots and pilot reports.

Aztec Books

`http://world.std.com/~aztec/`

Features books on UFOs, ghosts and the spirit world, unexplained phenomena, freemasonry, ancient and lost civilizations, science, ESP and psychic phenomena, holy grail, apocrypha, Kabbalah, Gnostic texts, astral projection, occult sciences, knights templar, theosophy, Nikola Tesla, Wilhelm Reich, and more.

Bacterial Nomenclature Up-To-Date

`http://www.ftpt.br/cgi-bin/bdtnet/bacterianame`

Provides the latest nomenclature information on bacteria. Enables user to enter a search word and receive information on the genus, species, status, and hazard group of known bacteria.

Ballooning Online!

`http://sunsite.unc.edu:80/ballooning/`

A reference for pilots and people interested in ballooning. Includes a glossary, information on clubs, a photogallery, ballooning prayers, catalogs, and historical information.

Basics of Space Flight Learners' Workbook

`http://oel-www.jpl.nasa.gov/basics/bsf.htm`

Provides orientation to space flight and related topics, including the solar system, gravity and mechanics, interplanetary trajectories, orbits, electromagnetic phenomena, space craft types, telecommunications, onboard subsystems, navigation, and phases of flight.

BCRI On-Line

`http://www.bcr.bc.ca`

Centre for Alternative Transportation Fuels. Focuses on forest biotechnology, environment, advanced transportation systems, ocean engineering, and ergonomics.

The Beauty of Chaos

`http://i30www.ira.uka.de/~ukrueger/fractals/`

Provides interactive journey through fractal images. Takes you through most of the database, which consists of hundreds of images.

Ben Cheng's Home Page

`http://198.68.160.16/~benny/benny.htm`

Offers a weekly math teaser (which also appears in the journal *Matematika*) to entertain and stretch your advanced math knowledge. Also presents an art gallery that contains chaos images.

BiochemWeb

`http://biochemweb.slu.edu/`

Provides a service for people involved in biochemistry and molecular biology: those considering applying to the St Louis University graduate program, those involved in the graduate program, and professors.

Biodiversity and Biological Collections Web Server

`http://muse.bio.cornell.edu/`

Provides information about specimens in biological collections, taxonomic authority files, directories of biologists, reports by various standards bodies (IOPI, ASC, SA2000, and so on), an archive of the Taxacom (MUSE-L and CICHLID-L listservs), access to online journals (including Flora On-line), and MUSE and Delta.

BioForce Labs

http://mac10201.zool.iastate.edu

Focuses on expanding the use of scanning probe microscopy and molecular force detection in basic and applied research and molecular diagnostics. Focuses in particular on manufacturing and selling BioTips™, biologically modified force transducers for molecular detection. Includes the following services and activities: on-site SPM setup and training, collaborations, providing services, and supply sales.

BioSupplyNet

http://www.biosupplynet.com/bsn/

Serves as an online product directory for the biomedical/lifescience research community. Offers searchable database that contains more than 15,000 products from 1,400 vendors. Provides information on new products and special offers, an opportunity for users to share expertise through product user groups, and immediate access to suppliers via e-mail for technical support and ordering information.

Bosco's RockPile

http://www.best.com/~bosco

Offers site for sharing paleontology and geology infomation, sites, and pictures.

Brain Page

http://maui.net/~jms/brainuse.html

Presents study of how brain chemicals affect emotion, personality, and sexuality. Also offers links to related sites.

A Brief Overview of the National Herbarium

http://nmnhwww.si.edu/botany/collover.html

Includes information about the National Herbarium, a government organization. Includes searchable databases of plants and historical documents.

A Brief Tour of Our Universe!

http://www.holli.com/~jshoup/space/index.html

Presents an image-enhanced interactive virtual tour of the universe.

Britannica Online

http://www.eb.com/

Online reference source (for a price, unfortunately). Contains articles in the *Encyclopedia Britannica*, as well as articles not yet published.

British Trees

http://www.u-net.com/trees/

Presents the "Introductory Guide to Native British Trees," which enables you to search by common English or Latin names to find information on family, description, habitat, distribution, timber, uses, and so on.

Brussels Free University (ULB) Computer Science Department: Bookmarks

http://www.ulb.ac.be/di/bookmarks/book.html

Collects bookmarks about computer science, mathematic, computer firms, technical reports in these fields, bibliographies, and more.

Calculus&amp— *Mathematica* Home Page

http://www-cm.math.uiuc.edu/

Calculus& *Mathematica* is a calculus-reform project started at the University of Illinois and Ohio State University. Uses *Mathematica*, a software package from Wolfram Research, to teach calculus to high school and college students.

California Academy of Sciences

http://www.calacademy.org/

Contains online exhibits among other museum information.

Caltech Space Society

http://www.seds.org/seds/chapters/css/CSS.html

Provides information about space-related projects, such as conferences and educational programs, that are open to the public.

The Canard's Aviator's Page

http://www.intercom.net/local/aviation/

Provides information for the aviation enthusiast. Offers links to Canard aircraft that provide information on each aircraft and other related information.

CCD Images of Galaxies

http://zebu.uoregon.edu/galaxy.html

Presents a collection of images that specializes in photographs of galaxies. Also offers educational resources.

Center for Advanced Space Studies (CASS) Home Page

http://cass.jsc.nasa.gov/CASS_home.html

Provides information about this national research center, as well as general information about space science.

The Center for Anthropology and Journalism

http://pegasus.acs.ttu.edu/~wurlr/index.html

Serves as a resource site for journalists, media, and science writers who want to contact anthropologists and for anthropologists who want information about communicating with a wider audience.

Center for Soybean Tissue and Genetic Engineering

http://mars.cropsoil.uga.edu/homesoybean/index.htm

Describes efforts to develop and refine a complete soybean genetic engineering system.

Centre for Earth and Ocean Research—University of Victoria

http://wikyonos.seaoar.uvic.ca/ceor.home.html

Focuses on earth and ocean research.

Centro de Pesquisa e Desenvolvimento da Telebras—CPqD

http://www.cpqd.br

Covers research and development in telecommunications: ISDN, switching, optical communications, inductive technology (telephone cards), systems, materials, and more.

CERN European Laboratory for Particle Physics

http://www.cern.ch/

Birthplace of the World Wide Web. Provides general information on the Web and maintains archives of information on particle physics and listings of links to other sites pertaining to the field of physics.

Chaos at Maryland

http://www-chaos.umd.edu/chaos.html

Provides information on the various applications of chaos theory. Includes dimensions, fractal basin boundaries, chaotic scattering, and controlling chaos. Includes online papers, a searchable database, and general references. Also offers the Chaos Gallery.

Chaos Network Sign-In

http://www.prairienet.org/business/ptech/

Offers many links to topics relating to chaos theory, such as fractal mathematics. Recommends books to peruse.

Charles University Department of Physiology

http://www.lf1.cuni.cz/~wittner/physiol.htm

Includes teaching and research information and a collection of pages related to physiology.

Chartwell-Bratt

http://www.studli.se/brattint/welcUSE.html

Provides an online catalog for Swedish book publisher, Chartwell-Bratt. Offers English- or Swedish-database you can search by title, author, or subject. Includes books on mathematics, computer science, and engineering.

ChemCAI: Instructional Software for Chemistry

http://www.sfu.ca:80/chemed/

Contains links to software sources, demonstration materials, and other information for chemists.

Chemical Engineering URLs Directory

http://www.ciw.uni-karlsruhe.de/chem-eng.html

Offers a collection of links to information about chemical engineering resources outside the United States. Also offers a collection of links to chemical engineering sites all over the world. Provides information on upcoming conferences and includes many search links.

The Chemistry Hypermedia Project

http://www.chem.vt.edu/chem-ed/vt-chem-ed.html

Provides library of hypermedia tutorials related to chemistry.

Chemistry Teacher Resources

http://rampages.onramp.net/~jaldr/chemtchr.html

Provides resources for teachers and high school students of chemistry, original documents created by a science teacher.

Civil Engineer's Calendar

http://audrey.fagg.uni-lj.si/ICARIS/dates.ce/

Provides information about upcoming events of interest to civil engineers, in a searchable index or obtainable by e-mail.

Classics on Evolution

http://www.uib.no/zoo/darwin.html

Contains links to some classic papers on evolution, from Charles Darwin and Alfred Russel Wallace. Includes the famous *Origin of Species*.

CMB Astrophysics Research Program

http://spectrum.lbl.gov

Surveys ongoing research and lists current personnel in the George Smoot Astrophysics Research Group.

CMU Artificial Intelligence Repository

http://www.cs.cmu.edu/Web/Groups/AI/html/air.html

Contains public domain and freely distributable software, publications, and other materials of interest to AI researchers, educators, students, and practitioners.

CNC Relief Maps

http://www.nerosworld.com/www/MassProduction/reliefmap.html

Provides models of any size, scale, or vertical exaggeration. Serves the National Forest Service for interpretive centers, fire/watershed analysis, and maintenance.

Comet Observation Home Page

http://encke.jpl.nasa.gov/

Contains a wide variety of information on comets, including links to online resources and data archives of articles and images.

Comet Shoemaker-Levy Collision with Jupiter

http://newproducts.jpl.nasa.gov/sl9/

Provides information about the impact with Jupiter last year. Includes images, animations, and information about the event.

Common Weights and Measures

http://www.cchem.berkeley.edu/ChemResources/Weights-n-Measures/index.html

Contains information on converting to and from metric and United States measurements.

Composite Materials Research Group—University of Mississippi

http://cypress.mcsr.olemiss.edu/~melackey

Features research conducted by the Composite Materials Research Group at the University of Mississippi. Focuses on the optimization of the pultrusion process for the manufacture of composite materials and mechanical and physical property characterization of composite materials. Features faculty research, facilities and equipment, and graduate school opportunites.

Compton Observatory Science Support Center

http://cossc.gsfc.nasa.gov/cossc/cossc.html

Contains links to various instrument home pages, bulletin board access, announcements, and public data archives.

Computational Logic, Inc.

http://www.cli.com/

Performs advanced research and development in math modeling of digital hardware and software systems. Includes software and technical reports. Also provides education and consulting services. Offers jumps to university sites that contain information on the mathematical modeling of digital systems.

Computer Vision and Image Processing Group

http://poseidon.csd.auth.gr:80/

Covers digital image processing and related areas. Includes the areas of multichannel and color image processing, parallel image processing, medical signal processing, ultrasonic image processing and storage, fast algorithms and architectures for digital filtering and image processing, morphological image analysis.

Computing Center, Academy of Sciences, Russia

http://sunny.ccas.ru/web/.index.html

Provides computing services to the institutes of the Academy and other users.

Consciousness Research Laboratory

http://eeyore.lv-hrc.nevada.edu/~cogno/cogno.html

Contains a bibliography of alternative research, parapsychology, cognitive science, human factors, and science fiction. Includes an online experiment in which the visitor can participate.

Coral Health and Monitoring Home Page

http://coral.aoml.erl.gov/

Provides services to help improve and sustain coral reef health throughout the world. Contains general information about coral as well as a listing of links to other sites about coral.

The Coral Health and Monitoring Program

Ocean Chemistry Division
Atlantic Oceanographic and Meteorological Laboratory
National Oceanic and Atmospheric Administration

Cornell Ornithology Collection

http://muse.bio.cornell.edu/museums/cubird.html

Provides information about the history of the ornithology program at Cornell. Offers a useful link to a gopher search tool for scientific information on bird species.

Cornell Theory Center

http://www.tc.cornell.edu/

Contains information about high-end computing theory. Offers a visualization link that includes animations, graphics, and tools.

CPLEX Optimization, Inc. Home Page

http://www.cplex.com/

Develops large-scale mathematical programming software and services. Provides list of products and services and offers linear and mixed-integer programming software.

Crazy about Constraints!

http://www.lm.com/~dshu/toc/cac.html

Provides information regarding mechanical engineering manufacturing issues, such as the theory of constraints, the thinking processes, and other Goldratt techniques.

CSC Mathematical Topics

http://www.csc.fi/math_topics/

Provides information about mathematical software and guidebooks available at the Center for Scientific Computing (CSC, Finland). Also points to application specialists at CSC for help on specific topics. Provides several kinds of search mechanisms to help find documents. Displays examples of mathematical animations and visualisations made at CSC. Also contains some guidebooks and newsletters published by CSC.

CSC Mathematical Topics: Visualizations

http://www.csc.fi/math_topics/Movies

Displays animations (MPG format) of various mathematical theories and areas. Includes Klein bottle, genetic algorithms, Fourier series, and so on.

CSIRO Division of Oceanography

http://www.ml.csiro.au/~wilkin/public/do.html

Offers two links: The Climate and Ocean Processes link provides information on research in this area, and the Marine Environment and Resources link contains additional information on current research.

CSU BIOWEB

http://130.17.2.215/index.html

Consolidates existing WWW biological science teaching and research resources and creates and distributes original multimedia resources for teaching biology. Offers general biology links and short descriptions of the sites as well as the separate category for multimedia sites related to biology, which consist mostly of image databases on the Internet.

CTI Centre for Chemistry Software Catalogue

http://www.liv.ac.uk/ctichem/catmain.html

Lists software you can use in many areas of science, including general science, crystallography, and all areas of chemistry. Covers a wide variety of software types and platforms.

Current Weather Maps/ Movies

http://clunix.cl.msu.edu/weather/

Offers timely JPEG weather maps and MPEG movies of radar motion (also offers a text version).

CyberSky

http://www.astro.ucla.edu/staff/stephen/cybersky.html

CyberSky is a shareware program that you download and run on a 386 or higher PC, running Windows 3.1 or higher.

D Banks— Microengineering/MEMS

http://www.ee.surrey.ac.uk/Personal/D.Banks/ueng.html

Provides information on microengineering. Offers a small collection of tutorials and documents. Focuses on micromachining and the fabrication of structures the size of microns.

Dalton Chemical Laboratories, Inc.

http://www.dalton.com/dalton

Specializes in the synthesis of phosporamidites, oligonucleotides, custom synthesis, and research contracts.

Data Catalog

http://rainbow.ldgo.columbia.edu/datacatalog.html

Presents a catalog of climate-related datasets, with an interface that enables you to make plots, tables, and files from any dataset, its subsets, or processed versions thereof.

Data Modeling Web Site

http://www.fred.net/mandalay/

Offers links to many other sites. Builds custom nonlinear curve-fitting software based on your problem.

The Data Zoo

http://www-ccs.ucsd.edu/ccs/about_datazoo.html

Contains data collected by various California coastal data collection programs and studies.

Dave's Math Links

http://www.azstarnet.com/~maxinfo/index.htm

Provides a Mathcad files library, links to math resources on the Web, and image-processing applications.

Defense Meteorological Satellite Program

http://web.ngdc.noaa.gov/dmsp/dmsp.html

Two satellite constellation of near-polar orbiting, sun-synchronous satellites that monitor meteorological, oceanographic, and solar-terrestrial physics environments. Features currently occurring meteorological phenomena.

Desert

http://www.iiasa.ac.at/Research/WAT/docs/desert.html

Offers software program to use PC and Windows to provide "decision support in water quality management on a river basin scale."

Design-By-Example

http://www.uta.fi/~hs/dbe.html

Develops tools for database design and reverse engineering.

Discovery of a Palaeolithic Painted Cave at Vallon— Pont-d'Arc (Ardèche)

http://www.culture.fr/culture/gvpda-en.htm

Presents recently discovered ancient cave paintings from the south of France, created during the last ice-age, which makes them between 17,000 and 20,000 years old.

Discovery Program Home Page

http://mercury.hq.nasa.gov/office/discovery/

Contains information about the different missions that NASA hopes to undertake.

Dynamical Systems and Technology Project

http://math.bu.edu/DYSYS/dysys.html

Provides information on contemporary mathematics, such as fractals and chaos. Includes computer demos, as well as movies on some famous fractal sets.

e-Math Home Page

http://www.ams.org/

Home of the American Mathematical Society. Offers professional memberships. Publishes electronic journals, books on math, and the fee-based MathSci database, which features comprehensive coverage of research in mathematics, computer science, and statistics. Also provides information about Math Awareness Week 1995 and good jumps to other math sites.

Earth Sciences and Resources Institute

http://www.esri.utah.edu

Focuses on university-based research applied to fossil fuel, mineral, geothermal, and environmental assessment. Presents an electronic brochure about the Institute. Also offers links to energy/environmental/mineral/geothermal relevant reference sites. Includes a photo and quote of the week.

Earth Viewer

http://www.fourmilab.ch/earthview/vplanet.html

Enables you to use the Earth Viewer online mapping tool to see Earth from above by setting specifications such as longitude and latitude, look at satellite imagery, composite the image with cloud cover, and much more. Presents the Solar System Live, which shows the locations of the planets at any time. Also presents Terranova, a series of images of hypothetical planets created each day.

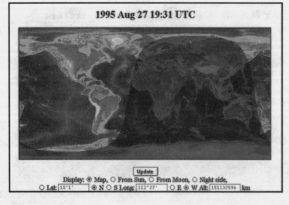

Earth Watch Communications, Inc.

http://www.earthwatch.com/

Contains many images of 3-D satellite views from space. Also plugs its 3-D software package that integrates 3-D weather visualization with a global database to create a virtual world.

Earthquake Info from the U.S.G.S.

http://quake.wr.usgs.gov/

Provides earthquake information. Includes plots, news, regional studies, maps, and references.

The Ebola Page

http://ichiban.objarts.com/ebola/ebola.html

Claims to be "the most complete source of information about Ebola on the Net." Contains breaking news about the deadly African virus. Offers links to other sites, graphics, and hypotheses about the disease and its origins. Presents a chronology of events related to the ongoing crisis, each linked to a media or governmental source and updated daily.

Eckerd College Natural Sciences Summer Research

http://www.wta.com/eckerd/

Summarizes research activities this summer in the Natural Sciences department at Eckerd College.

EcoLink

http://www.medium.com/wendee/EcoLink

Online eco-web journal. Delves into one ecological topic each week, including real-life stories, photos, and scientific information. Offers links to related Net resources.

Eisenhower National Clearinghouse DCL

http://www.enc.org/

Supports improving teaching and learning in math and science in secondary school. Offers links to other Internet resources. Presents online catalog and databases, as well as a collection of Internet software and information.

El Nino Theme Page

http://www.pmel.noaa.gov/toga-tao/el-nino/home.html

Explains El Nino (frequently referred to on oceanography pages), a disruption of the ocean-atmosphere system in the tropical Pacific that affects weather around the globe.

Electronic Desktop Project Home Page

http://vflylab.calstatela.edu/Welcome.html

Focuses on improving the way science is taught and learned by bringing the power of advanced workstation technology to introductory science students in both major and general education classes. Details some of EDP's projects and offers links to interactive demonstrations.

The Electronic Textbook: Integrated Course in Chemistry, Mathematics, and Physics

http://dept.physics.upenn.edu/courses/gladney/mathphys/Contents.html

Contains information in the areas of trigonomics, velocity, acceleration, Newton's Laws, chaotic systems, and more.

Electronic Visualization Lab

http://www.ncsa.uiuc.edu/EVL/docs/html/homePage.html

Merges art, computers, and science in electronic visualization. Contains visualization projects as well as student home pages that display visualizations.

Electronic Zoo

http://netvet.wustl.edu/e-zoo.html

Contains information about animals and animal-related resources. Offers many links to information on nearly any animal.

EMF-Link

http://infoventures.com

Serves as a resource on biological effects of electric and magnetic fields for the general public and professionals. Contains key documents, resources, and literature for those interested in possible health effects from power lines, computer monitors, magnetic resonance imaging equipment, radio communications, cellular telephones, radar, microwave transmissions, and other sources.

Environmental Chemical Corporation

http://w3.one.net/~webcon/clients/environ/html/index.html

Deals with safety solvents, industrial cleaning, biological products, maintenance supplies, equipment cleaning, truck wash, sewage treatment, degreasers, disinfectant, food processing chemicals, food service, drain maintenance, HVAC, heating ventilation and air conditioning, vehicle

maintenance, vehicle cleaning, printing industry, de-icers, and odor control, among other things, as partners for a cleaner, safer environment.

European Software Institute (ESI)

http://www.esi.es/

Provides information about Europe's movement toward improving the competitiveness of the European software industry. Includes training information, a list of upcoming events, and new improvements to their server.

Exploratorium

http://www.exploratorium.edu

Provides this interactive science museum's exhibits, workshops, projects, programs, events, and schedules. Includes a quarterly magazine, gifts, learning publication tools and resources, and images and sounds.

Explorer Home Page

http://unite.ukans.edu/

Provides access to thousands of science and math documents, lesson plans, and software for use in educational settings. Provides information about each item before you download as well as how they fit into curriculum goals.

The Face of Venus Home Page

http://stoner.eps.mcgill.ca/bud/first.html

Offers an interactive tour of the surface of Venus.

Federal Aviation Regulations

http://acro.harvard.edu/GA/fars.html

Furnishes searchable database of FAA regulations.

A Fine Kettle of Fish

http://muse.bio.cornell.edu/cgi-bin/hl?fish

Enables the user to query online fish databases, find out about endangered fishes, and link to other fish resources on the Internet. Includes a database that returns information and maps of the location's of different species.

The First General Aviation WWW Server

http://aviation.jsc.nasa.gov/

Offers a resource on aviation. Provides information about learning to fly, piloting tips, model airplanes, simulator information, FAA information, and other aviation-related items.

Flicks of FLI Files Of Mathematical Models

http://www.infi.net/~rbduncan/

Offers a collection of FLI and GIF files that illustrate mathematatical models using computer graphics.

The Florida Center for Environmental Studies' Home Page

http://www.fau.edu/divdept/ces/homeg1.htm

Provides environmental resources concerning the management of Florida ecosystems and other tropical and subtropical water dominated freshwater and estuarine ecosystems worldwide.

fracintro.html

http://www.uckland.ac.nz./arch/pdbourke/fractals/fracintro.html

Provides introductory information about fractals. Includes strange attractors, chaotic systems, fractal landscapes, and more. Also offers a list of online references.

Fractal Gallery

http://eulero.cineca.it/~strumia/FractalGallery.htm

Presents downloadable color fractal images that show different mathematics problems. Includes the Curve of Von Koch, the Mandelbot Set, and trees, ferns, and mountains.

Fractal Image Compression

http://inls.ucsd.edu/y/Fractals

Contains links and information regarding fractal image compression. Offers an online bibliography, book reviews, conference announcements, and papers.

The Fractal Microscope

http://www.ncsa.uiuc.edu/Edu/Fractal/Fractal_Home.html

Provides information on basic fractals, why they should be discussed, their purposes in the real world, and why supercomputers are necessary for fractals.

The Fractals Calendar Home Page

http://fas.sfu.ca/O/cs/research/projects/FractalCal/cal.html

Provides information on obtaining the Fractal Calendar, a calendar specifically designed to show off some of the newer discoveries in fractal mathematics. Also offers previous editions of the calendar.

Fractals Frequently Asked Questions and Answers

http://www.marshall.edu/~stepp/fractal-faq/faq.html

Contains all of the frequently asked questions (FAQ) about fractals.

Fraunhofer Institut for Materials Physics and Surface Engineering

http://www.iws.fhg.de/ext/iwseng.htm

Focuses on basic and applied research for surface processing of materials and components by means of laser and other high-power energy sources.

Frequently Asked Questions about Parapsychology

http://eeyore.lv-hrc.nevada.edu/~cogno/para1.html

Attempts to explain the current thinking about parapsychology from a scientific point of view. Includes discussions of ESP, ghosts, channeling, and a review of the criticisms.

The Froggy Page

http://www.cs.yale.edu/homes/sjl/froggy.html

Offers links to frog resources on the Internet. Includes links to frog sounds (including the Budweiser frogs), frogs in fairy tales, rewritten frog songs, famous frogs, and scientific information.

Future Graph, Inc. Home Page

http://www.futuregraph.com/

Offers many links to math-related sites.

GAMS:Guide to Available Mathematical Software

http://gams.nist.gov/

Gateway to NIST guide to available mathematical software. Allows searching by package name or, more interestingly, by what problem it solves

Gardening List WWW

http://www.cog.brown.edu/gardening/

Offers resources concerning gardening. Cyndi's Catalog of Catalogs provides information on obtaining catalogs. Also provides several gardening articles.

GDB Human Genome Database

http://gdbwww.gdb.org/

Supports biomedical research, clinical practice, and professional and scientific education by providing human gene mapping information. Includes DNA sequences for genes.

Ge210: Earthquakes, Volcanoes, and Other Hazards

http://wombat.princeton.edu/Ge210/welcome.html

Contains links to images (volcanoes, oceans, earthquakes, and seismic graphs), a glossary, lecture and lab notes, and geology information on the Internet.

General Astronomy Information on the World Wide Web

http://heasarc.gsfc.nasa.gov/docs/www_info/genastro.html

Provides general information on astronomy.

GenoBase Database Gateway

http://specter.dcrt.nih.gov:8004/

Allows you to search the NIH copy of GenoBase for biological data.

Geographic Nameserver

http://www.mit.edu:8001/geo

Provides geographic information about the location—including: county, state, country, population, area code, latitude, longitude, and elevation—when you enter a city name.

Giovanni Guglielmo's Research Page on Salt Tectonics

http://www.utexas.edu/research/beg/giovanni

Contains free computer animations, 3-D visualization, and interpretations of physical and finite element models of salt tectonics.

Global Network News Weather Page

http://nearnet.gnn.com/gnn/news/weather.html

Lists six major links to weather information on the Web, including the University of Michigan Weather Underground and the Weather Machine at the University of Illinois.

GLOBEC Information

http://www.ccpo.odu.edu/globec_menu.html

Designed to be a collaborative effort between physicists, biologists, and chemists. Attempts to more rapidly further research on oceanography through collaboration (made possible by Internet technology, including this Website).

Gnuplot

http://www.cs.dartmouth.edu/gnuplot_info.html

Supplies downloadable command-line driven plotting utility for Unix, DOS, and VMS.

Great Canadian Scientists

http://fas.sfu.ca/css/gcs/main.html

Presents a collection of material on Canadian scientists and science. Includes biographies of several scientists, descriptions of their greatest claims to fame, and activities. Presents an interactive quiz that tests knowledge and guides users around the site looking for answers. Also includes images and text.

Greenspan Technology

http://peg.pegasus.oz.au/~greenspan/

Specializes in leading-edge water quality monitoring technology for the water resources, environmental, and pollution markets. Offers services ranging from the deployment of single water quality sensors, installation of sophisticated multiparameter monitors, to project management of major hydrological studies worldwide.

A Guide to Math Resources

http://www.ama.caltech.edu/resources.html

Offers resource jump list to various math resources, including the Latex, Tex, and Maple packages. Also contains jumps to math-related Gopher sites, newsgroups, math institues, and a math software index.

Gulf Of St. Lawrence Microfossil Catalogue

http://www.cs.uwindsor.ca/meta-index/mcat/html-docs/woop.html

Contains searchable database of microfossil images.

The Health and Retirement Study (HRS)

http://www.umich.edu/~hrswww

Studies retirement and the aging of society.

The Heart: A Virtual Exploration

http://sln.fi.edu/TOC.biosci.html

Provides information suitable to elementary aged children on virtually every aspect of the cardiopulmonary system, including structure, function, and care. Includes downloadable information on everything from listening to heart murmurs to watching open heart surgery. Offers a few activities designed for the classroom to help children understand heart function and care.

The HEASARC Video Archive

http://heasarc.gsfc.nasa.gov/docs/heasarc/videos/
videos.html

Contains a directory of video clips that highlight high-energy astrophysics missions (in various formats).

Helicopter World

http://www.cs.umu.se/~dvamoa/heli.html

Provides information about helicopters. Includes a picture archive, a history of helicopters, information on schools, and technological information. Also includes a noteboard that visitors can read and respond to.

The Henrietta Leavitt Flat Screen Space Theater

http://ucsu.colorado.edu/~peterscc/Home.html

Explores astronomy topics in a planetarium-show style, designed to present astronomy to a wide variety of readers.

High Energy Astrophysics Science Archive Research Center

http://heasarc.gsfc.nasa.gov/docs/HEASARC_HOME_PAGE.html

Contains general information on supernovae, x-ray binaries, and black holes.

History of Mathematics

http://www-groups.dcs.st-and.ac.uk:80/~history/

Contains biographies of mathematicians, searchable by alphabetical or chronological index (and some include pictures).

Honolulu Community College Dinosaur Exhibit

http://www.hcc.hawaii.edu/dinos/dinos.1.html

Offers a free and permanent exhibit of dinosaur fossils for public viewing. Includes an audio narrative on each page.

Horizon Scientific Press: Molecular Biology Books

http://www.apollo.co.uk/a/horizon

A resource for books in molecular biology and microbiology. Contains useful links to other sites of interest to molecular biologists.

How Far Is It?

http://gs213.sp.cs.cmu.edu/prog/dist/

Allows you to enter two names and see basic information on both places. Also offers a link to a map that shows both places.

Hubble Space Telescope's Greatest Hits 1990–1995

http://www.stsci.edu/pubinfo/BestOfHST95.html

Houses the best images from the Hubble Space Telescope over the past five years.

Humans in Space

http://medlib.jsc.nasa.gov/intro/humans.html

Provides information on physiological needs, spacecraft systems, and general information about humans living in space.

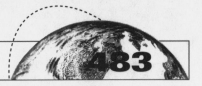

The Hyena Pages

http://www.csulb.edu/~persepha/hyena.html

Offers information, including frequently asked questions about hyenas, especially spotted hyenas.

HyperSpace at UBC

http://axion.physics.ubc.ca/hyperspace/

Contains articles related to gravity and relativity, current news on relativity, job listings, and conference information, among other information.

IEEE Home Page

http://www.ieee.org/

Provides information about new publications, joining the organization, job listings, student activities, a searchable database, and more.

IFIAS

http://www.ifias.ca

A global network of scientific research institutions that collaborate on projects relating to science, technology and innovation policy, ecosystem management, gender science and development, the implications of the human genome project for developing countries, and the international system of science.

IMA WWW Server

http://www.ima.umn.edu/

Institute for Mathematics and its Applications. Provides the newsletter and back issues of the newsletters of this professional organization.

IMSA Home Page

http://www.imsa.edu/

Provides information about the Illinois Mathematics and Science Academy, a residential public high school for students talented in the fields of math and science.

Information Leaflets

http://www.ast.cam.ac.uk/RGO/leaflets/

Lists online explanations of a variety of astronomy-related topics.

Infrastructure Technology Institute (ITI)

http://iti.acns.nwu.edu/

Provides information about current research, technology transfer, and education regarding America's infrastructure.

Institute for Space Astrophysics C.N.R.

http://titan.ias.fra.cnr.it/ias-home/ias-home.html

Offer some links in Italian but the majority in English. Includes the "Electronic Atlas of Dynamical Evolutions of Short-Period Comets."

The Institute for Work and Health

http://www.iwh.on.ca/home.htm

Ontario-based research, quality improvement, and education organization. Researches the underlying factors of workplace health and disability, evaluates designated Ontario rehabilitation facilities, and provides pertinent and timely information on workplace health and rehabilitation to health care workers and stakeholders through education products and workshops.

Institution of Electrical Engineers Home Page

http://www.iee.org.uk/

Provides information about membership in the Institution of Electrical Engineers, upcoming events, information services (including searchable databases), and a collection of links to other Internet resources.

Intellicast

http://www.intellicast.com/

Serves as guide to weather, ski reports, and ocean conditions. Provides information for weather novices and professionals.

Interactive Marine Observations

http://thunder.met.fsu.edu/~nws/buoy/

Gives access to meteorological and oceanographic data being reported by buoys and CMAN stations in the Atlantic, United States, and Pacific. Reloads automatically every two minutes if you have Netscape.

The Interactive Physics Problem Set

http://info.itp.berkeley.edu/Vol1/Contents.html

Contains almost 100 practice problems accompanied by detailed solutions and interactive computer experiments.

Interactive Weather Browser

http://rs560.cl.msu.edu/weather/interactive.html

Provides the capability to type any city's station ID and receive up-to-the-minute conditions. Also enables you to build a weather map, checking off only the options you want to include on the surface map.

Intercall

http://www.maths.monash.edu.au/people/tdr/welcome.html

Lets you import code into Mathematica. Gives users a way to organize and use Mathematica Notebooks. Also displays graphics rendered in Mathematica.

Interface Science Western

http://www.uwo.ca/isw/

Group of researchers from the Physics and Chemistry departments of the University of Western Ontario. Collaborates on a variety of experimental studies involving surfaces, interfaces, and thin films.

International Astronomical Union

http://www.lsw.uni-heidelberg.de/iau.html

Contains access to current and past bulletins as well as reports posted by association members.

The International Occultation Timing Association (I.O.T.A.) Home Page

http://www.sky.net/~robinson/iota.htm

Specializes in organizing reliable ways to view occultations and eclipses. Provides information on how nonmembers can become involved. Offers a list of members' addresses to help you locate a member near you who would be willing to help you properly view occultations and eclipses.

International Weather Watchers Official Home Page

http://groundhog.sprl.umich.edu/IWW/

Nonprofit group of weather enthusiasts. Includes information about the group, links to weather-related information, and an offer to receive a free bulletin the group puts out.

Internet Center for Mathematics Problems

http://www.mathpro.com/math/mathCenter.html

Attempts to identify and list all sources of math puzzles on the Internet. Lists problems from back issues of the *Missouri Journal of Mathematical Sciences* and the *Fibonacci Quarterly* and contains information about other sources of math puzzlers such as newsgroups and books.

An Introduction to Molecular Virology

http://www.uct.ac.za/microbiology/virtut1.html

Multimedia tutorial published by the University of Cape Town. Overviews the school.

Inventor's Resources

http://www.cashflow.com/database

Provides database of 8,700 manufacturers and marketing companies in the U.S. that have indicated an interest in reviewing new products.

Invertebrate and Vertebrate Paleontology Type Collection

http://www.flmnh.ufl.edu/databases/

Offers searchable database of information on various specimens by type.

Ionia "1 km AVHRR Global Land Data Set" Net-Browser

http://shark1.esrin.esa.it/

Presents a collection of 14,413 digital satellite images used to create the first comprehensive photographic map of the Earth.

ISB Working Group on Footwear Biomechanics

http://www.teleport.com/~biomech/sneakers.html

Organization of biomechanics experts who study footwear for sports and other functional applications. Includes information on the organization and abstracts of papers.

Jean-Marie Vaneskahian's Physics Home Page

http://www.fiu.edu/~jvanes01

Offers physics-realted links and software, including Net software.

Lawrence Livermore National Laboratory

http://www.llnl.gov/

Provides information about the laboratory and its research projects as well as links to other sites of general interest. Specializes in the study of nuclear, ecological, and bioscience topics.

The Laws List

http://www.spies.com/laws/

Online dictionary of physics terms and ideas. Covers laws, rules, principles, effects, paradoxes, limits, constants, experiments, and thought-experiments in physics.

List of Oceanography Resources

http://www.esdim.noaa.gov/ocean_page.html

Lists oceanography Web sites. Contains a listing of the major NOAA Web sites and links to some of the better Web sites of educational institutions.

A Listing of Physics Resources on the World Wide Web

http://aip.org/aip/physres.html

Lists various types of physics resources currently available on the Web.

Livermore Labs Atmospheric Research

http://www-ep.es.llnl.gov/www-ep/atm.html

Provides technical information with research on global and regional climate change, atmospheric physics and chemistry, biogeochemical cycles of anthropogenic gases and aerosols, cloud physics, and real-time modeling of the transport of contaminants in the atmosphere.

LLNL Biology and Biotechnology Research Program

http://www-bio.llnl.gov/bbrp/bbrp.homepage.html

Introduces you to the Lawrence Livermore National Laboratory's Biology and Biotechnology Research Program

(BBRP). Provides information related to their research projects in the areas of the human genome project, DNA repair, x-ray crystallography, and more.

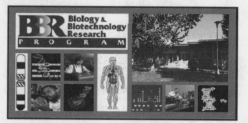

Logal Software Home Page

http://www.logal.com/

Develops and markets math software for middle school through college.

London & Middlesex Archaeological Society (UK)

http://orca.unl.ac.uk/lamas/

Provides a set of pages that examine the activities of the London and Middlesex Archaeological Society (LAMAS) and those of other heritage organizations in the area. Includes listings of lectures, conferences, new publications, and so on. Offers a comprehensive set of links to other WWW sites of interest to the archaeologist. Also presents the online version of the *Directory of British Archaeology*, which lists every known archaeological body in the United Kingdom.

The Long Duration Exposure Facility

http://setas-www.larc.nasa.gov/setas/ldef.html

Describes the LDEF satellite, which contained 57 experiments and spent 69 months in space. Provides the baseline on space environments and their effects.

Los Alamos Group XTM Home Page

http://www-xdiv.lanl.gov/XTM/

Supports X-Division's mission by developing state-of-the-art computational tools to investigate and solve complex problems in radiation hydrodynamics and transport. Applies these tools to problems that are important to the nation's security and well-being.

Los Alamos National Laboratory

http://www.lanl.gov/

Contains a library of information about and generated by this government laboratory.

Main Menu

http://www.sptimes.com/aquarium/default.html

Provides information (text and pictures) about the marine habitat and all the life in it. Includes a "Hands-On" section, which gives lots of marine-related experiments and lists the appropriate grade level for each.

Main Menu

http://curry.edschool.Virginia.edu:80/~insttech/frog/menu.html

Interactive frog dissection. Uses scanned video images to show frogs and leads you through the dissection process, including text instructions as well as downloadable QuickTime movies with audio tracks that tell you how to properly dissect a frog.

The Marine Biological Laboratory

http://alopias.mbl.edu/Default.html

Contains basic information about the Woods Hole Oceanographic Institution and laboratory and its research. Includes the MBL/WHOI library.

Math Teaching Assistant

http://www.csun.edu/~vcact00g/math.html

Contains a math tutoring program developed for classroom computer labs aimed at secondary school students.

Mathematica World

http://www.vut.edu.au/MW/

Electronic distribution center and support center for various math-related newsletters, most of which are based on Mathematica software.

Mathematics Archives WWW Server

http://archives.math.utk.edu/

Provides FTP access to shareware and public domain software for teaching math on the college level. Also provides information and software for people interested in math as well as links to secondary school software. Includes considerable information on software.

Mathlab

http://www.scar.utoronto.ca/homes/mathlab/mathlab.html

A mathematics computer lab. Features downloadable undergraduate level courseware (designed to run under Unix and Mathematica) on geometry, graph theory, and complex analysis.

MathSearch—Search a Collection of Mathematical Web Material

http://www.maths.usyd.edu.au:8000/MathSearch.html

Allows you to search a collection of over 19,000 documents on mathematics and statistics servers.

MathSoft Home Page

http://www.mathsoft.com/

Offers technical support, news, and product catalog.

MathSolutions, Inc. Home Page

http://christensen.cybernetics.net/MathSolutions.html

Distributes MathTensor, an add-on for Mathematica that performs tensor analysis. Also provides links to resources and offers papers.

MathSource Home Page

http://www.wri.com/WWWDocs/mathsource/

Provides a collection of downloadable Mathematica packages, notebooks, examples, and programs. Offers list of related Web sites.

MathType Home Page

http://www.mathtype.com/mathtype/

Houses an equation editor for Mac and Windows machines. Offers technical support, registration, and product information.

Mathware Home Page

http://www.xmission.com/~mathware/

Lists software and books.

MathWorks Home Page

http://www.mathworks.com/

Offers MATLAB, a high-end mathematics software package, as well as links to jobs, news, and books. Provides information on the Pentium chip flaw. Also presents products and services and an online copy of the MATLAB newsletter.

Meetings Information

http://www.tms.org

Provides information about materials-related resources and publications. Also offers a list of national or international conferences and seminars on materials engineering.

Mendeleev Communications

http://mc.ioc.ac.ru/mc.htm

International journal of short communications in chemistry, published jointly by The Royal Society of Chemistry and The Russian Academy of Sciences since 1991. Presents preliminary accounts of original and significant work from Russia, other states of the former Soviet Union, and elsewhere.

Michal Wittner's Bookmarks

http://www.lf1.cuni.cz/~wittner/

Includes a collection of links related to biology and medicine; in particular to neuroscience, molecular biology, biocomputing, and human physiology.

Micromath's Home Page

http://www.micromath.com/~mminfo

Develops software for scientists and engineers, primarily for solving equation systems and fitting experimental data. Offers Mac and IBM software. Also offers MMCalc, a downloadable Macintosh desktop utility program (free).

Microworlds: Exploring the Structure of Materials

http://www.lbl.gov/MicroWorlds/

Explores scientific issues being investigated at the Lawrence Berkeley Laboratory in an understandable and fun way. Provides information on research dealing with issues such as light, conductivity, and wetlands.

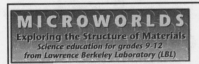

Miscellaneous Meteorological and Environmental Information

http://www.atm.ch.cam.ac.uk/MiscMet.html

Provides weather and earthquake links to Internet resources.

Mission Report: Apollo 13

http://liftoff.msfc.nasa.gov/home/cool/mission-report.html

Contains the story of Apollo 13. Includes images and sound files.

MIT Artificial Intelligence Laboratory

http://www.ai.mit.edu/http://www.ai.mit.edu/

Provides information and publications about MIT's latest work on artificial intelligence, including information on computer vision, humanoid robotics, and artificial muscles.

More Fractal Pictures

http://www.lerc.nasa.gov/Other_Groups/K-12/fracpage.html

Serves as a resource for fractal images that show the concepts of chaos theory (geared to grades K through 12).

Mount Wilson Observatory

http://www.mtwilson.edu/

Overviews several ongoing projects using innovative techniques and modern detectors. Provides information for professionals, amateurs, tourists, and educators.

Nanotechnology

http://nano.xerox.com/nano

Nanotechnology is an expected future manufacturing technology that should enable us to inexpensively build almost any structure consistent with the laws of chemistry and physics with molecular precision.

The Nanoworld Home Page

http://www.uq.oz.au/nanoworld/nanohome.html

Provides links to several resources. Offers database of microscopic images.

The NASA Astrophysics Data System Home Page— Classic System

http://adswww.colorado.edu/adswww/adshomepg.html

Offers free software, developed and operated on behalf of NASA, aimed at the astrophysics community. Provides access to a variety of astronomical data for the scientific user community. Presents a tutorial that allows users to get a taste of the software.

NASA Dryden Flight Research Center

http://www.dfrf.nasa.gov/dryden.html

Provides information about the activities of this research center. Includes a photo archive of research aircraft, research documents, and program information.

NASA Information Services via World Wide Web

http://www.nasa.gov/

Acts as the starting point for all of NASA's Web-based information. Offers links to resources, including space shuttle information, home pages for the NASA centers around the country, space images, and educational resources.

NASA Television on CU-SeeMe

http://btree.lerc.nasa.gov/NASA_TV/NASA_TV.html

Helps visitors learn how to access live images and audio from NASA using CU-SeeMe software. Provides a link for obtaining the CU-SeeMe software.

NASA Weather Archive

ftp://explorer.arc.nasa.gov/pub/Weather/

Provides archive of weather images taken by the space shuttle and NASA satellite systems.

NASA World Wide Web Information Services

http://www.gsfc.nasa.gov/NASA_homepage.html

Contains news and resources of value to a variety of people. Provides scientific information for professionals as well as educational information for teachers and students.

NASA-JSC Digital Image Collection

http://images.jsc.nasa.gov/html/home.htm

Feature more than 9,000 images since the Mercury space program.

National Center for Atmospheric Research

http://www.ucar.edu/

Consists of several scientific divisions and programs working together with member universities on research activities to better understand Earth's climate systems. Includes information on resources, facilities, and services; the research data archives; and weather-related information.

The National Center for Atmospheric Research

http://www.ucar.edu/oceanmodel.html

Presents a high-resolution simulation of the North Atlantic Ocean that represents circulation, designed to show the

utility of some current scientific visualization tools to interpret highly complex data—making these data both meaningful and instructive to the viewer.

National Center for Biotechnology Information

http://www.ncbi.nlm.nih.gov/

Responsible for building, maintaining, and distributing GenBank, the NIH genetic sequence database that collects all known DNA sequences from scientists worldwide. Also provides searchable database for DNA sequences.

National Chipcard Forum

http://www.dds.nl/~ncp/indexe.html

Provides information about smartcards and chipcards on the Net, as well as on the outcome of the forum's studies and projects. Also presents brochures and more.

National Hurricane Center Tropical Prediction Center

http://nhc-hp3.nhc.noaa.gov/index.html

Contains resources for the researcher, advanced student, and hobbyist interested in the latest information on tropical weather conditions, as well as archival information on weather data and maps. Provides links to other NOAA information and satellite data.

National Marine Fisheries Service

http://kingfish.ssp.nmfs.gov/home-page.html

Provides services and products to support domestic and international fisheries management operations, fisheries development, trade and industry assistance activities, enforcement, protected species and habitat conservation operations, and the scientific and technical aspects of

NOAA's marine fisheries program. Offers links to oceanographic information, particularly data concerning fish life.

National Museum of Natural History

http://nmnhwww.si.edu/nmnhweb.html

Provides information about the museum, exhibits, and what a visitor might expect. Contains useful information about various programs and several searchable databases.

National Radio Astronomy Observatory

http://zia.nrao.edu/doc/NRAO.html

Contains information about various radio astronomy labs as well as information on a variety of subjects broken down into the following major categories: telescopes, major initiatives, astronomical tools, and general information.

National Science Foundation

http://www.nsf.gov/

Provides information on government funded efforts to improve science in this country. Also provides information on past and present grant information and presents NSF publications.

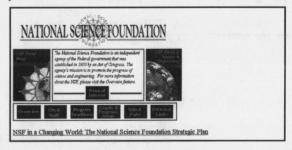

National Severe Storms Laboratory

http://www.nssl.uoknor.edu/

Provides information about the laboratory, including current research and programs. Does not offer specific information on severe weather but does provide links to sites that do. Also includes an extensive list of links to "Web literacy" sites.

National Society Of Black Engineers at SDSU

http://rohan.sdsu.edu/home/nsbe/index.html

Provides information about the organization, links to other chapter home pages, and an assortment of links to other Web sites. Also includes membership information.

National Weather Service

http://www.nws.noaa.gov/

Provides all information output by the NWS, including national and international weather in graphical and textual formats, and information about regional offices. Also offers links to NOAA and other NWS programs.

Nature Described: Learning to Look at the World

http://www.ncsa.uiuc.edu/SDG/Experimental/
vatican.exhibit/exhibit/g-nature/Nature.html

Provides historical data about nature and botany.

Nature Pictures

gopher://olt.et.tudelft.nl:1251/11/nature

Contains numerous images of animals and natural landscapes.

NCSA Relativity Group

http://jean-luc.ncsa.uiuc.edu/

Provides software tools, original documents (on black holes, cosmology, hydrodynamics, and so on), scientific movies, multimedia exhibits, and visualization projects.

NEMO—Oceanographic Data Server

http://nemo.ucsd.edu/

Provides a collection of data sets for physical oceanographers. Offers many holdings only to local users. Offers information on shore temperature and winds to all users.

Netlib Repository at UTK/ORNL

http://www.netlib.org/

Contains a large number of downloadable math-related programs (most of the software is shareware). Contains papers about different research on mathematical topics, many of which involve computers. Also offers links to other math-related databases.

NetVet Veterinary Resources

http://netvet.wustl.edu/

Provides information related to veterinary medicine. Offers the Electronic Zoo, a large collection of animal-related computer resources.

NetVet Veterinary Resources and the Electronic Zoo

http://netvet.wustl.edu/

Provides lists for animal resources. Includes links organized by animal (cats, dogs, insects, and so forth), electronic publications, legislation, organizations, biology, and medicine.

Neurosciences on the Internet

http://www.lm.com/~nab

Lists sites suggested as starting points for exploring neuroscience. Also lists some essential biological and medical resource sites and some World Wide Web sites invaluable for any type of information retrieval.

Nevada Bureau of Mines and Geology

http://www.nbmg.unr.edu

Conducts research and publishes results of the studies for the general public as well as geologic and minerals specialists.

New Mexico Bureau of Mines and Mineral Resources

http://nmt.edu/~nmbmmr/homepage.html

Provides a database of mineral images from New Mexico as well as a geologic map.

Niel's Timelines and Scales of Measurement List

http://xalph.ast.cam.ac.uk/public/niel/scales.html

Provides information in the areas of evolutionary time, geological time, scales of measurement, and so forth.

The NIH Guide to Molecular Modeling

http://www.nih.gov/molecular_modeling/gateway.html

Features information on modeling, software, and images.

The Nine Planets

http://seds.lpl.arizona.edu/billa/tnp/nineplanets.html

An online textbook about the nine planets and their moons. Contains basic factual information. Presents a multimedia tour of the solar system; an essay about the solar system using text, pictures, sounds; and an occasional movie. Describes each of the planets and major moons briefly and illustrates them using pictures from NASA spacecraft.

NOAA Coastal & Estuarine Oceanography Branch

http://www-ceob.nos.noaa.gov/

Contains information on the physics of coastal waterways and the movement of the waters and the causes of those movements.

NOAA Home Page

http://www.noaa.gov

Provides information about National Oceanic and Atmospheric Administration (NOAA) research, current weather information, and links to all other NOAA projects. Also includes latest news involving NOAA and the NOAA mission statement. Includes information about seasonal forecasts, fisheries, protected species, coastal ecosystems, and navigation.

NOAA Paleoclimatology Program

http://www.ngdc.noaa.gov/paleo/paleo.html

Includes searchable databases on climate modeling, ice cores, paleoceanographic, paleovegetation, tree-ring, and other data. Provides alternate search engines for users who cannot use tables.

Nondestructive Testing Information Analysis Center Home Page

http://www.dtic.dla.mil/iac/ntiac/ntiachome.html

Contains current and past issues of the *NTIAC Newsletter*, calendars of events, calls for papers, NDE book reviews, cross links to other NDE sites, and other information.

The North West Artificial Intelligence Applications Group

http://www.airtime.co.uk/NWAIAG/Welcome.html

Promotes the application of artificial intelligence.

Northridge Earthquake Simulation Using Tres3D with Recursive Grid Refinement

http://www.scubed.com/products/Tres3D.northridge.html

Contains movies, graphics, audio, and background information on the January 17, 1994 Northridge earthquake.

NRC Biotechnology Research Institute

http://www.bri.nrc.ca/irbgenen.html

Provides information about the Biotechnology Research Institute (BRI) of the National Research Council of Canada. BRI has more than 400 specialists and state-of-the-art facilities and equipment to perform cutting-edge R&D in biopharmaceuticals, environmental biotechnology, and bioprocess.

NU Student Chapter ASCE

http://pubweb.acns.nwu.edu/~chinners/asce.html

Provides information regarding the American Society of Civil Engineers. Includes information concerning membership, and offers a calendar and information about other chapters.

Nuclear Physics

http://www.riken.go.jp/rarf/np/nplab.html

Contains a catalog of sites pertaining to the field of physics. Contains a variety of links to sites, and an alphabetical listing that consists predominately of links to research centers around the world but that also includes links to a variety of associations.

The Numerical Algorithms Group Ltd.

http://www.nag.co.uk:70/

Produces numerical, symbolic, statistical, and visualization software for science, engineering, financial analysis, and research.

Nye Labs

http://www.seanet.com/Vendors/billnye/nyelabs.html

Houses PBS's Bill Nye the Science Guy. Serves as a place for students to learn science and have fun at the same time. Includes a set of links to science on the Web, show listings, and activities to do at home.

Ocean Planet Home Page

http://seawifs.gsfc.nasa.gov/ocean_planet.html

Presents an online version of an exhibition at the Smithsonian Institution's National Museum of Natural History. Also contains many resources.

Threatened Habitats: Intertidal Zones

Intertidal zones may support as many as two thousand species, but these interfaces between land and sea are in jeopardy from coastal development, land-based runoff, and ocean pollution.

photo © by Art Wolfe

Oceanography Links: Oceanography on the World Wide Web

http://www.ocgy.ubc.ca/oceanography.links.html

Lists Web sites dealing with the field of oceanography. There are sublistings of educational and government institutions as well as listings of other online resources such as images, project descriptions, and research articles.

The Oceanography Society

http://www.tos.org/

Offers general membership information. Maintains a news posting system. Covers a wide variety of topics ranging from highly scientific issues to elementary level oceanography education under the "News System" heading.

Olivetti Research Laboratory

http://www.cam-orl.co.uk/index.html

Contains research reports on various activities of the Lab in the area of computer multimedia architecture, gestural input, face recognition, and so on. Also of interest is the link to "The World Right Now," which shows live outdoor images from different parts of the world. Also available in Italian.

On Being a Scientist: Responsible Conduct in Research

http://xerxes.nas.edu:70/1/nap/online/obas

Presents a publication that addresses issues relevant to being a responsible scientist and researcher. Covers issues such as values, experimental technique, authorship practices, and the scientist in society.

On Board STS-70

http://shuttle.nasa.gov/

Provides data about the current space shuttle mission. Includes images, schedules, mission information, video clips, technical information. Lets you access status reports for every day for the last two years, including things to be done, concerns, and activities undertaken that day.

Online Earth Science Journals

http://www.glg.ed.ac.uk/~ajsw/doc/journals_FAQ.html

Lists online resources for earth science.

Online Image Archiver

http://www.maths.tcd.ie/pub/images/images.html

Presents math-related images, such as Mobius strips and Kleinband.

Online Resources for Groundwater Studies

http://vsc.washington.edu/resources/journals.html

List online resources for groundwater studies.

Parallel Ocean Program (POP) Simulation

http://dubhe.cc.nps.navy.mil/~braccio/

Simulates the global ocean circulation. Covers research being conducted by scientists at Los Alamos National Laboratory and the Naval Postgraduate School. Contains an array of images as well as MPEG movies.

The Pathfinder Cafe

http://satori.gso.uri.edu/archive/images.html

Contains more than 28,000 images. Serves as resource for finding oceanography images. Provides an interface for acquiring and viewing Pathfinder images.

Periodic Table of the Elements

http://www-c8.lanl.gov/infosys/html/periodic/periodic-main.html

Contains a periodic table from which you can select an element and get more information, including atomic number, weight, electrons, and a history of its discovery.

Periodic Table of the Elements: WebElements

http://ripple.bu.edu/Gavin/PeriodicTable/web-elements-home.html

Contains a periodic table from which you can select an element and get more information, including atomic number, weight, electrons, radii, nuclear charge, temperatures, and other highly specific information.

Physical Science

http://www-sci.lib.uci.edu/SEP/physical.html

Offers links of science resources on the Web, indexed according to California curriculum guidelines.

Physics and Space Technology Directorate

http://www-phys.llnl.gov/

Provides information on physics—particularly physics pertaining to space technology.

Physics around the World

http://www.physics.mcgill.ca/physics-services/

Provides a catalog of physics and related resources on the Web. Includes all major fields in physics, science education, history of science, physical constants, laws, data and tables, journals, software, and more. Also includes bulletin boards for summer schools and workshops and for buying and selling used instruments and equipment.

Physics Demonstrations at UC Berkeley

http://www.mip.berkeley.edu/physics/physics.html

Demonstrations for the subjects of mechanics, waves, heat and matter, electricity, magnetism, and optics.

Physics Education Group, Kansas State University

http://bluegiant.phys.ksu.edu/

Focuses on research and development in physics learning with emphasis on applications and technology and quantum physics.

Physics News

http://www.het.brown.edu/news/index.html

Contains up-to-date information on current events in the world of physics. Offers a listing of various online publications and resource sites.

Physics Problems

`http://zebu.uoregon.edu/~dmason/probs/probm.html`

Contains more than 30 problems in basic concepts, mechanics, and thermal physics.

Physics Problems

Physics Servers and Services around the World

`http://www.physics.mcgill.ca/deptdocs/physics_services.html`

Serves as a starting place to find physics resources on the Internet. Includes links to academic institutions, organizations, documents, and mailing lists.

Physics Unbound

`http://uptown.turnpike.net/L/lindeman/physics_ub.html`

Contains collection of texts about issues and topics in physics. Encourages readers to add to the wealth of knowledge already present.

Physics World Electronic News

`http://www.ioppublishing.com/PWEN/pwenwelcome.html`

An online newsletter. Allows subscribers to receive e-mail that provides an up-to-date account of news in the field of physics.

The Planetary Society Home Page

`http://wea.mankato.mn.us:80/tps/`

Encourages the exploration of the solar system and the search for extraterrestrial life. Provides information about organization projects, urgent space news, activities for the classroom, and links to information on the Internet.

WELCOME TO THE PLANETARY SOCIETY!

The Planetary Society
65 North Catalina Avenue
Pasadena, CA 91106-2301
voice: (818) 793-5100
fax: (818) 793-5528
e-mail: tps@genie.geis.com

Point Source Ltd.

`http://www.hpsource.com/psource/html`

Designs and manufactures customized fiberoptic and laser diode systems for the photonics industry. Provides flexible fiberoptic solutions to equipment manufacturers and research establishments throughout the world.

Precision Large-Scale Dimensional Metrology/ Measurement

`http://worldmall.com/et/ethome.htm`

Offers precision large-scale measurement, typically dimensional measurements with .001 inch accuracy.

Principia Consulting Home Page

`http://www.csn.net/princon/`

Offers training on Mathematica; gives Mathematica support; and does custom programming. Lists fees and availability of training. Provides information on fine-tuning performance with Mathematica.

Projects in Scientific Computing

http://pscinfo.psc.edu/MetaCenter/MetaScience/Articles/Contents.html

National Science Foundation Research Center. Online version of the Pittsburgh Supercomputing Center (PSC)'s annual publication. Features current research in various fields, written at a nonspecialist level.

Purdue SEDS (Students for the Exploration and Development of Space)

http://expert.cc.purdue.edu/~puseds

Provides information about the Purdue SEDS group and serves as place to discuss space exploration and development.

Quantum Books Home Page

http://www.shore.net/~quantum/

Online technical bookstore. Specializes in computer topics such as the Internet, programming, and graphics, as well as in books pertaining to mathematics and physics.

Quantum Magazine Home Page

http://www.nsta.org:80/quantum/

Provides information about *Quantum* magazine. Contains primarily physics-related contents, but does include a "toy store" of "mathematical amusements." Includes back issues and a sample.

Rain Forest Action Network Home Page

http://www.ran.org/ran/

Discusses environmental issues of the rain forest. Includes numerous reports, statistics, information on other groups, and lists of companies to boycott. Also presents a children's corner and information about what you can do.

Rainforest Workshop Home Page

http://mh.osd.wednet.edu/

Provides information about the rainforest. Contains many links to Internet resources, including lesson plans, plant and animal information, ecology, and more.

REINAS Instrumentation Tour

http://sapphire.cse.ucsc.edu/MosaicMet/top-view.html

Attempts to create a laboratory for real-time and retrospective meteorological and oceanographic science. Lets you visit each of the REINAS instrument sites scattered around the Monterey Bay area and query the various meteorological and oceanographic instruments at these sites, as well as create real-time plots of recent instrument data.

Reliability Analysis Center (RAC) Home Page

http://www.iitri.com/RAC/

Provides many links to information about reliability engineering. Also provides information on RAC products and offers a large collection of learning resources.

Reliability Analysis Center Web Server

http://www.iitri.com/RAC/

Collects, analyzes, and disseminates data and information to improve the reliability, maintainability, and quality of components and systems. Publishes databooks, standards, procedural manuals, and a quarterly journal. Provides experts for small and large consulting efforts, with many funding mechanisms available for government agencies and contractors. Offers a bibliographic search form and a database of reliability-related software tools, along with descriptions of products and training courses.

SAE at Michigan Tech

http://www.me.mtu.edu/~sae

The Society of Automotive Engineers Student Chapter at Michigan Technological University. Provides information about current projects that focus on redesigning car engines.

Safari Splash

http://oberon.educ.sfu.ca/splash.htm

Links people around the world and in classrooms to students and experts diving in an ocean environment. Features the Safari Touch Tank, in which you click on an image of plants and animals to call up a description, large image, 3D animation, and Webster definition of the item you choose.

San Diego Supercomputer Center

http://www.sdsc.edu

National laboratory for computational science and engineering established in 1985. Advances research and promotes United States economic competitiveness with state-of-the-art computational tools. Features a variety of collaborative research and educational programs, high-performance computational and visualization tools, and a nationally recognized staff.

Sargent Welch Scientific Company

http://www.sargentwelch.com

Lists catalog items and links them to science education references on the Web. Includes MSDS, safety checklist, and other references.

Satellite Oceanography Laboratory

http://satftp.soest.hawaii.edu/

Contains real-time data for meteorology and oceanography, as well as images and archives of publications. Includes video footage and offers the capability to make comments on the site and its contents.

Saxon Publishers, Inc. Home Page

http://www.saxonpub.com/

Presents an online catalog and a math challenge program.

School of Chemistry, Queensland University of Technology

http://www.sci.qut.edu.au/chem/

Provides staff contact information, courses, activities and research profiles, and other items of interest. Also contains pages for the Centre of Instrumental and Developmental Chemistry and the Queensland Branch of the Royal Australian Chemical Institute.

School of Civil Engineering—Curtin Univ., Perth, Western Australia

http://www.cage.curtin.edu.au/civil/links/

Focuses on civil engineering around the world.

School of Zoology, La Trobe University

http://www.zoo.latrobe.edu.au/

Contains a library of downloadable GIF images.

Science and Technology Corporation (STC)

http://www.stcnet.com

Specializes in the atmospheric and environmental sciences.

Science Television

http://www.service.com/stv/

Specializes in producing programs for the professional and educational use of the scientific community. Provides MPEG clips that help visualize complex sets of scientific data.

Scripps Institution of Oceanography Library

http://orpheus.ucsd.edu/sio/inst/index.html

Caters to the information needs of the research and educational activities of Scripps Institution.

Sea Surface Temperature Satellite Images

http://dcz.gso.uri.edu/avhrr-archive/archive.html

Provides access to the University of Rhode Island, Graduate School of Oceanography's archive of sea surface temperature satellite images. Also includes an online lesson plan for teachers who want to incorporate the images into a lesson.

Sea World Animal Information Database

http://www.bev.net/education/SeaWorld/

Provides teachers' guides, visitors' guides, preschool program information, and an "Ask Shamu" page.

DIURNAL BIRDS OF PREY

Sea World/Busch Gardens

http://www.bev.net/education/SeaWorld/homepage.html

Contains several information booklets pertaining to numerous areas of study. Provides kids with information on killer whales, bottlenose dolphins, gorillas, lions, manatees and more in the Animal Information Database. Also tells how to set up an aquarium.

SeaWiFS Project Home Page

http://seawifs.gsfc.nasa.gov/scripts/SEAWIFS.html

Provides access into the background, status, and documentation for NASA's upcoming global ocean color monitoring mission. Offers online documentation on this project, including educational resources.

SEDS Internet Space Warehouse

http://seds.lpl.arizona.edu/

Contains many links to space resources on the Internet, a few multimedia documents, and information about the organization.

Seismological Laboratory

http://www.gps.caltech.edu/seismo/seismo.page.html

Provides many seismology-related resources, including the record of the day, recent earthquake activity, and publications.

SelectSite Ocean Technology

http://www.selectsite.com/oceantech/

Provides pointers to businesses that specialize in ocean technology. Also lists conferences and reference sites, some of which might have something to offer someone doing nonbusiness research.

Sensors and Instrument Technology Planetary Tour Guide

http://ranier.oact.hq.nasa.gov/Sensors_page/Planets.html

Contains links to Web sites that have tours of the planets.

Sky Online Home Page

http://www.skypub.com/

Contains information and a large number of resources. Also contains a regularly updated listing of astronomical events.

Smithsonian Gem and Mineral Collection

http://galaxy.einet.net/images/gems/gems-icons.html

Contains nearly 100 images and short descriptions of gems and minerals.

The Society for Scientific Exploration

http://valley.interact.nl/av/kiosk/SSE/home.html

Explores issues ignored or not studied adequately in the mainstream scientific community. Contains abstracts to some articles published in their journal.

The SocioWeb

http://www.socioweb.com/~markbl/socioweb/

Provides sociological information.

SoftShell Online

http://www.softshell.com

Offers discussions and information on chemistry topics, including electronic publishing, the free ChemWeb GIF structure editor, and other chemistry software (such as ChemWindow and ChemIntosh). Focuses on world-wide access to chemical information. Presents a magazine in which anything can be published. Serves as a resource, a classroom, a library, a bulletin board, and a hangout.

Software Engineering Archives

http://www.qucis.queensu.ca/Software-Engineering/

Provides information regarding software engineering. Offers links to other related information. Includes archives searchable by vendor, category, or name.

Software Reviews from the CTI Centre for Chemistry

http://www.liv.ac.uk/ctichem/swrev.html

Reprints software reviews from the Centre's journal *Software Reviews*. Helps educators and researchers locate appropriate chemistry-related software.

Solar System Live

http://www.fourmilab.ch/solar/solar.html

Allows you to view a model of the solar system. Offers adjustable settings so you can see how the solar system would be at any given time or on any given date.

Southern Cross Astronomical Society

http://www.emi.net/~mike/scas.html

Lets you check out the Southern Cross Astronomical Society.

Space Explorer's Guide

http://nyquist.ee.ualberta.ca/~wanigar/spacelink/space_explorer.html

Contains links to space resources all over the globe by country. Provides information on space news and jobs.

Space Science and Engineering Center (SSEC) Real-Time Data

http://www.ssec.wisc.edu/data/index.html

Includes weather information and ocean temperatures.

Space Settlement

http://www.nas.nasa.gov/NAS/SpaceSettlement/

Provides information on developing orbital space settlements, including who, what, where, when, and how much.

Spie Home Page

http://www.spie.org/

Provides membership information. Lets you order publications online and search publication archives.

SRI's Optical Technology Group

http://aeol-www.sri.com/optics.html

Performs research in optics and related disciplines and applies optical and infrared technologies to practical problems. Includes research in optical oceanography and laser eye and sensor protection.

StarBits—Acronyms, Abbreviations, and More

http://cdsweb.u-strasbg.fr/~heck/sfbits.htm

Furnishes a searchable dictionary/glossary of astronomy acronyms, abbreviations, and so on.

StarWorlds—Astronomy and Related Organizations

http://cdsweb.u-strasbg.fr/~heck/sfworlds.htm

Furnishes a searchable listing of the addresses of organizations, institutions, associations, companies, and so on involved in astronomy and related space sciences.

Statistical Reports on United States Science and Engineering

http://www.nsf.gov/sbe/srs/stats.htm

Includes the education of scientists and engineers, the science and engineering work force, research and development expenditures and performance, science and technology outputs and impacts, and public attitudes on science.

STELAR Project Demos

http://hypatia.gsfc.nasa.gov/stelar/stelar_demos.html

Study of Electronic Literature for Astronomical Research. Explores the use of electronic means for improving access to scientific literature, and using astronomical publications to evaluate distribution, search, and retrieval techniques for full text and graphics display. Contains a listing of hypertext journal articles on astronomy.

Stellwagen Bank Information System

http://vineyard.er.usgs.gov/

Contains information on a variety of subjects.

Steven M. Christensen and Associates, Inc.

http://christensen.cybernetics.net/Christensen/html

Offers scientific computing software. Provides information on MathTensor, Schur, and Mathematica. Also offers consulting, which includes porting software to Sun systems. Offers links to Mathgroup, a Mathematica support group.

The Storm Chaser Home Page

http://taiga.geog.niu.edu/chaser.html

Includes information about storm chasers, a photo gallery of storms, and the latest news about the Storm Chasers group. Also provides information about storm chasing at home, including how to contact the NWS.

Stream Technologies, Inc.

http://www.sti.fi/

Produces and markets advanced object-oriented software tools for multimedia document processing.

A Summary of Personality Typing

http://sunsite.unc.edu/jem/faq-mbti.html

Provides online Myers-Briggs personality test and describes results.

Superplasticity

http://www.mm.mtu.edu/~drjohn/superplasticity.html

Provides information relating to the topic of superplasticity. Offers literature databases, experimental results, and software relating to superplasticity.

Supplements to Atmospheric & Oceanic Publications

http://www-cmpo.mit.edu/met_links/index.html

Provides data sets, source codes, and other supplements to published papers on the Web. Includes the means for visitors to the listing to add their own supplemental material if appropriate.

Systems Realization Laboratory

http://www.srl.gatech.edu/

Develops mechanical design techniques, higher learning, and environmentally friendly designs.

TAMU Oceanography Welcome Page

http://www-ocean.tamu.edu/welcome.html

Contains a variety of information. Includes a section on questions about careers in oceanography. Also offers links to online journals and research articles and resources.

Technology Review Magazine

http://web.mit.edu/techreview/www/

Covers technology and its implications. Addresses the practical applications of science, as opposed to laboratory breakthroughs and theoretical abstractions. Emphasizes policy issues rather than nuts and bolts.

Threatened Fauna in Australia: A Select Bibliography

http://mac-ra26.sci.deakin.edu.au/fauna.html

Provides peferences on Australia's threatened species, conservation, the greenhouse effect, and environmental legislation.

TIGER Mapping Service

http://tiger.census.gov/

Allows you to generate a high-quality, detailed map of anywhere in the United States, using public geographic data.

TMP at Imperial College London

http://othello.ma.ic.ac.uk/

Uses Mathematica to make learning modules for first year university science and engineering students. Provides learning modules for calculus, algebra, matrices, and so on.

Todd's Atomic Home Page

http://www.nuc.berkeley.edu/neutronics/todd.html

Provides a collection of nuclear energy-related resources, ranging from detailed designs of atomic bombs to comprehensive reviews of advanced nuclear reactors.

Topex/Poseidon—The Ocean Topography Experiment

http://topex-www.jpl.nasa.gov/

Cooperative project between the United States and France to develop and operate an advanced satellite system dedicated to observing the Earth's oceans. Contains archives and updates for the project.

Transmath—A CBL Mathematics Tutor

http://caliban.leeds.ac.uk/

Offers mathematics courseware using Toolbook (hypertext) documents with Microsoft Windows. Provides instruction on algebra, matrices, vectors, and sequences.

The Tree of Life

http://phylogeny.arizona.edu/tree/phylogeny.html

Serves as "a map to biological information," a cooperative group of WWW sites on the Internet. Provides information on biology arranged like a phylogenetic tree: the further along you go, the more specific the information becomes.

Tropical Storms

http://milo.ifa.hawaii.edu/Tropical/tropical.html

Displays images of hurricanes from around the world and provides data pertaining to those storms: where they're going, their strength, and more. Also provides numerous links to other related sites, including FAQs and text files.

U.I.A. Freshwater Biology (The Chironomid Home Page)

http://www.uia.ac.be/u/intpanis/index.html

Focuses on chironomidae (nonbiting midges). Provides several bibliographies with scientific papers, lists of colleagues around the world, and more. Also provides the opportunity to ask questions or share general messages.

UAB Thermal and Fluids Engineering Group

http://138.26.80.156/me

Focuses on computational/experimental research related to modeling problems, primarily those involving fluids and heat transfer interactions.

UCF ASET

http://pegasus.cc.ucf.edu/~aset/

Provides information about the Electric Car project and offers a collection of links to student engineering groups and organizations, along with research-related links.

UCSD Optoelectronic Computing Group

http://soliton.ucsd.edu

Researches and develops massively parallel optoelectronic computer systems using the optimal utilization of microelectronic and photonic technologies. Pursues a plan of research that spans the areas of optoelectronic materials and devices, diffractive and micro-optics, nonlinear optics, optical storage technologies, parallel computing algorithms and architectures, including database and neural systems, computer modeling, and optoelectronic packaging.

Understanding Our Planet Through Chemistry

http://helios.cr.usgs.gov/gips/aii-home.htm

Explains the history of the Earth and the chemistry involved in its formation.

UniData Corporation

http://unidata.ucar.edu/

Provides information about UniData's weather-related products and services. Also includes up-to-date meteorological examples of its products and information.

Union Matematica Argentina

http://www.famaf.uncor.edu/uma/

Organizes workshops, talks, and so on, and edits several magazines in mathematics and eduaction.

United Nations Environment Programme (UNEP), Geneva

http://www.unep.ch/

Contains many treaties and programs on preserving the environment. Includes information on topics including the "Convention on Biodiversity," climate change, endangered species, and toxic chemicals.

United States Department of the Interior/Geological Survey/Pacific Marine Geology

http://walrus.wr.usgs.gov/

Contains different resources. Strives to address key marine and coastal issues, increase understanding of geological processes affecting these realms, and ultimately improve predictive capabilities to help guide the preservation and sustainable development of the Nation's marine and coastal regions. Offers links to information on seismic activity, information on the Monteray bay area, and sea floor images. Also features a link to a more graphic intensive version of the site.

United States Gazetteer

http://tiger.census.gov/cgi-bin/gazetteer

Identifies places you can use the Tiger Map Server and the 1990 Census Lookup to view. Lets you search for a place by entering the name and state abbreviation.

United States Geological Survey: Earth and Environmental Science

http://info.er.usgs.gov/network/science/earth/earthquake.html

Offers links to pages about earthquakes, federal emergency management, oceanography, earth science, geology, and more.

United States JGOFS Home Page

http://www1.whoi.edu/

Contains information on current professional programs and studies. Includes current images of the world's major oceans as viewed with satellite technology. Also contains recent oceanography references on the Web.

United States WOCE Home Page

http://www-ocean.tamu.edu/WOCE/uswoce.html

Provides information about the present United States WOCE plans and details the status of current work.

The University of California Museum of Paleontology: Bringing Life's Past and People Together

http://ucmp1.berkeley.edu/

Presents dinosaurs and fossils. Simulates a visit to a real museum of paleontology. Enables you to visit different exhibits to discover fossil images, background data, and geological information.

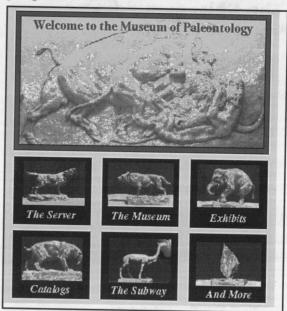

University of Houston Industrial Engineering

http://www.egr.uh.edu/Departments/IE/IJIE/Welcome.html

Provides information on how to contact the editors, the requirements for submissions, subscription information, and highlights of the current issue. Also enables you to search the old issues from 1994 and 1995.

University of Illinois Weather Machine

gopher://wx.atmos.uiuc.edu/1

Provides up-to-the-minute graphical and textual weather information from around the United States. Includes satellite imagery, infrared imagery, and visible shots taken from NOAA satellites. Also includes archives of weather events and links to other weather-related Gopher sites around the world.

University of Illinois— Institute of Aviation Wx Page

http://www.cen.uiuc.edu/~ny4065/aviwx.html

Offers list of several aviation-related images and textual information.

University of Utah Physics Department

http://www.physics.utah.edu

Offers information about undergraduate and graduate degrees in physics and instrumentation. Includes experimental astroparticle physics, relativity theory, high energy particle theory, experimental and theoretical condensed matter physics, and medical physics.

An Unofficial Chemical Engineering Home Page

http://turnpike.net/metro/eng40705/

Describes chemical engineering and offers a collection of links to information about or for chemical engineers.

USC's Mercury Project

http://www.usc.edu/dept/raiders/

The Mercury Project. Involves a tele-garden with which you can view and interact—water the plants, plant more plants, and view the the progress of the garden using the Web and a robotic arm you can control.

Usenet FAQs: Space

http://www.cis.ohio-state.edu/hypertext/faq/usenet/space/top.html

Presents FAQ list of general questions about planetary probes or information about solar system bodies.

UTK Office of Research Administration

http://www.ra.utk.edu/ora/

Promotes and adminsters research and creative programs at the University of Tennessee, Knoxville. Offers information on funding sources, university research policies and procedures, and information about research and creative accomplishments at UTK.

UW Sea Grant Home Page

http://h2o.seagrant.wisc.edu/home.html

"The University of Wisconsin Sea Grant Institute is part of a national network of 29 university-based programs of research, outreach, and education dedicated to the protection and sustainable use of the United States' ocean and Great Lakes resources. UW Sea Grant research and outreach are currently focused on Great Lakes fisheries, toxic contaminants, water quality, aquaculture, seafood

technology, estuarine and coastal processes, policy studies, biotechnology, diving safety, nonindigenous aquatic species, and education."

Vibrant Technology, Inc.

http://www.mlode.com/~vibrant/

Offers a downloadable application demo for a modal analysis system for viewing and analyzing noise and vibration in structures.

Video Vita

http://jaka.eecs.uic.edu/~spiff/videovita/index.html

Produces edutainment products in mathematics, science, and technology. Offers an online video sample.

Views of the Solar System

http://www.c3.lanl.gov/~cjhamil/solarsystem/homepage.html

Offers an educational view of the solar system. Contains images and information about the sun, planets, moons, asteroids, comets, and meteoroids.

Virginia Geotechnical Services

http://www.infi.net/~vageo

Specializes in geotechnical engineering, geoenvironmental services, and construction monitoring. Provides useful information concerning professional consulting, the environment, and business practice.

The Virtual Emu

http://www.vicnet.net.au/vicnet/RAOU/RAOU2WWW.html

A biodiversity and bird conservation group in Australia. Features a library of bird images and listings of threatened birds.

Virtually Hawaii

http://www.satlab.hawaii.edu/space/hawaii/

Provides easy access to Earth and space science data. Focuses on Hawaii. Offers a database of satellite, space shuttle, and aircraft remote sensing images of Hawaii. Enables you to view image navigators for Landsat, Spaceborne Radar, or Aerial photographic images. Also includes a collection of images in oceanography, meteorology, and volcanology.

Virus Databases Online

http://life.anu.edu.au/viruses/welcome.html

Provides links to Internet resources on biological viruses. Includes links to plant and animal viruses, tutorials, genome sequences, and virus news.

VolcanoWorld

http://volcano.und.nodak.edu/

Provides information on volcanos. Includes current news, images and articles about eruptions, background information, and an online expert who answers questions.

Mount Spurr, Alaska

View north of Crater Peak, the active vent of Mount Spurr, Alaska, on 26 September 1992. Crater Peak erupted in June, August, and September 1992. Ash from the August eruption closed Anchorage International Airport. Behind the small steam plume is Mount Spurr. Mt. Spurr and the peak visible on the left define the rim of caldera, evacuated by a huge debris avalanche about 10,000 years ago. Photo courtesy of USGS Cascades Volcano Observatory.

WARP Home

http://www.hia.com/hia/pcr/home.html

Offers a collection of multimedia documents pertaining to various aspects of "alternative" science, including warp technology, fantasy stories of time travel, quantum mechanics, and so on.

Warren Faidley's Storm Chasing Home Page

http://www.indirect.com/www/storm5/

Presents photos of severe weather taken by Warren Faisley, full-time storm chaser.

Waterloo Fractal Compression Page

http://links.uwaterloo.ca/

Provides information on fractal compression software and papers on fractal compression.

Weather and Climate Images

http://grads.iges.org/pix/head.html

Offers short- and medium-range forecasts for North America and current weather maps and climate anomaly models for the rest of the world. Provides a key to the weather maps and a table of weather symbols.

Weather and Global Monitoring

http://life.anu.edu.au/weather.html

Provides pointers to various weather services worldwide.

The Weather Channel

http://www.infi.net/weather/

Includes information about the Weather Channel and also provides novice weather enthusiasts with simple weather maps.

Weather Information Server

http://www.aviation.uiuc.edu/institute/weather.html

Provides weather information.

Weather Net

http://cirrus.sprl.umich.edu/wxnet/

Tries to list every weather-related link on the Internet. Includes not only WWW sites, but ftp sites, gophers, and Telnet sites. Includes commercial sites as well as educational and governmental sites.

Weather Page

http://acro.harvard.edu/GA/weather.html

Lists weather links out of Harvard University. Includes brief descriptions of each link. Also provides links to aviation information.

WeatherBoy's Weather Tools

http://www.cybercom.com/~weather/wx1.html

Lists links to earth science sites. Focuses on weather-related sites.

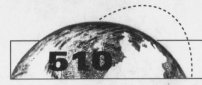

The Web Nebulae

http://seds.lpl.arizona.edu/billa/twn/top.html

Contains a collection of images of various objects in our galaxy. Includes images and explains how to classify nebulae.

The Web Station—New Media Science

http://www.mediascience.no/

Serves Nordic companies and institutions that want to strengthen their position in their markets by using multimedia as one of several business tools.

WebStars: Astrophysics in Cyberspace

http://guinan.gsfc.nasa.gov/WebStars.html

Provides information about astronomy. Contains online journals as well as searchable indexes and listings of other sites.

Welcome to Coastal America's Home Page

http://kingfish.ssp.nmfs.gov/coastamer/coastamer.html

The Coastal America program is a collaborative effort between organizations to protect the ecological systems and wildlife of America's coastal regions. Provides general information on the program itself and placeholders for more specific information yet to come.

Welcome to Internet Directory of Biotechnology Resources

http://biotech.chem.indiana.edu/

Provides information on biotechnology engineering on the Internet.

Welcome to Loch Ness Productions

http://www.entertain.com:80/lochness/

Specializes in producing planetarium program materials. Includes access to samples of planetarium music and art, as well as a listing of planetariums around the world.

Welcome to OCEANIC

http://diu.cms.udel.edu/

Maintains information on World Ocean Circulation Experiment (WOCE), TOGA Coupled Ocean-Atmosphere Response Experiment (TOGA COARE), research ship information and cruise schedules, and other oceanographic information sources.

Welcome to Project CLEA

http://www.gettysburg.edu/project/physics/clea/CLEAhome.html

Contemporary Laboratory Experiences in Astronomy. Contains educational resources that can be used to incorporate astronomy into science curriculum.

Welcome to SkyView

http://skview.gsfc.nasa.gov/skyview.html

Serves as a virtual observatory on the Net that enables visitors to view a generated image of any part of the sky in a variety of wavelengths.

Welcome to the Institute of Physics

`http://www.ioppublishing.com/iopwelcome.html`

Provides information in the field of physics. Restricts use of some items and aspects to registered members only. Users who choose to register can browse text abstracts or download full text versions of any article. To register, you must be a member of a subscribing institution.

Welcome to the Laboratory for Terrestrial Physics

`http://ltpwww.gsfc.nasa.gov/`

Provides information, documents and simulations related to terrestrial physics. Features links to images of various terrestrial phenomena, such as magnetic models of the crust.

Welcome to the Planets

`http://stardust.jpl.nasa.gov/planets/`

Presents collection of photos from NASA, organized by planet and the space craft that took the picture. Also includes textual explanations of the photos.

Wolfram Research; Makers of Mathematica

`http://www.wri.com/`

Provides product information, news releases, a demo, and an electronic library. Also offers a training tour and a graphics and sound gallery.

Woods Hole Oceanographic Institution (WHOI)

`http://www.whoi.edu/index.html`

Contains general oceanographic information. Includes a listing of oceanography Web sites.

Word about the International Oceanographic Foundation

`http://www.rsmas.miami.edu/iof.html`

Explains the mission of the International Oceanographic and contains an excellent definition/explanation of the field of oceanography.

The World Factbook 1994

`http://www.odci.gov/cia/publications/94fact/fb94toc/fb94toc.html`

CIA publication. Contains geographic, government, and demographic information about all the countries in the world. Includes maps.

World Forum for Acoustic Ecology

`http://interact.uoregon.edu/MediaLit/WFAEHomePage`

Seeks to investigate natural and human-made soundscapes. Offers links to sound resources and links to the online discussion forum.

World List of Insect Families

`http://nmnhwww.si.edu/gopher-menus/WorldListofInsectFamilies.html`

Contains a searchable list of insect families around the world.

The World of Soaring

http://www4.ncsu.edu/eos/users/j/jcturner/pub/
soaring.html

Contains links to sailplane information around the world, organized by country.

The World-Wide Web Home Page of the Canadian Astronomy Data Centre (CADC)

http://cadcwww.dao.nrc.ca/CADC-homepage.html

Contains general information on astronomy. Enables users to access programs and full-text copies of articles from several CD-ROMs.

The World-Wide Web Virtual Library: Aerospace

http://macwww.db.erau.edu/www_virtual_lib/aerospace.html

Offers collection of links on aerospace engineering.

The World-Wide Web Virtual Library: Electrical Engineering

http://epims1.gsfc.nasa.gov/engineering/ee.html

Provides links to information useful for electric engineers. Includes links to manufacturers of products and to academic institutions. Also includes announcements of upcoming events.

The World-Wide Web Virtual Library: Industrial Engineering

http://isye.gatech.edu/www-ie/

Provides a collection of links to resources concerning industrial engineering. Includes academic programs, other relevant places, and commercial and professional entities.

The World-Wide Web Virtual Library: Mathematics

http://euclid.math.fsu.edu/Science/math.html

Provides links to all things mathematical. Includes jumps to math software, gophers, newsgroups, electronic journals, preprints, bibliographies, TeX Archives, and high school and university math sites.

The World-Wide Web Virtual Library: Oceanography

http://www.mth.uea.ac.uk/ocean/oceanography.html

Provides links to a variety of Internet resources on oceanography. Offers links to Web resources by geographic area. Links to the "What's New" link, which contains a listing of sites that have recently announced or renovated their Web sites.

The World-Wide Web Virtual Library: Physics

http://www.w3.org/hypertext/DataSources/bySubject/
Physics/Overview.html

Offers a general listing of physics sites. Also contains links to listings of more specific sites on geophysics, astrophysics, nuclear physics, and energy science.

Wormhole Interactive

http://www.intr.net/bertwillco/

Serves both educational and entertaining purposes. Focuses on wormholes.

WWW Archive for Electric Power Engineering Education

http://www.uow.edu.au/public/pwrsysed/homepage.html

Provides resources for electric power educators. Focuses on the Asia-Pacific region. Also provides information about books and software packages.

X-Ray and Gamma-Ray Coefficients

http://www1.usa1.com/~aic/2121.html

Displays graphic presentation of all X-ray and gamma-ray coefficients. Includes links to other nuclear data and a program for calculating shielding and dose deposition.

Xerox PARC Map Viewer

http://www.xerox.com/map

Enables you to click on a region and zoom in to to see more detailed areas. Offers an easy way to generate regional maps of the world.

Yale NMR Research Group

http://mri.med.yale.edu

Concentrates on biomedical magnetic resonance imaging and spectroscopy.

The Young Scientists' Network

http://snorri.chem.washington.edu/ysnarchive/index.html

Tries to help new scientists get established in the scientific community. Presents a newsletter and provides job listings.

Zoological Record

http://www.york.biosis.org/index.htm

Contains links to various zoological resources. Provides an online glossary.

1995 Ryder Cup Matches

http://www.RochesterDandC.com/sports/ryder/rydhome.html

Offers complete coverage of the 1995 Ryder Cup Matches in Rochester, New York.

The 19th Hole

http://www.sport.net

Serves as a place where fans and participants in the sport of golf can gather, share a few stories, and settle a bet or two. Provides Daily Golf News and Almanac sections that let you keep up with the game on a daily basis and an Art section that brings a little laughter and color to your day. Also includes a Classified Ads area.

A1 Horse Breeders and Trading International

http://www.nscnet.com/horse001.htm

Targets horse lovers, breeders, and traders.

Adventure Schools, Inc.

http://jstart.com/kayak/kayak.html

Offers kayaking lessons for people of every ability level and kayaking vacations all over the world.

AFMWeb

http://www.afmracing.org

Focuses on motorcycle roadracing. Offers a New Rider School, practices, and races.

Alberta

http://www.cuug.ab.ca:8001/~mcleods/golf/golf.html

Provides in-depth descriptions of the many golf courses located in and around Alberta.

Alex's Mountain Biking Page

http://www.moscow.com/homepages/greeneg@pixi.com.html

Focuses on biking. Offers links, stories, and pictures.

American Football in Ireland

http://fiachra.ucd.ie:80/~alan/american_football.html

Presents a brief document that describes American football. Also covers the National League, teams, and the current Shamrock Bowl holders—the Dublin Tornadoes.

Arkatents USA—High Quality Camping Accessories

http://www.homepage.com/mall/arkatent/tents.html

Offers a catalog of camping accessories and tents.

Aro-Tek LTD.

http://coolworld.com/Outdoor/aro-tek/index.htm

Produces Glock accessories. Includes Glock accessories, laser sights, lasersikfet, tritium sights, night sights, leucht visier, handgun sights, and customized Glock firearms.

Autoracing Archive

http://www.eng.hawaii.edu/Contribs/carina/ra.home.page.html

Provides information about Formula One, IndyCar, and NASCAR racing. Also includes race results, point standings, schedules, and more.

INTERNET RACING SERVICE

AWESOME Sports Site of the Week

http://www.mmgco.com/online/awesome.html

Scans the Web looking for the best, the coolest, the most awesome sports site of the week.

Ballistic Batteries

http://cybermart.com/web/ballistic/

Provides reliable high-quality batteries for use in your R/C cars, trucks, planes, helicopters, or boats. Also carries Pro Gear travel bags.

Barrett's Climbing Page

http://www.intellinet.com/~btilley/climb.htm

Provides information on climbing in Arkansas. Usually includes pictures and maps/guides to areas in Arkansas. Offers links to 50 classic climbs.

Bay Area Fantasy Football League

http://www.phoenix.net/~sydex/baffl.html

Lets you watch the season progress and learn how to play in the BAFFL.

Bay View Yacht Sales

http://www.bayviewyacht.com/yachts/

Multiple listing yacht brokerage firm, located at Marina Bay in North Quincy, Massachusetts. Specializes in recreational power- and sailboats.

Bernie's Sports Center

http://www.mindspring.com/~imarcon/bernie.html

Provides gun enthusiasts in the Atlanta area with all their hunting and self-defense needs. Carries many calibers of rifles, a wide variety of handguns, and a large assortment of ammunition, and can handle your gunsmithing needs.

Big Deal Snow/ Skateboarding Co.

http://www.swmm.com/bigdeal/

Offers deals on snow/skateboarding equipment and some cheap entertainment.

British Society of Sports History

http://info.mcc.ac.uk/UMIST_Sport/bssh.html

Promotes research and publications about sports history and physical education. Also provides information about past and upcoming sports conferences.

Business, Hobbies & Sports Page

http://www.shadow.net/~mcruz

Provides information on business, music, and sports.

Calgary Flames Home Page

http://www.magic.mb.ca:80/~ciampa/flames/

Provides information about the Flames. Presents an electronic almanac of Flames information, including team standings and scoring leaders, rosters, and player images. Also offers a link to ESPN's NHL Live Scoreboard and pointers to other Calgary information.

Calgary Minor Soccer Association

`http://www.cadvision.com/Home_Pages/accounts/storm/toppage`

Focuses on Youth Soccer. Contains tournament information and links to other soccer-related sites.

Camelback Ski Resort Home Page

`http://silo.com/poconos/camelb~1/home.htm`

Promotes this ski area in the Poconos that also offers 14 summertime fun attractions.

Canada's Sports Hall of Fame

`http://www.inforamp.net/~cshof`

A guide to Canada's best and most honoured athletes, and to Canada's Sports Hall of Fame, located in Toronto, Ontario, Canada.

candelaMotorsport

`http://www.ozemail.com.au/~candela`

Provides all the latest news, press releases, pictures, and generally, anything involving motorsports in AUSTRALIA and the rest of the world.

Chehalis Composites

`http://www.europa.com/chehalis/skate.htm`

Offers Armadillo-brand extreme performance skateboard decks, a new product on the market. Provides information on composite materials and design, photos, and links.

The Commissioner's Assistant

`http://woodtech.com/~fanaticosu/tca.html`

Performs fantasy league management.

Common Sense Design's Home Page

`http://www.hevanet.com/berniew/index.htm`

Offers boat plans designed by the world famous designer Phil Bolger especially for first-time boat builders who want a quick, easy, and inexpensive boat.

Conway's Sports Research

`http://www.wwcd.com/conway/sport/odds.html`

Offers all the daily and future gaming odds.

CRN—Colorado Resort Net

`http://www.toski.com`

Serves as a guide to Colorado resort communities, including hotel, restaurant, arts, events, real estate, and shopping information.

CyberSoccer

`http://www.cybersports.co.uk/soccer/index.html`

Presents fantasy football (soccer) based on English FA Premiership.

CyberSports—at the Spectra.Net Mall

`http://www.spectra.net/mall/cybersports/`

Acts as a source for a wide variety of sports-related products and services on the Web.

Dallas Cowboys Training Camp Page

http://www.eden.com/~fgoodwin/cowboys.htm

Provides training camp information, including roster and schedule, a draft FAQ, and more.

The Danzan-Ryu Jujitsu Homepage

http://www.radix.net/~danzan

Contains authoritative information on Danzan-Ryu Jujitsu, the martial art of Henry Seishiro Okazaki.

Data Boat International CD-ROM

http://media1.hypernet.com/databoat.html

Includes an interactive CD-ROM that contains a catalog of more than 500 boat plan designs, information about hundreds of marine books and videos, a sample of yacht design software, color photos, video clips, an original sound track, and more.

David B. Martin's Water Polo Page

http://www.kfu.com/~dbmartin/polo.html

Focuses on water polo and offers many water polo links.

David Marc Nieporent's Unofficial Orioles Home Page

http://pluto.njcc.com/~nieporen/oriole.html

Focuses on the Baltimore Orioles.

Devizes to Westminster International Canoe & Kayak Marathon

http://www.sjr.com/sjr/www/gr

Provides information about the DW Canoe and Kayak Marathon, known as "The Canoeist's Everest," and which includes 125 miles, 76 portages paddled nonstop.

DIVE DESTINATIONS.em

http://www.atonet.com/dive/

Online magazine. Covers scuba diving and dive travel. Includes regularly updated feature articles, destination previews of diving hotspots world-wide, geo-data, and a traveler's center to assist your travel planning, as well as diver chat forums and an interactive photo-gallery of dive photos from around the world.

Eastern Virginia Mountain Biking

http://www.pinn.net/~wosborg/bike_hm.html

Provides information for mountain biking enthusiasts in Eastern Virginia, including information on trails and locations, riding and maintenance groups, and local bike shops.

Edge Magazine

http://www.fanzine.se/edgemag/

Covers snowboard, skateboard, surf, sound, and daredevil sports. Lets you download movie clips, some really radical photos, a preview of the latest issue of *Edge Magazine*, and more. Also offers many links to Internet sites on the edge.

Emory Bicycle Manufacturing Company

http://www.tdg.com/emory/emory.html

Factory direct bicycles. Forty years in the bicycle business. Offers products ranging from beach cruisers to collectables to mountain bikes, all for sale.

The Endurance Connection

http://www.endurance.com

Serves as an information center for endurance horse riding. Includes competitive ride schedules, maps, entry forms, horses and accessories for sale, a riders' forum, tips, and techniques.

Enternet Communications' Web Site

http://www.enternet.com/

Contains *Influx Digital Skate Culture*, an online magazine dedicated to skateboarding and related subjects; and SkateTalk, a real time discussion group dedicated to skateboarders, but open to all.

ESPNET Sports Zone

http://espnet.sportszone.com

Provides up-to-date information for the following sports: football, basketball, hockey, baseball (for professional and college teams/players). Also offers scores, previews, statistics, and highlight photos for some of the big games.

Fantasy Football sign-up ends Saturday | Publisher's letter | ❖ NFL team previews

SPORTSZONE
A SERVICE OF STARWAVE AND ESPN

| SELECT SPORT | ZONED OUT! | SPORTSTALK | ESPN STUDIOS |

The top stories as of August 23, 1995, 5:47pm ET

Life of Riley: Knicks, Heat reach agreement

ATP takes its whack$ at Tarango, too

Tyson gets another shot at Buster — Mathis that is

Siberia swimmer sets world record

Graf gets nod over Seles for top seed at U.S. Open

The FALL LINE

http://www.uvm.edu/~smiller/fallline.html

Furnishes a noncommercial directory to skiing resources on the Web. Includes a guide to the best expert skiing in New England.

Fantasy Baseball

http://arachnid.cm.cf.ac.uk/User/Gwyn.Price/fantasy_baseball/

Offers a collection of fantasy baseball information.

Fencing

http://www.ii.uib.no/~arild/fencing.html

Offers information concerning fencing clubs, books, drawings, and events. Provides an Internet fencing encyclopedia. Also includes resources for the United States, Europe, and Japan.

Fly Fishing in Patagonia

http://www.webzonecom.com/nesc/andes/

Promotes fly fishing in the vast estancias, perhaps the best and most peaceful fly fishing in the world.

The Flying Scot Page

http://www.ansoft.com/palmer/sail/fs.html

Provides information about Flying Scot sailboats, news about regattas and results, new and used boats and equipment for sale, tips on boatspeed and tactics, and more.

Football Stats Analyzer Shareware

http://www.webcom.com/~liberty

Offers shareware you can use to predict future football game outcomes by analyzing historical statistics.

Fore Play Golf Shop

http://www.4play.com/sports/4play

Offers pro-line and custom golf equipment for sale. Features newsletters and tips from pros.

GALE FORCE F1

http://www.monaco.mc/f1/

Provides Formula 1 motor racing results and track information.

George Ferguson's Ultimate Frisbee

http://www.cs.rochester.edu/u/ferguson/ultimate/

Provides fun for Ultimate Frisbee enthusiasts and links to game descriptions, rules, and tournament information.

Golf Courses of British Columbia

http://interchange.idc.uvic.ca/~golf/golfbc.html

Offers much to golfers of all skill levels. Provides links to more than 100 golf courses, as well as other golf-related Web servers.

The Golf Depot

http://www.golfdepot.com

Offers a line of Australian-made DINT putters.

The Golf Net

http://www.sdgolf.com/

Offers golf products for sale. Provides the PGA schedule. Features many golf related topics and provides tips on everything from putting to the psychology of golf.

GolfData On-Line Home Page

http://www.gdol.com/

Offers a bundle of links related to golf, including travel packages, golf publications, course information, a golf channel, and tournament and association information. Provides additional links to other golf servers.

GolfNet Website

http://www.digital-press.com/golfnet/

An interactive golf-related site that offers merchandising, golf news, stories, business opportunities in the field of golf, and tour information.

The Grandstand

http://www.gstand.com

Offers fantasy leagues, simulation leagues, and contests. Serves as a forum where sports fans can watch, talk, and play sports.

GT Olympic Project

http://www.gatech.edu/olympics/intro.html

Serves as a guide to the upcoming 1996 Olympic Games in Atlanta. Offers useful information concerning events, venues, and ticket sales. Provides up-to-date event results.

Highlight Fantasy—The Draft Kit

http://gmg.gmgnet.com/fantasy/

Presents The Draft Kit for fantasy and rotisserie sports, such as football, baseball, hockey, and basketball. Includes jumbo size 10-foot draft boards. Also offers a line of fantasy sports T-shirts.

Home Page for United States Swimming, Inc.

http://www.usswim.org/usswim

Presents United States Swimming, Inc., the national governing body for amateur competitive swimming in the United States.

The House (a.k.a. Sailboard Warehouse)

http://www.rscomm.com/adsports/house/index.html

Provides a complete windsurfing catalog.

Houston Hotshots

http://www.cpy.com/hotshots/hotshots.html

Focuses on Houston's indoor soccer team. Provides information about Nebo Bandovic, an opportunity to win free tickets. Features an interview with Diego Lopez (y Maradona), nephew of the famed forward from Argentina.

HyperBills: Buffalo Bills Football Coverage

http://www.RochesterDandC.com/sports/bills/bhhom.html

Offers complete coverage of the Buffalo Bills, including game stories, player profiles, stats, and photos.

The IndyCar Enthusiast

http://ucsu.colorado.edu/~sauerb/Home.html

Provides information, with special consideration given to Indy cars. Also offers links to other sites.

Inside Hockey

http://www.fanzine.se/hockey/

Features stats, interviews, contests, gossip, and news. Also hosts the home pages of several NHL superstars.

Instant Sports Info

http://www.webknx.com/jmassoc/900.shtml

Provides instant sports score information, for all sports, updated every five minutes.

International Aerobatics Club Home Page

http://acro.harvard.edu/IAC/iac_homepg.html

Boasts of competition results and upcoming events. Lists chapters within the organization, some of which offer their

own home pages. Provides information on other aviation servers, some aviation images, and weather information.

International Aerobatics Club Home Page

Last Update: Wednesday, 23-Aug-95 15:30:20 EDT

Internet Athlete

http://www.athlete.com

Provides an extensive calendar of events for running, swimming, cycling, and triathlon/duathlon. Offers results, team and training directories, and features.

Irish Sports Report

http://irishsports.com/

Focuses on Notre Dame sports. Offers Irish news, trivia, photographs and chances to win. Provides a feature article, game summary, photo of the week, plus insider information you won't find anywhere else, 22 times a year.

ISF World Snowboarding Rankings

http://deepcove.com/isf/

Presents International Snowboard Federation World & National Ranking lists, compiled from snowboarding competition results received from all over. Covers primarily Parallel Slalom, GS, Halfpipe, and Boarder Cross.

Judo Information Site

http://www.rain.org/~ssa/judo.htm

Provides information on the sport and martial art of Judo, brought to you by Neil Ohlenkamp and the Encino Judo Club.

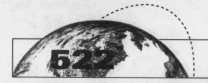

Kansas City Royals Home Page

http://www2.dtc.net/~crchrdsn/billding/royals/

Focuses on the Kansas City Royals.

KFAN Radio

http://www.kfan.com/

Offers hundreds of sports links and a new contest every month.

King of the Hill Fly Fishing Co.

http://www.kinghill.com

Full service fly fishing outfitter and supplier carries a complete line of fly tying and fly fishing products. Also represents worldwide fishing destinations.

Kosciusko Thredbo Australian Ski Site

http://www.thredbo.com.au/skiweb/

Offers information on the Thredbo resort, ticket and ski hire prices, and ski school, plus comprehensive snow reports and satellite images of snowfields.

Lacrosse Web

http://www.tol.net/lacrosse/

Serves the Bay Area and Lake Tahoe. Supplies college and club lacrosse information for California. Includes links to other lacrosse information sites.

Lawn Bowls in Tuggeranong

http://tyndale.apana.org.au/~paddo/clubtxt.html

Provides information about lawn bowls, a sport made famous by Sir Francis Drake and enjoyed by hundreds of thousands of Australians each week.

A Light-Tackle Sport Fishing Charter—West Central Gulf Coast, Florida

http://www.cftnet.com/members/duclon/capt2.htm

Presents light-tackle sport fishing on the west central Gulf coast of Florida with Captain Mike Duclon.

Mad Dog Expeditions

http://www.mad-dog.net/

Seeks to expand the experience of sport diving into realms traditionally reserved for scientists and heavily sponsored exploration teams. Offers challenging expeditions and training for serious divers of all ability levels.

Magic 693—Australian Rules Football

http://www.magic.com.au

Covers any AFL football game played anywhere in Australia for Melbourne.

Matt's Solar Car Page

http://www-lips.ece.utexas.edu/~delayman/solar.html

Provides race information, team listings (United States and Canada), and official results of previous races. Also offers images of solar cars, as well as a race route map across Australia.

Maui Scuba Page— Ed Robinson's Diving Adventures

http://www.maui.net/robinson/erd.html

Provides information on dive sites, weather, and other dive-related aspects of island life.

The Maui Windsurfing Report

http://maui.net/~mauiwind/MWR/mwr.html

The MWR is the center of windsurfing on the WWW. Offers action, news and views, and beautiful bikini-clad women.

Metts Sports Tours

http://www.gc.net/metts/metts.html

Operates sports vacations across the nation. Specializes in NFL football, Winston Cup NASCAR racing, and the '96 Summer Olympics in Atlanta.

Midwest Express Fantasy Game Co.

http://www.iquest.net/~mwexp

Headquarters for Online Fantasy Sports. Hosts the World Wide Weekly Challenge. Enables you to pick, trade, or waive your players online. Also the home of Weebe Technologies (Statmaster Football and Baseball).

MIT Women's Soccer Team Home Page

http://www-swiss.ai.mit.edu/soccer/home.html

Offers the action-packed soccer graphics of the MIT women's soccer team.

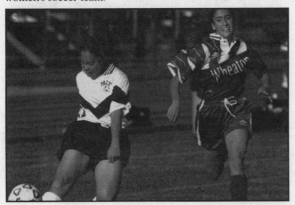

Motorsports Media Service International Home Page

http://www.west.net/~webpages

Provides information about auto racing—drivers, teams, sponsors, art and photography, merchandise, and more.

Mountaineering Council of Ireland

http://www.ul.ie/~mci

Represents Irish climbers and hill walkers. Provides news and links to other related sites.

Nando X

http://www.nando.net/baseball/bbserv.html

Hosts Beyond the Boxscore—a commentary by columnists Bill Arnold and Mark Camps that offers the inside scoop on baseball.

National Hockey League— Hawaii's NHL Home Page

http://maxwell.uhh.hawaii.edu/hockey/hockey.html

Provides present league standings, the latest NHL scores, leading scorers, and 1995 Stanley Cup playoffs. Also provides information on the history of the Stanley Cup finals and NHL awards, as well as NHL images and movies.

NAUI (National Association of Underwater Instructors)

http://www.what.com/naui/

Serves as the official site for the National Association of Underwater Instructors (NAUI) for use by scuba divers of all associations to promote diving safety and education.

Nautical Net

http://www.nauticalnet.com

Contains a tackle shop, marine electronics, boat brokers and manufacturers, clubs, fishing reports, and charter boats.

New England Windsurfing Journal

http://www.rscomm.com/adsports/newj/index.html

New England Windsurfing Journal—online.

Newt's Fantasy Football Page

http://www.servtech.com/public/newt

Provides draft tips, stats, and other various bits of information for fantasy footballers.

NFL Executive Accessories

http://www.executive-accessories.com

Offers NFL executive accessories, including : NFL golf accessories, NFL desk accessories, NFL personal accessories, NFL travel luggage, NFL business luggage, and more.

NFL POOL

http://webcom.net/~dunny/nfl.htm

Offers information on the National Football League and a shareware program that runs a recreational football pool on the NFL.

NHL OPEN NET

http://www.nhl.com

Official home page site of the National Hockey League and its teams. Includes daily press releases, hockey stats, and other information.

NHL Schedule

http://www.cs.ubc.ca/nhl

Provides the schedules for each of the 26 NHL hockey teams. Also includes individual team information and links to other data.

Nor'east Saltwater Magazine

http://www.noreast.com

A weekly sportfishing magazine for New York's saltwater anglers. Includes weeky fishing reports, sportfishing news, new product information, boats for charter, partyboat schedules, weekly saltwater flyfishing column, editorials, reader feedback, classifieds, and more.

North American Arms, Inc.

http://www.utw.com/NAA/naahome.html

Offers a catalog of these small, finely crafted mini-revolvers in .22 caliber. Also offers custom accessories. Includes links to other firearms-related sites.

Northern Vermont X-Country, Backcountry, and Telemark Skiing

http://salus.uvm.edu/VTXCSki.html

Provides information about free heel skiing in Northern Vermont. Includes trail maps, trail discriptions, and and links to resorts related to x-country or telemark skiing.

NY Roller Hockey

http://www.panix.com/~petern/HOCKEY.html

Features the statistics, standings, and schedules for the major roller hockey leagues in Manhattan. Provides contact information and photos as well.

Official PGA Championship Web Site

http://www.championship.pga.org/

Features live results from the Riviera Country Club. Provides results and features information about every hole, all the players, news and daily photographs/artwork, past and future PGA Championship events, other events run by the PGA of America, and more.

Offshore Powerboat Racing

http://ccwf.cc.utexas.edu/~aalbert/offshore.html

Provides results, recaps, schedules, current news, and team information.

Offshore Powerboat Racing

Welcome to the world of offshore powerboat racing. There are several organizations involved in this sport, the most active and recognized of which is the American Powerboat Association (APBA). Within this organization, and others, there are several classes of competition, and two types of boats, catamarans and V-hulls.

Open Cockpit Biplane Flights on the Big Island of Hawaii

http://planet-hawaii.com/biplane

Lets you fly in a modern-day replica of a 1934 WACO biplane. Offers aerial tours over the Big Island of Hawaii, which includes views of waterfalls, live volcano eruptions, and pristine hidden valleys.

The Oregon Wrestling Report

http://www.teleport.com/~mitchell/oregon

Covers amateur wrestling in Oregon, from kids clubs through the college level.

Orienteering and Rogaining Home Page

http://www2.aos.Princeton.EDU:80/rdslater/orienteering/

Offers a general description of the two sports (which are types of skiing), and provides announcements, a schedule of events, and club activities. Also offers links to other orienteering and rogaining servers.

Parachute Industry Association

http://www.eskimo.com/~pia

The objectives of the Parachute Industry Association are to advance and promote the growth, development, and safety of parachuting and to engage and serve participants in the parachute industry. The PIA consists of companies and individuals united by a common desire to improve business opportunities in this segment of aviation.

Pedersen's Ski and Sport

http://www.pedersens.com

Sells mountain bikes, inline skates, skis, snowboards, accessories, clothing, and more. Provides free shipping within the continental Unites States. Includes contests and links to other resources.

Penn State

http://www.psu.edu

Presents a Rose Bowl site and movies of past events. Provides some general information about the university, including student policies, online course materials, and topics of academia and research. Also offers job listings.

Perception, Inc.'s Kayaking Home Page—20 Years of Fun

http://www.kayaker.com/perception/

Kayak manufacturer. Celebrates 20 years of fun and invites you to visit.

Physique Techniques Fitness Consultants

http://www.unicomp.net/users/pthomas/index.html

Offers complete fitness programs, nutritional analysis, personal training, supplementation, steroid information, bodybuilding, training advice, fitness columns, and so on. Specializes in *metabolic manipulation* (making your body work for you; not being trapped by your body).

Piedmont Budokan (Judo and JuJitsu)

http://www.cpcc.cc.nc.us/clubs/judo.htm

Emphasizes developing the individual and provides information on judo throws and the proper way to work out.

Planet Reebok

http://planetreebok.com/

Offers information about Reebok's corporate history and news about fitness, human rights, activism, and research.

Powder Hound Ski Report

http://www.icw.com/skireport.html

Provides information about ski conditions and weather reports throughout the world. Also offers specific resort forecasts for Utah.

Princeton Golf Archives

http://dunkin.princeton.edu/.golf

Offers an education in designing a golf club and calculating slope and handicaps. Provides information about GolfData On-line—a bulletin board that offers a database of 14,000 golf courses, tips from Jeff Maggert (PGA professional), discount coupons, and more (including GIF and BMP).

Pyde Vista Golf Course

http://www.interspace.com/bus/realty/mgood/listings.html

Provides information about this executive, nine hole golf course and the original owners, who are now retiring.

Radio Control Sailors of Finland

http://honeybee.helsinki.fi/surcp/rcsail.htm

Offers descriptions and pictures of radio control sailing, the Finnish competition schedule, and online results. Provides the results of all Finnish competitions and some international competitions.

Random Swim Information for Swimmers

http://www.kfu.com/~jethro/swim.html

Provides information for swimmers of all kinds. Offers links to other swim sites, workouts, and meet results.

Real Madrid

http://www.laeff.esa.es/~crb/EntradaRM.html

Presents the football team, including its history, titles, players, trainers, presidents (and it's in Spanish).

The Richmond Braves

http://emporium.turnpike.net/V/vanet/rbraves/index.html

Includes information about local and team history, ballpark extras, attractions, dining, lodging, directions, and ticket information.

Roller Warehouse News

http://albert.bu.edu/~spectre/rw-news.html

Provides information and an archive for the *Roller Warehouse News* newsletter, disributed via mailing list. Also contains deals from Roller Warehouse and articles from the newsletter editor.

Rowing

http://www.comlab.ox.ac.uk/archive/other/rowing.html

Provides definitions, rules, statistics, and photographs for the sport of rowing. Also provides Regatta results and a link to the River and Rowing Museum.

Rugby

http://rugby.phys.uidaho.edu/rugby.html

Provides rules of the game, as well as a listing of competitive events.

Running Page

http://sunsite.unc.edu/drears/running/running.html

Provides information on notable trails, clubs, races, marathons, race results, and "the running scene" worldwide.

Sailboard Vacations

http://www.sccsi.com/Club_Mistral/welcome.html

Serves as a travel agency for windsurfers. Offers detailed travel information on the finest windsurfing spots. Features the latest in quality windsurfing equipment from Mistral. Provides information on how to windsurf.

Sk8er's Home Page

http://www.eden.com/~sk8er/

Offers instructions on inline skating technique. Reviews equipment and places to skate. Provides a messages bulletin board. Also provides information on figureblade skating school programs.

Sky Adventure Tours

http://www.mainelink.net/SKYADVENTURES/

Hang gliding tours of Maine. Includes lodging and transportation. Provides boat tow instruction and tandem instruction. Includes mountain images and a directory of pilot home pages.

Small World Baseball

http://www.smallworld.com/promotions/promo_baseball.html

Presents Small World Baseball, an online sports strategy game that allows fans to draft and trade a team of real players on an active, national market. Lets you organize a league with your friends and compete with thousands of opponents from across the globe.

Small World Hockey

http://www.smallworld.com/promotions/promo_hockey.html

Presents Small World Hockey, an online sports strategy game that allows fans to draft and trade teams of real players on an active national market. Lets you compete against your friends and against thousands of other opponents.

The Snow Page

http://rmd-www.mr.ic.ac.uk/snow/snowpage.html

Provides information about winter sports, including skiing and snow boarding, as well as information on resorts, weather reports, and trail maps. Also offers a picture gallery.

The Sonic Spot

http://weber.u.washington.edu/~jgurney/sonics/

Contains many photos, audio clips, statistics, and other information related to the Seattle Sonics of the NBA.

South Carolina Golf Courses

http://www.gdol.com/sc/

Provides access to a database that lists every golf course in the state.

Southern Utah Golf Courses

http://sci.dixie.edu/StGeorge/Golf/golf.html

Provides a map that designates Utah's more famous golf courses. Also offers course descriptions and other useful information.

Specialty Car Page

http://www.infiniteweb.com/cars.html

Includes free classified ads with photos of hundreds of cars, as well as vendor, car club, and car show pages.

Sportfishing Industry Newsletter

http://www.kinghill.com/sportfishing

Offers a comprehensive closeup of the business of sportfishing: what's new, what's hot, who's who and why. Targets fishing tackle manufacturers, ad agencies, marketers, and informed consumers.

The Sports SHAK

http://www.csn.net/~mhand/SportsSHAK

A fantasy sporting service. Lets users sign up free of charge, receive their own home page, and become team owners and league commissioners. Gives each league and team its own set of pages. Does all stats, updates all the standings, and lets you concentrate on your team.

Sports Souvenirs & Memorabilia

http://nashville.net/~mold

Presents Team Fan, which carries a wide variety of sports memorabilia and souvenirs. Carries items from NHL, MLB, and NFL. Includes a list of hard-to-find items, including many for the Dallas Cowboys.

Sports Videos

http://www.intellinet.com/~jdutton/sports.html

Offers basketball, football, baseball, hockey, golf, tennis, track and field, fishing, camping, hunting, skiing, and more. Features dozens of selections of sports videos and includes

plenty of tips and instructions from Dave Stockton, Billy Casper, Andre Aggasi, and many other well-known sports heroes.

Sportsworld

http://sportsworld.com/

The Sports Information Resource. Provides worldwide sports information, merchandise, and results (both professional and amateur). Includes results for running, triathalons, duathalons, and cycling (with a unique individual results page for each athlete).

Sprague Mat Club

http://www.teleport.com/~mitchell

A kids' wrestling club.

Spring City Cycles

http://iquest.com/~topcycle/

Provides fun and useful information on cycling and an online ordering scheme is in the works. Includes the stats on your favorite bike.

Stadiums and Arenas

http://www.wwcd.com/stadiums.html

Enables you to purchase tickets for sporting events.

Steve Perkins' Home Page

http://www.indy.net/~sperkins/

Contains links to IndyCar, Jimmy Buffett, NFL, and several other sites.

Steven Louie's New York Yankees Home Page

http://www.interport.net/~slouie/yankees/index.html

Provides graphical New York Yankees home page and loads of information on the Yankees.

Stretching and Flexibility

http://archie.ac.il/papers/rma/stretching_toc.html

Provides information concerning stretching.

Sykkeldelisk

http://www.oslonett.no/sp/sy/

Offers a catalog that contains plenty of color images of mountain bikes, ordering information, and links to related information.

Texas SportsGuide

http://mcia.com/~circfish/tsg.htm

Fishing magazine online. Provides fishing, camping, travel, and outdoor information and articles on Texas' lakes, rivers and gulf coast.

Three Chimneys Farm Home Page

http://www.threechimney.com/farm/

Provides photos and statistics of some of the world's leading thoroughbred stallions, as well as information and photographs of Three Chimneys Farm, among the world's leading thoroughbred breeding farms.

THRIL—Thoroughbred Horse Racing Information Link

http://www.thril.com/

Provides news, information, services, and products (much of the information is free to all, but requires a small subscription price if you want access to professional handicapping services, columns by top writers, and other services).

Timber! The Ottawa Loggers d'Ottawa Home Page

http://www.synapse.net/~stargate/loggers/loggers.htm

Focuses on the Ottawa Loggers Roller Hockey team. Le site Web bilingue dedie a l'equipe de roller hockey Les Loggers d'Ottawa.

Tracy's Karate Canada Homepage

http://www.islandnet.com/~karate/karate.html

Contains information on owning and running a karate school. Includes a short history of Kenpo Karate.

TSI Soccer

http://www.tsisoccer.com/tsi/

Provides catalogs of soccer products for teams and individuals. Includes information about TSI services.

BROWSE TSI SOCCER'S CATALOG

The Ultimate Internet Sports Guide

http://www.sportinfo.com/sportinfo/

Serves as an Internet guide to professional sporting events.

The Ultimate Sports Page

http://sportsone.radix.net

Provides sports information: includes the pros, college sports, and the Olympics.

United States Fencing Association Online

http://www.usfa.org/

Official online resource of the United States Fencing Association.

United States Power Squadrons Web Page

http://www.ronin.com/USPS/

Presents USPS, a private boating organization. Focuses on USPS's Basic Boating Course.

United States Tennis Association/Mid-Atlantic Section

http://www.clark.net/pub/mrosen/usta.html

Provides information about the USTA/Mid-Atlantic section, USTA programs, tournament schedules, and more.

University of Iowa Hawkeyes

http://www.biz.uiowa.edu/hawkeyes

Focuses on the University of Iowa Hawkeyes.

Unofficial Australian National Basketball League (NBL) Page

http://natsem.canberra.edu.au/nbl/nbl.html

Provides the latest Australian NBL results and news. Includes complete team, player, and game statistics.

The Unofficial NBA Visual Directory

http://www.primenet.com/~hantla/nba/nba.html

Provides a complete listing of all current NBA players and teams.

The Upper Midwest Traveler and Adventure Guide

http://www.execpc.com/~midwest

Provides information about this splendid region known as the Upper Midwest. Covers recreation activities ranging from participation sports to pure travel and adventure. Tells you where to hike, bike, golf, ride, and canoe in the summer and fall, and where to downhill and cross-country ski in the winter. Also leads you to unique attractions, festivals, and events the Upper Midwest has to offer.

USA Football Center Online

http://cybergsi.com/foot2.htm

Provides scores and updates to college and pro football games, betting lines, and weekly stats. Also features a pregame show that talks about the games to be played that day, and provides the picks of the day.

VeloLinQ

http://www.wsmith.com/velolinq

Serves as a source for current cycling news, cutting edge racing results, product information, online cycling publications, and more.

Velonews Experimental Tour de France Service

http://www.velonews.com/VeloNews/

Offers news on the Tour de France, including course maps, team lineups, TV schedules, and results. Also includes an article by John Healey that explains the Tour de France in depth.

Virtual Flyshop

http://rmii.com/~flyshop/flyshop.html

Provides a hypermedia collection for easy access. Includes pictures, stories, movies, knots, and additional links to newsgroups and other related Web pages.

Wasatch Powderbird Guides

http://www.xmission.com/~act/wpb.htm

Offers helicopter powder skiing in Snowbird, Utah, just 35 minutes from Salt Lake City International Airport.

The Washington Handicapper

http://www.aa.net/~strchrun/wahandicapper.html

Serves thoroughbred horse racing fans in the state of Washington by providing pre-race analyses and post-race summaries about stakes races run at Washington race tracks. Provides occasional stats-based features about racing in the state and offers links to related sites.

Wilmington Blue Rocks Baseball

http://www2.interpath.net/baseball/wilmington/

Includes schedules, ticket information and ordering, merchandise, and stats for the Class-A Carolina League affiliate of the Kansas City Royals.

WinAmerica! Fantasy Football

http://www.cdmnet.com/winAmerica/winam.html

Lets you engage in fantasy football on the Internet, licensed by The NFL Players Association, sponsored by Dodge. Provides weekly results via Internet and on Prime Sports cable Thursday nights.

Windsight Windsurfing Wind Reports

http://www.gorge.net/windsight

Provides text, graphic, and video coverage of windsurfing sites in the Columbia River Gorge, Oregon Coast, San Francisco Bay, Baja, and Maui. Also covers meteorological concepts as they apply to windsurfing. Explains how to use Windsight's 800 number voice phone service and the Windsight software.

Windsurfing in Texas

http://www.sccsi.com/Windsurfing/windsurfing.html

Provides information on windsurfing in the Houston area, including sailing sites, wind and weather, lessons, and more.

World of Fishing

http://www.fishingworld.com

Offers all types of fishing information, services, products, tournaments information, magazines, and servers as a place to visit other fishermen.

World Skiing

`http://www.cs.colorado.edu/homes/mcbryan/public_html/bb/ski/ski.html`

Provides information on skiing conditions throughout the world (for both downhill and cross-country skiing).

World Wide Web of Sports

`http://tns-www.lcs.mit.edu/cgi-bin/sports`

Offers a collection of sports statistics, schedules, rosters, facts, figures, and information. Covers the NBA, NFL, NHL, soccer, golf, frisbee, rowing, fencing, and rugby, among other sports.

World Wide Web Tennis Server

`http://arganet.tenagra.com/Racquet_Workshop/Tennis.html`

Offers monthly tennis tips on skills and equipment, daily tennis news, and hyperlinks to the Tennis Rules and Tennis Code. Also offers extensive list other links.

Above It All

http://hoohana.aloha.net/~above/index.htm

Serves as a charter service for Hawaii and the islands. Includes flight reservation, charter information, and flight lessons.

Hawaii
The Big Island

Photo by Brad Lewis...click for larger image
(135k)

In 1990, inhabitants of the southern-most part of the U.S. watched their town be completely destroyed as

Adventures in Paradise

Adventure Cruising in the North Atlantic

http://www.centrum.is/com/vinland.html

Provides information on the pleasure cruiser, *Liefur Eriksson*, which sails in the North Atlantic.

Aer Lingus

http://www.hursley.ibm.com/aer/

Includes departures, news, special business programs, and a photo gallery that shows Aer Lingus history.

Aeroflot

http://www.seanet.com/Bazar/Aeroflot/Aeroflot.html

Includes pictures of aircraft, departure schedules, and a map of Moscow's Sheremetyevo-2 Airport.

Air Canada

http://www.aircanada.ca/

The official Web site for Air Canada. Includes a news desk, schedules, a program, and a special section called Netguide, which provides information on Internet and HTML basics. Also provides a French version.

Air Charter Guide

http://www.shore.net/acg/

The online edition of *The Air Charter Guide*, a limited version of the book. Serves as a guide for locating charter operators, arranged by state, name. Also includes tips on planning and pricing a charter

Air Travel Card Control Tower

http://air-travel-card.com/atc/home.htm

Provides news and trends in the business travel industry and information on Air Travel Card.

Air Traveler's Handbook

http://www.cs.cmu.edu/afs/cs/user/mkant/Public/Travel/airfare.html

Offers links to information on courier travel, consolidators and bucket shops, charters, newsgroups, mailing lists, general travel information, background notes, tourist information, destination information, Embassies car rental agencies, hotels, bed and breakfasts, hosteling, home exchanges, health, money and currency, weather, foreign languages, packing, insurance, maps travel publishers, publications, periodicals, travel bookstores, travel software student/budget travel, round-the-world, travelogues, aviation, miscellaneous usage statistics, and entry submissions.

Air UK

http://www.neptune.com/scotland/airuk.html

Provides information on the airline for travel to Scotland, but no schedule or service information. Offers links to a site that provides information on Scotland.

Airlines of the Web

http://haas.berkeley.edu/~seidel/airline.html

Provides information about airlines, organized by geographic region. Also provides information about cargo airlines, newsgroups, and airports.

Alaska Information Cache

http://www.neptune.com/alaska/alaska.html

Overviews things to see and do in Alaska. Includes tour information.

Alchemy of Africa

http://www.aztec.co.za/biz/africa

Provides information all about Africa. Lets you download African Music while you stroll through the Art Gallery, browse the Market for shops and business listings, chat online in the Chat rooms, arm chair travel to African destinations via the Mystical Launch pad, and more.

America's Caribbean Paradise

http://noc.usvi.net:80/

Provides information on the Virgin Islands, including wedding and vacation information, holidays, carnivals and other events, and weather forecasts. Also offers a section on real estate, vacation rentals, recipes, and Caribbean products.

American Airlines

http://www.amrcorp.com/aa_home/aa_home.htm

Includes schedules, travel awards program information, special products, and a helpful alphabetical index to access information quickly. Also includes an employment opportunity section.

Ansett Australia

http://www.ansett.com.au/homepage.html

Features an airline that flies to exotic places such as Norfolk Island, Bali, Christmas Island, in addition to places in Australia.

Arctic Adventours, Inc.

http://www.oslonett.no/html/adv/AA/AA.html

Advertises Arctic Adventours, a Norwegian company that specializes in creating exciting expeditions and explorations in the Arctic area, including Northern Norway, Jan Mayen, Spitzbergen (Svalbard), Franz Josef's Land, and Northern Russia / Siberia.

Arizona's WebHub

http://www.emerald.net/webhub/

Presents a subject-sorted listing of Web links about Arizona.

Australia Travel Directory

http://www.anzac.com/aust/aust.htm

Offers links to information on tourism, VISA, individual states, and transportation.

Bahamas Online

http://TheBahamas.com/

Provides information on facts, accommodations, restaurants, banks, and bars.

Belgium Online—Tourist Information

http://www.online.be/online/nl/tourist.html

Offers links to other sites. Overviews Belgium and features prominent cities such as Brussels, Ghent, and Antwerp.

Big Island Air

http://www.ilhawaii.net:80/pt/bigair.html

Offers tours of Hawaii, including volcano tours. Also offers a reservation service.

Boston Information and Resources

http://www.pn.com/Services/Boston/

Provides information about clubs, restaurants, weather, movie listings, and more in the metropolitan Boston area.

Boulder, Colorado

http://bcn.boulder.co.us/government/boulder_city/center.html

Provides information about Boulder's government and neighborhoods. Includes weekly calendars, press releases, and information about city departments.

Cambridge, Massachusetts

http://www.ai.mit.edu/projects/iiip/Cambridge/homepage.html

Features Cambridge City resources and more. Offers links to such sites as Art, Employment, Government, and others.

Canadian Airlines Intl.

http://www.cdnair.ca/

Includes the usual airline Web information, such as news, schedules, destinations. Also offers links to a QuickTime movie.

The Caribbean Connection

http://mrlxp2.mrl.uiuc.edu/~stuart/caribbean.html

Serves as a starting point for the traveler who wants to become familar with the Caribbean. Offers links to travel and tourism, country profiles, and entertainment.

CaribWeb

http://www.caribweb.com/caribweb/

Serves as a resource for travelers and Caribophiles alike. Provides online travel publications and a conversation area. Also provides information from all the Caribbean tourist-board home pages and other relevant links to the Caribbean. Includes a searchable database, called CaribSearch, which contains information on hundreds of hotels, yacht charter companies, and restaurants.

The Source for Caribbean Travellers & Explorers

Cathay Pacific

http://www.cathay-usa.com/

Offers service to locations in Asia, such as Hong Kong, Bangkok, and Singapore. Includes services and special deals, but no schedule information.

Chicago Information System

http://reagan.eecs.uic.edu

Provides visitor and resident information about Chicago. Includes up-to-date weather forecasts and a calendar of events. Also lists demographic information about Chicago and its suburbs.

City Net

http://www.city.net/

Offers links to various cities that have Web pages of their own (in the United States, Canada, Germany, United Kingdom, France, Italy, Australia, or the Netherlands). Lets you take a virtual tour of Marseille, check the subway schedule for Philadelphia, or find out what types of entertainment are available in Victoria.

The Civilized Explorer

http://www.crl.com/~philip/home.html

Contains information on places around the world, including beaches, restaurants, activities, and places to stay. Also includes photographs and links to maps, satellite pictures, and other resources.

CLEVE.NET: A Guided Tour of the North Coast

http://www.en.com/cleve.net/

Invites you to take a tour of the "North Coast." Presents Cleveland, a city once full of urban decay, as a beautiful mecca you can visit and enjoy.

Clever Ways to Travel for Free or Little Cost

http://adam.cs.uwec.edu/~andersts/travel.html

Provides information for people traveling on a budget. Includes tips on money, documents, protection against theft, travel organizations, and so on.

Comair

http://www.iac.net/~flypba/COMAIR/COMAIR/ COMAIR.home.html

Includes an Information Skyway section, which provides information on commerical aviation, such as aircraft manufacturers, airport index, airline stock quotes. Also includes a Table of Contents section.

Country Flags

gopher://gopher.stolaf.edu:70/11/InternetResources/US-State-Department-Travel-Advisories/FTP-Archive/gifs/ flags/world-almanac-1992

Presents GIF picture files of flags.

Country Maps of Europe

http://www.tue.nl/maps.html

Presents country maps of Europe.

Country Specific Pages— Africa

http://www.sas.upenn.edu/African_Studies/Home_Page/ Country.html

Lists African countries and offers links to related information, such as country maps and country home pages. Highlights links to "Ethnologues: Languages of the World."

Cruise Review Library

http://www.digimark.net/rec-travel/cruises/rtc.html

Serves as a usenet newsgroup forum for discussing travel by cruise ships. Offers reviews on any of the major cruise ship lines.

Currency Exchange Rates

http://www.dna.lth.se/cgi-bin/kurt/rates

Presents the exchange rate for 23 currencies. Lets you select any currency and compare it to another (based on values obtained at 6 P.M. Swedish time).

Cyprus

http://www.wam.umd.edu/~cyprus/tourist.html

Serves as a general guide to Cyprus. Includes sections on cities and advice on where to stay. Provides information on where to shop, what to buy, the cuisine of Cyprus, music sites, and where to have fun.

Czech Republic

http://turnpike.net/metro/muselik/index.html

Presents a guide to the Czech Republic. Includes general information, bulletin boards (such as finding an ancestor), travel, and a section on the city of Prague.

Digital Commercial Services

http://www.commerce.digital.com/

Demonstrates Digital's commercial services (uses Palo Alto, California). Contains an abundance of local and tourist information about Palo Alto. Also offers a link to the Ohio Online Export Directory.

Dublin Pub Review

http://www.dsg.cs.tcd.ie:/dsg_people/czimmerm/pubs.html

Provides a self-admittedly biased opinion of pubs and nightclubs in Dublin. Takes you on a tour of pubs and provides a price and visitability rating for each one.

Eagle Canyon Airlines

http://cybermart.com/eagle/

The airline to tour the Grand Canyon. Tour information available in German, French, Spanish, Italian, Chinese, Korean, and Japanese.

Easynet S.r.l.—Internet Service Provider

http://www.easynet.interbusiness.it/Welcome.html

Contains news from the city and province of Verona, with links to commercial activities and services for the citizens. A Virtual Tour of the city is available.

The Electronic Embassy

http://www.embassy.org/

Serves as a source for information that is useful to the staff of embassies in Washington, D.C., as well as for those interested in embassy affairs. Offers link to embassy Web sites, an index of all D.C. embassies, and jumps to federal executive agencies and a list of Washington events.

ELVIS+, Co.

http://www.elvis.msk.su/

Provides information about USD exchange rates in Russia, a Russian-English dictionary, advertisements, and more. Offers a keyword search engine. Provides English and Russian versions.

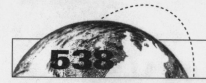

The Emirates Intl. Airline of the United Arab Emirates

http://www.onu.edu/~mparham/uae/emirates/emirates.html

Emphasizes the variety of services this airline offers; however, provides no information on schedules or special vacations, and so on.

Environmental Recycling Hotline

http://www.primenet.com/erh.html

Gives you immediate information about recycling in your area when you enter your zip code. Provides information about drop sites, hazardous materials, and even buying recycled products.

Eugene, Oregon

http://www.efn.org/

Provides many links pertaining to Eugene, its sponsors, its community, the government, and the community. Also enables you to search the Web or find out what's new.

European Rail Passes

http://www.xmission.com/~aoi/d000.html

Provides information on the Eurailpass and rail passes for other countries such as Germany, Austria, Italy, Czech Republic, and Scandinavia.

The Eurostar: English Channel

http://www.iihe.ac.be/hep/pp/evrard/eurostar.html

Presents Eurostar, direct passenger train service that connects Paris and Brussels and London using the Chunnel (English Channel Tunnel). Includes timetables and prices

and pictures of trains that travel this engineering masterpiece.

Finnair

http://www.interactive.line.com/finland/finair.home.html

Provides background information on Finland and the other locations Finnair services. Includes a section on available tours.

Foreign Language for Travelers

http://insti.physics.sunysb.edu/~mmartin/languages/languages.html

Discusses common words and phrases of just about any language you might be interested in, including German, French, Italian, Russian, Czech, Turkish, Finnish, Danish Esperanto, English, Spanish, Portuguese, Dutch, Polish, Romanian, Swedish, Norwegian, and Icelandic. Furnishes sound files for each language. Offers links to other sites that feature translation dictionaries and general information.

Freighter World Cruises

http://www.gus.com/travel/fwc/fwc.html

Advertises Freighter World Cruises, Inc., a travel agency that focuses on freighter travel. Provides information on various freighter lines and their destinations.

Frontier Airlines

http://www.cuug.ab.ca:8001/~busew/frontier.html

Serves Denver-based Rocky Mountain locations. Provides the history of Frontier Airlines. Includes many airplane graphics.

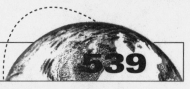
A Future Corporation Australian Experience

http://peg.apc.org/~futurecom

Presents a collection of graphics concerning life online, from Queensland, Australia. Offers links to many facets of Web lifestyle, including education, vacationing, and travel.

GENinc Bed and Breakfast Inns: USA

http://www.geninc.com/geni/b_and_b/

Provides information on various bed and breakfasts throughout the United States.

GENinc's World-wide Travel/Tourism and Convention and Visitor Bureaus

http://www.geninc.com/geni/maps/travel_world.html

Offers links to other sites that contain travel information on various destinations.

Global Network Navigator/ Koblas Money Converter

http://bin.gnn.com/cgi-bin/gnn/currency/

Presents a currency converter, updated weekly. Lets you select a currency and displays all other currencies relative to that one.

GNN TC Internet Resources—Countries

http://gnn.com/gnn/meta/travel/res/countries.html

Provides a collection of traveler's guides for almost any place in the world. Provides information about local customs, accommodations, and more.

GNN Travel Center

http://nearnet.gnn.com/gnn/meta/travel/index.html

GNN, a publisher of travel books, furnishes a Web site for feature stories on special travel sites and links to other travel-related Web sites.

Grand Rapids, Michigan

http://www.grfn.org/

Provides information about Grand Rapids. Includes weather updates and attractions. Also includes information about FreeNets.

The Guide to Iceland and Its People

http://www.primenet.com/~peetah/iceland/IsMenu.html

Presents a guide to Iceland, its attractions, history, people, language, and economy. Includes many pictures and provides information. Also includes lists of common phrases and words, such as *Hvernig gengur?* (How are you?).

Helinet Helicopter Tours

http://travelassist.com/tcd/helinet.html

Presents an unusual tour of Los Angeles—a Helinet helicoptor tour might be the way to go. Provides information on beach tours and a dinner tour in which you land atop a skyscraper.

HobokenX

http://www.stevens-tech.edu/hobokenx/hobokenx.html

Provides information about Hoboken, New Jersey, and about its government, entertainment, and more.

Hong Kong Online Guide

http://www.hk.super.net/~webzone/hongkong.html

Provides information on Hong Kong, including shopping,

dining, culture, and places of interest listings. Offers links to sites on Hong Kong culture and on Chinese culture.

Houston Area Real-Time Traffic Report

http://herman.tamu.edu/houston-real.html

Provides real-time information about the traffic situation on Houston freeways. Consists of data collected by volunteer probes. Invites you to sign up to become a volunteer, too.

Indonesia

http://www.sino.net/asean/indonesa.html

Serves as a guide to Indonesia and its customs, traveling within the country, entertainment, and more. Includes a recording of the National Anthem of Indonesia and a soon-to-be-available video clip.

Information about Duty Free/Tax Free Shopping

http://www.webscope.com/duty-free/

Provides shopping-related information. Also offers links to sites related to cruise lines. Contains information on duty-free and/or tax-free products.

The Information Skyway

http://www.iac.net/~flypba/net.airlines.html

Covers airlines (arranged geographically).

The Inn Traveler— International Bed & Breakfast and Country Inn Guide

http://www.biddeford.com/inntravel/home.html

Provides information about bed and breakfast inns. Currently covers the United States (arranged alphabetically) and Canada. Includes room descriptions, reservations (forms), newsletters, and audio clips recorded by the innkeepers.

International Airport Codes

http://www-iwi.unisg.ch/~mmarchon/airline/worldapt.txt

Sports an inclusive list of the codes for all United States and world airports, arranged alphabetically by airport code.

International Traveler's Clinic

http://www.intmed.mcw.edu/ITC/Health.html

Provides information on diseases and immunizations for travelers. Includes tips on what to pack in your travel medicine kit.

The Internet Guide to Hostels

http://www.hostels.com/hostels/

Includes a *Worldwide Hostel Guide* for throughout the world; "Talk Backpacking," a forum for asking questions, and a guide to Budget guidebooks.

Japan Airlines

http://www.spin.ad.jp/jal/home-e.html

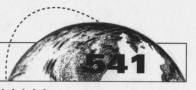

Focuses on Japan Airlines Frequent Flyer information. Also provides a Japanese language version.

Jerusalem Mosaic

http://www1.huji.ac.il/jeru/jerusalem.html

Provides a virtual welcome to the city of Jerusalem. Offers many interesting historical and religious fact and pictures pertaining to Jerusalem. Includes a view of Jerusalem from the sky, and an option to hear the song of Jerusalem.

Jordan

http://www.mit.edu:8001/activities/jordanians/jordan/

Serves as a guide to the Hashemite Kingdom of Jordan, its culture, people, and tourism. Includes links to Jordanian sites of interest.

KLM

http://www.ib.com:8080/business/klm/klm.html

Includes "a historic photographic diary" of the past 75 years of KLM.

LA Weather

http://www.vortex.com/weather1.Z

Provides meteorological coverage of the greater Los Angeles area.

Lake Tahoe News Network

http://www.tahoe.com/

Serves as a visitor's guide to Lake Tahoe. Contains information on history, news and events, hiking trails, and more. Also offers some images of the Tahoe area.

Las Vegas

http://www.vegas.com

Includes a wide range of vacation-planning information concerning Las Vegas, ranging from hotel information and reservations, to show schedules, sports, conventions, betting tips, and business services.

Lauda Air

http://www.laudaair.com/engl/indexe.htm

Promotes an Austrian airline that services Milan, Munich, London, Brussels, and Paris. Includes basic schedule and airline information.

List of Servers—District of Columbia

http://www.fie.com/www/district.htm

Offers lists, lists, and more lists. Offers the opportunity to connect to anything and everything D.C.-related, from government to entertainment and beyond.

Lonely Planet Travel Centre

http://www.lonelyplanet.com.au/

Offers *Lonely Planet* guides, which provide travelers information somewhat off the beaten path. Provides information about the guides and also information about the travel resources on the Internet.

Los Angeles Traffic Report

http://www.scubed.com/caltrans/la/la_transnet.html

Features real-time traffic data for Los Angeles, updated once a minute. Contains current area of congestion, five minute and real-time map, and tables of current speeds on freeways.

Louisville Visitors Center

http://iglou.com/lou/lou_main.html

Provides visitor information, attractions, area organizations, economic and business information, and more.

Lufthansa Timetable Info

http://www.tkz.fh-rpl.de/tii/lh/lhflug-e.html

Focuses on departure information on Lufthansa flights to and from Europe. Furnishes a German version of the page.

Maui Interactive

http://maui.net/~kelii/MIA/MI.html

Serves as an interactive guide to Maui. Contains information on travel, entertainment, maps, photography, magazines, and art.

Mexicana Airlines

http://www.catalog.com/cgibin/var/mx/index.html

Provides a graphic-intensive airline Web site for Mexico. Includes maps, vacation specials, and current testing of reservation system.

Milwaukee Marketplace

http://www.mixcom.com/index.html

Lists hundreds of places to visit, shop, or just see in Milwaukee.

The Monaco Home Page

http://www.monaco.mc/

Presents the Principality of Monaco. Provides information on tourism, business, and motor racing. Includes English and French versions.

The Monaco Home Page

Mount Cook Airlines

http://www.clearfield.co.nz/mount_cook/

Offers information on New Zealand, in additon to schedules and exchange rates.

NetWeb Bermuda Home Page

http://www.bermuda.com/

Provides information about Bermuda. Offers links to Bermuda travel information and cultural information. Also serves as an advertising site for Bermuda businesses.

New Brunswick, Canada: Outdoor Adventures

http://www.csi.nb.ca/tourism/

Advertises Outdoor Adventures vacation packages, which include whale watching, scuba-diving, sailing, kayaking, canoing, hiking, bird-watching, and cycling in various national parks and other locations.

New England Airlines

http://www.ids.net/flybi/

Offers flights to Block Island, Nantucket, Martha's Vineyard, and Cape Cod. Emphasizes Block Island and provides information on the island itself.

Northwest Airlines

http://www.winternet.com/~tela/nwa-info.html

Includes background about Northwest Airlines, recent developments, and its fleet of aircraft.

Norwegian Cruise Line

http://www.explore.com/ncl/ncl.html

Provides information on Norwegian Cruise Line's specific cruise ships, their destinations, itineraries, and travel fees.

Palo Alto, California

http://www.city.palo-alto.ca.us/home.html

Provides information about medical facilities, schools, parks, recreation, and government in Palo Alto, California.

Quantas Airlines

http://www.anzac.com/qantas/qantas.htm

Includes schedules, a history of the airline, links to related sites on Australia and other airlines. Offers pictures of koalas, too.

Qantas Airways Ltd

Railroad Timetables

http://www-cse.ucsd.edu/users/bowdidge/railroad/rail-gopher.html

Offers links to timetables for United (Amtrak) and commuter lines; Canada, Europe, Asia, and Oceania.

rec.travel. library

http://www.digimark.net/rec-travel/

Provides travel information. Features travel-related newsgroups with searching capability for archives. Also includes hotel, tour operators, and world-wide rail information.

Reno Airlines

http://www.renoair.com/

Provides minimal information on the background of the airlines, but does offer maps and a referral to reservation service.

Resort Sports Network

http://www.resortsportsnet.com/biz/rsn/

Provides information for the avid vacationer. Includes weather, activities, and more for various vacation spots.

RING. Online: Michigan's Electronic Magazine

http://www.ring.com/michigan.html

Offers information on Michigan, such as local news and events, sightseeing and travel, entertainment, and more.

Round-The-World Travel Guide

http://www.digimark.net/rec-travel/rtw/html/faq.html

Offers links to sites that help you make travel decisions, choose transportation and accommodations, and provide information on money matters and communications. Covers travel-related newsgroups.

Royal Caribbean Cruise Line

http://mmink.com/mmink/kiosks/costa/rccl.html

Provides information on Royal Caribbean Cruise Line cruise ships and their destinations, itineraries, and travel fees.

Safari Helicopters

http://hoohana.aloha.net/safari/

Offers helicopter tours of Kauai and the Big Island. Includes a "Virtual Helicopter Tour" of QuickTime movies of locations.

Salzburg, Austria

http://www.tcs.co.at/fvp.html

Provides information about Salzburg (in German and English).

San Diego, California

http://white.nosc.mil/sandiego.html

Provides information about San Diego. Features include restaurant listings, local school information, attractions, and disaster and emergency response procedures.

Santa Barbara County

http://www.internet-cafe.com/sb/sb.html

Provides information about businesses, community service, events and leisure activities, and visitor information.

Scenic Airlines

http://www.best.com/~pcap/scenic.htm

Specializes in tours of the Grand Canyon, Monument Valley, Bryce, and more. Includes current prices. Lets you make reservations online.

St. Louis, Missouri

http://www.st-louis.mo.us/

Invites you to visit the "Gateway to the West." Provides information about tourist sites, restaurants, museums, and more.

Staunton, Virginia

http://www.elpress.com:80/staunton/

Invites you to visit historical Staunton, Virginia, founded in the 1740s. Offers virtual historical tours, maps, and access to many visitor attractions.

TexasAustin

http://www.quadralay.com/www/Austin/Austin.html

Provides information about Austin's government, the local area, including attractions and universities, and more.

TGV: French High Speed Train

http://www-leland.stanford.edu/~ctillier/tgv/tgvindex.html

Features TGV, the French high-speed train. Includes background, graphics, and schedules (in French) and links to other high-speed train sites around the world.

TII—Tourism Info Internet

http://www.tkz.fh-rpl.de/tii/tii-e.html

Provides an index to information on flights, rail, hotels, tourist news, newsgroups, and country information around the world. Includes English and German versions.

Tour Canada without Leaving Your Desk

http://www.cs.cmu.edu/Web/Unofficial/Canadiana/Travelogue.html

Offers a page of links to many different sites about Canada and each of its provinces.

Travel & Entertainment Network (TEN-IO) Home Page

http://www.ten-io.com/index.html

Maintains a searchable database of travel-related information, including a seperate Frequent Flyer information database. Also offers a downloadable demo copy of their Trip Finder for Travelers software.

Travel Discounts

http://www.boms.com/discount/index.html

Provides information about discounts and information on car rentals, railroads, tours, cruises, airlines, and specific tour packages arranged by region.

Travel Discounts Cruise Index

http://www.traveldiscounts.com/cruises/cruindex.html

Provides discount cruise information, arranged by region. Includes up-to-date information and the option to make a reservation online.

Travel Information

http://galaxy.einet.net/GJ/travel.html

Offers information links to many different places, including all the states and Africa.

Travel Online

http://tol.com/tol/

Provides information about travel locations, tour packages, accomodations, travel bargains and many more travel topics. Also lets you make reservations and purchases online.

The Travel Page

http://www.travelpage.com/

Provides information on hotels and reservations, cruises, and air travel.

Travel to Finland

http://www.travel.fi/Welcome.html

Provides information on Finland, including the usual fare of information a tourist might want, as hotels, shopping, and maps (clickable). Offers the pages in English and Suomi.

The Travel Web

http://www.travelweb.com/

Targets the traveler looking for hotel information on the Web. Lets you specify criteria for a hotel room, such as location, chain, amenities, and rates. Also offers links to a comprehensive list of major hotel chains and travel agencies.

Travel Web Search Page

http://www.travelweb.com/thisco/global/travel.html?

Lists hotels by city and country. Lets you search for the right type of hotel by location, property type, and lodging chain. Also offers links to the required hotels.

TravelASIA

http://silkroute.com/silkroute/travel/index.html

Contains information about what you need to know before you travel to several Asian destinations. Provides information on topics such as climate, entry regulations, customs regulations, tipping policies, local transportation options, health issues, and even information on local electricity, water, and banking. Also provides a list of TravelASIA hotels, along with links to other Asian travel resources.

TravelASSIST—Online Travel Information

http://travelassist.com/ta_home.html

Serves as an online mall in which companies in the tourism and travel industry can describe their services. Features the Register of Bed and Breakfast Inns and Small Hotels. Contains more than 600 listings for bed-and-breakfasts submitted by owners.

TravelBase

http://www.travelbase.com/

Focuses primarily on ski and scuba vacation spots. Claims to have a list of all the ski resorts available on the Web. Also offers extensive information on Orlando, Florida, and the Florida Keys. Lets you conduct by clicking on a map or using a search form.

TravelSearch

http://www.bendnet.com/travelsearch.html

Offers to provide a concise destination sheet telling you the worthwhile things to do in your destination city (for a fee).

TravelSource

http://www.travelsource.com/

Includes topics such as resorts, hotels, sports, golfing, ranches, cycling, yachts, and more.

U/Seattle

http://useattle.uspan.com

Serves as a guide to events in the greater Seattle area. Also includes a weather link and news information.

United Kingdom Pages

http://www.neosoft.com/~dlgates/uk/ukindex.html

Provides information about the United Kingdom in many categories: higher education, cities, countryside, culture, government, travel and employment, and miscellaneous. Provides more than a thousand links to other sites, primarily within the United Kingdon. Also lists bed-and-breakfast accommodations, picturesque pubs, and so forth. Offers several photo albums of downloadable images, including a page of photographs of the Royals.

United Kingdom— Manchester Geology Department

http://info.mcc.ac.uk/Geology/home-page.html

Presents the Department of Earth Sciences at the University of Manchester. Offers links to research about geology and other education issues. Also invites you to take a tour of the city.

United States State Department Travel Warnings and Consular Info Sheets

http://www.stolaf.edu/network/travel-advisories.html

Provides up-to-date information on traveling to countries around the world, including warnings, entry requirements, and crime information. Lets you subscribe via e-mail to receive travel advisories throughout this site.

USA City Link

http://www.NeoSoft.com/citylink/

Focuses on travel and tourism information about individual states and cities in the United States, arranged by states in alphabetical order.

USA CityLink

http://www.NeoSoft.com:80/citylink/

Lists cities and their states. Lets you look up almost any city in the United States and find information about schools, government, the local community, and more. Offers many links.

ValleyWeb

http://www.nstn.ca:80/valley/

Serves as the virtual home of the Nova Scotia's Annapolis Valley, "where the land and sea merge, the past lingers in the present, and both the French and English have found a home." Provides information about the Valley's towns and villages, businesses, tourist sites, historical sites, Acadia University, and many links to other places.

Vancouver, British Columbia

http://freenet.vancouver.bc.ca

Provides FreeNet's information and links. Also offers links to the British Columbian home page and other Canadian home pages.

Victoria, British Columbia

http://freenet.victoria.bc.ca/vifa.html

A community-based network available at no cost to residents and visitors of Victoria. Provides easy access to businesses, individuals, government, and more.

Virgin Atlantic Airlines

http://www.fly.virgin.com/atlantic/

Provides information about special offers, frequent flyer miles, and more. Lets you plan your flight online. Also furnishes articles from their magazine, *Hot Air*.

Virtual Tourist II

http://wings.buffalo.edu/world/vt2/europe.html

Provides information on various countries, including city information, culture and language, education, maps, news, and so forth. Presents a graphical interface composed of maps—you click on the map to select a country's page. Provides a text-based version for faster access of the information.

Web Travel Review

http://webtravel.org/webtravel/

Includes more than 600 pages of text and more than 2,000 photographs of the personal travel experiences of travel writer, Philip Greenspun. Showcases many pictures.

The Webfoot's Travel Guides

http://www.webfoot.com/travel/guides/guides.top.html

Serves as a "thinking person's guide" to traveling to Austria, British Virgin Islands, France, Germany, Italy, Spain, Vatican City, and the state of Hawaii. Provides links to good overall information about each location, such as general information, city/site information, public transportation, language, literature and culture, and tips for tourists.

The West Virginia Web

http://wvweb.com

Serves as West Virginia's main entry ramp to the worldwide information superhighway and the Internet. Pertains to the West Virginia travel industry, economic development, government and virtually any other area of interest within West Virginia.

Western Pacific Airlines

http://www.cucruising.com/cu/wpair.html

Provides detailed schedule and fare information.

Where to Stay in the Caribbean

http://www.christwh.com/islands/index.html

Serves as an online guide to more than 200 resorts and hotels in the Caribbean, arranged by Island, topic, and alphabetically by resort.

Wholesale Travel Centre

http://www.dgsys.com/~airfare/index.html

Serves as an airfare quoting reservation service. Lets you enter where and when you want to go and e-mails you back a quote on what it will cost.

The Yankee Traveler

http://www.tiac.net/users/macgyver/ne.html

Provides a compilation of travel-related sources relating to New England. Includes state Web pages, information on Cape Cod and the Islands, bed-and-breakfast inns, and map links. Provides information on real estate, local businesses, and more.

The American Humanist Association

http://freethought.tamu.edu/org/aha/#weddings

Contains a collection of articles, essays, commentaries, lists, and so on. Contains information in the Special Occasions section on how to conduct various types of Humanist wedding ceremonies.

Ans Bolk Personal Design Bridal Couture

http://www.xs4all.nl/~gijs/ansbolk.htm

Creates exclusive bridal and evening gowns. Designs gowns that suit the personality of the client in style and cut. Offers a large selection of materials appropriate to the design, including silks and laces imported from various countries. Also offers to adorn the fabrics with exclusive embroidery.

Bridal Net: Online Bridal Registry

http://204.96.64.1/bridalnet/

Provides an online shopping and bridal registry with images of china and silverware patterns. Features information about major retailers' Bridal Registries, including tips and advice on how to register, color pictures of products, and store locations and phone numbers. Also offers links to other online bridal services and honeymoon destinations.

The Bridal Veil Home Page

http://www.hooked.net/users/sraney/

Provides information about bridal veils. Offers a short history of bridal attire and information on matching your veil and hair.

Caribmoon

http://www.caribweb.com/caribweb/caribmoon/

Provides information for couples wanting to get married or honeymoon in the Caribbean Islands. Offers specific wedding instructions and requirements pertaining to each island.

Celebration Vineyards

http://www.deltanet.com/intersphere/cv/

Advertises Vineyard Celebrations, which provides personalized wedding favors, such as customized labels for champagne and sparkling cider table favors. Shows examples of each.

Club Wed Press

http://www.io.org/~clubwed/

Advertises a service, which provides a personal *Club Wed Press Newsletter* that introduces you to guests and helps them plan for the ceremony, reception, and other special events. Also offers some tips on how to use the newsletter.

Coconut Coast Weddings and Honeymoons

http://hoohana.aloha.net/cocowed/

Advertises the services of Coconut Coast Weddings and Honeymoons, which specializes in planning and coordinating weddings, vow renewals, and honeymoons. Also offers a list of various packages and the marriage license requirements for Hawaii.

Aloha and Welcome to Coconut Coast Weddings and Honeymoons!

Collected Domestic Partners Information

http://www.cs.cmu.edu/afs/cs.cmu.edu/user/scotts/domestic-partners/mainpage.html

Contains information and links to information on topics related to domestic partnerships and same-sex marriages. Offers excellent resources on policies in various companies and universities, family leave and adoption policies, and legal opinions.

Engagement Diamond FAQ

http://www.wam.umd.edu/~sek/wedding/diamonds2.txt

Provides a list of frequently asked questions (FAQs) about buying a diamond, written by Peter Mlynek (not a gemologist but rather, an experienced diamond buyer).

The Fabulous Northwest Wedding Page

http://www.halcyon.com/lavender/wed.html

Contains wedding information "for all those who have a passion for the Grand Spectacle and an aversion for printed matchbooks . . . ." Offers information on etiquette, personal style, locations, and other topics.

Hora Bridal Accessories

http://www.netmart.com/hora/

Advertises bridal accessories offered by Hora.

HvH Video Productions

http://www.epix.net/~johnvh/hvh.html

Advertises the services of HvH Video Productions, which offers to transfer slides, photos, 8 mm movies, or printed materials to video, convert videos to various formats, or dub and edit videos.

Imagemaker's Kalendarized Keepsakes

http://www.onramp.net/imagemaker/calendar.html

Put your favorite photos in a 12-month calendar.

Imagi-Nations

http://www.netmart.com/imagi-nations/

Advertises bridal gowns offered by Imagi-Nations, styles by Watters and Watters.

Indian Matrimonial Service

http://mammen.clark.net/marriage/

Contains classified ads with proposals for marriage. Lets you post your own ad or reply to existing ads.

Island Wedding SuperClubs, Jamaica

http://www.kaiwan.com/~travel/island.html

Advertises the services of SuperClubs Resorts. Offers honeymoon escapes, but now couples are electing to have their wedding at these resorts.

Jewish Marriage Enhancement

http://peewee.chinalake.navy.mil/computational_sciences/staff/carey/JME/index.html

Advertises the Jewish Marriage Enhancement, a weekend program for married couples to explore the fullest potential for their relationship. Emphasizes communication.

The Jim Harmon Group, Inc.

http://www.usit.net/harmon

Offers wedding games, guides, and prayers. Describes the products offered and provides ordering information.

Leslie's Guide to Wedding Planning

http://acm.vt.edu/~lfowler/wed/wedding.html

Provides information in the format of a wedding planning guide. Contains information on ceremony and reception music, readings, flowers and their meanings, links to other wedding Web sites, a bride's emergency kit, shower games, a photo checklist, a list of places to register, honeymoons in Hawaii, ceremonies, cookware, invitations, and miscellaneous other things.

Love, Sex, and Marriage

http://intertain.com/store/new-browse/
Love_Sex_and_Marriage.html

Online bookstore. Offers many titles on various topics relating to relationships, marriage, sex, and family. Includes a search tool you can use to look for certain titles or authors.

Marriage Enrichment

http://www.io.org/~enrich/

Advertises the Marriage Enrichment computerized program developed by Dr. Charles Dorothy and Pastor Kenneth Westby. Also contains a collection of self-help resources that you can order, as well as links to other sites.

Mary and Michael Wedding Photography

http://www.commerce.digital.com/palo-alto/WeddingPhoto/
home.html

Advertises photographic services offered by Mary and Michael of Palo Alto, California. Also provides a section on "Tips for Togetherness" for couples.

Match.com

http://www.match.com/

Serves as an interactive matchmaking site at which you can read descriptions of people looking for a match or leave your own description.

Melanet Online African Wedding Guide

http://www.melanet.com/melanet/wedding/

Focuses on giving you ideas and guiding you to resources. Represents a hodgepodge of African traditions, as well as adaptations to the ways of African Americans. Includes examples of how others have had African-centered weddings. Also provides consumer and retail information.

Meryl and Yusuf's Wedding Page

http://www.eecs.nwu.edu/~yusuf/meryl-yusuf-wedding.html

Presents a personal wedding page. Meryl and Yusef provide their before-wedding plans and then details of how it went. They also have their wedding announcement in both English and Turkish.

Music for Weddings and Receptions

http://www.wam.umd.edu/~sek/wedding/music.html

Contains a listing of music titles for weddings and receptions.

Ninga Software Corporation: "The Wedding Planner"

http://www.freenet.calgary.ab.ca/trade/ninga.html#wedding

Advertises Ninga Software Corporation's "The Wedding Planner," a program that helps the organizer (usually the bride) with the invitations, RSVPs, gifts, and thank-you cards.

P.S. I Love You

http://www.psiloveyou.com/

Serves as a matchmaking center for women from all over the world. Includes helping establish initial electronic introductions and in-person meetings.

Peachtree Circle, Inc.

http://www.mindspring.com/~pcircle/pcircle.html

Offers distinctive gifts for wedding attendants.

Personal Wedding Pages on the Net

http://www.wam.umd.edu/~sek/readwed/readwed.html

Helps you announce your wedding over the Web. Offers to link to your wedding page or create a page for you. Lists couples by the year of wedding and includes many photos.

PeterLink

http://www.infopro.spb.su/

Contains information on St. Petersburg, Russia. Also offers links to an area where you can become acquainted with Russian males or females. Lets you leave your own personal information through a form.

Poems for Disposable Cameras

http://www.wam.umd.edu/~sek/wedding/camerapoems.html

Provides some examples of poems you can use to let the guests know what you expect them to do with the disposable cameras you've provided at your wedding.

Rialto Archive: Period and SCA Weddings

http://fermi.clas.virginia.edu/~gl8f/rialto/weddings.html

Provides a collection of messages about various types of weddings, including medieval, early Christian, middle Eastern, and SCA (Society for Creative Anachronism).

Same-Sex Marriage Home Page

http://www.nether.net/~rod/html/sub/marriage.html

Contains links to Internet resources, state news, lobby groups, articles, and general information related to same-sex marriages.

Simply Software: "Brides-maids for Windows"

http://infolane.com/infolane/simply/bride.html

Advertises "Bridesmaids for Windows," a Windows application that helps the wedding planner organize invitations, gifts, RSVPs, thank-you notes, expenses, and important dates.

soc.couples.wedding WWW Page

http://www.wam.umd.edu/~sek/wedding.html

Web page for the newsgroup soc.couples.wedding, a forum for discussing all aspects of wedding planning, from engagement through honeymoon. Includes, but isn't limited to, topics such as purchasing engagement/wedding jewelry and gifts, announcing the engagement, setting a wedding date, hiring professionals such as caterers and photographers, renting facilities such as churches and halls, planning the ceremony, wedding-related etiquette, registering for gifts, selecting wedding attire, and dealing with relationship/family problems associated with wedding planning. Doesn't limit discussions to weddings between one man and one woman. Invites same-sex couples and groups of more than two people planning a wedding to participate. Also welcomes discussions of wedding traditions from around the world.

Sophisticated Chocolates

http://branch.com/sophisticated/

Advertises services by Sophisticated Chocolates Mfg., Inc. Specializes in supplying gift box chocolate assortments, chocolate corporate logo's, chocolate-filled gift baskets, personalized wedding favors, and many other chocolate products.

Sposabella Bridal— La Sposa Veil

http://www.hydra.com/sposa/sposa.html

Shows veils and head attire offered by Sposabella Bridal of New York. Offers images of their products.

Talking Personals

http://204.239.18.1/vanpersonals/

Contains the Vancouver Talking Personals, which contains descriptions of more than 3,000 men and women in online advertisements. Uses both community newspapers and the Web. All ads are currently running or have appeared in print in one of the 14 VanNet community newspapers with a circulation of over 650,000 at least twice per week. Ads are placed for free in one of the community newspapers via audiotext system. The system asks questions to match you with prospective partners. Voice ads are transcribed and published in the community newspaper at least once. Also offers a section on relationship tips.

The TouchSoft: "I Do Ultimate Wedding Planner"

http://www.worldport.com:80/touchsoft/

Advertises a Windows-based software application that helps you organize, plan, and budget your wedding. Provides information on its features, how it works, and how to order it.

Wedding Announcement Circle Home Page

http://www.cipsinc.com/wedding/announce/

Offers free announcement space for couples.

Wedding Bell Blueprint

http://www.videomaker.com/edit/wedding.html

Provides an article that tells the professional secrets of how to videotape a wedding with a single camera. Gives advice on story visualization, rehearsals, and how to best capture the ceremony.

Wedding Cam

http://www.webcom.com/~camera/wedding.html

Advertises the single use camera made by Custom Camera Design, Inc. Provides instructions on how to get your wedding guests involved in the picture-taking process.

Wedding Gardens

http://www.olympus.net/gardens/gwedd.htm

Serves as a complete guide to gardens in the United States. Offers a detailed description of each garden along with contact information.

A Wedding Made in Paradise

http://www.maui.net/~wedmaui/

Advertises wedding locations and custom planning services for couples getting married in Maui, Hawaii.

Wedding Photography Guide and FAQ

http://www.wam.umd.edu/~sek/wedding/photofaq.txt

Focuses on helping you understand wedding photography from the behind-the-camera-side to make wiser choices in your own purchase, as well as get the most from it after you have contracted.

Wedding Planning Timetable

http://www.wam.umd.edu/~sek/wedding/schedule.html

Contains a timetable for wedding planning.

The Wedding Source

http://www.pep.com/pep/tws/tws.html

Provides information on wedding vendors and serves as a place to find and exchange ideas. Contains links to other sites relating to weddings or wedding-related products.

Weddings, with Makana

http://204.182.49.10/wed1.html

Advertises a private estate that offers wedding locations and a full range of onsite wedding services, including videographers, musicians, vocalists, dancers and drummers, photographers, florals, champagnes, and wedding cakes.

Weddings Online

http://sensemedia.net/sprawl/weddings

Provides an online shopping guide with links to bridal service providers, such as jewelers, photography, stylists, bands, and so on. Also provides a wedding guide section with links to a wedding planning timeline, planning software, marriage laws, and tips from pros.

The World Wide Web Dating Game

http://www.cid.com/cid/date/

Imitates the TV version of the dating game. Lets you participate either as a voting member of the "audience," where you decide who the entrant should go out with, or fill out a form and try to get in the Dating Game yourself.

WorldWide Marriage Encounter

http://www.scri.fsu.edu/~sollohub/wwme/wwme.html

Advertises WorldWide Marriage Encounter, a program designed to give married couples the opportunity to examine their lives together. Emphasizes communication between husband and wife.

APPENDIX A:
COLLEGES AND UNIVERSITIES

The following list contains the names and *Uniform Resource Locators* (URLs) of more than 1,500 World Wide Web sites maintained by colleges and universities. These sites provide information about degree programs, curricula, research, student life, and other areas of interest associated with institutions of higher learning.

A.C.C. College

http://www.hk.linkage.net/~cat/avcc.html

Aachen University of Technology

http://www.informatik.rwth-aachen.de/RWTH/

Aalborg Business College

http://www.aalborges.dk/

Aalborg University

http://www.auc.dk/

Abilene Christian University

http://cteserver.acu.edu/

Academy Canada

http://www.compusult.nf.ca/~micronet/academycanada/

Acadia University

http://www.acadiau.ca/

Adam Mickiewicz University

http://www.amu.edu.pl/welcome.html

Agder College

http://www.aid.no/

Agnes Scott College

http://www.scottlan.edu/

Agricultural University of Norway

http://www.nlh.no/Studie_kontor/info_eng/info_eng.html

Akita University

http://quartet.bb.akita-u.ac.jp/index-e.html

Albert Szentgyorgyi Medical University

http://www.szote.u-szeged.hu/

Albertson College of Idaho

http://www.acofi.edu/

Albion College

http://www.albion.edu/

Alfred University

http://www.alfred.edu

Algarve University

http://strauss.si.ualg.pt:8080/

Allentown College

http://www.allencol.edu/

Altay State University

http://dcn-asu.altai.su/ENTRY.en.html

American University

http://www.american.edu/

American University in Bulgaria

http://www.aubg.bg/

Amherst College

http://www.amherst.edu/

Andrews University School of Business

http://www.cs.andrews.edu/index.html

Anglia Polytechnic University

http://www.anglia.ac.uk/

Anna University

http://www.engr.uky.edu/~arunp/anna.html

Annamalai University

http://wwwvms.utexas.edu/~thaths/auhome.html

Antioch University

http://college.antioch.edu/

Aoyama Gakuin

http://www.bb.aoyama.ac.jp/index-e.html

Appalachian State University

http://www.acs.appstate.edu/

Aristotle University of Thessaloniki

http://www.lance.colostate.edu/auth/

Arizona State University

http://www.asu.edu/

Arizona Western College

http://www.awc.cc.az.us/

Armstrong State College

http://www.armstrong.edu/

Ashland University

http://www.ashland.edu/

Asian Institute of Technology

http://emailhost.ait.ac.th/

Askeri Elektronik Sanayi

http://www.aselsan.com.tr/

Assumption College

http://www.assumption.edu:80/

Assumption University

http://www.au.ac.th/

Aston University

http://www.aston.ac.uk/

Ateneo de Manila University

http://kilaw.admu.edu.ph/

Athena University

http://symnet.net/~VOU/au.html

Atlantic Community College

http://www.atlantic.edu/

Attila Jozsef University

http://www.jate.u-szeged.hu/

Auburn University

http://mallard.duc.auburn.edu/

Augsburg College

http://www.augsburg.edu/

Augustana College, Rock Island, Illinois

http://www.augustana.edu/

Austin College

http://www.austinc.edu/

Australian International Hotel School

http://hotelschool.cornell.edu/aihs/

Azusa Pacific University

http://apu.edu/

Baker University

http://www.bakeru.edu/

Ball State University

http://virgo.bsu.edu:8080/

Bangkok University

http://www.bu.ac.th/

Barnard College

http://www.barnard.columbia.edu/

Bates College

http://abacus.bates.edu/

Baylor College of Dentistry

http://www.ont.com/baylords/

Baylor College of Medicine

http://www.bcm.tmc.edu/

Baylor University

http://www.baylor.edu/

Beaver College

http://www.beaver.edu/

Beijing Agricultural University

http://www.ihep.ac.cn:3000/uni/BAU/agri.html

Beijing University of Chemical Technology

http://www.buct.edu.cn/

Belmont University

http://acklen.belmont.edu/

Beloit College

http://stu.beloit.edu/

Bemidji State University

http://bsuweb.bemidji.msus.edu/

Ben-Gurion University of the Negev

http://www.cs.bgu.ac.il/

Benedictine College

http://www.benedictine.edu/

Berea College

http://www.berea.edu/

Bergen College

http://www.hib.no/

Bergen University

http://www.uib.no/index-eng.html

Bermuda College

http://www.bercol.bm/

Berufsakademie Ravensburg

http://www.ba-ravensburg.de/home.htm

Bessenyei Gyorgy Teachers' Training College

http://www.bgytf.hu/

Bethany College

http://info.bethany.wvnet.edu/

Bethel College and Seminary, St. Paul, Minnesota

http://www.bethel.edu/

Bethel College, Newton, Kansas

http://www.bethelks.edu/

Bilkent University

http://www.bilkent.edu.tr/bilkent.html

Binghamton University

http://www.binghamton.edu/

Biola University

http://www.biola.edu/

Birkbeck College

http://www.bbk.ac.uk/

Birmingham-Southern College

http://www.bsc.edu/

Bishop's University

http://venus.ubishops.ca/

Black Hills State University

http://www.bhsu.edu/

Blackburn College

http://www.mcs.net/~kwplace/bc.htm

Bloomsburg University

http://www.bloomu.edu/

Bluffton College

http://www.bluffton.edu/

Bogazici University

http://www.boun.edu.tr/

Boise State University

http://www.idbsu.edu/

Bond University

http://bond.edu.au/

Boston College

http://infoeagle.bc.edu/

Boston University

http://web.bu.edu

Bowdoin College

http://www.bowdoin.edu/

Bowling Green State University

http://www.bgsu.edu/

Bradley University

http://www.bradley.edu/

Brandeis University

http://www.cs.brandeis.edu/

Bridgewater College

http://www.bridgewater.edu/

Brigham Young University

http://www.byu.edu/

Brigham Young University, Hawaii

http://www.byuh.edu/

Bristol University

http://www.bris.ac.uk/

Brock University

http://spartan.ac.brocku.ca/

Brookdale Community College

http://soho.ios.com/~andrewjr/

Brooklyn College

http://146.245.2.151/

Brown University

http://www.brown.edu/

Brunel University

http://http1.brunel.ac.uk:8080/

Brussels University

http://sun4.iihe.ac.be/

Bryant College

http://www.bryant.edu/

Bryn Mawr College

http://www.brynmawr.edu/

Bucknell University

http://www.bucknell.edu/

Buena Vista College, Storm Lake, Iowa

http://othmar.bvc.edu/

Butler University

http://www.butler.edu/

Butte Community College

http://www.cin.butte.cc.ca.us/

Cabot College of Applied Arts, Technology, and Continuing Education

http://www.cabot.nf.ca/

California Coast University

http://www.calcoastuniv.edu/ccu/

California Institute of Technology

http://www.caltech.edu/

California Institute of the Arts

http://www.calarts.edu/

California Lutheran University

http://callutheran.edu/

California Polytechnic State University, San Luis Obispo

http://www.calpoly.edu/

California State Polytechnic University, Pomona

http://www.csupomona.edu/

California State University

http://www.calstate.edu/

California State University, Bakersfield

http://www.csubak.edu/

California State University, Chico

http://www.csuchico.edu/

California State University, Dominguez Hills

http://dolphin.csudh.edu/

California State University, Fresno

http://athena.lib.csufresno.edu/csuf.htm

California State University, Hayward

http://www.mcs.csuhayward.edu/

California State University, Long Beach

http://www.csulb.edu/

California State University, Los Angeles

http://www.calstatela.edu/

California State University, Northridge

http://www.csun.edu/

California State University, Sacramento

http://www.csus.edu/

California State University, San Bernardino

http://www.csusb.edu/

California State University, San Marcos

http://coyote.csusm.edu/

California State University, Stanislaus

http://lead.csustan.edu/

Calvin College

http://www.calvin.edu/

Cambridge University

http://www.cam.ac.uk/

Camosun College

http://www.camosun.bc.ca/camosun.html

Canadore College

http://www.canadorec.on.ca/

Capital Community-Technical College

http://neo-oreo.commnet.edu/

Cardinal Stritch College

http://acs.stritch.edu/

Carleton College

http://www.carleton.edu/

Carleton University

http://www.carleton.ca/

Carnegie Mellon University

http://www.cmu.edu/

Carroll College

http://carroll1.cc.edu/

Case Western Reserve University

http://litwww.cwru.edu/

Catholic University of America

http://www.cua.edu/

Catholic University of Louvain

http://www.sc.ucl.ac.be/UCL/gb/intro.html

Cedarville College

http://www.cedarville.edu/DPMA/Cedarville.html

Centenary College of Louisiana

http://alpha.centenary.edu/

Central Connecticut State University

http://neal.ctstateu.edu/Home.html

Central Florida Community College

http://205.129.12.3/

Central Institute of Technology

http://www.cit.ac.nz/

Central Michigan University

http://www.cmich.edu/

Central Missouri State University

http://cmsuvmb.cmsu.edu/

Central Oregon Community College

http://www.cocc.edu/

Central Queensland University

http://www.cqu.edu.au/

Central Washington University

http://www.cwu.edu/

Centre College

http://www.centre.edu/

Centre Universitaire Saint-Louis-Maillet

http://www.cuslm.ca/index-e.htm

Cerritos College

http://www.cerritos.edu

Chalmers University of Technology

http://www.chalmers.se/Home-E.html

Chandler-Gilbert Community College

http://140.198.129.30/

Chapman University

http://www.chapman.edu/

Charles Sturt University

http://www.csu.edu.au/

Charles University, Prague

http://www.cuni.cz/

Chase College of Law

http://nku.edu/~fooks/Chase.html

Chemeketa Community College

http://web.chemek.cc.or.us/

Chiba University

http://www.hike.te.chiba-u.ac.jp/chiba-u/

Chicago-Kent College of Law

http://www.kentlaw.edu/

Chinese University of Hong Kong

http://www.cuhk.hk/

Christchurch Polytechnic

http://vesta.chch.planet.co.nz/polytech/polytech.html

Christian Brothers University

http://www.cbu.edu/

Christopher Newport University

http://www.pcs.cnu.edu/

Chukyo University

http://www.sccs.chukyo-u.ac.jp/

Chulalongkorn University

http://www.netserv.chula.ac.th/

Chung Hua Polytechnic Institute

http://www.chpi.edu.tw/

Chung-Ang University

http://bbs.cba.cau.ac.kr/

Chungbuk National University

http://cbubbs.chungbuk.ac.kr/~jeongjh/cbnu/welcome.html

ChungNam National University

http://infocomm2.chungnam.ac.kr/

Citadel

http://macs01.mathcs.citadel.edu/

City University

http://web.city.ac.uk/

City University of Hong Kong

http://www.cityu.edu.hk/

City University of New York

http://www.cuny.edu/

City University, Seattle, Washington

http://www.cityu.edu/inroads/welcome1.html

Claremont College

http://www.clare.tased.edu.au/

Clark Atlanta University

http://www.cau.auc.edu/

Clark University

http://www.clarku.edu/

Clarkson University

http://fire.clarkson.edu/

Clemson University

http://www.clemson.edu/home.html

Cleveland State University

http://www.csuohio.edu/

Coe College

http://www.coe.edu

Colby College

http://www.colby.edu/

Colgate University

http://arachnid.colgate.edu/

Collaborative Information Technology Research Institute

http://www.citri.edu.au/

College of Aeronautics

http://www.mordor.com/coa/coa.html

College of Charleston

http://www.cofc.edu/

College of Eastern Utah

http://www.ceu.edu/

College of St. Catherine

http://www.stkate.edu/

College of Staten Island

http://www.csi.cuny.edu/

College of William and Mary

http://www.wm.edu/

College of Wooster

http://www.wooster.edu/

Colorado Christian University

http://www.ccu.edu/

Colorado College

http://www.cc.colorado.edu/

Colorado School of Mines

http://gn.mines.colorado.edu:80/

Colorado State University

http://www.colostate.edu/

Columbia College

http://www.colum.edu/

Columbia University

http://www.columbia.edu/

Concordia College

http://www.cord.edu/

Concordia University

http://www.concordia.ca/

Concordia University, River Forest

http://www.cuis.edu/www/curf/home.html

Connecticut College

http://camel.conncoll.edu/

Cooper Union

http://www.cooper.edu/

Copenhagen Business School

http://www.cbs.dk/

Cornell College

http://www.cornell-iowa.edu/

Cornell University

http://www.cornell.edu/

Cornerstone College

http://www.grfn.org/~cstone/

Cranfield University

http://www.cranfield.ac.uk/

Creighton University

http://bluejay.creighton.edu/

Curtin University, Western Australia

http://www.curtin.edu.au/

Czech Technical University, Prague

http://www.cvut.cz/

Da-Yeh Institute of Technology

http://www.dyit.edu.tw/

Dakota State University

http://www.dsu.edu/

Dalhousie University

http://www.dal.ca/

Dalian University of Technology

http://www-personal.engin.umich.edu/~leijiang/DUT/index.html

Dallas County Community College District

http://www.dcccd.edu/

Dana College

http://www.dana.edu/

Daniel Webster College

http://www.mv.com/users/shardy/dwc.htm

Dartmouth College

http://www.dartmouth.edu/

Davidson College

http://www.davidson.edu/

De La Salle University

http://www.dlsu.edu.ph/

De Montfort University

http://www.dmu.ac.uk/

Deakin University

http://www.deakin.edu.au/

Delaware Technical & Community College

http://www.dtcc.edu/

Delft University of Technology

http://www.tudelft.nl/

Democritus University

http://www.cc.duth.gr/

Denison University

http://www.denison.edu/

DePaul University

http://www.depaul.edu/

Devry Institute of Technology

http://www.devrycols.edu/

Diablo Valley College

http://www.dvc.edu/

Dixie College

http://sci.dixie.edu/

Dokkyo University School of Medicine

http://www.dokkyomed.ac.jp/

Dongguk University

http://www.dongguk.ac.kr/DGU/

DongSeo University

http://www.dongseo.ac.kr/

Dortmund University

http://www.uni-dortmund.de/

Downing College

http://www.dow.cam.ac.uk/

Drake University

http://www.drake.edu/default.html

Drew University

http://tarzan.drew.edu/athome.html

Drexel University

http://www.drexel.edu/

Dublin City University

http://www.compapp.dcu.ie/DCU_home.html

Dublin Institute of Technology

http://147.252.133.152/

Duke University

http://www.duke.edu/

Dundee University

http://alpha.mic.dundee.ac.uk/dusa/dusa.html

Duquesne University

http://www.duq.edu/

Earlham College

http://www.earlham.edu/

East Carolina University

http://ecuvax.cis.ecu.edu/

East Central University, Ada, Oklahoma

http://student.ecok.edu/

East Stroudsburg State University

http://www.esu.edu/

East Tennessee State University

http://etsu.east-tenn-st.edu

East Texas State University

http://www.etsu.edu/

Eastern Illinois University

http://www.eiu.edu/

Eastern Mediteranean University

http://salamis.emu.edu.tr/

Eastern Mennonite University

http://www.emu.edu/

Eastern Michigan University

http://www.emich.edu/

Eastern New Mexico State University

http://www.enmu.edu/

Eastern Washington University

http://www.ewu.edu/

Ecole Centrale Paris

http://www.ecp.fr/

Ecole Nationale Superieure des Telecomunnications de Paris

http://www.enst.fr/

Ecole Polytechnique de Montreal

http://www.polymtl.ca/

Edinboro University

http://www.edinboro.edu/

Edith Cowan University

http://www.cowan.edu.au/

Edmonds Community College

http://www.edmonds.ctc.edu/

Ege University

http://www.ege.edu.tr/

Ehime University

http://ccs42.dpc.ehime-u.ac.jp:8000/

Eindhoven University of Technology

http://www.tue.nl/

Embry Riddle Aeronautical University

http://macwww.db.erau.edu/

Emerson College

http://www.emerson.edu/

Emmanuel College

http://www.emmanuel.edu/

Emory University

http://www.cc.emory.edu/welcome.html

Engineering School of St. Gallen

http://www.bodan.net/isg/index.html

Eotvos Lorand University of Sciences

http://dtalk.elte.hu/www/welcome.html

Erasmus University of Rotterdam

http://www.eur.nl/

Erie Community College

http://davey.sunyerie.edu/

Ernst-Moritz-Arndt-University Greifswald

http://www.uni-greifswald.de/

Escuela de Administracion de Negocios para Graduados

http://www.esan.edu.pe/

Estrella Mountain Community College

http://www.emc.maricopa.edu/

Europa-University Viadrina Frankfurt

http://www.euv-frankfurt-o.de/

European Institute of Business Administration

http://www.insead.fr/

Ewha Women's University

http://arch.ewha.ac.kr/

Fayetteville State University

http://www.fsufay.edu/

Feng Chia University

http://www.fcu.edu.tw/

Ferris State University

http://about.ferris.edu/

Findhorn College

http://www.tiac.net/biz/fcie/

Fisk University

http://www.fisk.edu/

Flinders University

http://www.flinders.edu.au/

Florida A&M University

http://www-wane-leon.scri.fsu.edu:80/~jippolit/
FAMU_html/html_s/FAMU_top.html

Florida Atlantic University

http://www.fau.edu/

Florida Institute of Technology

http://www.fit.edu/

Florida International University

http://www.fiu.edu/

Florida State University

http://www.fsu.edu

Foothill College

http://www.fhda.edu/foothill/

Fort Hays State University

http://fhsuvm.fhsu.edu/

Franklin and Marshall College

http://www.fandm.edu/

Franklin Pierce College

http://www.fpc.edu/

Franklin Pierce Law Center

http://www.fplc.edu/

Fredonia State University

http://www.cs.fredonia.edu/

Freie University Berlin

http://www.chemie.fu-berlin.de/fub/index.html

Friends University

http://www.friends.edu/

Fudan University

http://www.cs.wisc.edu/~mshen/fudan.html

Fujita Health University

http://pathy.fujita-hu.ac.jp/

Fukuoka Institute of Technology

http://www.fit.ac.jp/

Fukuoka Junior College of Technology

http://www.fjct.fit.ac.jp/

Fukushima Medical College

http://www.fmu.ac.jp/index.html

Fukushima University

http://www.fukushima-u.ac.jp/

Fullerton College

http://www.fullcoll.edu/

Furman University

http://www.furman.edu/

Gainesville College

http://www.gc.peachnet.edu/

Gallaudet University

http://www.gallaudet.edu/

Gannon University

http://www.gannon.edu/

Gazi University

http://cc.gazi.edu.tr/

Gdansk Medical Academy

http://www.amg.gda.pl/

Gdansk Technical University

http://www.pg.gda.pl/pg.html

George Mason University

http://www.gmu.edu/

George Washington University

http://gwis.circ.gwu.edu/

Georgetown University

http://www.georgetown.edu/

Georgia Institute of Technology

http://www.gatech.edu/TechHome.html

Georgia State University

http://www.gsu.edu/

Gettysburg College

http://www.gettysburg.edu/

Glasgow University

http://www.gla.ac.uk/

GMI Engineering & Management Institute

http://www.gmi.edu/

Gödöllõ University of Agricultural Sciences

http://www.ktg.gau.hu/

Golden West College

http://www.gwc.cccd.edu/

Goldsmiths College, University of London

http://www.gold.ac.uk/

Gonzaga University

http://www.gonzaga.edu/

Goshen College

http://www.goshen.edu/

Goucher College

http://www.goucher.edu/

Grace College

http://www.grace.edu/

Graceland College

http://www.graceland.edu/

Graduate Institute of International Studies

http://heiwww.unige.ch/

Grant MacEwan Community College

http://www.gmcc.ab.ca/

Graz University of Technology

http://www.tu-graz.ac.at/

Griffith University

http://www.gu.edu.au/

Grinnell College

http://www.math.grin.edu/

Grossmont-Cuyamaca Community College District

http://www.gcccd.cc.ca.us/

Guilford College

http://www.guilford.edu/

Gunma University

http://www.la.gunma-u.ac.jp/

Gustavus Adolphus College

http://www.gac.edu/

Haagse Hogeschool

http://www.hhs.nl/Welcome.html

Hacettepe University

http://www.ee.hun.edu.tr/

Hachinohe Institute of Technology

http://www.hi-tech.ac.jp/

Hahnemann University

http://www.hahnemann.edu/

Hallym University

http://myrinae.hallym.ac.kr/welcome.html

Halmstad University

http://www.hh.se:7777/

Hamilton College

http://www.hamilton.edu/

Hamline University

http://www.hamline.edu/

Hampden-Sydney College

http://www.hsc.edu/

Hampshire College

http://www.hampshire.edu/

Hampton University

http://cs.hamptonu.edu/

Hangzhou University

http://bronze.ucs.indiana.edu/~zerping/hangda.htm

Hanover College

http://www.hanover.edu/

Hanyang University

http://166.104.36.75/

Harbin Engineering University

http://www.tuns.ca/~hey/hsei.html

Harding University

http://www.harding.edu/

Harvard University

http://www.harvard.edu/

Harvey Mudd College

http://www.hmc.edu/

Hastings College of Law

http://www.uchastings.edu

Haverford College

http://www.haverford.com/

Hawaii Pacific University

http://www.hpu.edu/

Heald Institute of Technology

http://www.heald.edu/

Hebrew University of Jerusalem

http://www1.huji.ac.il/

Heidelberg College

http://www.heidelberg.edu/

Heinrich-Heine-University Duesseldorf

http://www.rz.uni-duesseldorf.de/

Helsinki Business Polytechnic

http://www.helbp.fi/

Helsinki School of Economics

http://www.hkkk.fi/

Helsinki University

http://www.helsinki.fi/

Helsinki University of Technology

http://www.hut.fi/index.html

Hendrix College

http://192.131.98.11/

Heriot-Watt University

http://www.cee.hw.ac.uk/

Hillsdale College

http://www.hillsdale.edu/

Hiram College

http://www.hiram.edu/

Hirosaki University

http://www.hirosaki-u.ac.jp/

Hiroshima City University

http://www.hiroshima-cu.ac.jp/

Hiroshima Institute of Technology

http://www.cc.it-hiroshima.ac.jp/

Hiroshima Shudo University

http://www.shudo-u.ac.jp/

Hiroshima University

http://www.hiroshima-u.ac.jp/

Hiroshima-Denki Institute of Technology

http://www.c.hiroshima-dit.ac.jp/

Hitotsubashi University

http://www.higashi.hit-u.ac.jp/info-ind.html

Hobart and William Smith Colleges

http://hws3.hws.edu:9000/

Hofstra University

http://www.hofstra.edu/

Hogeschool Eindhoven

http://www.hi.ft.hse.nl/

Hogeschool van Amsterdam

http://www.hva.nl

Hogeschool van Utrecht

http://www.hvu.nl/index_english.html

Hokkaido University

http://www.hokudai.ac.jp/welcome-e.html

Hokkaido University of Education

http://www.iwa.hokkyodai.ac.jp/

Hong Kong Baptist University

http://www.hkbu.edu.hk/

Hong Kong Polytechnic University

http://www.bs.hkp.hk/

Hong Kong University of Science and Technology

http://sunsite.ust.hk/

Honolulu Community College

http://www.hcc.hawaii.edu/

Hope College

http://www.hope.edu/

Howard Community College

http://www.howardcc.edu/

Howard University

http://www.howard.edu/

Hudson Valley Community College

http://www.hvcc.edu/

Humber College of Applied Arts and Technology

http://www.humberC.on.ca/

Humboldt State University

http://rocky.humboldt.edu/

Humboldt-University, Berlin

http://www.hu-berlin.de/

Huntingdon College

http://www.huntingdon.edu/

Huntington College

http://www.huntcol.edu/

ICI University

http://www.ici.edu/

Idaho State University

http://www.isu.edu/

IJselland Polytechnic

http://htoc11.hto.rhij.nl/engels.htm

Illinois Benedictine College

http://www.ibc.edu/

Illinois Institute of Technology

http://www.iit.edu/

Illinois State University

http://www.ilstu.edu/

Imperial College of Science and Technology

http://www.doc.ic.ac.uk/

Incarnate Word College

http://www.iwctx.edu/

Indian Institute of Science, Bangalore

http://ece.iisc.ernet.in/iisc.html

Indian Institute of Technology, Bombay

http://sarang.ee.iitb.ernet.in/

Indian Institute of Technology, Delhi

http://kriti.iitd.ernet.in/menu/iitd-home.html

Indian Institute of Technology, Kanpur

http://www.cs.wisc.edu/~shubu/iitk/iitk.html

Indian Institute of Technology, Kharagpur

http://www.asel.udel.edu/~jayachan/iit.html

Indian Institute of Technology, Madras

http://sol.rutgers.edu/~sabesan/iit.html

Indiana Institute of Technology

http://www.indtech.edu/

Indiana State University

http://www-isu.indstate.edu/

Indiana University

http://www.indiana.edu/

Indiana University–Purdue University, Indianapolis

http://indyunix.iupui.edu/

Indiana University, South Bend

http://www.iusb.edu/

Indiana University, Bloomington

http://www-iub.indiana.edu/

Indiana University of Pennsylvania

http://www.lib.iup.edu/

Inha University

http://nms.inha.ac.kr/

Institut d'Informatique d'Entreprise

http://iie.cnam.fr/

Institut des Mathematiques Appliquees de Grenoble

http://imag.fr/

Institut f. Semantische Informationsverarbeitung

http://hal.cl-ki.uni-osnabrueck.de/

Institut fur Lasertechnik

http://www.ilt.fhg.de/WELCOME.HTML

Institut Jozef Stefan

http://www.ijs.si/

Institut National de Physique Nucleaire et de Physique des Particules

http://info.in2p3.fr/

Institut National des Sciences Appliquees de Toulouse

http://www.insa-tlse.fr/

Institut National des Télécommunications

http://arctique.int-evry.fr/eng/menu_eng.html

Institut Universitari de l'Audiovisual

http://www.iua.upf.es/

Institute for Mathematical Sciences

http://www.imsc.ernet.in/

Institute of Paper Science and Technology

http://www.ipst.edu/

Institute of Telecommunications and Information Technology

http://ittm.com.my/

Instituto Politecnico Nacional

http://www.ipn.mx/

Instituto Tecnologico y de Estudios Superiores de Monterrey

http://www.mty.itesm.mx/

Instituto Tecnologico y de Estudios Superiores de Occidente

http://www.gdl.iteso.mx/

International College Penang

http://mimos.my/icp/start.html

International Islamic University, Malaysia

http://scc.mimos.my/uia/uia.html

International School for Advanced Studies

http://www.sissa.it/

Iowa State University

http://www.iastate.edu/

Istanbul Technical University

http://www.itu.edu.tr/

Ithaca College

http://www.ithaca.edu/

Jackson State University

http://tiger.jsums.edu/html/homepage.html

Jacksonville State University

http://jsucc.jsu.edu/welcome.html

Jacksonville University

http://junix.ju.edu/

Jagiellonian Univeristy

http://www.if.uj.edu.pl/

James Cook University

http://www.jcu.edu.au/

James Madison University

http://www.jmu.edu/

Janus Pannonius University of Sciences

http://ipisun.jpte.hu/

Japan Advanced Institute of Science and Technology

http://www.jaist.ac.jp/

Japan Women's University

http://www.jwu.ac.jp/

Johannes Kepler University of Linz

http://www.ifs.uni-linz.ac.at/home.html

John Brown University

http://www.jbu.edu/

John Marshall Law School

http://www.jmls.edu/

Johns Hopkins University

http://www.jhu.edu/

Juhasz Gyula Teacher Training College

http://berreh.cab.jgytf.u-szeged.hu/jgytfeng.html

Kagoshima University

http://www.kagoshima-u.ac.jp/

Kalamazoo College

http://kzoo.edu/

Kanazawa University

http://kipcwww.ipc.kanazawa-u.ac.jp:8080/

Kansas State University

http://www.ksu.edu/

Kara Harb Okulu

http://www.kho.edu.tr/

Karl Franzens University

http://www.kfunigraz.ac.at/

Karolinska Institute

http://www.ki.se/

Katholieke Universiteit Leuven

http://www.kuleuven.ac.be/

Kazan University

http://www.ksu.ras.ru/

Keele University

http://www.keele.ac.uk/

Keene State College

http://kilburn.keene.edu/

Keimyung University

http://kmucc.keimyung.ac.kr/

Keio University

http://www.sfc.keio.ac.jp/index.en.html

Keio University of Science and Technology

http://www.st.keio.ac.jp/

Kent State University

http://www.kent.edu/homepage.html

Kenyon College

http://www.kenyon.edu/

King's College, London

http://www.kcl.ac.uk/

Kingston University

http://www.kingston.ac.uk/

Kinjo Gakuin University

http://www.kinjo-u.ac.jp/Welcome.html

Kitasato University

http://www.kitasato-u.ac.jp/

Kobe University

http://www.kobe-u.ac.jp/

Koc University

http://u6065.ku.edu.tr:70/0h/ku/ku.guide.html/

Kochi National College of Technology

http://www.kochi-ct.ac.jp/

Kochi University

http://www.is.kochi-u.ac.jp/

Koga Kuin University

http://www.kogakuin.ac.jp/

Konan University

http://www.ipc.konan-u.ac.jp/

Kookmin University

http://bukak.kookmin.ac.kr/

Korea Advanced Institute of Science & Technology

http://camis.kaist.ac.kr:8080/

Korea University

http://www.cs.columbia.edu/~dongwon/KU/

Kossuth Lajos University of Sciences

http://www.lib.klte.hu/index.english.html

Kumamoto National College of Technology

http://www.cs.knct.ac.jp/

Kumamoto Prefecture College

http://www.pu-kumamoto.ac.jp/

Kumamoto University

http://www.eecs.kumamoto-u.ac.jp/

Kurume Institute of Technology

http://www.kurume-it.ac.jp/

Kutztown University of Pennsylvania

http://www.kutztown.edu/

Kuwait University

http://kuc01.kuniv.edu.kw/

Kwangwoon University

http://128.134.70.44/main-eng.html

Kyoto Institute of Technology

http://www.kit.ac.jp/

Kyoto University

http://www.kyoto-u.ac.jp/English/

KyungSung University

http://sarang.kyungsung.ac.kr/

Kyushu Institute of Design

http://www.kyushu-id.ac.jp/

Kyushu Institute of Technology

http://www.kyutech.ac.jp/

Kyushu Sangyo University

http://www.ip.kyusan-u.ac.jp/

Kyushu University

http://www.kyushu-u.ac.jp/

La Salle University

http://www.lasalle.edu/home.html

La Sierra University

http://www.lasierra.edu/

La Trobe University

http://www.latrobe.edu.au/

Lafayette College

http://www.lafayette.edu/

LaGrange College

http://www.lgc.peachnet.edu/

Lahti Polytechnic

http://web.lahti-poly.fi/

Lake Forest College

http://www.lfc.edu/

Lake Superior State University

http://www.lssu.edu/

Lakehead University

http://www.lakeheadu.ca/menu.html

Lamar University

http://www.lamar.edu/

Lambton College

http://www.lambton.on.ca/

Lancaster University

http://www.lancs.ac.uk/

Langston University

http://www.lunet.edu/

Lappeenranta University of Technology

http://www.lut.fi/english.html

Lawrence University

http://www.lawrence.edu/

Lehigh University

http://www.lehigh.edu/

Leiden University

http://www.leidenuniv.nl/cwis/default.html

Lewis & Clark College

http://www.lclark.edu/

Lewisham College

http://www.lewisham.ac.uk/college/index.html

Liberec University of Technology

http://www.vslib.cz/

Libero Istituto Universitario Carlo Cattaneo

http://www.liuc.it/

Liberty University

http://www.liberty.edu/

Lillehammer College

http://www.hil.no/

Limburgs Universitair Centrum

http://www.luc.ac.be/

Lincoln University

http://www.lincoln.ac.nz/

Linkoping University

http://www.liu.se/

Liverpool John Moores University

http://www.livjm.ac.uk/

Lock Haven University of Pennsylvania

http://www.lhup.edu/

Lodz Technical University

http://zsku.p.lodz.pl/

London Business School

http://www.lbs.lon.ac.uk/

London School of Economics

http://www.blpes.lse.ac.uk/

Loughborough University of Technology

http://info.lut.ac.uk/

Louisiana State University

http://unix1.sncc.lsu.edu/

Louisiana Tech University

http://aurora.latech.edu/

Lousiana College

http://www.lacollege.edu/

Loyola College

http://www.loyola.edu/

Loyola Marymount University

http://www.lmu.edu/

Loyola University, Chicago

http://www.luc.edu/

Lulea University

http://www.luth.se/

Lund Institute of Technology

http://www.lth.se/

Lund University

http://www.lu.se/

Lycoming College

http://www.lycoming.edu/

M. S. Ramaiah Institute of Technology

http://www.cs.okstate.edu/~dpravee/msrit.html

Macalester College

http://www.macalstr.edu/

Macquarie University

http://www.mq.edu.au/

Madison Area Technical College

http://www.madison.tec.wi.us/

Mahidol University

http://www.mahidol.ac.th/mahidol.html

Malaspina University-College

http://www.mala.bc.ca/

Manchester Metropolitan University

http://www.mmu.ac.uk/

Manhattan College

http://www.cc.mancol.edu/

Mankato State University

http://www.mankato.msus.edu/

Mansfield University

http://157.62.12.80/

Maria Curie-Sklodowska University

http://www.umcs.lublin.pl/

Maricopa Community Colleges

http://www.maricopa.edu/

Marine Institute St. John's

http://inseine.ifmt.nf.ca/mi.html

Marist College

http://148.100.176.70/mcollege.htm

Marlboro College

http://www.marlboro.edu/

Marquette University

http://vinny.csd.mu.edu/marquette.html

Marshall University

http://www.marshall.edu/

Martin Luther University Halle-Wittenberg

http://www.uni-halle.de/

Mary Washington College

http://www.mwc.edu/

Maryland Institute, College of Art

http://www.mica.edu/

Marymount College

http://www.marymt.edu/

Marywood College

http://www.marywood.edu/

Masaryk University

http://www.fi.muni.cz/

Massachusetts Institute of Technology

http://web.mit.edu/

Massachusetts Maritime Academy

http://www.mma.mass.edu/mma.html

Massey University

http://www.massey.ac.nz/

Masters College

http://www.masters.edu/

Matej Bel University

http://nic.uakom.sk/hypertext/home.html

Mathematical Institute of the Hungarian Academy of Sciences

http://www.math-inst.hu/

Matsuyama University

http://iyokan.cc.matsuyama-u.ac.jp/

McGill University

http://www.mcgill.ca/

McMaster University

http://www.mcmaster.ca/

Medical College of Georgia

http://www.mcg.edu/

Medical College of Ohio

http://www.mco.edu/

Medical College of Wisconsin

http://www.mcw.edu/

Medical University of South Carolina

http://www.radonc.musc.edu/

Meharry Medical College

http://ccmac.mmc.edu/

Meiji University

http://www.meiji.ac.jp/

Meisei University

http://www.meisei-u.ac.jp/

Memorial University of Newfoundland

http://www.ucs.mun.ca/

Mercer University

http://www.mercer.peachnet.edu/

Mercyhurst College

http://utopia.mercy.edu/

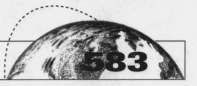

Meredith College

http://www.meredith.edu/meredith/

Merton College, Oxford

http://info.ox.ac.uk/~mertinfo/

Mesa Community College

http://www.mc.maricopa.edu/

Messiah College

http://www.messiah.edu/

Metropolitan State College of Denver

http://www.mscd.edu/

Miami Bible Institute

http://www.fiu.edu/~wgreen01/mbi.html

Miami University, Ohio

http://www.muohio.edu/

Miami-Dade Community College

http://www.mdcc.edu/

Michigan State University

http://www.msu.edu/

Michigan Technological University

http://www.mtu.edu/

Mid Sweden University

http://www.forv.mh.se/estart.html

Middle East Technical University

http://www.metu.edu.tr/

Middle Tennessee State University

http://www.mtsu.edu/

Middlebury College

http://www.middlebury.edu/

Middlesex University

http://www.mdx.ac.uk/

Midwestern State University

http://www.mwsu.edu/

Mie University

http://www.mie-u.ac.jp/english.html

Millersville University

http://cs.millersv.edu/

Millsaps College

http://www.millsaps.edu/

Milwaukee School of Engineering

http://www.msoe.edu/

Mindanao State University–Iligan Institute of Technology

http://www.msuiit.edu.ph/

Minneapolis College of Art and Design

http://www.mcad.edu/

Minot State University

http://warp6.cs.misu.nodak.edu/

Mississippi College

http://www.mc.edu/

Mississippi State University

http://www.msstate.edu/

Missouri Western State College

http://www.mwsc.edu/

Miyazaki International College

http://www.miyazaki-mic.ac.jp/

Miyazaki Medical College

http://www.miyazaki-med.ac.jp/

Miyazaki University

http://www.miyazaki-u.ac.jp/

Molde College

http://www.dhmolde.no/

Monash University

http://www.monash.edu.au/

Monmouth College

http://www.monmouth.edu/

Montana State University—Bozeman

http://www.montana.edu/

Montana State University—Northern Havre

http://www.nmclites.edu

Montan University, Leoben

http://www.unileoben.ac.at/oehwww/

Montclair State University

http://www.montclair.edu/

Monterey Institute of International Studies

http://www.miis.edu/

Moscow Institute of Physics and Technology

http://www.crec.mipt.ru/MIPT

Moscow State University

http://www.rector.msu.su/

Mount Allison University

http://www.mta.ca/

Mount Holyoke College

http://www.mtholyoke.edu/

Mount Saint Mary College

http://www.msmc.edu/

Mount Saint Mary's College

http://www.msmary.edu/

Mount Saint Vincent University

http://www.msvu.ca/

Mount Union College

http://www.muc.edu/

Munich University of Technology

http://www.informatik.tu-muenchen.de/HOME-PAGE_e.html

Murdoch University

http://www.murdoch.edu.au/

Muroran Institute of Technology

http://www.muroran-it.ac.jp/

Musashi Institute of Technology

http://www.musashi-tech.ac.jp/

Musashi University

http://www.cc.musashi.ac.jp/

Muskingum College

http://www.muskingum.edu/

Nagano University

http://www.nagano.ac.jp/

Nagasaki University

http://www.cc.nagasaki-u.ac.jp/

Nagoya Institute of Technology

http://www.nitech.ac.jp/

Nagoya University

http://www.nagoya-u.ac.jp/

Nanyang Polytechnic

http://WWW.nyp.ac.sg/

Nanyang Technological University, Singapore

http://www.ntu.ac.sg/

Nanzan University

http://www.nanzan-u.ac.jp/

Napier University

http://www.napier.ac.uk/

Nara Institute of Science and Technology

http://www.aist-nara.ac.jp/

Naruto University of Education

http://www.naruto-u.ac.jp/

National Central University

http://www.mgt.ncu.edu.tw/

National Cheng Kung University

http://www.ncku.edu.tw/

National Chengchi University

http://www.nccu.edu.tw/

National Chiao Tung University

http://www.nctu.edu.tw/

National Chung Cheng University

http://www.ccu.edu.tw/

National College of Art & Design, Norway

http://samson.shks.no/

National Defense University

http://www.ndu.edu/

National Sun Yat-sen University

http://www.nsysu.edu.tw/

National Taichung Institute of Commerce

http://alpha.ntcic.edu.tw/

National Taiwan Normal University

http://www.ntnu.edu.tw/

National Taiwan University

http://www.ntu.edu.tw/

National Technological University

http://www.ntu.edu/

National Tsing-Hua University

http://www.nthu.edu.tw/

National University

http://nunic.nu.edu/

National University of Mexico

http://www.noc.unam.mx/UNAM/hpunam.html

National University of Singapore

http://nuscc.nus.sg/NUShome.html

Naval Postgraduate School

http://www.nps.navy.mil/

Nesna College

http://oter.hinesna.no/

New Jersey Institute of Technology

http://www.njit.edu/

New Mexico Institute of Mining and Technology

http://www.nmt.edu/

New Mexico State University

http://www.nmsu.edu/

New School for Social Research

http://dialnsa.edu/home.html

New York Institute of Technology

http://ftp.nyit.edu/

New York University

http://www.nyu.edu/

Nicholls State University

http://server.nich.edu/

Nicolaus Copernicus University

http://www.cc.uni.torun.pl/

Nihon University

http://ftp.nc.nihon-u.ac.jp/

Niigata University

http://www.cc.niigata-u.ac.jp/

Nijenrode University

http://www.nijenrode.nl/

Nippon Bunri University

http://www.mc.nbu.ac.jp/NBU/e/nbu-e.html

Nippon Medical School

http://www.nms.ac.jp/

Noordelijke Hogeschool Leeuwarden

http://www.tem.nhl.nl/

North Carolina Agricultural and Technical State University

http://www.ncat.edu/

North Carolina State University

http://www.ncsu.edu/

North Central Bible College

http://www.ncbc.edu/

North Dakota State University

http://toons.cc.ndsu.nodak.edu/ndsu/Home.html

North Dakota University System

http://www.nodak.edu/

North East Wales Institute of Higher Education

http://www.newi.ac.uk/

North Park College and Theological Seminary

http://www.npcts.edu/

Northeast Louisiana University

http://www.nlu.edu/

Northeast Missouri State University

http://www.nemostate.edu/

Northeastern University

http://www.dac.neu.edu/

Northern Arizona University

http://www.nau.edu/

Northern Michigan University

http://www.nmu.edu/

Northern Statue University

http://www.northern.edu/

Northern Territory University

http://www.ntu.edu.au/

Northern University of Malaysia

http://161.142.40.1/0c:\versi.htm¦/

Northwest Nazarene College

http://www.nnc.edu/Homepage.html

Northwestern Michigan College

http://leo.nmc.edu/

Northwestern State University

http://server.nsula.edu/

Northwestern University

http://www.nwu.edu/

Norwegian Institute of Technology, Trondheim

http://www.unit.no/NTH

Notre Dame Women's College

http://www.notredame.ac.jp/

Nova Southeastern University

http://alpha.acast.nova.edu/start.html

Novgorod State University

http://www.novsu.ac.ru/

Novosibirsk State University

http://www.nsu.nsk.su/

Oakland University

http://www.acs.oakland.edu/

Oberlin College

http://www.oberlin.edu/

Occidental College

http://www.oxy.edu/

Ohio Northern University

http://www.onu.edu/

Ohio State University, The

http://www.acs.ohio-state.edu/

Ohio University

http://www.ohiou.edu/

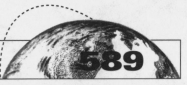

Ohio Wesleyan University

http://192.68.223.4:8000/

Oita University

http://www.oita-u.ac.jp/

Okanagan University College

http://oksw01.okanagan.bc.ca/home.html

Okayama Prefectural University

http://www.oka-pu.ac.jp/

Oklahoma City University

http://frodo.okcu.edu/

Oklahoma State University

http://www.okstate.edu/

Old Dominion University

http://www.odu.edu/

Olivet Nazarene University

http://www.olivet.edu/

Open University of the Netherlands

http://www.ouh.nl/

Oppland College

http://www.odh.no/

Oral Roberts University

http://www.oru.edu/

Orange Coast College

http://www.lib.occ.cccd.edu/OCC/OCCHomePage.html

Oregon Graduate Institute of Science and Technology

http://www.ogi.edu/welcome.html

Oregon Health Sciences University

http://www.ohsu.edu/

Oregon State University

http://www.orst.edu/

Osaka Kyoiku University

http://okumedia.cc.osaka-kyoiku.ac.jp/

Osaka Medical College

http://www.osaka-med.ac.jp/

Osaka University

http://www.osaka-u.ac.jp/Osaka-u.html

Oulu Institute of Tecnology

http://www.otol.fi/index.uk.html

Oxford Brookes University

http://www.brookes.ac.uk/

Oxford University

http://www.ox.ac.uk/

Pace University

http://pacevm.dac.pace.edu/

Pacific Lutheran University

http://plu.edu/

Palomar College

http://www.palomar.edu/

Peking University

http://www.pku.edu.cn/

Pennsylvania State System of Higher Education

http://sshe2.sshechan.edu/sshe.html

Pennsylvania State University

http://www.psu.edu/

Pepperdine University

http://moon.pepperdine.edu/HomeSBM.html

Perugia University

http://www.unipg.it/welcomeEn.html

Phoenix College

http://www.pc.maricopa.edu/

Pima Community College

http://www.pima.edu/

Pittsburg State University

http://www.pittstate.edu/

Pitzer College

http://www.pitzer.edu/

Plymouth State College

http://www.plymouth.edu/

Pohang University of Science and Technology

http://firefox.postech.ac.kr/

Point Loma Nazarene College

http://192.147.249.89/

Point Park College

http://www.lm.com/~markv20/ppc.html

Politecnico di Milano

http://www.polimi.it/

Politecnico di Torino

http://www.polito.it/

Polytechnic University of New York

http://www.poly.edu/

Polytechnical University of Bucharest

http://www.cs.pub.ro/

Pomona College

http://www.pomona.claremont.edu/

Pontifica University Catolica de Chile

http://www.puc.cl/

Portland Community College

http://www.pcc.edu/

Portland State University

http://www.pdx.edu/

Princeton University

http://www.princeton.edu/

PUC-Rio

http://www.puc-rio.br/

Purdue University

http://www.purdue.edu/

Pusan National University

http://164.125.64.41/pnu/pnu.html

Pusan Women's University

http://lotus.pwu.ac.kr/

Queen's University, Belfast

http://www.qub.ac.uk/

Queen's University, Kingston, Ontario

http://info.queensu.ca/index.html

Queensland University of Technology

http://www.qut.edu.au/

Quincy University

http://www.quincy.edu/

Radford University

http://www.runet.edu/

Rand Afrikaans University

http://www.rau.ac.za/

Randolph-Macon College

http://www.rmc.edu/

Randolph-Macon Women's College

http://www.rmwc.edu/

Reading University

http://www.reading.ac.uk/

Reed College

http://www.reed.edu/

Regent University

http://www.regent.edu/

Regional Engineering College

http://www.cis.ufl.edu/~sk0/recw.html

Regional Engineering College, Tiruchirappalli, India

http://tam2k.tamu.edu/~ssk8291/rect.html

Reitaku University

http://www.reitaku-u.ac.jp/

Rensselaer Polytechnic Institute

http://www.rpi.edu/

Rhodes College

http://www.rhodes.edu/

Rhodes University

http://www.ru.ac.za/rhodes.html

Rice University

http://www.rice.edu/

Richard Stockton University

http://odin.stockton.edu/

Richland College

http://www.rlc.dcccd.edu/

Rider University

http://www.rider.edu/

Riga Technical University

http://www.eef.rtu.lv/

Ritsumeikan University

http://www.ritsumei.ac.jp/

Roanoke College

http://www.roanoke.edu/

Rochester Institute of Technology

http://www.rit.edu/

Rockefeller University

http://www.rockefeller.edu/

Rockhurst College

http://vax1.rockhurst.edu/

Rollins College

http://www.rollins.edu/

Rose-Hulman Institute of Technology

http://www.rose-hulman.edu/

Roskilde University

http://frederik.ruc.dk/

Rowan College of New Jersey

http://www.rowan.edu/

Royal Danish School of Pharmacy

http://info.dfh.dk/

Royal Holloway College

http://www.rhbnc.ac.uk/

Royal Institute of Technology, Stockholm

http://www.kth.se/

Royal Melbourne Institute of Technology

http://www.rmit.edu.au/

Royal Military Academy

http://www.rma.ac.be/

Royal Military College of Canada

http://www.rmc.ca/

Royal Postgraduate Medical School

http://www.rpms.ac.uk/index.html

Ruhr-University Bochum

http://www.ruhr-uni-bochum.de/

Russian Academy of Sciences

http://www.ras.ru/

Rutgers University

http://www.rutgers.edu/index.html

Rutgers University, Camden

http://camden-www.rutgers.edu/

Ryerson Polytechnic University

http://www.acs.ryerson.ca/

Sacramento City College

http://wheel.ucdavis.edu/~btcarrol/sac_city/
Sac_City.html

Saga University

http://www.cc.saga-u.ac.jp/

Sage Colleges

http://www.sage.edu/

Saint Joseph College

http://www.sjc.edu/

Saint Joseph's College

http://www.saintjoe.edu/

Saint Joseph's University

http://www.sju.edu/

Saint Mary's University

http://www.stmarys.ca:70/

Saint Xavier University

http://www.sxu.edu/

Saitama University

http://www.ke.ics.saitama-u.ac.jp/index_english.html

Sam Houston State University

http://www.shsu.edu/

Samford University

http://www.samford.edu/

San Diego State University

http://www.sdsu.edu/

San Francisco State University

http://www.sfsu.edu/

San Joaquin Delta College

http://www.sjdccd.cc.ca.us/

San Jose State University

http://www.sjsu.edu/

Sangamon State University

http://www.sangamon.edu/

Santa Clara University

http://www.scu.edu/

Santa Fe Community College

http://www.santafe.cc.fl.us/

Santa Rosa Junior College

http://www.santarosa.edu/

Sapporo Medical University

http://www.sapmed.ac.jp/

Saskatchewan Institute of Applied Science and Technology

http://www.siast.sk.ca/

Scarborough College, University of Toronto

http://www.scar.toronto.edu/

School of Engineering of Bern HTL

http://www.isbe.ch/index_e.html

School of Engineering of Burgdorf HTL

http://www.isburg.ch/hpageeng.html

School of Oriental and African Studies

http://www.soas.ac.uk/

School of the Art Institute of Chicago

http://www.artic.edu/saic/saichome.html

School of the Visual Arts

http://www.sva.edu/

Science University of Tokyo

http://www.sut.ac.jp/

Scuola Superiore di Studi Universitari e di Perfezionamento Sant'Anna

http://www.sssup.it/

Seattle Central Community College

http://scc.cc.wa.us/

Seattle Pacific University

http://www.spu.edu/

Seattle University

http://www.seattleu.edu/

Semmelweis University of Medical Sciences

http://www.sote.hu/

Sendai National College of Technology

http://www.sendai-ct.ac.jp/welcome-e.html

Seoul National University

http://www.snu.ac.kr/

Seton Hall University

http://www.shu.edu/

Shandong University

http://www.inf-wiss.uni-konstanz.de/~zhang/SDUni/sduni.html

Shanghai Medical University

http://www.ucc.uconn.edu/~xuchen/smu.html

Sheffield Hallam University

http://pine.shu.ac.uk/

Sheffield University

http://www.shef.ac.uk/

Shiga Polytechnic College

http://www.shiga-pc.ac.jp:8080/

Shimane Medical University

http://www.shimane-med.ac.jp/

Shippensburg University

http://www.ship.edu/

Silesian Technical University

http://www.gliwice.edu.pl/

Simon Fraser University

http://www.sfu.ca/

Simon's Rock College

http://www.simons-rock.edu/

Simpson College

http://www.simpson.edu/

Skidmore College

http://www.skidmore.edu/

Slippery Rock University

http://www.sru.edu/

Slovak Technical University

http://sun.sanet.sk/info/efstu-sl.html

Smith Chapel Bible College

http://144.174.145.13/

Smith College

http://www.smith.edu/

Sogang University

http://www.sogang.ac.kr/

Soka University

http://www.t.soka.ac.jp/

Sonoma State University

http://www.sonoma.edu/

Sophia University

http://www.sophia.ac.jp/

South Bank University

http://www.sbu.ac.uk/

South Dakota School of Mines and Technology

http://www.sdsmt.edu/

South Dakota State University

http://www.sdstate.edu/

Southeast Missouri State University

http://www.semo.edu/

Southern College of Seventh-Day Adventists

http://www.southern.edu/

Southern College of Technology

http://www.sct.edu/

Southern Connecticut State University

http://scwww.ctstateu.edu/

Southern Cross University

http://www.scu.edu.au/

Southern Denmark Business School

http://www.hhs.dk/

Southern Illinois University

http://www.siu.edu/

Southern Illinois University at Edwardsville

http://www.siue.edu/

Southern Methodist University

http://www.smu.edu/

Southern University

http://www.subr.edu/

Southern Utah University

http://www.suu.edu/suuhome.html

Southwest Missouri State University

http://www.smsu.edu/

Southwest Texas State University

http://www.swt.edu/

Southwestern Adventist College

http://www.swac.edu/

St. Cloud State University

http://www.stcloud.msus.edu/

St. Edward's University

http://www.cs.stedwards.edu/

St. Francis Xavier University

http://www.stfx.ca/

St. John's College, Annapolis

http://www.sjca.edu/

St. John's University

http://www.stjohns.edu/

St. John's University, College of St. Benedict

http://www.csbsju.edu/

St. Louis College of Pharmacy

http://www.stlcop.edu/

St. Louis University, Baguio

http://www.slu.edu.ph/

St. Mary's College of California

http://www.stmarys-ca.edu/

St. Mary's College of Minnesota

http://140.190.128.190/SMC/HomePage.html

St. Olaf College

http://www.stolaf.edu/

St. Petersburg University

http://www.pu.ru/

St. Thomas University

http://www.stthomasu.ca/

St. Andrews University

http://www.st-and.ac.uk/~www_/index.html

Stanford University

http://www.stanford.edu/

Stanislaw Staszic University of Mining and Metallurgy

http://www.uci.agh.edu.pl/

State Engineering University of Armenia

http://www.darmstadt.gmd.de/~dressler/seua.html

State University of New York at Geneseo

http://mosaic.cc.geneseo.edu/geneseo.html

State University of New York at Oswego

http://www.oswego.edu/

State University of New York at Potsdam

http://www.potsdam.edu/

State University of New York College at Cortland

http://www.cortland.edu/

State University of New York Institute of Technology

http://woody.c2tc.rl.af.mil/

State University of New York, Albany

http://cscmosaic.albany.edu/

State University of New York, Brockport

http://www.acs.brockport.edu/

State University of New York, Buffalo

http://wings.buffalo.edu/

State University of New York, New Platz

http://npeeserv.eelab.newpaltz.edu/

State University of New York, Oneonta

http://137.141.153.38/

State University of New York, Plattsburgh

http://bio420.hawk.plattsburgh.edu/SUNYHomePage.html

State University of New York, Stony Brook

http://www.sunysb.edu/

Stavanger College

http://www.hsr.no/

Stephen F. Austin State University

http://www.sfasu.edu/

Stetson University

http://www.stetson.edu/

Stevens Institute of Technology

http://www.stevens-tech.edu/

Stockholm School of Economics

http://www.hhs.se/

Stockholm University

http://www.su.se/

Stord/Haugesund College

http://www.ssh.no/

Strasbourg University

http://www.u-strasbg.fr/

Susquehanna University

http://www.susqu.edu/

Suzhou University

http://kantaro.sk.tsukuba.ac.jp/Shi/public_html/Suzhou_U.html

Swansea University

http://www.swan.ac.uk/

Swarthmore College

http://www.swarthmore.edu

Swedish School of Economics and Business Administration, Finland

http://www.shh.fi/

Swedish University of Agricultural Sciences

http://www.radek.slu.se/

Sweet Briar College

http://www.sbc.edu/

Swinburne University of Technology

http://www.swin.edu.au/

Swiss Federal Institute of Technology, Zurich

http://www.ethz.ch/

Syracuse University

http://cwis.syr.edu/

Szeged University

http://www.u-szeged.hu/

Taegu University

http://www.taegu.ac.kr/

Takuma National College of Technology

http://www.takuma-ct.ac.jp/

Tallinn Technical University

http://zaphod.cc.ttu.ee/

Tama Institute of Management and Information Sciences

http://www.timis.ac.jp/Timishome.html

Tamkang University

http://www.tku.edu.tw/

Tampere Institute of Technology

http://www.tit.fi/

Tampere University of Technology

http://www.cc.tut.fi/

Tartu University

http://www.ut.ee/

Tatung Institute of Technology

http://www.cse.ttit.edu.tw/

Technical University Kosice

http://hron.ef.tuke.sk/tu/tuke-a.html

Technical University of Budapest, Hungary

http://www.bme.hu/

Technical University of Denmark

http://www.dtu.dk/cwis/welcome.html

Technical University of Nova Scotia

http://www.tuns.ca/

Technical University of Timisoara

http://www.utt.ro/

Technikum Vorarlberg

http://www.tvlbg.ac.at/

Technion, Israel Institute of Technology

http://www.technion.ac.il/

Technische University Berlin

http://www.tu-berlin.de/

Technische University Braunschweig

http://www.tu-bs.de/

Technische University Chemnitz-Zwickau

http://www.tu-chemnitz.de/index-e.html

Technische University Clausthal

http://www.tu-clausthal.de/

Technische University Darmstadt

http://www.th-darmstadt.de/

Technische University Dresden

http://www.tu-dresden.de/

Technische University Hamburg-Harburg

http://www.tu-harburg.de/indexus.html

Technische University Ilmenau

http://www.tu-ilmenau.de/

Teikyo University

http://www.teikyo-u.ac.jp/

Tel Aviv University

http://www.tau.ac.il/

Telemark College

http://www.tdh.no/

Temple University

http://astro.ocis.temple.edu/

Tennessee Technological University

http://www.tntech.edu/

Texas A&M University

http://www.tamu.edu

Texas Christian University

http://www.tcu.edu/

Texas State Technical College

http://www.tstc.edu/

Texas Tech University

http://www.ttu.edu/

Texas Women's University

http://192.135.186.50/twu/1.html

Thamasat University

http://ipied.tu.ac.th/

Thomas College

http://www.thomas.edu

Thomas Jefferson University

http://www.tju.edu/

Thomas More College

http://www.thomasmore.edu/welcome.html

Tianjin University

http://www.tju.edu.cn/

Tilburg University

http://www.kub.nl:2080/

Tohoku University

http://www.tohoku.ac.jp/

Tokai University

http://www.cc.u-tokai.ac.jp/

Tokyo Institute of Technology

http://www.titech.ac.jp/

Tokyo International University

http://www.tiu.ac.jp/

Tokyo Kaseigakuin Tsukuba Junior College

http://www.kasei.ac.jp/

Tokyo Kogei Tanki University

http://www.win.or.jp/~takahara/

Tokyo Medical and Dental University

http://www.i-mde.tmd.ac.jp/I-MDE.html

Tokyo Metropolitan College of Aeronautical Engineering

http://www.kouku-k.ac.jp/

Tokyo University of Agriculture & Technology

http://www.tuat.ac.jp/

Tokyo Women's Christian University

http://www.twcu.ac.jp/

Tokyo Women's Medical College

http://www.twmc.ac.jp/

Tomsk State University

http://www.tsu.tomsk.su/

Towson State University

http://www.towson.edu/

Toyama Medical and Pharmaceutical University

http://www.toyama-mpu.ac.jp/

Toyama University

http://www.toyama-u.ac.jp/

Transylvania University

http://www.transy.edu/

Trenton State College

http://www.trenton.edu/

Trinity College

http://www.trincoll.edu/homepage.html

Trinity University

http://www.trinity.edu/

Tsinghua University

http://www.net.edu.cn/

Tufts University

http://www.tufts.edu/

Tulane University

http://www.tulane.edu/

Ube College

http://www.ube-c.ac.jp

Ulsan University

http://munsu.ulsan.ac.kr:8080/

Uludag

http://www.uludag.edu.tr/

Umea University

http://macavity.umdc.umu.se/~roland/

Uniformed Services University of the Health Sciences

http://www.usuhs.mil/

UNIK - Center for Technology at Kjeller, University of Oslo

http://www.unik.no/ENGELSK/presentengelsk.html

Union College

http://www.union.edu/

United Medical and Dental Schools of Guy's and St. Thomas's Hospitals

http://www.umds.ac.uk/

United States Air Force Academy

http://www.usafa.af.mil/

United States Military Academy

http://euler.math.usma.edu/Introduction.html

United States Naval Academy

http://xtreme2.acc.iit.edu/~trygray/USNA.html

United States Sports Academy

http://www.sport.ussa.edu/

Universiti du Quibec

http://www.uquebec.ca/

University degli studi di Brescia

http://www.unibs.it/

University of Connecticut

http://www.uconn.edu/

University of Dallas

http://www.udallas.edu/

University Anahuac

http://www.dcc.anahuac.mx/

University Anahuac del Sur

http://www.uas.mx/

University Autonoma de Barcelona

http://www.uab.es/

University Autonoma de Nayarit

http://www.uan.mx/

University Autonoma de Nuevo Leon

http://www.dsi.uanl.mx/

University Autonoma Metropolitana

http://tonatiuh.uam.mx/

University Bamberg

http://www.uni-bamberg.de/

University Basel

http://www.unibas.ch/

University Bayreuth

http://www.uni-bayreuth.de/homes/bayreuth.html

University Bielefeld

http://www.techfak.uni-bielefeld.de/indexengl.html

University Bonn

http://www.informatik.uni-bonn.de/unibo.html

University Bremen

http://www.uni-bremen.de/

University Central de Venezuela

http://www.sagi.ucv.edu.ve/

University College London

http://www.ucl.ac.uk/home.html

University College of Kalmar

http://www.hik.se/

University College Salford

http://www.ucsalf.ac.uk/

University College, Cork

http://www.ucc.ie/webentry.html

University College, Dublin

http://www.ucd.ie/

University College, Galway

http://www.ucg.ie/

University Complutense de Madrid

http://www.ucm.es/UCMD.html

University de Barcelona

http://www.ub.es/

University de Chile

http://www.uchile.cl/

University de Colima

http://www.ucol.mx/

University de Cordoba

http://www.uco.es/UCOhome.english.html

University de Costa Rica

http://www.ucr.ac.cr/

University de Granada

http://www.ugr.es/

University de Guadalajara

http://www.udg.mx/Ingles/udg.html

University de Guanajuato

http://www.ugto.mx/

University de la Frontera

http://www.enlaces.ufro.cl/

University de la Republica Oriental del Uruguay

http://fisica.edu.uy/

University de las Palmas de Gran Canaria

http://www.ulpgc.es/

University de Lausanne

http://www.unil.ch/

University de Los Andes

http://mozart.ing.ula.ve/ula.html

University de Marne la Vallée

http://indy.univ-mlv.fr/

University de Oviedo

http://www.uniovi.es/

University de Savoie

http://www.univ-savoie.fr/

University de Technologie Compiegne

http://delta.si.univ-compiegne.fr/

University del Valle

http://www.univalle.edu.co/

University del Zulia

http://www.luz.ve/

University des Saarlandes

http://www.rz.uni-sb.de/

University des Sciences et Technologies de Lille

http://www.univ-lille1.fr/

University di Cagliari

http://www.unica.it/welcome.html

University do Estado do Rio de Janeiro

http://www.uerj.br/

University du Quebec a Hull

http://www.uqah.uquebec.ca/welcome.htm

University EAFIT

http://www.eafit.edu.co/home.html

University Erlangen-Nuremberg

http://www.uni-erlangen.de/docs/index_e.html

University Federal de Minas Gerais

http://www.cpdee.ufmg.br/

University Federal de Pernambuco

http://www.di.ufpe.br/

University Federal de Santa Catarina

http://www.inf.ufsc.br/

University Federal de Santa Maria

http://www.ufsm.br/

University Federal do Rio de Janeiro

http://www.ufrj.br/

University Federal do Rio Grande do Sul

http://www.cesup.ufrgs.br/

University Freiburg

http://www.uni-freiburg.de/

University G.d'Annunzio

http://mars.unich.it/

University Gesamthochschule Essen

http://www.uni-essen.de/

University Hamburg

http://www.uni-hamburg.de/welcome_english.html

University Hannover

http://www.tnt.uni-hannover.de/data/info/www/tnt/welcome.html

University Heidelberg

http://www.urz.uni-heidelberg.de/index.html

University Hildesheim

http://www.uni-hildesheim.de/EWelcome.html

University Institute of Architecture

http://www.iuav.unive.it/

University Javeriana

http://javercol.javeriana.edu.co/

University Kaiserslautern

http://www.uni-kl.de/

University Karlsruhe

http://www.rz.uni-karlsruhe.de/Uni/

University Konstanz

http://www.uni-konstanz.de/index.html

University Laval

http://www.rsvs.ulaval.ca/

University Leipzig

http://www.uni-leipzig.de/

University Libre de Bruxelles

http://www.ulb.ac.be/

University Lumiere Lyon

http://web.univ-lyon2.fr/Universite.html

University Malaysia Sarawak

http://www.fit.unimas.my:8080/

University Mannheim

http://www.uni-mannheim.de/

University Medical School of Debrecen

http://www.dote.hu/

University Michoacana

http://www.ccu.umich.mx/

University Nacional Autonoma de Mexico

http://www.noc.unam.mx/unam/historia.html

University Nacional de La Plata

http://www.unlp.edu.ar/

University Nueva Esparta

http://www.une.edu.ve/

University of Aarhus

http://www.aau.dk/

University of Aberdeen

http://www.abdn.ac.uk/

University of Abertay Dundee

http://www.dct.ac.uk/

University of Adelaide

http://www.adelaide.edu.au/

University of Aizu

http://www.u-aizu.ac.jp/

University of Akron

http://www.uakron.edu/

University of Alabama

http://www.ua.edu/

University of Alabama, Birmingham

http://www.lhl.uab.edu/

University of Alabama, Huntsville

http://info.uah.edu/

University of Alaska

http://www.alaska.edu/

University of Alaska, Anchorage

http://orion.alaska.edu/www/cwis.html

University of Alaska, Fairbanks

http://zorba.uafadm.alaska.edu/

University of Alberta

http://web.cs.ualberta.ca/UAlberta.html

University of Amsterdam

http://www.uva.nl/00/english.html

University of Antwerp

http://www.ua.ac.be/

University of Arizona

http://www.arizona.edu/

University of Arkansas, Fayetteville

http://www.uark.edu/

University of Arkansas, Little Rock

http://www.ualr.edu/

University of Arkansas, Monticello

http://cotton.uamont.edu/

University of Art and Design, Helsinki

http://www.uiah.fi/default.html

University of Auckland

http://www.auckland.ac.nz/

University of Baltimore

http://www.ubalt.edu/

University of Bath

http://www.bath.ac.uk/home.html

University of Bergen

http://www.uib.no/

University of Berne

http://arwen.unibe.ch/

University of Birmingham

http://www.bham.ac.uk/

University of Bologna Department of Computer Science

http://www.cs.unibo.it/

University of Boras

http://www.hb.se/

University of Bradford

http://www.brad.ac.uk/bradinfo/bradinfo.html

University of British Columbia

http://view.ubc.ca/

University of Calgary

http://www.ucalgary.ca/

University of California at Santa Barbara

http://id-www.ucsb.edu/

University of California, Berkeley

http://www.berkeley.edu/

University of California, Davis

http://www.ucdavis.edu/

University of California, Irvine

http://www.uci.edu/

University of California, Los Angeles

http://www.ucla.edu/

University of California, Riverside

http://www.ucr.edu/

University of California, San Diego

http://www.ucsd.edu/

University of California, San Francisco

http://www.ucsf.edu/

University of California, Santa Cruz

http://www.ucsc.edu/

University of Campinas

http://www.unicamp.br/

University of Canberra

http://services.canberra.edu.au/home.html

University of Cantabria

http://www.gae.unican.es/

University of Canterbury

http://www.canterbury.ac.nz/

University of Capetown

http://www.uct.ac.za/

University of Central Arkansas

http://aix1.uca.edu/

University of Central Florida

http://www.ucf.edu/home.html

University of Chicago

http://www.uchicago.edu/

University of Cincinnati

http://www.uc.edu/

University of Colorado at Denver

http://www.cudenver.edu/

University of Colorado, Boulder

http://www.colorado.edu/

University of Colorado, Colorado Springs

http://www.uccs.edu/

University of Copenhagen

http://www.ku.dk/welcome-e.html

University of Dallas

http://acad.udallas.edu/

University of Dayton

http://www.udayton.edu

University of Delaware

http://www.udel.edu/

University of Denver

http://www.du.edu/

University of Dublin— Trinity College

http://www.tcd.ie/

University of Duisburg

http://www.uni-duisburg.de/

University of Durham

http://www.dur.ac.uk/

University of East Anglia

http://cpca3.uea.ac.uk/welcome.html

University of East London

http://www.uel.ac.uk/

University of Economics, Vienna

http://www.wu-wien.ac.at/

University of Edinburgh

http://www.ed.ac.uk/

University of Electro-Communications

http://www.uec.ac.jp/

University of Essex

http://www.essex.ac.uk/

University of Evansville

http://www.evansville.edu/

University of Exeter

http://info.ex.ac.uk/

University of Florida

http://www.ufl.edu/

University of Fribourg

http://www.unifr.ch/

University of Gazi Antep

http://www.gantep.edu.tr/

University of Geneva

http://www.unige.ch/

University of Georgia

http://www.uga.edu/

University of Ghent

http://www.rug.ac.be/

University of Glamorgan

http://www.glam.ac.uk/home.html

University of Greenwich

http://www.gre.ac.uk/

University of Groningen

http://www.rug.nl/rug/startuk.html

University of Guelph

http://www.uoguelph.ca/

University of Haifa

http://www.haifa.ac.il/

University of Hartford

http://www.hartford.edu/UofHWelcome.html

University of Hawaii

http://www.hawaii.edu/uhinfo.html

University of Hawaii, West Oahu

http://www.uhwo.hawaii.edu/

University of Hertfordshire

http://www.herts.ac.uk/

University of Hong Kong

http://www.hku.hk/

University of Houston

http://www.uh.edu/

University of Houston, Clear Lake

http://129.7.160.115/

University of Hull

http://www.hull.ac.uk/

University of Iceland

http://www.rhi.hi.is/

University of Idaho

http://www.uidaho.edu/

University of Illinois, Chicago

http://www.uic.edu/

University of Illinois, Urbana-Champaign

http://www.uiuc.edu/

University of Indianapolis

http://www.uindy.edu/

University of Indonesia

http://www.ui.ac.id/

University of Innsbruck

http://info.uibk.ac.at/

University of Iowa

http://www.uiowa.edu/

University of Joensuu

http://cc.joensuu.fi/

University of Kansas

http://kuhttp.cc.ukans.edu/cwis/UDK/KUhome/KUHome.html

University of Kansas Medical Center

http://www.kumc.edu/

University of Karlskrona/ Ronneby

http://www.hk-r.se/

University of Karlstad

http://www.hks.se/

University of Kent at Canterbury

http://www.ukc.ac.uk/

University of Kentucky

http://www.uky.edu/

University of King's College

http://www.ukings.ns.ca/Docs/

University of Klagenfurt

http://info.uni-klu.ac.at/

University of Kuopio

http://www.uku.fi/

University of L'Aquila

http://www.univaq.it/EnglishIndex.html

University of Latvia

http://www.latnet.lv/

University of Leeds

http://www.leeds.ac.uk/

University of Leicester

http://www.le.ac.uk/

University of Lethbridge

http://www.uleth.ca/

University of Library and Information Science

http://ulispsn.ulis.ac.jp:8001/html/ENG_homepage.html

University of Liège

http://www.ulg.ac.be/

University of Limburg

http://www.cs.rulimburg.nl/

University of Limerick

http://www.ul.ie/

University of Liverpool

http://www.liv.ac.uk/

University of Ljubljana

http://www.uni-lj.si/

University of London

http://www.ulcc.ac.uk/

University of Los Andes

http://www.uniandes.edu.co/

University of Louisville

http://www.louisville.edu/

University of Macau

http://sftw.umac.mo:8000/

University of Maine

http://www.maine.edu/

University of Maine at Farmington

http://www.umf.maine.edu/

University of Maine at Fort Kent

http://www.umfk.maine.edu/

University of Manchester

http://info.mcc.ac.uk/UofM.html

University of Manitoba

http://www.umanitoba.ca/UofM_homepage.html

University of Maribor

http://www.uni-mb.si/

University of Maryland

http://www.umd.edu/

University of Maryland University College

http://www.umuc.edu/

University of Maryland, Baltimore County

http://www.umbc.edu/

University of Maryland, College Park

http://inform.umd.edu/

University of Massachusetts

http://www.umassp.edu/

University of Massachusetts, Amherst

http://www.umass.edu/

University of Massachusetts, Boston

http://www.umb.edu/

University of Massachusetts, Dartmouth

http://www.umassd.edu/welcome.html

University of Massachusetts, Lowell

http://www.uml.edu/

University of Medicine and Dentistry of New Jersey

http://njmsa.umdnj.edu/umdnj.html

University of Melbourne

http://www.unimelb.edu.au/

University of Memphis

http://www.memphis.edu

University of Miami

http://www.ir.miami.edu/

University of Michigan, Ann Arbor

http://www.umich.edu/

University of Michigan, Dearborn

http://www.umd.umich.edu/

University of Milano

http://www.dsi.unimi.it/home.html

University of Minho

http://www.uminho.pt/

University of Minnesota

http://www.umn.edu/

University of Minnesota, Duluth

http://www.d.umn.edu/

University of Minnesota, Morris

http://www.mrs.umn.edu/

University of Miskolc

http://silver.uni-miskolc.hu:8080/

University of Miskolc, Hungary

http://gold.uni-miskolc.hu/

University of Mississippi

http://www.olemiss.edu/

University of Missouri, Columbia

http://www.missouri.edu/

University of Missouri, Kansas City

http://www.umkc.edu/

University of Missouri, Rolla

http://www.umr.edu/

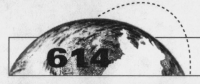

University of Missouri, St. Louis

http://www.umsl.edu/

University of Modena

http://www.casa.unimo.it/

University of Montana

http://www.umt.edu

University of Montreal

http://www.iro.umontreal.ca/

University of Namur

http://www.fundp.ac.be/

University of Natal

http://www.und.ac.za/

University of Natal, Pietermaritzburg

http://www.unp.ac.za/

University of Nebraska at Kearney

http://betty-boop.unk.edu/

University of Nebraska, Lincoln

http://www.unl.edu/index.html

University of Nebraska, Omaha

http://www.unomaha.edu/

University of Neuchatel

http://www.unine.ch/www/welcome-e.html

University of Nevada System

http://www.nevada.edu/

University of Nevada, Las Vegas

http://www.nscee.edu/

University of Nevada, Reno

http://www.scs.unr.edu/

University of New Brunswick

http://www.unb.ca/

University of New England

http://www.une.edu.au/

University of New Hampshire, Durham

http://samizdat.unh.edu:70/1/unh

University of New Haven

http://www.newhaven.edu/

University of New Mexico

http://www.unm.edu/

University of New Orleans

http://www.uno.edu/

University of New South Wales

http://www.unsw.edu.au/

University of Newcastle

http://www.newcastle.edu.au/

University of Newcastle upon Tyne

http://www.ncl.ac.uk/

University of Nijmegen

http://www.kun.nl/

University of North Carolina at Wilmington

http://www.uncwil.edu/

University of North Carolina, Asheville

http://www.unca.edu/

University of North Carolina, Chapel Hill

http://www.unc.edu/

University of North Carolina, Charlotte

http://unccvm.uncc.edu/

University of North Carolina, Greensboro

http://www2.uncg.edu/

University of North Dakota, Grand Forks

http://www.und.nodak.edu/

University of North Florida

http://www.unf.edu/

University of North London

http://www.unl.ac.uk:80/welcome.html

University of North Texas

http://www.unt.edu/

University of Northern Colorado

http://www.univnorthco.edu/

University of Northern Iowa

http://www.uni.edu/

University of Notre Dame

http://www.nd.edu/NDHomePage/NDHomePage.html

University of Nottingham

http://www.nott.ac.uk/

University of Oklahoma

http://www.uoknor.edu/

University of Oldenburg

http://www.informatik.uni-oldenburg.de/homepage.e.html

University of Oregon

http://www.uoregon.edu/

University of Oslo

http://www.uio.no/

University of Otago

http://www.otago.ac.nz/

University of Ottawa

http://www.uottawa.ca/

University of Oulu

http://www.oulu.fi/homepage.html

University of Padua

http://www.unipd.it/

University of Palermo

http://cucaix.cuc.unipa.it/Public/welcome.html

University of Parma

http://www.unipr.it/

University of Pavol Jozef Safarik

http://kosice.upjs.sk/upjs.html

University of Pennsylvania

http://www.upenn.edu/

University of Pereslavl

http://u-pereslavl.botik.ru/UP/

University of Phoenix

http://www.uophx.edu/

University of Picardie

http://www.u-picardie.fr/

University of Pisa

http://www.unipi.it/welcome.html

University of Pittsburgh

http://www.pitt.edu/

University of Port Elizabeth

http://www.upe.ac.za/

University of Portland

http://www.up.edu/

University of Portsmouth

http://www.port.ac.uk/

University of Pretoria

http://www.up.ac.za/

University of Prince Edward Island

http://www.upei.ca/

University of Puerto Rico

http://www.upr.clu.edu/english/home.html

University of Puget Sound

http://www.ups.edu/

University of Quebec, Montreal

http://www.uqam.ca/

University of Queensland

http://www.uq.edu.au/

University of Reading

http://www.rdg.ac.uk/

University of Redlands

http://www.uor.edu/

University of Regina

http://www.uregina.ca/

University of Rennes 1

http://www.univ-rennes1.fr/welcome.html

University of Rhode Island

http://www.uri.edu/

University of Richmond

http://www.urich.edu/

University of Rochester

http://www.rochester.edu/

University of Salford

http://www.salford.ac.uk/

University of Salzburg

http://www.edvz.sbg.ac.at/home.html

University of San Carlos

http://www.usc.edu.ph/

University of San Diego

http://www.acusd.edu/

University of San Francisco

http://www.usfca.edu/

University of Saskatchewan

http://www.usask.ca/

University of Science and Technology of China

http://math.wisc.edu/~cliu/ustc/

University of South Africa

http://www.unisa.ac.za/

University of South Australia

http://cutl.city.unisa.edu.au/

University of South Carolina

http://www.csd.scarolina.edu/

University of South Carolina at Aiken

http://www.usca.scarolina.edu/

University of South Dakota

http://www.usd.edu/

University of South Florida

http://www.usf.edu/

University of Southampton

http://ilc.ecs.soton.ac.uk/welcome.html

University of Southern California

http://cwis.usc.edu/

University of Southern Indiana

http://www.usi.edu/

University of Southern Maine

http://www.usm.maine.edu/

University of Southern Mississippi

http://www.usm.edu/

University of Southern Queensland

http://www.usq.edu.au/

University of Southwestern Louisiana

http://www.usl.edu/

University of St. Andrews

http://www.st-andrews.ac.uk/

University of St. Gallen

http://www-iwi.unisg.ch/

University of St. Thomas

http://www.stthomas.edu/

University of Stellenbosch

http://lib.sun.ac.za/

University of Stirling

http://www.stir.ac.uk/

University of Strathclyde

http://www.strath.ac.uk/

University of Sunderland

http://www.sunderland.ac.uk/

University of Surrey

http://www.surrey.ac.uk/

University of Sussex

http://www.susx.ac.uk/

University of Sydney

http://www.usyd.edu.au/

University of Tampere

http://www.uta.fi/

University of Tasmania

http://info.utas.edu.au/

University of Technology, Sydney

http://www.uts.edu.au/

University of Teesside

http://www.tees.ac.uk/

University of Tennessee, Chattanooga

http://www.utc.edu/

University of Tennessee, Knoxville

http://www.utk.edu/

University of Tennessee, Martin

http://www.utm.edu/

University of Texas at Arlington

http://www.uta.edu/

University of Texas at Austin

http://www.utexas.edu/

University of Texas at Dallas

http://www.utdallas.edu/

University of Texas at El Paso

http://cs.utep.edu/utep/utep.html

University of Texas at Houston

http://www.uth.tmc.edu/

University of Texas at San Antonio

http://rabbit.cs.utsa.edu/Welcome.html

University of Texas Health Center at Tyler

http://pegasus.uthct.edu/UTHCT-Home/Welcome.html

University of Texas Health Science Center, San Antonio

http://www.uthscsa.edu/

University of Texas Medical Branch

http://www.utmb.edu/

University of Texas Southwestern Medical Center

http://www.swmed.edu/

University of Texas-Pan American

http://www.panam.edu/

University of the Americas

http://info.pue.udlap.mx/

University of the Basque Country

http://www.sc.ehu.es/

University of the Pacific

http://www.uop.edu/

University of the Philippines, Diliman

http://www.upd.edu.ph/

University of the Ryukyus

http://www.ie.u-ryukyu.ac.jp/

University of the Virgin Islands

http://www.uvi.edu/

University of the West Indies

http://www.uwimona.edu.jm/

University of the West of England

http://gate.uwe.ac.uk:8000/uwe/uwe.html

University of Tokushima

http://www.tokushima-u.ac.jp/

University of Tokyo

http://web.yl.is.s.u-tokyo.ac.jp/ut/ut.html

University of Tokyo, Institute of Industrial Science

http://www.iis.u-tokyo.ac.jp/

University of Toledo

http://www.utoledo.edu/

University of Toronto

http://www.utoronto.ca/uoft.html

University of Trieste

http://www.univ.trieste.it/e_utshom.html

University of Trondheim

http://www.unit.no/

University of Tsukuba

http://www.tsukuba.ac.jp/

University of Tulsa

http://www.utulsa.edu/

University of Turku

http://www.utu.fi/

University of Twente

http://www.nic.utwente.nl/

University of Udine

http://www.uniud.it/www/welcome.html

University of Ulster

http://www.ulst.ac.uk/

University of Utah

http://www.utah.edu/

University of Vaasa

http://www.uwasa.fi/samjay/index.html

University of Valladolid

http://www.uva.es/

University of Venice

http://www.unive.it/HomePage.html

University of Vermont

http://www.uvm.edu/

University of Veterinary Medicine, Vienna

http://www.vu-wien.ac.at/

University of Victoria

http://www.uvic.ca/

University of Vienna

http://www.univie.ac.at/

University of Virginia

http://www.virginia.edu/

University of Waikato

http://www.waikato.ac.nz/default.html

University of Wales

http://WWW.Lamp.Ac.UK/

University of Wales College of Medicine

http://www.uwcm.ac.uk/

University of Wales, Bangor

http://www.bangor.ac.uk/

University of Wales, Cardiff

http://www.cf.ac.uk/index.html

University of Warwick

http://www.csv.warwick.ac.uk/default.html

University of Washington

http://www.washington.edu/

University of Waterloo

http://www.uwaterloo.ca/

University of Western Australia

http://www.uwa.edu.au/

University of Western Ontario

http://www.uwo.ca/

University of Western Sydney, Hawkesbury

http://www.hawkesbury.uws.edu.au/

University of Western Sydney, Macarthur

http://www.macarthur.uws.edu.au/

University of Western Sydney, Nepean

http://www.nepean.uws.edu.au/

University of Westminster

http://www.wmin.ac.uk/

University of Windsor

http://www.uwindsor.ca/

University of Wisconsin, Eau Claire

http://www.uwec.edu/

University of Wisconsin, Madison

http://www.wiscinfo.wisc.edu/

University of Wisconsin, Milwaukee

http://www.uwm.edu/

University of Wisconsin, Oshkosh

http://www.uwosh.edu/

University of Wisconsin, Parkside

http://www.uwp.edu/

University of Wisconsin, River Falls

http://www.uwrf.edu/

University of Wisconsin, Steven's Point

http://www.uwsp.edu/

University of Wisconsin, Stout

http://www.uwstout.edu/

University of Wisconsin-Platteville

http://www.uwplatt.edu/

University of Wisconsin-Whitewater

http://www.uww.edu/

University of Witwatersrand

http://www.wits.ac.za/

University of Wollongong

http://www.uow.edu.au/

University of Wolverhampton

http://www.wlv.ac.uk/

University of Wyoming

http://www.uwyo.edu/

University of York

http://www.york.ac.uk/

University of Zambia

http://www.zamnet.zm/unza/unza.html

University of Zurich

http://www.unizh.ch/

University Paris IX Dauphine

http://www.bu.dauphine.fr/

University Passau

http://www.uni-passau.de/welcome.html

University Pertanian Malaysia

http://w3.cs.upm.my/

University Potsdam

http://www.uni-potsdam.de/

University Regensburg

http://www.wiwi.uni-regensburg.de/

University Regiomontana

http://www.ur.mx/

University Rostock

http://www.informatik.uni-rostock.de/Uni/

University Rovira i Virgili

http://www.urv.es/

University Sains Malaysia

http://www.cs.usm.my/

University San Francisco de Quito

http://mail.usfq.edu.ec/

University Santa Maria La Antigua

http://www.usma.pa/

University Stuttgart

http://www.uni-stuttgart.de/

University Tecnica Federico Santa Maria

http://www.inf.utfsm.cl/

University Teknologi Malaysia

http://www.utm.my/

University Trier

http://www.uni-trier.de/

University Ulm

http://www.informatik.uni-ulm.de/index.eng.html

University Zagreb

http://www.zvne.etf.hr/uniinfo.html

University-GH Paderborn

http://www.uni-paderborn.de/

Uppsala University

http://www.uu.se/

Ursinus College

http://www.ursinus.edu

Utah State University

http://www.usu.edu/

Utah Valley State College

http://www.uvsc.edu/

Utrecht University

http://www.ruu.nl/

Utsunomiya University

http://www.utsunomiya-u.ac.jp/

Valdosta State University

http://www.valdosta.peachnet.edu/home.html

Valparaiso University

http://www.valpo.edu/

Vanderbilt University

http://www.vanderbilt.edu/

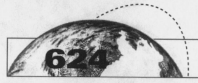
Vassar College

http://vasweb.vassar.edu/

Vaxjo University

http://www.hv.se/eng/eng_home.html

Vermont Technical College

http://www.vtc.vsu.edu/

Vesalius College

http://www.vub.ac.be/VECO/VECO-intro.html

Victoria Jubilee Technical Institute

http://www.ece.iit.edu/~hchhaya/vjti/vjti.html

Victoria University of Technology

http://www.vut.edu.au/

Victoria University of Wellington

http://www.vuw.ac.nz/

Vienna University of Technology

http://info.tuwien.ac.at/ROOT

Villanova University

http://www.vill.edu/

Virginia Commonwealth University

http://www.vcu.edu/

Virginia Tech

http://www.vt.edu/

Volda College

http://www.hivolda.no/

Vrije University

http://www.cca.vu.nl/

Wabash College

http://ruby.wabash.edu/

Wageningen Agricultural University

http://www.wau.nl/welcome.html

Wakayama University

http://www.wakayama-u.ac.jp/

Wake Forest University

http://www.wfu.edu/start.html

Walden University

http://www.waldenu.edu/

Walla Walla College

http://www.wwc.edu/

Warren Wilson College

http://www.warren-wilson.edu/

Warsaw Technical University

http://www.ia.pw.edu.pl/

Warsaw University

http://info.fuw.edu.pl/

Washburn University

http://www.wuacc.edu/

Washington & Lee University

http://liberty.uc.wlu.edu/

Washington College

http://www.washcoll.edu/

Washington State University

http://www.wsu.edu/

Washington University in St. Louis

http://www.wustl.edu/

Washtenaw Community College

http://northernspy.washtenaw.cc.mi.us/

Wayne State University

http://www.wayne.edu/

Waynesburg College

http://waynesburg.edu/

Weber State University

http://www.weber.edu/

Weizmann Institute of Science

http://wissgi.weizmann.ac.il/

Wellesley College

http://www.wellesley.edu/

Wesleyan University

http://www.wesleyan.edu/

West Chester University of Pennsylvania

http://albie.wcupa.edu/

West Coast University

http://katz.wcula.edu/

West Georgia College

http://www.westga.edu/

West Texas A&M University

http://www.wtamu.edu/

West Virginia University

http://www.wvu.edu/

Western Baptist College

http://www.wbc.edu/

Western Carolina University

http://www.wcu.edu/

Western Iowa Community College

http://www.witcc.ia.us/

Western Kentucky University

http://www.wku.edu/

Western Maryland College

http://ns1.wmc.car.md.us/

Western Michigan University

http://www.wmich.edu/

Western State College of Colorado

http://www.wester.edu/Welcome.html

Western Washington University

http://www.wwu.edu/

Westmont College

http://www.westmont.edu/

Wharton School

http://www.wharton.upenn.edu/

Wheaton College

http://www.wheatonma.edu/

Whitman College

http://www.whitman.edu/

Whittier College

http://www.whittier.edu/

WHU Koblenz School of Corporate Management

http://www.whu-koblenz.de/

Wichita State University

http://www.twsu.edu/

Wilkes University

http://www.wilkes.edu/

Willamette University

http://www.willamette.edu/

William Penn College

http://www.wmpenn.edu/

William Rainey Harper College

http://www.harper.cc.il.us/

William Woods University

http://www.wmwoods.edu/

Williams College

http://www.williams.edu/

Wilmington College

http://www.wilmington.edu/

Winona State University, Minnesota

http://gopher.winona.msus.edu/

Winthrop University

http://lurch.winthrop.edu/WinthropHomePage.html

Wolfson College, Oxford

http://www.wolfson.ox.ac.uk/

Worcester Polytechnic Institute

http://www.wpi.edu/

Wright State University

http://pogo.wright.edu/

Wroclaw Technical University

http://www.ict.pwr.wroc.pl/

Xavier University

http://www.xu.edu.ph/

Xi'an Jiao Tong University

http://www.cs.bham.ac.uk/~yxh/xjtu.html

Yale University

http://www.yale.edu/

Yamanashi University

http://www.yamanashi.ac.jp/

Yasuda Women's University

http://www.yasuda-u.ac.jp/

Yerevan Physics Institute

http://www.yerphi.am/

Yeshiva University, Albert Einstein College of Medicine

http://www.aecom.yu.edu/

Yeungnam University

http://165.229.11.3/

Yildiz Technical University

http://www.ce.yildiz.edu.tr/

York College

http://www.yorkcol.edu/

York University

http://www.yorku.ca/

Youngstown State University

http://gateway.cis.ysu.edu/

Yuan-Ze Institute of Technology

http://www.yzit.edu.tw/

Zhongshan University

http://www.sci.ccny.cuny.edu:80/~jdong/zhongda/index.html

This section supplements the earlier business section by listing nearly 2,500 selected commercial enterprises that maintain Web sites. A more complete compendium of business-related sites is available on the CD-ROM that accompanies this book.

1-800-FLY-ASAP

http://www.indirect.com/user/ecs/

123 Consulting

http://www.webplaza.com/pages/Computers/123Consulting/
123Consulting.html

1st Choice Travel

http://physc1.byu.edu/~astrosoc/first.html

1st Solutions, Inc.

http://www.firstsol.com/

20/20 Sofware, Inc.

http://www.twenty.com/~twenty/

3220 Sacramento St. Videoconference Center

http://www.hia.com/hia/pcr/advert.html

3D Scanners, Ltd.

http://www.3dscanners.com/

3DO

http://www.3do.com/

4GL Computing, Ltd.

http://www.demon.co.uk/4gl/

508/617 Frame Relay Internet Service

http://www.harvardnet.com/

7th Wave Productions

http://www.speakeasy.org/~herc/

A&M Networking, Inc.

http://voyager.bei.net/am/index.html

A-Link Network Services, Inc.

http://www.alink.net/

A.M.I. Records

http://jax.jaxnet.com/~ejerue/ami.html

A.R.K Distribution

http://www.maires.co.uk/nw2n/headbutt/arc.html

AAA Advertising Info

http://cybersight.com/cgi-bin/market/s?info.gmml

AAA Love Records

http://www.goodies.com/biz/alr/aaa0.htm

AAA Villas of Hawaii

http://www.hula.net/~cyber/villas.html

AArising Records

http://www.aarising.com/

ABA Net

http://www.abanet.it/

Abacus Niagara

http://www.niagara.com/~abacus/

Ablaze Business Systems, Inc.

http://www.radix.net/~ablaze

About Time Music Company

http://www.numenet.com/sc/about_time/

Absoft Corporation

http://www.absoft.com/

Abstract Technologies

http://www.abstract.co.nz/

Abundant Discoveries

http://amsquare.com/abundant/index.html

Abut Oy

http://www.ttl.fi/abut/

Academy of Learning

http://www_wol.info-mine.com/aol/

ACC Corp., Inc.

http://www.acc-corp.com/

Accelerated Computer Training, Inc.

http://www.earthlink.net/~actinc/

Accent's Cruise Connection

http://www.premier.net/~accent/

ACCESS Computer Hardware

http://www.electriciti.com/~access/

Access Global Information Services, Inc.

http://www.ag.net/

AccessManager

http://www.icl.co.uk/access

Accidental Software

http://www.primenet.com/~accident/accident.html

Accsys Corporation

http://info.acm.org/~rkaplan/homepage.html

ACD Systems

http://vvv.com/acd/

ACE InfoSystems

http://www.aceinfo.com/

Acer America Career Opportunities

http://www.acer.com/aac/about/jobs.htm

Acer America What's New

http://www.acer.com/aac/whatsnew.htm

Acer Group

http://www.acer.com/index.htm

Achieve Technology

http://www.mv.com/biz/achieve-tech/

Acorn Music

http://www.sirius.com/~acorn/

ACS Custom Manufacturing

http://www.btsweb.com/cable/

Action Staff, Inc.

http://www.tulsa.com/action/paulhagl.htm

Active Vacations

http://www.castles.com/vs/vacation_station.html

Activision

http://www.activision.com/

Acumart

http://www.acumart.com/

Ad Methods Halpern and Eurich Advertising, Inc.

http://www.li.net/admethod/

Ada's Store

http://adaweb.com/adaweb/items/store.html

Adams Networks

http://www.ltm.com/atc/atc1.html

Adept Scientific plc

http://www.adeptscience.co.uk/

adfx

http://www.halcyon.com/zz/top.html

Adjacency, Inc.

http://adjacency.com

Admins, Inc.

http://www.admins.com/

AdMorInk

http://www.focusoc.com/admorink/

Adnet

http://www.adnet.ie/Adnet/

ADSTAR Distributed Storage Manager (ADSM)

http://www-i.almaden.ibm.com/storage/hardsoft/software/html/adsmhome.htm

Adtran

http://www.adtran.com/

Advance Network Solutions

http://www.halcyon.com/routers/

Advanced Computer Technologies

http://www.mountain.net/hp/act/

Advanced Cultural Technologies

http://www.ACTinc.bc.ca/

Advanced Instruments Corporation

http://www.ai.com/

Advanced Paradigms, Inc.

http://www.paradigms.com/

Advanced Quick Circuits, L.P.

http://www.iu.net/aqc/

Advanced Software Technology, Inc.

http://www.aescon.com/asti/index.htm

Advantage Computers, Ltd.

http://www.advantage.com/

ADVANTIS Networking Technology Services

http://www.ibm.com/globalnetwork

Adventure Travel

http://www.rscomm.com/adsports/at.html

Advertising Media Internet Center (AMIC)

http://www.amic.com

Advertising, Boelter & Lincoln

http://www.advbl.com/

AdWaves Communications

http://www.pepperdine.edu/seaver/communic/adwaves.htm

Aer Lingus

http://www.hursley.ibm.com/aer/

Aeroflot

http://www.seanet.com/Bazar/Aeroflot/Aeroflot.html

AFL Consulting

http://www.interport.net/~aflcons/

After Hours Media

http://www.afterhours.com/cd-backup.html

After Hours Media Duplication Service

http://www.afterhours.com/

AfterHours Communications Corp.

http://www.primenet.com/~ahours/

AgentCentral

http://www.mindspring.com/~jon-tom/AgentCentral.html

Agorics, Inc.

http://www.agorics.com/~agorics/

AHK & Associates

http://www.value.net/ahk/html/

Ainsworth Group of Companies

http://wchat.on.ca/ainsworth/ati.htm

Air Brokers International World Travel Specialist

http://www.aimnet.com/~airbrokr/

Air Havoc Controller for Windows

http://com.primenet.com/rainbow/

Airtime Internet Resources, Ltd.

http://www.airtime.co.uk/

AIT

http://access.digex.net/~solson/

Aladdin Knowledge Systems, Ltd.

http://www.hasp.com/

Albion Books

http://www.bookport.com/source/albion9501.html

Alcatel Data Networks

http://www.adn.alcatel.com/

Alchemy Records

http://www.musicpro.com/alchemy/

Alfers Advertising & Publishing, Inc.

http://fox.nstn.ca/~alfers/

AlgoRhythm Music

http://www.io.org/~arhythm/

Aliah, Inc.

http://www.aliah.com/

All About Computers, Inc.

http://www.magic.mb.ca/~allabout/

All Around Travel Network

http://www.sims.net/aatn/

All Ways Travel

http://www.empnet.com/all_ways/

Alldata

http://www.alldata.tsb.com/

Allegro Group, The

http://www.allegro.net/

Allen & Associates, Ltd.

http://www.radix.net/~eallen/

Allen, Victoria

http://www.goworldnet.com/vallen.htm

Allied Percival International

http://www.miint.net/api/api.html

Allon Computer, Inc.

http://www.promedia.net/allon/allon.html

Alpha Microsystems Services Operation

http://www.alphamicro.com/

Alphanet South Corporation

http://www.ansouth.net/

Alps Electric USA

http://www.alpsusa.com/

Altera

http://www.altera.com/

AlternaKids Records

http://tfnet.ils.unc.edu/~kids/

Alternate Image

http://www.suspects.com/AlternateImage

Alternet Sonic Realities

http://www.iuma.com/ASR/

Amadeus Consulting

http://www.wolfgang.com/

Amass Systems, Inc.

http://www.supernet.ab.ca/Mall/Computer/amass.html

Amcan Travel

http://www.halcyon.com/amcan/welcome.html

Amdahl Open Enterprise Systems

http://www.amdahl.com/doc/products/oes.html

Amecon, Inc.

http://www.tiac.net/users/amecon/index.html

American Computer Resources, Inc.

http://www.the-acr.com/

American Digital Network

http://www.adnc.com/

American Gramaphone Records

http://www.amgram.com/

American Power Conversion

http://www.apcc.com/

American Reporter

http://www.newshare.com/Reporter/today.html

American Supply International, Inc.

http://www.dgsys.com/~asii/

American Trans Air

http://www.xmission.com/~aoi/fata.html

Americas, The

http://www.integctr.com/americas/

AmeriNet

http://amerinet.com/

Amida Press

http://users.aimnet.com/~amidaprs/

AMOC (A Matter of Clay)

http://www.systemv.com/infonet/gtg/

Amris, Ltd.

http://www.iijnet.or.jp/amris/elead_pp/ad_ele_e.html

Analytical Software Packages, Inc.

http://www.emi.net/~asp

Anchors Away

http://www.onestop.com/cruise/

AND Idenfication

http://www.and.nl/corporate_review/identification/

Andrews, Chris

http://fox.nstn.ca/~candrews

Anduril Design

http://www.acm.iit.edu/~trygray/anduril.html

Angel Thorne Music

http://www.e-MediaWeb.com/ATM.html

AniCom, Inc.

http://www2.interpath.net/anicom/

AnimaTek, Inc.

http://www.animatek.com/

Animation Rendering & Image Processing

http://www.maui.com/~rendernet/

Another Color, Inc.

http://www.csgi.com/AC/

Ansett Australia

http://www.ansett.com.au/

Antigua & Barbuda

http://www.candw.ag/

Anzen

http://www.tesser.com/anzen/

Apache Digital Corporation

http://www.apache.com/

APCiNet

http://www.apci.net/

Apollo Advertising

http://apollo.co.uk/

App Foundation, Inc.

http://www.onthego.com/taf/

Applied Computer Services, Inc.

http://www.acsil.com/

Applied Signal Technology

http://www.appsig.com/

Applix, Inc.

http://www.applix.com/

APSC Informatique

http://www.montrealnet.ca/apsc/

AquaNet

http://www.finite-tech.com/fti/aquanet.htmld

ARC

http://www.arcfile.com

Arcada Software

http://www.arcada.com/

Architext Software

http://www.atext.com/

Archtek Telecom Corp.

http://www.archtek.com.tw/

Arcland, Inc.

http://www.xensei.com/flowmodel/

ARGUS

http://www.tcel.com/~argus/

Aris Technologies

http://www.aris.com/

Aristoplay, Ltd.

http://intergalactic.com/aris.htm

Armstrong Design Consultants

http://www.nando.net/prof/farmland/farmhouse.html

ArosNet

http://www.aros.net/Welcome.html

Arrow Publishing Company

http://www.spadion.com/spadion/arrow/

Art Design & Sign/Gaines-Brosseau Gallery

http://www.artdsign.com/graphics/

Art Net

http://telescope.com/telescope/artnet/

Art Planet

http://www.artplanet.com/

Artful Surroundings

http://aspin.asu.edu/~stevea1/index.html

Artifice, Inc.

http://artifice.com/foyer.html

Artix

http://www.artix.com/biz/artix/

Arvore

http://www.arvore.pt/arvore/

AS220

http://www.ids.net/~as220/home.html

Asante Technologies

http://www.asante.com/

Ash International

http://iuma.southern.com/Ash/

Ashlar, Inc.

http://www.ashlar.com

Asia PC Yellow Pages

http://206.17.44.3/pcasia/pcasia.htm

AsiaOne

http://www.asia1.com.sg/zaobao/

askSam Systems

http://199.44.46.2/askSam.htm

Aslan Computing, Inc.

http://www.aslaninc.com/

Aspen Grafix

http://rainbow.rmii.com/~tuffgong/

Aspen Technology, Inc.

http://www.aspentec.com/

Asphodel Records

http://www.w2.com/docs2/a3/asphodel.html

Association of American University Presses (AAUP) Online Catalog/Bookstore

http://aaup.pupress.princeton.edu/

Astrobyte

http://www.astrobyte.com/

Astrology et al Bookstore

http://www.wolfe.net/~astroetl/index.html

AT&T Enterprise Modelling

http://www.edd.co.uk/em/intro

AT&T Paradyne

http://www.paradyne.att.com/

Athena International L.L.C.

http://www.smartpages.com/athena/index.html

ATI Technologies

http://www.atitech.ca/

Atlantic Information Systems, Inc.

http://www.learning.com/AIS/AISHome

Atlantic Systems Group

http://www.ASG.unb.ca/

ATM Publishing

http://warlight.com/warlight/CLIENTS/cc194.html

Atomic Games

http://atomic.neosoft.com/Atomic.html

Atomic Vision, Inc.

http://www.atomicvision.com/

Audio Help Systems

http://apollo.co.uk/a/audiohelp/

AudioWav

http://www.tc.net/audiowav/html/audiowav.html

Auricle Control Systems

http://www.webcom.com/~auricle/

Austin Knight

http://www.aone.net.au/ak

Australasian World Publishing Systems

http://www.wps.com.au/

Australian Pacific Advertising

http://www.nt.com.au/apa/

Auto-Graphics Inc.

http://www.agfx.com/

Automata Design, Inc. (ADI)

http://www.adiva.com/

Automated Design Systems

http://www.niagara.com/autodes/autodes.html

Automated Travel Center

http://www.ananda.com/plg/travel/

Automation Soecialists

http://www.cyberport.com/mall/autospec/

Autotime Corp.

http://www.teleport.com/~autotime/

Avalan Technology, Inc.

http://www.ultranet.com/~dtemple/

Avalanche Systems, Inc.

http://www.avsi.com/

Avazpour Systems

http://www.tyrell.net/~avazsys/

AveryJohn Technologies

http://www.mordor.com/averyjohn/

AVM Summit

http://www.well.com/www/manatee/summit.html

Axess Communications

http://www.axess.com/

Axiom/Laswell Web Site

http://hyperreal.com/music/labels/axiom/

Axis Communications AB

http://www.axis.se/

Aydelu Computer, Inc.

http://www.magi.com/~aydelu/

AztecK Online

http://www.mcs.net/~lavalos/

B & E Technology Group

http://www.cnct.com/~bgriffin/

B&B Computer Specialists, Inc.

http://204.89.187.1

B.M. Software Solutions

http://www.interlog.com/~bmynarsk/BMSolutions.html

Bachman Information Systems

http://www.novalink.com/bachman/index.html

Back Institute of Beverly Hills

http://www.mdle.com/backinst.htm

Badcat Records

http://www.opendoor.com/badcat/BCR_Home.html

Baltzer Science Publishers

http://www.NL.net/~baltzer/

Bandwidth Brokers International (BBI)

http://www.bbi.com/

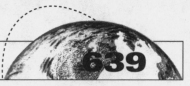

Barlow Wilson PowerBuilder Consultancy

http://www.ibmpcug.co.uk/~jtyndale/

Barrett Consultants

http://wchat.on.ca/barretcj/barrett.htm

Basic Communications, Ltd.

http://www.bcl.net/

Batey Ads Singapore

http://bateyads.com.sg/

BATS, Inc.

http://www.bats.com/bats/

Bay Area Internet Solutions

http://www.bayarea.net/

Bayou Internet BBS

http://www.bayou.com/

Beach Holme Publishing

http://www.swifty.com/Beach/

Beaconway Press, Inc.

http://sunsite.unc.edu/owl/home.html

BelCom Dacha

http://solar.rtd.utk.edu/~belcom/

Belhaven

http://www.owt.com/belhaven/

Bell Microproducts, Inc.

http://www.bellmicro.com/

Benaroya

http://www.portal.com/~sedit/rexxgrph.html

Bentley Systems

http://www.bentley.com/

Bernstein & Associates, Inc.

http://www.b-and-a.com/

Best Computer Service

http://www.winternet.com/~wcdc/bcs.html

Beta-Books

http://www.webcom.com/~unlearn/

BetBasics

http://www.vegas.com/vegascom/betbasc/betbasc.html

Beyond 2000 Systems

http://www.beyond2000.com/

BGS Systems

http://www.bgs.com/

Biddeford Internet Corp.

http://www.biddeford.com/

Big Home Productions

http://www.magna.com.au/woodwire/BHP.html

Big Noise Music Software

http://www.icba.com/bignoise/index.html

Biggs Gilmore Communications

http://www.Biggs-Gilmore.com/icecream/

Bioenergetics Press

http://www.msn.fullfeed.com/rschenk/bioecat.html

BIOS Scientific Press

http://www.demon.co.uk/bookshop/bicat.html

Birdsong Enterprises

http://www.ioa.com/users/birdsong/

Bismarck Group

http://www.bismarck.com/

Bitronics, Inc.

http://www.infop.com/bitron/index.html

BitWise Solutions, Inc.

http://www.bit-wise.com/bitwise/

Black Box Corporation

http://www.blackbox.com/

BlackMagic Enterprises

http://www.blackmagic.com/

Blackwell Science

http://www.blacksci.co.uk/

Blithedale Books

http://199.164.192.154/

Blue Bonnet Books

http://www.maestro.com/ing/literature/bluebonnet/bluebind

Blue Heron Publishing

http://www.teleport.com/~bhp/

Blue Peter Books

http://www.discribe.ca/other/bluep.htm

Blue Ridge Technologies

http://ios.com/~brt/

Blue Sky Research

http://www.bluesky.com/

BlueGoat Records

http://www.iuma.com/Bluegoat/

Bluestone, Inc.

http://www.bluestone.com/

Blyth

http://www.crocker.com/~pistrang/bcsOmnis.html

BMP DDB Needham

http://www.bmp.co.uk/bmp/home.htm

Bob Book Online

http://www.gigaplex.com/wow/books/bob/index.htm

Boca Research

http://www.boca.org/

Bonder Bookstore Inc,

http://www.bonder.com

Bonneville International Corporation, Utah Wired

http://www.utw.com/bonneville/bonn.html

Book Hunter

http://www.i1.net/~bhunter/

Bookish

http://www.bic.org.uk/bic/

Bookmasters

http://www.bookmasters.com/elecmkt.htm

Bookport

http://www.bookport.com/welcome/yahoo_ent_bks/

BookSite

http://www.booksite.com/

Bookstore at Houghton Mifflin

http://www.hmco.com/trade/

BookWorld

http://www.bookworld.com/

Borg Internet Services

http://www.borg.com/

Boss Net

http://www.isisnet.com/jeff/index.html

Boston Ibex Technologies

http://www.tiac.net/users/dinerman/

Bouncing Buddha Productions

http://www.sirius.com/~zola/zola.html

Boy's Life Records

http://www.iuma.com/Boy's_Life/

BPE Technologies

http://www.wta.com/bpe/

BrainLINK International

http://www.brainlink.com/

Branson Gray Line Travel

http://www.branson.net/branson/grayline/

Brazilnet BBS

http://www.win.net/~brazilnet/bbs.html

Brickell Research, Inc.

http://www.shadow.net/~roland/soap.html

Bridger Records

http://www.numenet.com/sc/bridger/

Brightware Corporation

http://www.brightware.com/

Broadcast Management Plus

http://www.bmp.com/

Broadway Video, Inc.

http://www.broadwayvideo.com/

Brochure Flow

http://www.broflo.com.au/broflo.html

Bryant Software

http://www.bryant.com/

Bubble Technology Industries, Inc.

http://intranet.on.ca/~bubble/

Budding Artists

http://www.wwcd.com/budart/b_art.html

Bulb Records

http://www.umich.edu/~anfangen/bulb-catalog.html

Bullfrog

http://www.bullfrog.co.uk/

Bureau of Electronic Publishing, Inc.

http://www.bep.com/

Business Access Technologies

http://www.batech.com/

Business Computer Products

http://www.america.com/mall/store/dcw.html

Business Edge

http://pcixous.deltanet.com/behomepage.html

Business Systems of America, Inc.

http://www.webcom.com/~bsa/

Business Volunteers for the Arts

http://www.fine-art.com/org/bva.html

BusLogic, Inc.

http://www.buslogic.com/

Buz Design Group

http://www.netoutfit.com/buz/index.html

BVM

http://www.bvmltd.co.uk/welcome/

BwanaK's Software Super Store

http://www.mindspring.com/~bwanak/bwanaks/bwanaks.html

ByteBox Computer Enclosures

http://www.bytebox.com/bytebox/

C G Enterprises

http://usa.net/cge/cybergat.htm

C I Travel

http://www.infi.net/citravel/

C.O.S. Productions

http://www.caprica.com/0/parkplace/videostore/cos/cos.html

C/M Online Media, Inc.

http://zeus.cybernetics.net/cm.html

CA Natalie Associates

http://www.cana.com/cana/

CACI Company

http://www.caciasl.com/

CAD Cut, Inc.

http://plainfield.bypass.com/bypass/users/cadcut/
cadcut2.html

Cadkey Corp.

http://www.cadkey.com/

Caema Ltd.

http://www.sci.fi/~tsuomine/caema.htm

Caldera Inc.

http://www.caldera.com/

Calico Coop

http://www.dsmnet.com/iowebios/calico/

California Software, Incorporated

http://www.calsoft.com/

Callhaven Computing

http://www.londonmall.co.uk/callhav/

CallWare Technologies

http://www.tdc.on.ca/CTI.html

Calypso Online Services

http://www.calypso.com/

Cambridge Computer Corp.

http://cam.com/~cam

Cambridge Technology Partners

http://www.ctp.com/

Campbell Family Travel

http://198.175.15.221/familytravel/index.html

Campus Network Solutions

http://www.halcyon.com/routers/campus/

Can Am Partners, Inc.

http://canam.dgsys.com/

Canadian Medical Association

http://www.hwc.ca:8400/pubs.htm

Candle Corporation

http://www.candle.com/

Capella Networking

http://plaza.xor.com/capella/

Capital, The

http://www.infi.net/capital/

Capstone Software

http://www.gate.net/~intracor/capstone.html

Caravelle Networks Corporation

http://www.caravelle.com/

Caribbean Internet Service (CISCorp)

http://www.caribe.net/

Carl Yaffey Computer Consulting

http://www.infinet.com/~clydss/

Carney, Hood, and Pancost, Inc.

http://www.halcyon.com/tomas/welcome.html

Carroll-Net

http://www.carroll.com/

Carswell Publishing

http://www.carswell.com/carswell.home

Carter Waxman

http://www.carwax.com

Casa De Toad Records

http://www.nacs.net/~cdtoad/

Cascade Consulting

http://www.omix.com/sites/cascade/home.html

Casino ConXtion

http://conxtion.com/casino.htm

CastCAE

http://www.castech.fi/

Castle Network

http://www.castle.net/

Castle von Buhler Records

http://world.std.com/~amb/

CatchWord Ltd

http://www.catchword.co.uk/

Catron Custom Software

http://www.tiac.net/users/cgb/catron/

Caulfield Records

http://www.acton.com/bernie/

CB-Byte Computersolutions

http://www.worldport.co.at/worldport/cb_byte/cb_home.htm

CCAT Limited

http://www.hk.linkage.net/~cat/index.html

CCI Consulting

http://cciworld.com/ccieng.html

CD-ROM Paradise Srl

http://www.cdrom-paradise.com/

CD Solutions, Inc.

http://www.cdarchive.com/cd_solutions/welcome.htm

CD Works

http://www.tiac.net/users/cdworks/

CD-ROM Software by Telecentral

http://www.a1.com/tlcental/

CDE Technologies

http://www.ipac.net/cde/cdehome.html

CDM Distributors

http://www.iquest.net/cdm/index.html

CE Software

http://www.cesoft.com/

Celebrity Rubbings from the Grave

http://www.pixi.com/~seagull/grave.html

Celtic Internet Services

http://www.imaginet.co.uk/celt/CN_Home.html

Center for Anxiety and Stress Treatment

http://www.cts.com/~health/

Center for Software Development

http://www.service.com/csd/home.html

Centerline Computers

http://www.centercomp.com/

Central Data

http://www.cd.com/

Central Penn Comnet

http://boss.cpcnet.com/home/cpcnet.html

Centrumls Communication

http://www.centrum.is/english/index.html

CEO Software

http://www.the-wire.com/usr/ceo/

Ceram, Inc.

http://www.csn.net/~stinger/

Certified Network Educators

http://www.comnet.com/cne/cnehome.html

CGD.Graphix

http://www.cgd.graphix.co.at/cgd/

CGI Systems, Inc.

http://www.cgisystems.com/

Chameleon Concept, Inc.

http://www.lizardlink.com/home.html

Changing Tones Records

http://www.inch.com/~macmusic/chngtone.html

Chapter Music

http://multiline.com.au/~langham/chapter/

Charles Chickadel Communications

http://www.webcom.com/~home/ccc/

Charleston: A Magical History Tour

http://sc.net/organizations/farrow/magic-tour.html

Charm.Net

http://www.charm.net/

CharterHouse Software Corporation

http://www.earthlink.net/~charterhouse/

Chemical Safety

http://www.portal.com/~austin/chemsafe/index.html

ChemTech Publishing

http://www.io.org/~chemtec/

Cherry Communications, Incorporated

http://teletron.com/cherry/cherry.html

Chiat/Day Inc.

http://www.chiatday.com/factory/

Chick Enterprises Ltd.

http://www.infomatch.com/~chick/chick.htm

China Records

http://www.china.co.uk/china/

Chrysalis Counseling Services

http://www.omix.com/sites/drSandy/home.html

CIAO Software Solutions, Inc.

http://www1.usa1.com/~jurgen/

Cinax Designs Inc.

http://www.cinax.com/

Circa Informatique

http://www.globale.net/~circa/

Circlet Press

http://www.apocalypse.org/circlet/home.html

Circuit Technology, Inc.

http://www.halcyon.com/sverne/home.html

Citac Corporation

http://www.wta.com/citac/

City Lights Publishers and Booksellers

http://town.hall.org/places/city_lights/

City Paper

http://www.cpcn.com/

CJC Graphic Design, Inc.

http://www.panix.com/~charl/

Clara Vista Corporation

http://www.fiesta.com/CVista/

Clarion for Windows

http://www.io.com/~hanover/cw.html

Classic

http://info.cv.nrao.edu/aips/aips-home.html

Clayton Wallis

http://www.crl.com/~clwallis/

Clean Machine

http://wchat.on.ca/cleanmch.htm

Clean Well-Lighted Place For Books, A

http://www.well.com/www/jwscott

Cleopatra

http://www.hallucinet.com/cleopatra

Click 3x

http://www.click3x.com

Client Systems, Inc.

http://www.clientsys.com/

Cloverleaf Communications

http://www.cloverleaf.com/

clySmic Software

http://www.albany.net/~rsmith/

CM&D Online Bookstore

http://www.apk.net/cmd/bookstore/

CN Software

http://www.cns-nj.com/cnsoft/

CNI Communications Network International GmbH

http://www.cni.net/

Cobb Group

http://www.cobb.ziff.com/~cobb/

Coconut Info

http://www.dublclick.com/coconutinfo

Cody's Books

http://www.parentsplace.com/shopping/codys/index.cgi

Cogent Software, Inc.

http://www.cogsoft.com/

Coherent Communications

http://www.coherent.com/

Cohn & Wells

http://www.cohn-wells.com/

Cold Spring Harbor Laboratory Press

http://www.cshl.org/about_cshl_press.html

Collabra Software, Inc.

http://www.collabra.com/

Collection, The

http://www.thecollection.com

Collideascope Digital

http://collideascope.com/empire/

Colorado Independent Publisher's Association

http://usa.net/cipa/

Colorgraphic Communications Corporation

http://www.colorgfx.com/

Columbia Data Products, Inc.

http://www.magicnet.net/cdpi/

COMAIR, The Delta Connection

http://www.iac.net/~flypba/COMAIR/COMAIR/COMAIR.home.html

Comdisco, Inc.

http://www.comdisco.com/

Commax Technologies, Inc.

http://www.commax.com/

CommNet Data Systems

http://www.comm.net/

Commonwealth Data Systems, Inc.

http://www.mnsinc.com/bradshaw/cds_inc1.html

CommTech Systems, Inc.

http://www.ctsystems.com/commtech/

Communicopia Environmental Research and Communications

http://interchange.idc.uvic.ca/communicopia/index.html

Community ConneXion

http://www.c2.org/

Compact Disc Authoring

http://www.ph.kcl.ac.uk/cd/

Compass Point Software, Inc.

http://www.cais.com/aevans/cpsi/cpsi.html

Compass.Net

http://www.compass.net/

CompCo, Incorporated

http://cu.comp-unltd.com/~brett/compcohp.html

Complete Las Vegas Casinos and Hotels Guide

http://www.pcap.com/hotel.htm

Comport Consulting Corporation

http://www.comport.com/

Compris, Inc.

http://infoweb.magi.com/~compris/

CompuGraph International

http://www.cybergate.com/~marc/cg/index.html

CompuHelp Online

http://www.connix.com/~shpilber/

CompuNet USA

http://www.compunetusa.com/cnet/

CompuSmart (Ottawa)

http://infoweb.magi.com/~compsmrt

Compusult Limited

http://www.compusult.nf.ca/

CompuTek International

http://www.computek.net/

Computer Chrome Presentation Graphics

http://www.compchrome.com/

Computer Clinic

http://www.vistech.net/users/pvignola/clinic.html

Computer Company Belgium

http://www.coco.be/

Computer Consumables Buyer's Club

http://www.inforamp.net/~ccbc

Computer Crime Research Laboratories

http://crimelab.com/

Computer Direct

http://www.worldgate.com/compdirect/

Computer Engineering Technologies, Ltd.

http://www.cet.net/

Computer Gate

http://www.aimnet.com/~cgate/cgate.htm

Computer Graphics Systems Development Corporation (CGSD)

http://www.cgsd.com

Computer Hardware Page

http://infotique.lm.com/cgi-bin/phpl.cgi?comphard.html

Computer House/ISMAX

http://emanate.com/ismax/

Computer Marketplace, Inc.

http://www.mkpl.com/

Computer Power Group

http://www.cpsg.com.au/cpg/welcome.html

Computer Price Cruncher

http://www.killerapp.com/

Computer Recycler

http://www.coolsville.com/recycler/

Computer Salvage Company

http://www.charm.net/~creative/salvage/index.html

Computer Shopper Magazine [zdnet.com]

http://www.zdnet.com/~cshopper/

Computer Solutions GSD, Inc.

http://www.csgsd.com/

Computer System Architects

http://itchy.itsnet.com/commercial/csa/public_html/

Computer Systems Design Company

http://www.csd.net/Welcome.html

Computer Telephone Integrators, Inc.

http://www.inforamp.net/mainstay/cti/

Computer Warehouse

http://usashopping.com/cgi-win/cw/cwnet.exe

Computerbücher am Obelisk

http://www.obelisk.netplace.com

ComputerDen, Inc.

http://www.gate.net/~compden/

ComputerPeople/Dci

http://www.computerppl.com/

Computers and Learning A/S

http://www.oslonett.no/html/adv/Candle/candle.html

Computervision Corp.

http://www.cv.com/

Compuware Corporation

http://www.compuware.com/

Comstar

http://www.comstarinc.com/

Conari Press

http://www.organic.com/Books/Conari/index.html

Config.Sys

http://www.apk.net/1/cdrom

Conlin Faber Travel

http://www.branch.com/conlin/conlin.html

connect.com.au pty ltd

http://www.connect.com.au/

Connectivity Custom Controls

http://www.toupin.com/~etoupin/ccc.html

CONNECTnet

http://www.connectnet.com/

ConnectUSA

http://www.connectusa.com/

Consensus Development

http://www.consensus.com:8300/

Constant Synthesis Project

http://www.sanctuary.com/haven/consynpro/

Consumer Network Group

http://www.msen.com/~niser/

Continuum Information Services

http://pages.prodigy.com/GA/continuum_is/
continuum_is.html

Contrib.Net

http://www.contrib.net/

Convergence Communications

http://www.pcnet.com/~convrge/Convergencecomm.HTML

Cook's Web Services

http://www.metronet.com/~fec/

CooperSoft

http://www.getnet.com/~joeco/

CoPilot

http://www.leadgroup.com/

Core Systems

http://www.win.net/~core/

CoreLAN Communications, Inc.

http://www.corelan.com/

Cornelius Concepts

http://www.teleport.com/~concepts/

Cornett & Associates, Inc.

http://www.accunet.com/cornett.htm

Cornucopia First Class Travel

http://iquest.com/~marla/

Corporate Book Services, Inc.

http://www.njcc.com/~corbook/

Corporate Network Management

http://www.csz.com/cnm.html

Corporate Software Integration Services

http://www.csis.csof.com/

Cosmic JamStain

http://uptown.turnpike.net/~Makari/CJS/

Coteau Books

http://coteau.unibase.com/welcome.html

Countryman Press

http://www.cybermalls.com/cymont/countrym/

CouponNet

http://coupon.com/coupon.html

CP Systems

http://www.connix.com/~cps/

CPsoft Consulting

http://www.azstarnet.com/~cpsoft/index.html

Crafter's Showcase

http://www.northcoast.com/unlimited/product_directory/cs/cs.html

Crayola

http://www.crayola.com/crayola/

Crazy Dave's Used Computers

http://www.csiworld.com/hutchnet/daves.htm

Creation Records

http://www.elmail.co.uk/music/creation/

Creative Design

http://www.webcom.com/~cdesign/

Creative Eye

http://bensonassoc.com/bensonassoc/pct/pctres.html

Creative Interests Agency

http://www.sonic.net/cia/

Creative Services

http://sec.dgsys.com/creative.html

Creative Strategies Research

http://www.creative.net/

Creative Virtue Press

http://www.eskimo.com/~telical/

Credit Manager, Version 1.0

http://www.xmission.com/~rexm/tsb.html

Crescent Division

http://www.progress.com/crescent/

Cromack Industries, Inc.

http://www.cromack.com/

CrossComm Corporation

http://www.crosscomm.com/

CrossLink Internet Access

http://www.crosslink.net/

CrossWind Technologies, Inc.

http://www.crosswind.com/

Cruise Shoppes America, Ltd.

http://www.cruiseshoppes.com/

Cruises, Inc.

http://www2.csn.net/cruises/

Cruz Group, The

http://www.cruzgroup.com/directory/

CRUZIO

http://cruzio.com/cruzio/cruzio.html

CSI.NET, Inc.

http://www.csi.net/

CTC-Mundo

http://www.ctc-mundo.net/

CTE Computer Training Center

http://www.ctetrain.com/cte/

Cunningham & Cunningham, Inc.

http://www.c2.com/

Curb Records

http://www.curb.com/

curious pictures

http://found.cs.nyu.edu/curious/

Custom Innovative Solutions (CIS)

http://www.cisc.com/

CutterNet, Inc.

http://inetbsystems.us.com/CUTTERNET/CutterNet.html

CVS Bubbles

http://www.loria.fr/~molli/cvs-index.html

cyber exchange

http://www.chattanooga.net/cyberx/index.html

Cyber Reality Productions

http://Mindlink.net/Glenn_Giesbrecht/

Cyber Technologies International

http://shrine.cyber.ad.jp/

CyberDiner Internet Cafe Systems

http://www.cyberplace.com/cyberdiner.html

Cyberg8t Internet Services

http://www.cyberg8t.com/

Cybergate L.L.C.

http://web.cybergate.org/

CyberHighway

http://www.cyberhighway.net/

Cyberian Outpost

http://www.cybout.com/

CyberMedia

http://www.internet-is.com/cybermedia/in-iis.html

CyberNet Communications Corp.

http://www.cybernet.ca/

Cybernetic Stress Control

http://wchat.on.ca/romberg/

CyberRentals

http://opendoor.com/rentals/homepage.html

Cyberspace Promotions, Inc.

http://www.microserve.net/vradio/

CyberStar

http://www.vistech.net/users/cstar/

CyberTec Commercial Art, Inc.

http://www.wln.com/~grafx/index.html

Cybertzara

http://www.webcom.com/~cybertza/

CyberVision

http://www.edge.net/cybervision/index.htm

CyberWeb SoftWare

http://www.charm.net/~web/CWSW.html

Cyclic Software

http://www.cyclic.com/

CygnaCom Solutions, Inc.

http://www.cygnacom.com/

Cygnus Support Information Gallery

http://www.cygnus.com/

Cytopia Software Incorporated

http://www.cytopia.com/

D&M Sales

http://www.srv.net/~dia/vitamins/opening.html

D-Best Computer Center

http://fs.cei.net/dbest/

Da Capo Jazz/Blues Catalog

http://www.dnai.com/~lmcohen/dacapo.html

DAC Micro Computing

http://www.ultranet.com/~ward/

Daedalus Design Group

http://www.mainelink.net/~ddg/ddg.html

Daily Commercial Recorder

http://www.dcci.com/PTP/crecorder.html

DAIR Computer Systems Logo Design

http://www.vpm.com/dair/daircs.htm

DAKCO PC Products Division, Inc.

http://dakco.lm.com/

Dallas Morning News, The

http://www.pic.net/tdmn/tdmn.html

Dalton Maag

http://www.demon.co.uk/trash/DaltonMaag/type.html

Damar Group

http://www.dgl.com/

Dancing Dragon Designs

http://www.northcoast.com/unlimited/product_directory/
dancing_dragon/dancing_dragon.html

Danpex Corporation

http://sweb.srmc.com/danpex/

Darim Vision Co.

http://darvision.kaist.ac.kr/

Darwin Micro Systems

http://www.deltanet.com/users/darwin/

Das Computerhaus

http://www.syscon.co.at/

Dash Open Phone System

http://www.dashops.com/

Data Exchange Corporation

http://www.dex.com/

Data Image Systems

http://bigweb.com/mall/don/index.html

Data Logic

http://www.datlog.co.uk/

Data-Doc Electronics, Inc.

http://www.datadoc.com/

Database Excelleration Systems

http://www.desdbx.com/

DataCAD

http://www.cadkey.com/datacad/

Datalink Direct

http://www.datalinkrdy.com/

Datamini Systems

http://www.net1.net/comm/datamini.html

Dataprobe

http://www.dataprobe.com/

DataSoft

http://pulse.datasoftbus.com/

Datasync Internet Services

http://www.datasync.com/

Datateknik

http://www.et.se/datateknik

DataViz

http://199.186.148.129/

DataWave Technologies

http://usa.net/datawave/

Dataworld

http://www.datawld.com/

David Morrison Books

http://www.teleport.com/~morrison/

David Whitt & Associates, Inc.

http://www.gate.net/~pdwhitt/

Davis Studios

http://www.sirius.com/~jdavis/

DayStar Digital, Inc.

http://www.daystar.com/

DDB Needham Interactive Communications

http://www.ddbniac.com/

DDIX, Inc.

http://www.charm.net/~iscape/packview.html

Decoder Ring Records

http://jax.jaxnet.com/~theidiot/decoder.html

Deep Politics Bookstore

http://www.copi.com/deepbook.htm

DejaView

http://bigmac.gmg.com/

Delphi Information Systems

http://www.delphinfo.com/~delphi/

Delphic Medical Systems

http://www.delphic.co.nz/

Delta Tao, Inc. (unofficial)

http://www.cis.yale.edu/~casper/deltatao/deltatao.html

Denmac Systems

http://www.mixcom.com/wwggww/

denver.net

http://www.cook.net/denvrnet.html

Der Standard

http://www.derstandard.co.at/DerStandard/

Descartes Solutions

http://www.u-net.com/descartes/

Design Combus, Ltd.

http://www.sci.fi/combus/indexEng.html

Design OnLine Pty, Ltd.

http://www.design.net.au/

Designed Information Systems Corporation

http://www.aurora.net/disc.html

Designs for Health

http://branch.com/vitamin/vitamin.html

DesignSphere Online

http://www.dsphere.net/

Desktop Miracles

http://rampages.onramp.net/~desktop/

Destination Vegas

http://www.vegas.com/vegascom/dstnvegs/dstnveg.html

Destinations On-Line

http://dol.meer.net/

Detroit News

http://www.detnews.com/

Deutsche Telekom Asia

http://www.hk.super.net/~jtsinz/

Devonshire Travel

http://www.northcoast.com/travel/devonshire/travel.html

DGA

http://www.dga.co.uk/

DGS Group

http://www.edensys.com/edensys/dgs/index.html

DIA, Dansk Internet Adgang

http://www.ia.dk/

Dialogic

http://www.dialogic.com/

Diamond International Systems, Ltd.

http://www.hk.net/~drummond/diammain.html

Diane's Travel

http://www.tulsa.com/diane.html

DICO-SOFT GmbH

http://www.dicosoft.co.at/dicosoft/

Die Welt

http://www.welt.de/

DigiCraft Software

http://yallara.cs.rmit.edu.au/~s9312630/digicraft.html

Digio Media

http://www.digio.com/

Digital Ad Express

http://www.unicomp.net/digiad/

Digital Café

http://www.skypoint.com/members/digitalc/

Digital Creators

http://www.digitalcreators.com/dc/

Digital Dimensions

http://quasar.fastlane.net/homepages/lantz/digital.htm

Digital Dreamshop

http://www.indirect.com/www/steelep4/ddi.html

Digital Gateway Systems

http://dgs.dgsys.com

Digital Insight

http://www.csn.net/digins/

Digital MainStream

http://www.main.com/

Digital PC

http://www.pc.digital.com/

Digital Publishing Specialists

http://www.slip.net/~bsawyer/Welcome.html

Digital Service Consultants, Inc.

http://www.io.com/user/phoebus/dsc.html

Digital Tools

http://www.digit.com/dt/dt1.html

DigitalFacades

http://www.dfacades.com/

DigiTar Corporation

http://www.hooked.net/users/williams/digitar.htm

Dillon Technology Group, Inc.

http://www.fentonnet.com/dillon/

Dimension Specialist, Inc.

http://www.dspecialist.com/

Dinamika Computers s.r.l.

http://oasi.shiny.it/Firms/Dinamika/

Direct Response Design Studio, Inc.

http://www.drds.com/

DirectNet

http://www.directnet.com/

Discnet, Inc.

http://discnet.net/

Discovey Networks

http://www.shopping2000.com/shopping2000/discovery/

Disk-O-Tape, Inc.

http://branch.com/disko/disko.html

Distinct Corporation

http://www.distinct.com/

DM Records

http://www.iuma.com/DM/

DMS Marketing, Inc.

http://www.opennet.com/dms/

Dnevnik

http://www.k2.net/~dnevnik/index.html

Dog Computer Systems

http://hamton.eng.ua.edu/college/home/mh/grad/jtong/dog/

Dokken Consulting, Inc.

http://imt.net/~dokken

Dom America

http://www.teleport.com/~arcana/bands/dom_america/

Doody Publishing, Inc.

http://www.doody.com/

Dorling-Kindersley

http://www.main.com/~waynew/

Double Click Design (2CD)

http://www.Nashville.Net/dcd/

Downtown Digital

http://www.dtd.com/

DPI

http://www.digprod.com/

Dr. Computer Logick

http://www.barint.on.ca/cybermal/rsmith.html

Dragon's Eye Software

http://rampages.onramp.net/~desoftw/

Drama Book Publishers

http://www.interport.net/~dramapub/

Dream Garden Press

http://www.dreamgarden.com/

Dream Machine, The

http://www.skypoint.com/members/magic/

Dreams.com

http://www.dreams.com/welcome

DS Diagonal Systems

http://www.diagonal.com/

DSnet

http://www.dsnet.it/

DTK Computers, Inc.

http://www.gan.net/dtk/

Dube Cruise & Travel Center

http://www.maine.com/dube/

Due North

http://www.icw.com/duenorth/duenorth.html

Dun & Bradstreet Software

http://www.dbsoftware.com/

Duoforce Enterprises, Inc.

http://www.netwave.net/duoforce/

Durango Computer Classroom

http://animas.frontier.net/~mkatz/

DVC Company

http://www.edt.com/dvc/dvc.html

DX net

http://www.dx-net.fr/

E-Doc

http://www.edoc.com/

e.m.a.N.a.t.e.

http://emanate.com/

Eagle Canyon Airlines

http://cybermart.com/eagle/

Earl Tanny Miniatures

http://www.freenet.ufl.edu/~afn13406/Miniatures/
1._Introduction.html

Earth Resource Mapping

http://www.connectus.com/~aztech/ermapper/emuindex.html

EarthWise Journeys

http://www.teleport.com/~earthwyz/

Eastern Connecticut Computer Services

http://www.eastconn.com/

Easy Mail

http://www.worldserver.pipex.com/nc/ezmail/

Easy-Door Library

http://www.megatoon.com/~sincom/easydoor/

EBI Communications

http://www.ebicom.net/

Eccosys, Ltd.

http://www.eccosys.com/ECCOSYS/es.html

Echelon Company

http://www.skypoint.com/members/guymon

Eclipse Internet Access

http://www.eclipse.net/

Eco-Travel services

http://www.belgasoft.com/ets.html

edell

http://www.ios.com/~edell/

EDGE Interactive Media, Inc.

http://www.well.com/www/edgehome/

Edifika

http://ournet.clever.net/edifika/hp.html

Edit & Copy Communications

http://www.smartpages.com/editcopy/

Editorial Experts, Inc. (EEI)

http://www.eei-alex.com/

Edna's Consulting

http://www.sover.net/~edna/consult.html

EDS Unigraphics Division

http://www.ug.eds.com/

EduSelf Multimedia Publishers

http://www.webscope.com/eduself/homepage.html

EDV-Markt

http://www.edvmarkt.de/

EEG Records

http://www.w2.com/docs2/e/eeg.html

Egghead Software

http://www.egghead.com/

Einstein Investments & Trading

http://www.cyberpages.com/db/company&1&229

El Diario de Yucatan

http://www.yucatan.com.mx/

Élan Computer Group

http://www.elan.com/

Electric Bookstore, The

http://www.cadvision.com/bookstore/electric.html

Electric Gypsy Software & Consulting

http://www.tyrell.net/~elecgpsy/

Electro-Byte Technologies

http://www.ebtech.net/

Electronic Book Technologies

http://www.ebt.com/

Electronic Design Automation Companies

http://www.edac.org/

Electronic Learning Systems, Inc.

http://www.vector.net/~elstech/

Electronic Resources Ltd.

http://www.singnet.com.sg/~yllow/

Electronic Telegraph, The

http://www.telegraph.co.uk/

Electrotex

http://www.electrotex.com/

Elektropost HQ

http://www.ep.se/

Elite Computer & KC Vale

http://trojan.neta.com/~kc/

Elite Traveller

http://www.tcd.net/~elite/

Eltec International

http://www.ibmpcug.co.uk/~eltec

EMA Multimedia, Inc.

http://www.emamulti.com/

EMD Enterprises

http://www.iis.com/emd/

Emily Clarke

http://www.ior.com/~eeclarke

EMJ Data Systems, Limited

http://www.emj.ca/

emotion, Inc.

http://www.emotion.com/emotion/

EmpireNet

http://www.empirenet.com/

Emporium

http://www.vrsystem.com/

empreintes DIGITALes

http://www.cam.org/~dim/F/catED.html

Emulex Network Systems

http://www.emulex.com/

Endeavour Travel

http://www.anzac.com/endvr/endvr.htm

Engage Communication

http://www.engage.com/engage/

Engineering Graphical Solutions

http://www.tiac.net/users/eazl/egs/

Enköpings-Posten

http://www.netc.stuns.se/eposten/ep.html

Enrich International

http://www.enrich.com/

Enter.net

http://www.enter.net/

Enterprise Network Solutions

http://www.lanology.com/

Entertainment Through Technology Consortium

http://www.ibmpcug.co.uk/~ettc/

EnviroAccount Software

http://wheel.dcn.davis.ca.us/go/earthaware/

Environmental Systems Research Institute

http://www.esri.com/

ENVISIONET, Inc.

http://www.envisionet.net

Eòlas Technologies Incorporated

http://www.eolas.com/

EPMOD Consultants, Inc.

http://www.ibp.com/pit/epmod/

Epublish

http://www.fullfeed.com/epub/index.html

Equinox

http://www.forman.com/equinox/

ERDAS

http://www.erdas.com/

Eris Systems

http://erisys.org/

EroSpirit

http://www.gayweb.com/104/eros.html

ESDX

http://www.esdx.org/esdhome.html

eSoft, Inc.

http://www.esoft.com/

Essential Data, Inc.

http://netmar.com/mall/shops/edi/

Etcetera Graphics

http://www.scsn.net/~hwalsh/etcetera/etcetera.html

Ether Records

http://www.cityscape.co.uk/users/ej77/index.html

Eton Solutions

http://www.primenet.com/~etonsol/index.html

European Computer Industry Research Centre GmbH

http://www.ecrc.de/

Evans & Sutherland Computer Corporation

http://www.es.com/

Evansville Online

http://www.evansville.net/

evol design

http://www.cris.com/~dspiral/dmz/

EVPA

http://market.net/gaming/ev/index.html

Ex-Voto Records

http://www.vkool.com/exvoto/index.html

Exceller Software Corporation

http://www.infomall.org/exceller/

eXclaim!

http://www.unipress.com/cat/exclaim.html

Exec-PC

http://www.execpc.com/

Exide Electronics

http://www.exide.com/exide/

Exnet

http://www.exnet.com/

Exodus Online Services

http://www.eos.net/

Expert Macintosh Consulting

http://www.efn.org/~machelp/

ExperTelligence

http://www.expertelligence.com/

Explorer Communication

http://www.explorercomm.com/

Extra! Online

http://iquest.com/~extra/online/extraMP.html

EyE Candy Custom Graphics & T-Shirts

http://www.eyecandy.com/~eyecandy/

EZ Systems

http://register.com/drives/

F. F. Tronixs

http://www.fftron.com/fftron/

F.P. Publishing Co., Inc.

http://www.earthlink.net/~successpub/

Facet Collector's Showcase

http://www.inetbiz.com/facet/

Falcon BBS Systems

http://www.consulan.com/falcon/falcon.html

Falcon Systems

http://www.falcons.com/

Faludi Computing

http://www.faludi.com/

FAO Travel GmbH

http://www.fao.de/

Far & Away Travel Services

http://www.faraway.com/default.htm

Farago Advertising

http://www.farago.com

Fast Books

http://www.moreinfo.com.au/fastbooks/

Fastnet (Switzerland)

http://www.fastnet.ch/

Fat Messiah Games

http://io.com/user/wasson/fmg.html

FCR Software

http://www.fcr.com/homepage.html

Fell, Dan

http://www.goworldnet.com/dfell.htm

Fenestrae, Inc.

http://www.america.net/com/fenestrae/fen.html

FiberNet Communications

http://www.allware.com/fibernet/ldrates.html

The FIEN Group

http://nt.scbbs.com/tfg/

Financial Dynamics, Inc.

http://www.findyn.com/findyn/

Fine Art Print Emporium

http://www.airmail.net/~tself/

Finital Informatica Srl

http://www.ats.it/finital/index.html

Finite Technologies, Incorporated

http://www.finite-tech.com/fti/home.htmld

Fintronic USA, Inc.

http://www.fintronic.com/

First Coast On-Line

http://www.fcol.com/fcol.htm

First Floor Software

http://www.firstfloor.com/

First Step Research

http://www.fsr.com/

Fishnet Internet Services

http://www.fishnet.net/

Flamingo Communications, Inc.

http://www.fcom.com/

FlatCracker Software

http://www.fiber.net/flatcracker/

Florida Atlantic University

http://www.fau.edu/academic/cont-ed/cneip.htm

Florida Online

http://digital.net/

Fly Dirt Cheap, Anywhere!

http://netcenter.com/netcentr/travel/airtech.html

Focus GbR Software

http://www.liii.com/~louiev/focusgbr.html

Folio Corporation

http://www.folio.com/

fONOROLA i*internet

http://www.fonorola.net

For-to-Win

http://weber.ucsd.edu/~rtrippi/for2win.htm

FORE Systems, Inc.

http://www.fore.com/

Forest Green Media

http://fgreen.com/fgm/

Forté

http://www.forteinc.com/forte/forte.htm

Four Lakes Colorgraphics, Inc.

http://www.fourlakes.com/

Fourth Mesa, Inc.

http://best.gdb.org/mesa-data/fourthmesa/fmhome.html

FrameMakers

http://www.prairienet.org/arts/framing/homepage.html

France Telecom Network Services

http://www.transpac.se/

FranceCom, Inc.

http://www.trilogy.net/fcom

Freedom System Integrators, Inc.

http://southwind.net/fsi/

Freese-Notis Weather.Net

http://www.weather.net/html/internet.html

Freesun News

http://www.freesun.be/

Friedman/Fairfax Publishers

http://www.webcom.com/~friedman/

Front Desk

http://www.vegas.com/vegascom/front_desk/front.html

Frontier Airlines

http://www.cuug.ab.ca:8001/~busew/frontier.html

FrontLine Design

http://www.interaccess.com/frontlin

FRS Associates Training and Education Division

http://www.frsa.com/frs.shtml

Fuji Publishing Group

http://www.netins.net/showcase/fujipub

Full Spectrum Communications

http://www.fsc.com/fsc/

Fundamental Software

http://www.funsoft.com/funsoft.html

Funnel Cakes and Guidance Office Records

http://poe.acc.virginia.edu/~rae4a/wendy/fcgo.html

Fusion Advertising and Communications

http://usa.net/fusion/

Future Enterprises, Inc.

http://www.fei.com/fei.html

Future Net, Inc.

http://www.fn.net/

FutureMedia Services

http://www.futuremedia.com/

FutureTel, Inc.

http://www.ftelinc.com/

Futuristic Software & Computing Group

http://www.entrepreneurs.net/futuregroup/

G.A.C. Computer Services

http://rampages.onramp.net/~campbel/

G.T.A. Business Solutions

http://www.winternet.com/~hvgriner/gtahp.html

Gainesville Sun

http://news.jou.ufl.edu

Galaxy Communications, Inc.

http://www2.portal.ca/~galaxy/

Galaxy Systems, Inc.

http://www.interport.net/galaxy/

Galerie Woltjen

http://www.supernet.ab.ca/Mall/Arts/GalerieWoltjen/home.htm

Gamblers Spree

http://www.csn.net/zoom/casino.htm

GameNet

http://www.gamenet.com/

Gamma Productions, Inc.

http://www.gammapro.com/

Garbee and Garbee

http://www.gag.com/

Gareth Stevens Publishing

http://market.net/literary/gsinc/index.html

Garry's Web Services

http://www.azstarnet.com/~gar/

Gary Holmes Books

http://www.gmi.edu/~gholmes/Welcome.html

Gastroenterology Consultants

http://www.gastro.com/

Gates, Jeff

http://www.tmn.com/Community/jgates/home.html

GBH Handsfree Communication

http://nia.com/headsets/

GCR Computers Llc.

http://198.87.118.50/bus/gcr/pages/gcr.htm

Gebala Systems, Inc.

http://www.geopages.com/SiliconValley/1500/

Gemini Systems Software, Inc.

http://www.chataqua.com/GSSI/GSSI.html

GeneCraft

http://www.genecraft.com/vectdir/

Generator

http://www.iea.com/~stevem/brochure.html

Genetic Algorithm Solver for Excel™

http://www.iea.com/~stevem

Genoa Technology

http://www.gentech.com

GenText, Inc.

http://www.metronet.com/~gentext/homepage.htm

Georg Heeg

http://www.heeg.de/

George Coates Performance Works

http://www.georgecoates.org/

Gerald Green Consulting, Inc.

http://www.shadow.net/~grgreen/

Gestalt Systems, Inc.

http://www.clark.net/pub/gestalt

Get Outta Town Travel

http://adventure-vacations.com/gott/

GHG Corporation

http://www.ghgcorp.com/ghg/InternetServices/

GIC

http://www.gicorp.com/

Gilbert Paper

http://www.editelchi.com/gilbert/

GIS\Solutions, Inc.

http://www.gisedm.com/gisedm/gisedm.html

Glass Wings Press Home Page

http://www.aus.xanadu.com/1/gwp

Glistening Trail Records

http://membrane.com/

Global Computing, Inc.

http://www.pixi.com/~global/

Global Internet Technology Services

http://sunrayce.gmr.com/glits/

Global Music Outlet

http://www.iuma.com/GMO/

Global One

http://www.globalone.net/

Global Village Stock Footage

http://www.nbn.com:80/footage/

Global Visions Software

http://pages.prodigy.com/CO/gviscmr/gviscmr.html

GlobalNET

http://www.globalus.com/global3.html

Glyphic Technology

http://www.glyphic.com/glyphic/welcome.html

GNP Computers

http://www.gnp.com/

Go Kart Records

http://www.w2.com/gokart.html

GO! Online Communications

http://www.jumppoint.com

Godin London, Incorporated

http://www.godin.com/godin/

Gold Canyon Multimedia

http://www.goldcanyon.com

Golden Diamonds

http://haven.ios.com/~cbsa/

Golden Triangle On-Line

http://www.golden.org/

Goldsmith Yamasaki Specht, Inc.

http://www.interaccess.com/users/rgzinn/

goodDog Productions

http://www.sirius.com/~alyon/

Goswick Advertising

http://www.goswick.com/

Gotee Records House of Insomnia

http://www.netcentral.net/gotee/index.html

Graficas Art and Design

http://iquest.com/~tbuzbee/

GrafTek, Inc.

http://www.labelview.com/graftek/

Grail, Inc.

http://www.csn.net/~mhand/TheGrail.Inc/

Graphic Image

http://www.rmii.com/~briggs/strange1.htm

Graphic Simulations Corporation

http://www.computek.net/graphsim/gsc.html

Graphics Gallery, The

http://www.infi.net/~gallery/

Gray Design Associates

http://delta.com/gda.com/gda.htm

Great Australian Travel Co.

http://www.magna.com.au/~hideaway/snow_ind.html

Great Computer

http://www.a2z.com/a2z/cr00001a.html

Green Bay Online!

http://online.dct.com/

Greene Communications Design, Inc.

http://www.greene.com/

Greensleeves Records

http://www.easynet.co.uk/goodvibe/greens.htm

Grey-Tech Computer, Inc.

http://www.inforamp.net/~greytech/

Griffin Music

http://www.icom.ca/cgpinc/grifmain.htm

GroMedia

http://www.iea.com/~mikevm/

GroupWise Information

http://www.dws.net/groupwise.html

Gryphon Software Corporation

http://www.gryphonsw.com/

GSLink

http://www.gslink.net/

Gudbrandsdoelen-Lillehammer Tilskuer

http://www.hil.no/Lillehammer/glt/glt.html

Guildhall, Inc.

http://www.guildhall.com/artprints/

GulfNet Technologies

http://199.44.46.2/

Guru Technologies, Inc.

http://www.gurutech.com/

Gutter Press

http://www.io.org/~gutter/gutter.html

Gymboree

http://www.service.com/Gymboree/home.html

Habia Cable AB

http://www.habia.se/

HADCO Corporation

http://www.hadco.com:8080/

Hajjar/Kaufman New Media Lab

http://www.hkweb.com/

Halo Network Management

http://www.commerce.com/halonet/

Hamilton Rentals Place

http://www.hamilton.co.uk/

Hamrick Software

http://www.primenet.com/~hamrick/

Happy Puppy Software

http://happypuppy.com/games/link/index.html

Harbourside Travel Services

http://www.tagsys.com/Ads/Harbourside/

Harder Technologies

http://www.earthlink.net/free/bigbee/webdocs/index.html

Harlequin

http://www.harlequin.com/full/products/symbolic-processing.html

Harley Street Software

http://www.islandnet.com/~harley/homepage.html

HarperCollins Interactive

http://www.delphi.com/harpercollins/hcinteractive/hcinteractive.html

Harris Digital Telephone Systems

http://www.dts.harris.com/

Hart Advertising, Ltd.

http://www.microstate.com/pub/micros/Hart-Advertising-Bermuda/

Harter Image Archives

http://www.tddc.net/geo/harter/

Hastings Tribune Internet Edition

http://www.cnweb.com/tribune/index.html

Hauppauge Computer

http://www.hauppauge.com/hcw/index.htm

Hawaiian Express Unlimited

http://planet-hawaii.com/~hawnexp/

HCCI

http://www.cimteg.ists.ca/corp/hcci/hcci.htm

HD Industries

http://www.Infoservice.com/HDIndustries/

Headquarters.Com Internet

http://www.headquarters.com/

HealthCom, Inc.

http://www.gdesystems.com/healthcom.html

Hearne Scientific Software

http://www.hearne.com.au/

Hebel Computer

http://www.wco.com/~hebelcom/

Heirloom Art

http://www.desiderata.com/Art/Artists/Heirloom/

Helios Software

http://www.helios.de/

Hello America

http://www.helloamerica.com/~hello/education.html

Hemochromatosis Foundation, Inc.

http://branch.com/hemo/hemo.html

Henry Koren

http://turnpike.net/metro/tioga/hireme.html

Herald Sun Get Wired

http://www.ozonline.com.au/getwired/home.htm

Herzog System of Computer Keyboarding

http://www.tucson.com/herzog

HFSI

http://www.hfsi.com/

Hi-Bias Records, Inc.

http://www.maple.net/citw/hibias/

Hidden Treasures-Movie Madness

http://singnet.com.sg/~bspgod/

Hieroglyphics

http://www.webcom.com/~hiero/welcome.html

High Performance Cartridges

http://www.netpoint.net/hpcart/hpcart.html

Higher Octave Music

http://smartworld.com/hioctave/hioct.html

Hijinx

http://www.hijinx.com.au/

Hill Holliday Advertising

http://www.hhcc.com/

Hirt & Carter Owlnet

http://www.owlnet.co.za/

Hit The Beach!

http://www.hitthebeach.com/

Hitech Computers

http://www.mktmkt.com/hitech.html

HJF Digital Media

http://www.aloha.com/~redmond/

HMS Software

http://www.wst.com/hms

HNR Computers

http://www.hnr.com/

Hodder & Stoughton

http://www.u-net.com/hodder/

Holland Online

http://www.hol.nl/

Holman Travel

http://www.wwwa.com/holman/

Home News

http://www.injersey.com/Media/HomeNewsNet/doc/home.html

Home Run Pictures

http://www.zdepth.com/homerun/

Honeysuckle Computing

http://pages.prodigy.com/GA/honeysoft/honeysoft.html

Horizon Books

http://www.io.org/~errol/

Hot City Networking

http://www.hotcity.com/

hot-n-GUI

http://www.hotngui.com/

Houghton Mifflin Company

http://www.hmco.com/

Hourglass Internet Services

http://www.halcyon.com/hourglass/

House of Blues

http://underground.net/HOB/

Houston Creative Connection

http://www.insync.net/~creative/

How To Books

http://Intergal.com/dm_mgt_grp/

Howard Karno Books

http://www.cts.com/~karnobks/

HPS Simulations

http://www.cris.com/~sturmer/

HSiN Semiconductor Pte, Ltd.

http://www.singnet.com.sg/~hx1008/

HudsoNet

http://www.hudsonet.com/

Human Computer Interface

http://www.fortnet.org/HCI/

Humble Beginnings

http://rhumble.beginnings.com

Hummingbird Software

http://www.primenet.com/~awong/legaudit.html

Hybrid Communications

http://gs1.com/default.html

Hydromantis, Inc.

http://www.hydromantis.com/

Hyper Design Technologies

http://www.redshift.com/~montpres/hdt.html

HyperGlot, The Foreign Language Software Company

http://www.hyperglot.com/hyperglot.html

Hyperparallel Technologies

http://www.ppgsoft.com/ppgsoft/hc_main.html

HYPHECAN Fingertip Cap

http://www.eskimo.com/~vanming/hpc_intro.html

I-2000

http://i-2000.com/

I-Kinetics, Inc.

http://www.i-kinetics.com/

I. Net Solutions, Inc.

http://www.mke.com/

I/O 360 Digital Design, Inc.

http://www.inch.com/user/io360/welcome.html

iambic Software

http://www.iambic.com/iambic/

Ian Freed Consulting, Inc.

http://www.ifc.com/

IBM Client/Server Computing

http://www.csc.ibm.com

IBM Mainframe Software Helpers

http://pages.prodigy.com/MA/acs/acs.html

IBM Person-to-Person Conferencing

http://www.hursley.ibm.com/p2p/P2P.html

IC Group, Inc.

http://pobox.com/icg/fromyahoo.html

ICC Communications Centre

http://www1.usa1.com/~ibnet/iccomhp.html

ICE

http://www.iced.com/

ICEnet

http://www.ice.net

ICNet: The Original Internet provider for the Eastern Shore

http://www.intercom.net/

Icon Technologies, Inc.

http://www.icontech.com/

Iconomics

http://linden.fortnet.org/FORTNET/business/Iconomics/
Iconomics.html

ICS

http://www.relay.net/~gcw/memory.html

ID&T Records

http://www.dance.nl/id&t/

IDEAL Scanners & Systems

http://www.ideal.com/

IdeSYS

http://www.idepro.fr/

IDM

http://www.jaring.my/at-asia/idm/id_hpage.html

IES Technologies

http://www.hometeam.com/iestech.shtml

Ignatius Press

http://www.ignatius.com/

Iler Networking & Computing

http://teal.csn.net/~kenti/

Illustra Information Technologies, Inc.

http://www.illustra.com/

Image House Digital Photography Studio

http://www.concom.com/~whitcomb/ih_home.html

Image Manipulation Systems

http://www.imageman.com/

Image, The

http://www.lainet.com/image/

ImageFX

http://www.imagefx.com/imagefx/

Imagen Communications, Inc.

http://www.imagen.net/default.htm

Imageware

http://www.msen.com/~imagewar

imaginagency

http://www.charm.net/~imagine/IMAGINE.HTML

Imagination

http://www.imagin.com/imagination/

Imagine.com

http://www.imagine.com/

Imagix

http://www.teleport.com/~imagix

Imaja Home Page

http://www.imaja.com/imaja/

imedia

http://www.imedia-sf.com

Immedia Systems

http://www.netwest.com/~immedia/

Immortal Software Productions

http://www.synapse.net/~immortal/

Impediment, Inc.

http://www.impediment.com/

IMPULSE!

http://www.impulsetv.com/drtv/

IMT Systems

http://mfginfo.com/comp/imtsystems/imt.htm

Inacom Corp.

http://www.inacom.com/

Incite

http://www.incite.com/

InContext Systems

http://www.incontext.ca/

Index

http://www.telematrix.com/

Index

http://www.webtrack.com/adverts/adverts.html

Index

http://web.frontier.net/MEDMarket/indexes/indexmfr.html

Index

http://www.cs.ucl.ac.uk/~twicks/ill/index.html

Index

http://www.bookwire.com/links/other_booksellers/
other_booksellers.html

Index

http://www.vegas.com/whatcool.html

Index

http://pages.prodigy.com/IN/

Index

http://www.library.vanderbilt.edu/law/acqs/pub_alph.html

Index

http://199.201.186.116/info/casinos.htm

Indian Fonts

http://clarksville.mc.utexas.edu/~alim/Vijay/vijay.html

Indianapolis Star and News

http://www.starnews.com/

Indochina

http://www.china.co.uk/china/indochina/

Industrial Peer-to-Peer

http://www.callamer.com/~pfahey/

Industrial Strength Design

http://www.pangaea.net/ISD/

Inference

http://www.inference.com/

Infinity Software, Inc.

http://www.io.com/~isi_info/

InfoArt™

http://www.packet.net/hwyone/blkbear1/welcome.html

InfoCafé

http://www.infocafe.com/

Infogroup S.p.A.

http://infogroup.iunet.it/

infoLink Communications

http://www.webcom.com/~infolink/

InfoMedia

http://usa.net/cge/infomedi.htm

InfoPros

http://www.infopros.com/infopros/infohome.html

INFORIUM, The Information Atrium, Inc.

http://www.e-commerce.com/inforium.htm

Information Age, Inc.

http://www.informationage.com/

Information Builders, Inc.

http://www.ibi.com/

Information Data Products Corp.

http://www.planet.net/idpc/

Information Management Group

http://www.imginfo.com/

The Information Systems Manager, Inc.

http://www.infosysman.com/

Informatique RF

http://www.saglac.qc.ca/inforf/welcome.html

InfoScan

http://www.machinasapiens.qc.ca/machina/infoscanang.html

InfoSource

http://www.gate.net/~pctrain/

Infowerks Creative Web Services

http://www.infowerks.com/

Ingalls, Quinn & Johnson

http://www.iqj.com/

Ingres Consultant

http://www.cris.com/~Sb/cv.html

Inland Answering Service

http://www.citivu.com/usa/ias/index.html

Inmar

http://www.inmar.com/

Innervation Technology Corporation

http://www.innervation.com/inner/

Innovative Computer Associates, Inc.

http://www.icai.com/icai/

Innovative Systems of New York, Inc.

http://www.wp.com/ISON/

InReach

http://www.inreach.com/

Insight Designs, Inc.

http://www.phoenix.net/~insight/

Insignia Solutions

http://www.insignia.com/

Inspiration Software

http://www.rdrop.com/

InstaNet (Instant Internet Corporation)

http://www.instanet.com/

Instant Impact

http://cvinet.com/impact/

Instruction Set, Inc.

http://www.inset.com/

Intaglio

http://www.intaglio.com/intaglio/

Integra Software Corporation

http://www.xmission.com/~americom/integra-credit.html

Integrated Communications

http://www.intcom.net/

Integrated Research

http://www.zdepth.com/integ/

Integrated Systems Solutions Corporation

http://www.issc.ibm.com/

Integrated Technologies, Inc. (InTech)

http://204.17.76.3/intech.html

Intel Smart Network Devices

http://www.intel.com/comm-net/index.html

InteleTravel International

http://inteletravel.com/inteletravel/

InteliSys Technologica, Inc.

http://www.intelinet.net/

Intelligent Market Analytics

http://www.marketmind.com/

Inter-Modo

http://hyperreal.com/music/labels/inter-modo/index.html

Inter//Web Development

http://www.iwd.com/

Interactive Computer Systems, Ltd.

http://www.discribe.ca/ics/icshome.htm

Interactive Data Systems, Inc.

http://www.idsinc.com/

Interactive Effects

http://www.webcom.com/~ie/index.html

Interactive Software Engineering

http://www.eiffel.com/

Interactive Television [IBM]

http://www.raleigh.ibm.com/itv/itvprod.htm

Interactive Voice Applications

http://www.tc.net/voice/

INTERCAT

http://www.intercat.com/

Intercom

http://www.intercom.es/

InterComp Internet, UNIX, and World Wide Web Services

http://www.panix.com/~tab/intercomp/

Intergate

http://www.intergate.net/

Interglobal Mutltimedia

http://www.interglobal.com/

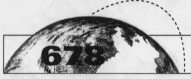

Intergraph Corporation

http://www.ingr.com/

InterLink Trondheim

http://www.interlink.no/

InterMind

http://www.intermind.com/

International Business Center

http://www.niagara.com/blmc

International Industrial Intelligence

http://international.com/

International Knowledge Systems

http://iks.com/

International Software Systems, Inc.

http://www.issi.com/issi/issi-home_page.html

International Travel Agency (ITA)

http://www.comprez.com/ita/

International Travel Guide

http://www.iisys.com/www/travel/itg.htm

International Typeface Corporation

http://www.esselte.com/itc/

Internet Access Phoenix Arizona

http://neta.com/

Internet Advertising Solutions

http://iaswww.com/

Internet Application Services, Inc.

http://mindspring.com/~netserve

Internet Business Solutions

http://inbs.coop.net/

Internet Channel

http://www.inch.com/

InterNET Computer Store

http://inetstore.com/

Internet Database Consultants

http://www.clark.net/infouser/endidc.htm

Internet Delaware

http://www.delnet.com/

Internet Direct [Toronto, Canada]

http://idirect.com/welcome.html

Internet Express, Inc.

http://www.inxpress.net/

Internet Front

http://www.internetfront.com/

Internet Home Users Group (IHUG)

http://ihug.co.nz/

Internet Interface Systems

http://www.webnet.com.au/

Internet Light and Power

http://www.ilap.com/

Internet MainStreet

http://www.mainstreet.net/

Internet North

http://www.internorth.com/

Internet of Shelby

http://shelby.vnet.net/

Internet On-Ramp, Inc.

http://www.ior.com/

Internet Pilots

http://www.xmission.com/~ip/ip.html

Internet ProLink SA/AG

http://www.iprolink.ch/

Internet Saguenay Lac St-Jean

http://www.saglac.qc.ca/

Internet Services Montana

http://www.ism.net/index.html

Internet Shopping Network

http://www.internet.net/index.html?source=DYHO

Internet Systems, Inc.

http://www.isi.net/

Internet Training & Consultancy

http://www.bitz.co.nz/itc/

Internet Travel Network

http://www.itn.net/cgi/get?itn/index/

Internet Trois-Rivieres

http://www.itr.qc.ca/

Interphase

http://www.iphase.com/

Interpretive Software

http://www.execpc.com/~isi/

InterServe Communications

http://www.interserve.com/

Interstate FiberNet

http://www.mindspring.com/~itchold/itc/ifn/ifn.html

InterStudio Limited

http://www.interstudio.co.uk/isl/

InterSys Technologies

http://www.inst.com/

Intertex

http://www.algonet.se/~intertex/

Intervid

http://www.intervid.co.uk/intervid/

InterWare Service Provider

http://www.interware.it/

Intra Travel

http://qb.island.net/~intra/

INTRANET Technologies, Inc.

http://intranet.on.ca/

IntrepidNet

http://www.intrepid.net/

IntuMediaWorks, Ltd.

http://www.intumedia.com/intumedia/

Investor's Business Daily

http://ibd.ensemble.com/

InVzn Development Corporation

http://www.invzn.com/

IPC Technologies, Inc.

http://www.ipctechinc.com/

Irdial Discs

http://www.ibmpcug.co.uk/~irdial/

Iris Development Coporation

http://irisdev.com/

Ironstone Technologies

http://www.ironstone.mb.ca/infopage/iron1.html

ISDN Internet Access

http://www.nettechsys.com/

ISDN*tek

http://www.isdntek.com/

Ishi Press

http://www.portal.com/~rww/pub_ishi.html

Island Parent

http://www.pacificrim.net/~ttillman/parent.html

Island Services Network

http://www.isn.net/

ISPW

http://www.ispw.com/

Isthmus Corporation

http://www.izzy.net/

It's a Mystery

http://www.mysterybooks.com/

Ivory Tower Information Systems

http://www.itis.com/

J P Mclaughlin & Associates, Inc.

http://www.uidaho.edu/~hend881/jpma.html

J-MAC System, Inc.

http://www.j-mac.co.jp/

Jack

http://www.cis.upenn.edu/~hms/jack.html

Jackson-Reed, Inc.

http://www.halcyon.com/prreed/jackreed.html

Jacobs Publishing, Ltd.

http://www.awa.com/jacobs/jacobs.html

Jandel Scientific Software

http://www.jandel.com

Janus Interactive

http://www.teleport.com/~janus/

Javiation

http://www.demon.co.uk/javiation

Jazz International Records

http://www.w2.com/docs2/j/jazz.html

JCA Télématique

http://www.jca.fr/jca/

JCICNet

http://www.jcic.org/

JCS Computers

http://www.vpm.com/jcs/jcscomp.html

JDG Designs

http://www.jdgdesign.com/

Jeffrey Wiener Studio

http://www.interport.net/~jwiener/

Jenkins Consulting Services, Inc.

http://www.mcs.com/~mjenkins/HTML/jcs.html

Jerusalem Post

http://www.jpost.co.il/

Jewell, Chris

http://www.wco.com/~jewellcj/

JimWare, Inc.

http://www.prairienet.org/~jdpierce/homepage.html

JM Consulting and Cheap Advice

http://pages.prodigy.com/IL/jomoor/

JMG Information Systems

http://jmg.lightspeed.net/

JOBSCOPE Manufacturing Management System

http://web.sunbelt.net/~jobscope

John Mayes & Associates

http://www.jma.com/

John T. Zubal, Inc.

http://www.zubal.com/

Johnson Consulting Network

http://www.jcn.com/

Jolly Games

http://www.callamer.com/~claudius/jolly

Joni Aveni & Associates

http://www.callnet.com/pub/joeav/

Joseph-Beth Booksellers

http://www.mis.net/jbeth/jbmain.html

JourneyWare Media

http://www.journeyware.com/

JR Gifts

http://www.olworld.com/olworld/mall/mall_us/c_jewelr/
m_jrgift/index.html

Jumbo Computer International

http://www.xmission.com/~wwwads/jumbo/home.htm

JunkYard, The

http://www.thejunkyard.com/junk/

Juta & Company

http://www.os2.iaccess.za/juta/index.htm

K Records

http://www.wln.com/~kpunk/

K-Net Ltd

http://www.k-net.co.uk/

KAB Konsult AB

http://www.dataphone.se/~kab/index.html

Kaiser Family Foundation

http://www.kff.org/kff/

Kamloops Daily News-Online

http://www.netshop.net/dailynews/daily_news.html

KAN Distributors'

http://www.widdl.com/Kan/

KarlBridge

http://www.demon.co.uk/kbridge/index.html

Karoma Publishers

http://www.infop.com/karoma/

Katalina Technologies

http://www.ozemail.com.au/~katalina/

KEEN art and design

http://www-scf.usc.edu/~akuehn/

Kennewick Computer Company, Inc.

http://www.kcc-computers.com/

KENTnet Internet Services

http://www.kentnet.co.uk/

Kern Media Associates

http://www.maine.com/kern/

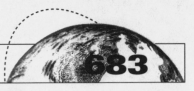
Keski-Uusimaa

http://www.cardinal.fi/keski-uusimaa/

Kewill-Xetal EDI Services

http://www.cityscape.co.uk/users/ew48/index.htm

Keystone Technology

http://www.keytech.com/

Khazana

http://www.winternet.com/~khazana/index.html

Kickin Records

http://www.musicbase.co.uk/music/kickin/

Kim Koch—Jewelry

http://www.netgains.com/koch/

Kinesix

http://www.kinesix.com/

Kinfonetics Technology

http://www.io.org/~cyourth/

Kitchen Wisdom Publishing

http://www.wiskit.com/

KKT Design Co.

http://www.interlog.com/~jrudnick/

Klever Computers

http://www.klever.com/

Knighted Computers

http://www.knighted.com/

Knossopolis

http://www.knosso.com/

Knowledge Engineering Pty, Ltd.

http://www.ke.com.au/

Knoxville News Sentinel

http://www.scripps.com/knoxnews/

Kodak Color Printers

http://www.kodak.com/productInfo/officeImaging/output/output.shtml

Koinonia House

http://www.khouse.org/

Kraken Press, Titles

http://webster.skypoint.net/members/mfinley/booklist.htm

Kratzer Computer Consultants

http://www.greatbasin.net/~kratzer/kratz.htm

KRON Computers

http://www.icon.net/commercial/kron/kron.html

Kudzu Creations

http://www.america.net/com/kudzu/kudzu.html

Kult Records

http://www.virtualf.com/kult/kult.html

L & H Computers

http://www.citivu.com/rc/lnh/index.html

L.C.P. Company Computer Sales

http://www.upstate.net/lcp.html

L@it2'd

http://www.primenet.com/~lati2d/

La Bancarella On Line

http://www.indesia.iunet.it/cct/bancarel/index.htm

La Nacion

http://www.nacion.co.cr/

LabCorp

http://www.labcorp.com/

Lahaina News

http://www.maui.net/~daveray/lahaina.html

Lake Tahoe News Network

http://cybermart.com/bonanza/LTNN.html

Lambda Systems, Ltd.

http://www.wimsey.com/~andy/

LAN Solutions

http://www.aimnet.com/~yungi/lansol.html

Lancom Technologies

http://www.inforamp.net/~lancom/

LandWare

http://www.planet.net/landware/

Langfield Associates, Ltd.

http://www.u-net.com/langfield/bet.htm

Lanka Internet Services

http://www.lanka.net

Lanop Corp.

http://www.maestro.com/lanop/lanop.html

LapTECH Systems

http://www.worldweb.com/Laptech/

Laser Express

http://emporium.turnpike.net/D/dcservice/wg/krantin.htm

Laser Products and Services Group

http://www.infoanalytic.com/laser/

Laser Renewal

http://www.infi.net/~elspence/

LaserSaver

http://www.sundaypaper.com/www/lsrsvr.htm

Last Gasp

http://www.woof.com/last_gasp.html

Last Unicorn, Ltd.

http://www.VirtualAd.com/browse/va/LastUnicorn/

Lavallée & Associates

http://www.io.org/~lcl/lassoc.html

LavaNet, Inc.

http://www.lava.net/

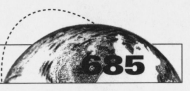
Law Enforcement/Police Software

http://www.augusta.net/alert1.htm

Le Beach Club

http://usa.net/~davef/travel.html

Leaping Frog Publishing

http://204.94.158.8/LeapingFrog/

Learning Edge Corp.

http://www.io.org/~tle/

Learning-Society Publications

http://www.intr.net/dc-online/resume/ad.html

Leather Tongue Video

http://www.sirius.com/~leather/

Legal Computer Solutions

http://www.lcsweb.com/

Lejé International

http://www.transport.com/~leje/homepg.html

Leo Electronics

http://www.earthlink.net/~leoelex/

Let's Fly & Cruise, Inc.

http://www.digimark.net/rec-travel/tagents/lets-fly-cruise/index.html

Lex Systems

http://www.link.ca/~lex/

Lexitech, Inc.

http://www.lexitech.com/

LI.Net

http://www.li.net/

Liberty Stats

http://www.webcom.com/~liberty/

Library Solutions Institute and Press

http://www.internet-is.com/library/

License Management Articles

http://www.globetrotter.com/articles.htm

LifeGuide

http://www.compuoffice.com/lg.html

Liggett Stashower

http://www.liggett.com/

Light Impressions

http://www.infopost.com/lt_impressions/index.html

Lighthouse Software, Inc.

http://www.lighth.com/~lighth/

Lightscape Technologies, Inc.

http://www.lightscape.com/

Lightspeed Communications & UNIServe Internet

http://haven.uniserve.com/~davem/

Lilly Software Associates, Inc.

http://mfginfo.com/cadcam/visual/visual.htm

Limit X

http://dino.ccm.itesm.mx/AM3/pageengl.html

Linda Sy Skin Care

http://www.fractals.com/sy/html/sy_intro.html

Link Technologies, Inc.

http://www.batnet.com/linktech/

Linkage Online

http://www.hk.linkage.net/

LinkStor

http://www.linkstor.com/

Little Dog Records Entertainment

http://www.iuma.com/Little_Dog/

Little, Brown and Company

http://pathfinder.com/twep/Little_Brown/
Little_Brown.html

Live Picture, Inc.

http://www.livepicture.com/

LMB Microcomputers

http://www.lmb.iquest.net/

LMSoft

http://geoserver.lmsoft.ca/

Local Internet Gateway Co.

http://www.lig.net/

Lockheed Martin REAL3D

http://www.mmc.com/real3d/real3d.html

Locus Computing Corporation

http://www.locus.com/

Lodestone Research, L.L.C.

http://www.aescon.com/lodeston/index.htm

Loganberry Books

http://www.logan.com/loganberry/

Logic Approach

http://www.eden.com/~logic/

LOGIC Records

http://www.germany.net/cebit/logic/homepage.htm

Logical Operations

http://www.logicalops.com

Login Brothers Book Company

http://www.lb.com/

Logos Research Systems, Inc.

http://islander.whidbey.net/~logos/welcome.html

Look Software Systems, Inc.

http://look.com/

Lopez Communications

http://www.interport.net/peoplelink/

Los Andes Publishing, Inc.

http://www.losandes.com/www/libros/

Loviel Computer Corporation

http://www.loviel.com/

LSD Online

http://www.southwind.net/~lshiney/

LucasArts Entertainment Company

http://www.lucasarts.com/menu.html

Luminous Flux Records

http://www.castlepoint.com/fluxnet/

LvNet

http://www.lvnet.lv/

LYNQS Internet Services

http://www.interstate.net/LYNQS/LYNQS.html

M&S Hourdakis SA

http://www.stepc.gr/~sweetie/hourd.html

M.E. Sharpe

http://usa.net/mesharpe/mesh.html

Mabry Software

http://www.halcyon.com/mabry/

Mac Zone and PC Zone

http://www2.pcy.mci.net/marketplace/mzone/

Macatawa Area Free-Net

http://www.macatawa.org/

Mach 5 Software

http://205.164.234.18/

MacMedic

http://www.pacificrim.net/~macmedic/

Macmillan Information SuperLibrary

http://www.mcp.com/

MacNeal-Schwendler Corporation

http://www.macsch.com/

MacSultants

http://www.macsultants.com/

MacToolKit

http://www.vsinet.com/mactoolkit/

Mad Opal Pseudo Corporate Page

http://www.mcs.com/~madopal/home.html

Mage Publishing

http://gpg.com/mage/

Magellan Media Services

http://www.webcom.com/~magellan

Magic Island

http://www.magicisland.com/

Magical Fox Interactive

http://www.magicalfox.com/

Magna Computer Corp.

http://magna.magna.net/

Magnacom Data Products, Inc.

http://www.webscope.com/magnacom/

Magnetic Page

http://www.magpage.com/

Magnett Internet Gateway

http://www.magnet.ca/

Mainframes, Minis, & Micros

http://www.kern.com/mmm.html

Make Systems, Inc.

http://www.makesys.com/makesys

Malahat Mountain Music

http://www.islandnet.com/~dobro/

MalSoft

http://www.usis.com/~draconis/

Management Concepts Incorporated

http://www.MgmtConcepts.com/

Management Graphics, Inc. USA

http://www.mgi.com/

Management Information Technologies, Inc.

http://www.vyp.com/miti/miti.html

Manhattan MultiMedia, Inc.

http://www.panix.com/~mmm

Manifest Records

http://www.pacifier.com/~coldwave/

Manta Ray

http://www.webology.com/adfit/

MapleNet Technologies, Inc.

http://www.maple.net/maple.html

Marathon Communications

http://www.marcomm.com/mc/home.html

Marathon Records

http://www.netads.com/netads/arts/music/marathon/

Marcus Advertising

http://www.marcusad.com/marcus/

Mare's Nest Publishing

http://www.poptel.org.uk/password/marenest.html

Marine Graphics, Inc.

http://nwlink.com/graphics/

Mark Palmer Design

http://navishow.web.aol.com/lab/m/mpalme/MPDWeb/
MPDHomePage.html

Market Place Media

http://www.marketmedia.com/

Marketing Masters

http://surveysaid.ostech.com:8080/

Martin Action Art

http://www.bluemarble.net/~bcs/cauldron/catalog.html

Massey Development

http://supernet.net/~tmassey/

MasterMind Technology, Inc.

http://www.telepath.com/mmti/

MathSolutions

http://christensen.cybernetics.net/MathSolutions.html

Matrix Computer Consulting, Inc.

http://ios.com/~matrixbb/index.html

Maui News

http://www.maui.net/~mauinews/news.html

Maxperts, Inc.

http://www.maxperts.com/

MaxVision Online

http://www.maxvision.com/

Mayflower Software

http://www.maysoft.com/

MBS Industries, Inc.

http://www.mbsii.com/mbs/

MC2 Cyberspace Research

http://www.mc2-csr.com/

MCAE, Inc.

http://www.ppgsoft.com/ppgsoft/inertia.html

McDonnell Information Systems

http://www.mdis.com/

McGrawHill

http://mexplaza.udg.mx/McGraw/

McIntyre's Fine Books & Bookends

http://zeus.cybernetics.net/cm-docs/mcintyre.html

McMonigle & Spooner

http://www.primenet.com/~mands/index.html

MDL Information Systems

http://www.mdli.com

MedConnect

http://netmar.com/medconnect/

Media House Films

http://www.ultranet.com/~msavino/MHFHome.html

Media Range

http://www.mediarange.com/media/welcome.htm

Media Solutions International

http://www.msi-usa.com/

MediaBox Communications

http://www.mediabox.com/

MediaGlobe

http://www.mediaglobe.com/

MediaLogic, ADL, Inc.

http://www.adlinc.com/adlinfo/

MediaSoft Telecom

http://www.cam.org/~mst/

MediaTel's Newsline

http://www.mediatel.co.uk/

Medical Multimedia Systems

http://www.webcom.com/~medmult/

Medlin Accounting Shareware

http://community.net/~medlinsw/

MEDMarket Virtual Industrial Park

http://www.frontier.net/MEDMarket/

Megaforce Records

http://www.iuma.com/Megaforce/

Megascore, Inc.

http://www.interactive.net/~jgm/megascore.html

MEGO

http://www.is.in-berlin.de/~mego/

Meir Kahtan Public Relations

http://www.aimnet.com/hia/mka/

Memory USA

http://www.mu.com/

Mentor Graphics Corporation

http://www.mentorg.com/

MentorPlus Software, Inc.

http://www.webcom.com/~criteria/mentorp/

Meridian Call Center

http://www.nortel.com/english/call_center/

Merisels Sun Division

http://www.merisel.com/

Merlin Software

http://www.deltanet.com/merlin/

Message Board System, The

http://www.netins.net/showcase/message/tmb.html

Meta Software Corporation

http://www.tiac.net/users/metasoft/

MetaCase Consulting

http://www.jsp.fi/metacase/

Metal Blade Records

http://www.iuma.com/Metal_Blade/

Metarose Group

http://metarose.netinterior.com/

Metatec Corporation

http://www.metatec.com/

MetaWare Incorporated

http://www.metaware.com/

Metropolis Records

http://www.w2.com/metropolis.html

Metrotel Multi-Media, Ltd.

http://mmm.wwa.com/mmm/why.html

MEX Multimedia Experts

http://www.mex.com/

MFD Consult

http://login.dknet.dk/~mortenf/

MGL Systems

http://www.mgl.ca/

Michael J. Motto Advertising

http://www.gti.net/motto/

Michigan Internet Cooperative Association

http://www.mica.net/

Micro Computer Systems, Inc.

http://www.mcsdallas.com/

Micro House International

http://www.microhouse.com/

Micro Service & Training

http://www.ici.net/cust_pages/jsouza/jsouza.html

Micro-Rent Corporation

http://www.deltanet.com/micro-rent/

Micro/Station at UIC

http://www.MicroStation.uic.edu/

MicroBiz

http://www.carroll.com/microbiz/

MicroExcel Software

http://www.microexcel.com/mxsoft/mxweb.htm

Microlytics

http://www.microlytics.com/

MicroMedium, Inc.

http://www.micromedium.com/

Micron Internet Services

http://www.micron.net/

Microplay Video Game Stores

http://www.canadamalls.com/provider/microp.html

Microprose

http://www.microprose.com/

Microstar Software, Ltd.

http://www.microstar.com/

Microsystems Engineering Company

http://www.interaccess.com/products/

Microtrader

http://www.magic.mb.ca/~microt/

MicroWarehouse, Inc.

http://www.warehouse.com/

MidiMan's Official Web Site

http://www.midifarm.com/midiman/

Midnight Special Bookstore

http://msbooks.com/msbooks/

Midware Technologies (SA)

http://www.os2.iaccess.za/midware/index.htm

Mike Salitter Consultant Services

http://knet.flemingc.on.ca/~msalitte/mscs.html

Milestone Technologies, Inc. (MTI)

http://www.spadion.com/spadion/mti/

Military Simulations, Inc.

http://www.military-sim.com/

Millberry Union Bookstore

http://www.mubooks.ucsf.edu/

Millennium Whole Earth Catalog

http://www.well.net/mwec/

Mimesis Technology

http://rampages.onramp.net/~mimesis/

Mind Logic

http://www.xmission.com/~wwwads/mind/logic.html

MindSphere Design for Communication

http://www.mindsphere.com/

Minerva Technology

http://www.minerva.ca/

MiNET Net3D

http://www.minet.com/net3d/

Minnesota MicroNet

http://www.mm.com/

Minnesota Regional Network (MRNet)

http://www.mr.net/MRNet.html

Mintz & Hoke Advertising and Public Relations

http://www.mintz-hoke.com/

Miramar Productions

http://useattle.uspan.com/miramar/

Miros

http://www.miros.com/biz/miros/

Mississippi Business Journal

http://www.inst.com/mbj/

MJC Inc. Computer Services

http://www.holonet.net/mjc/

MKS Source Integrity Product

http://www.mks.com/si/mkssi.htm

MLL Software and Computers

http://www.ppgsoft.com/ppgsoft/wz_main.html

MNW Records Group

http://www.iuma.com/MNW/

Mobile Planet

http://www.mplanet.com/

MobileWare Corporation

http://www.mobileware.com/

Modular Software Corporation

http://www.primenet.com/~modsoft/

MonadNet

http://www.monad.net/

Monkeyland Records

http://www.primenet.com/~tripmon/

Monsterbit Media

http://monsterbit.com/

Montana Communications Network (MCN)

http://www.mcn.net/index.html

Monterey Press

http://www.redshift.com/~montpres/

Moonlite Software

http://www.synapse.net/~moonlite/home.htm

Moonshine Music

http://www.moonshine.com/

Moran Communications Group

http://www.moran.com/

Morris Travel

http://eaglerock.if.scientech.com/morris/

Morse Telecommunication, Inc.

http://www.morse.net

Mosaic Multisoft Corporation

http://www.cts.com/~mosaic/

Moshofsky/Plant Creative Services

http://moshplant.com

Motorola Information Systems Group

http://www.motorola.com/MIMS/ISG/

Motorola University Press

http://www.mot.com/MotorolaUniversity/
MUPress_Catalog.html

Mountain CAD, Inc.

http://www.montana.com/MtCAD/MtCAD.html

Mountain Internet

http://www.mountain-inter.net/

Mountain Software

http://www.mountain.net/hp/mtnsoft/

Movie Madness

http://planet-hawaii.com/madness/

Movie Van, Inc., The

http://www.maui.net/~mvan/

MR Mac Software

http://www.ip.net/shops/MR_Mac_Software/

MSI Communications

http://www.msic.com/

MTW Network Solutions

http://web.sunbelt.net/~mtwsolutions

Multi-Media Communications

http://fuji.ixl.net:8000/MultiMedia/

Multi-Tech Systems, Inc.

http://www.multitech.com/

Multimedia Computing Corp.

http://asearch.mccmedia.com/

MultiMedia Enterprises

http://www.world-wide.com/multimedia/

Multimedia Solutions

http://www.noumenon.com/

Mundo Internet

http://w3mint.cieamer.conacyt.mx/

Murray MultiMedia

http://www.murraymedia.com/murray/

Muscovy Imports

http://branch.com/muscovy/muscovy.html

Mute Liberation Technologies

http://www.mutelibtech.com/mute/

MVS Training, Inc.

http://www.pittsburgh.net/MVS/

MyBody, Ltd.

http://www.Demon.Co.UK/mybody/

Myricom, Inc.

http://www.myri.com/

Mystech Enterprises

http://www.primenet.com/~valenti/index.html

N-Soul Records

http://198.4.164.52/N-Soul/

Nahariya Glass

http://www.fy.com/NG/

Nantucket.Net

http://www.Nantucket.net/NN/home.html

Narhex

http://www.odyssey.com.au/uspecies/narhex/welcome.html

National Health Video

http://www.frp.com/healthvid/

National Knowledge Networks, Inc.

http://www.nkn.edu/

National Parts Depot

http://www.megasoft.com/npd/

Nationwide Computer Support

http://navishow.web.aol.com/lab/n/ncs/index.htm

Native Guide

http://www.NativeGuide.com

Natracare, LLC

http://www.indra.com/natracare/

NaviSoft

http://www.navisoft.com/

Navrang, Inc.

http://www.xmission.com/~seer/navrang/index.html

NCA Computer Products

http://www.mediacity.com/NCA/

NDS Distributing

http://www.netrep.com/global/biz/nds/nds.html

Nebulus

http://nebulus.home.ubc.ca/

Nedbook International

http://qqq.com/nedbook/index.html

Nemesis Design

http://www.achilles.net/~nemesis/homepage.html

NeoLogic Systems

http://www.neologic.com/~neologic/

Neptune Interactive Designs

http://www.injersey.com/ijNET/ijNID/NIDWEBSITE.HTML

NESAK Records

http://www.nesak.com/kado/

Net Design Technology, Inc. St.Louis, MO USA

http://walden.mo.net/~netd/

Net Guru Technologies, Inc.

http://www.internet-is.com/netguru/

Net Trek Cafe

http://www.nettrek.com.au/

NetAxis [Montreal]

http://www.netaxis.qc.ca/

NetCasters, Inc.

http://www.netcasters.com/

NetConnect Consulting Services, Sacramento

http://www.portal.com/~nconnect/index.html

NetCount

http://www.digiplanet.com/DP1/netcount.html

NetDepot

http://www.netdepot.com/

NETHEAD

http://www.nethead.co.uk/

NETiS Technology, Inc.

http://www.netistech.com/

Netlife Health Products

http://www.interlog.com/~netlife/netlife.html

NetMagic, Inc.

http://www.aristosoft.com/netmagic/company.html

Netmare 1

http://netmare1.channel.co.uk/

NetMind Media

http://www.mindnet.com/

NetPoint Communications, Inc.

http://www.netpoint.net/

NetPress Communications

http://www.netpress.com/

NetReach

http://www.reach.net/

Netropolis

http://www.dash.com/

Netside Network

http://www.netside.com/index.html

Netsoft

http://voyager.bei.net/amni/netsoft/elite.html

Nettech Engineering

http://www.ebtech.net/users/nettech/

Nettwerk Records

http://www.wimsey.com/nettwerk/

NETWave Internet Access Provider

http://maui.netwave.net/info.html

Network Communication Computers and Arrays

http://tribeca.ios.com/~ideal/index.html

Network Consulting Group

http://www.comland.com/~mnorth

Network Data Services, Inc.

http://www.gate.net/~nds/index.html

Network Performance Institute

http://anshar.shadow.net/~npi/npipage.html

Network Support Center

http://guess.worldweb.net/webauth/newhome.htm

Network Systems Corporation

http://www.network.com/

Networking and Internet Connectivity Consultant

http://www.earthlink.net/free/tedv/webdocs/

Networks Incorporated

http://205.138.166.1/networks/

Networks Plus Computers

http://www.sierra.net/ntwkplus/

NeuroDimension, Inc.

http://www.nd.com/

Neuromedical Supplies, Inc.

http://www.neuro.com/

Neverland Records

http://www.netaxs.com/~dothar/never.htm

New England Airlines

http://www.ids.net/flybi/

New England Computer Supply

http://emanate.com/necs/

New Era Art

http://www.kajen.malmo.se/~nea/

New Image Slide Service

http://www.roccplex.com/newimage/

New Media Associates, Inc.

http://www.ip.net/NMA/

New Media Think Tank

http://www.webcom.com/~newmedia/

new stuff, inc.

http://www.newstuff.com/

New Technology Computers

http://www.indirect.com/www/newtech/

New World Books

http://branch.com/books/books.html

Newbridge Networks Corporation

http://www.newbridge.com/

Newman Group Computer Services

http://www.dpi.com/Newman/catalog.htm

Newmarket

http://www.newmarket.com/default.html

Newton Factory Direct

http://www.teleport.com/~newton/

Nexus srl Firenze Italy

http://www.trident.nettuno.it/~fabio/nexus.html

NH&A

http://www.nha.com/

nicejob Media

http://www.earthlink.net/~mrnicejob/

Nieuws Servers Overzicht (In Dutch)

http://cbil.humgen.upenn.edu/~marcovth/nieuws/nieuws.html

Nightwish Engineering

http://www.moscow.com/~nitewish/

Nine Pines Publishing

http://www.cygnus.nb.ca/bookstr/ninepines/ninepines.html

Nisa Communications Group

http://www.aurora.net/~jpenner/

Nisus Software Inc.

http://www.nisus-soft.com/~nisus/

Nokia

http://www.nokia.com/

Nomad Press

http://www.awa.com/nomad/

Norcov Research

http://www.norcov.com/

NORTH 45 Management Corp.

http://www.globalx.net/n45/n45.html

North American Digital

http://biz.rtd.com/nad/index.html

North American Stijl Life

http://buckaroo.bonsai.com/~nasl/

North Communications

http://www.infonorth.com/

North Tahoe/Truckee Week

http://www.sierra.net/nttw/nttw.html

Northstar

http://www.northstar-mn.com/

Northwest Link

http://nwlink.com/

Norwegian Bookshop

http://www.oslonett.no/home/paul/nw.html

Notes Solution Software

http://www.dct.com/NOTES/

Novagate

http://www.novagate.com

NovaNET

http://www.nn.com/

Novia Internetworking

http://www.novia.net/

NSM Services

http://www.nsm.co.uk/

NTG International

http://www.ntg-campus.com/ntg/

NTT Data Communications Systems

http://unisql.www.nttdata.jp/

Number Nine Visual Technologies

http://www.nine.com/

Numerical Algorithms Group, Ltd., The

http://www.nag.co.uk:70/

NuReality

http://www.nureality.com/

NutriGenie

http://pages.prodigy.com/CA/nutrigenie/

NYnet Computer Store

http://savvy.com/~nynet/comp/comp.html

O'Connor, Kenny, Swain

http://www.wspice.com/oks/homepage.html

O'Neills Thoroughbred Information

http://www.gc.net/oneill/index.html

Object Agency, Inc.

http://www.toa.com/

Object Technologies

http://www.objectech.com/NEXTSTEP/

Object Warehouse

http://www.wwww.com

ObjectWorks, Inc.

http://www.objectworks.com/

OBLIVION Entertainment

http://www.cybergate.com/~oblivion/index.html

OC Systems

http://ocsystems.com/

Ocean Software

http://odon.com/ocean/

Octel Communications Corp

http://www.octel.com/

Odegard Labs, Inc. Media Group

http://www.odegard.com/oli/media-main.html

Odyssey Systems, Inc.

http://www.stern.nyu.edu/~mnarayan/

Office Technology

http://www.officetech.com/

OffShore Music Group

http://ignatz.ucsd.edu/offshore/

Oh Yah! Records

http://www.mbnet.mb.ca/flatland/mall/ohyah/

Okanagan Computer Products Recycling, Inc.

http://www.awinc.com/OCPRI/

Oknet

http://www.oknet.com/

Olivetti

http://www.olivetti.it/

Olivetti Line

http://www.oli.it/

Olle Hallin

http://public-www.pi.se/~hit/

Olympus Software

http://www.mmrcorp.com/corporate/olympus/

Omega Research, Inc.

http://www.gate.net/~omegares/

Omicron Structured Software (Pty), Ltd.

http://www.onwe.co.za/alon/omicron.htm

Omnicron Data Systems Home Page

http://www.omnicron.com/omnicron.html

Omniscience

http://www.omniscience.com

Omtool, Inc.

http://www.omtool.com/

On-line Video Capture Services

http://www.galaxymedia.com/vcapsvcs.html

ONE A DAY Computer Greetings

http://www.automatrix.com/panzl/index.html

One Up Corporation

http://www.smallplanet.com/smallplanet/oneup/
1uphome.html

OneLiners, Inc.

http://www.HiWAAY.net/ONeLINERS/

ONet

http://www.onet.on.ca/onet/index.html

Online BookStore

http://www.obs-us.com/

Online Zone (San Francisco)

http://www.onlinezone.com/

OnPoint Communications, Inc.

http://www.mwbe.com/

ONRAMP Network Services

http://www.onramp.ca/

ONYX Music and Books

http://www.mindspring.com/~onyxpet/onyx.html

OpCode Factory

http://www.portal.com/~davidm/

Open Access

http://www.oa.net/

Open Market's University Program

http://www.openmarket.com/omi/nph-univ.cgi

Open Systems, Inc.

http://www.gmcclel.bossnt.com/osas/

Ophelia Publishing

http://www.digimark.net/Ophelia/

Optical Delusions

http://www.the-spa.com/optical.delusions/

Optimus

http://www.sigma.unb.ca/optimus/optimus.htm

Optivision, Inc.

http://www.optivision.com/

ORALink Web

http://oradb1.jinr.dubna.su/software/oralink/

Orangeville Citizen

http://www.headwaters.com/citizen/citizen.html

Orbik Records

http://www.earthlink.net/~orbik/

Organic Online

http://www.organic.com/

Oriflame International

http://voyager.bei.net/oriflame/index.html

Origin Communications, Inc.

http://io.com/~origins/

Orion Instruments, Inc.

http://www.oritools.com/

Orthotronics, Inc.

http://usa.net/cge/orthotro.htm

Ostfeld

http://www.graffiti.it/ostfeld/

Outbound Train

http://www.webcom.com/~outbound/

OutNOW!

http://www.zoom.com/outnow/

Output Technologies

http://www.tyrell.net/~succeed/

Oxford Books Online

http://www.ping.com/oxford/main.htm

Oxford Softworks

http://www.demon.co.uk/oxford-soft/

OZ Interactive

http://www.oz.is/OZ/Deps/Interactive/Page1.html

P.O.W.E.R. Net, Inc.

http://www.poweramp.net/

Pac Services, Inc.

http://www.cyberspace.com/pac/

Pace Publications

http://www.w2.com/pacepub.html

Pacific Book Auction Galleries

http://www.nbn.com/pba/

Pacific Computers

http://204.174.85.99/default.htm

Pacific Interconnect

http://pinc.com/pi/

Pacific Numerix Corporation

http://www.crl.com/~pacnum/pnc.html

Pacific Rim Network, Inc.

http://www.pacificrim.net/

Pacifier Computers (Pacifier Online Data Service)

http://www.pacifier.com/

PageSetters

http://www.pagesetters.com/

Paintball Headquarters

http://www.infop.com/paint/index.html

Palantir

http://pages.prodigy.com/MA/palantir/

Pamet River Partners

http://www.pamet.com/

Pan-Net

http://www.pan-net.de/

Pandemonium Group

http://www.pandemonium.fr/

Pangea Creative Media

http://www.magi.com/~brett/multimedia.html

Pangea Visions

http://www.lance.colostate.edu/~av398541/pangea/pangea.html

Pantera Publishing

http://www.iquest.net/~kingman/book.html

PaperFree Systems

http://paperfree.com/edi/index.htm

Pappalardo & Associates, Inc.

http://pai.iquest.net/index.html

Para Publishing

http://www.zpub.com/para/

Paradigm Communication Group

http://cymetric.com/paradigm/

Paradigm Systems Corporation Global Information Service

http://www.sf.psca.com/

Paradon Computer Systems

http://islandnet.com/~paradon/paradon.html

Parallel Performance Group

http://www.ppgsoft.com/ppgsoft/loox.html

Parametric Technology Corporation

http://www.ptc.com/

Paranormal Records

http://www.iuma.com/Paranormal/

Parlophone Records

http://www.parlophone.co.uk/parlophone/

Parsytec Computer GmbH

http://www.parsytec.de/

pas de chance

http://kzsu.stanford.edu/uwi/pas-de-chance/catalogue.html

Pathtrace Systems

http://mfginfo.com/cadcam/edgecam/pathtrace.htm

Pattern Corporation

http://www.panix.com/pattern/

Paul Mace Software

http://www.pmace.com/

PC DOCS, Inc.

http://www.pcdocs.com

PC Heidens

http://www.teleport.com/~pcheiden/

PC Innovation

http://www.nando.net/xwwwtemp/compad/pcinnov1.html

PC Shareware

http://www.cts.com/~pcs/

PC Tutoring

http://www.blvl.igs.net/~cunning/

Pc-Trans

http://kuhub.cc.ukans.edu/~pctrans/

PCS Health Systems

http://www.pcshs.com/

Peachpit Press

http://www.peachpit.com/

Peak Computing

http://peak.usa1.com

Peer Protocol

http://www.earthlink.net/~peer/

Pegasus Networks

http://www.peg.apc.org/

Pelican Airways

http://www.pwr.com/FLYHIGH/DEFAULT.html

Penguin Books

http://www.demon.co.uk/bookshop/pecat.html

Peninsula Advisors, Inc.

http://www.best.com/~iris/

PennWell Publishing Company

http://www.pennwell.com/

Perdido Bay Electronics

http://www.gulf.net/emall/perdido/

Perfection Services, Inc.

http://ivory.lm.com/~psi

Performance Engineering Corporation

http://www.p-e-c.com/

Performing Graphics Company

http://www.pgc.com/

Perilous Industries

http://www.csn.net/~djai/

Peripheral Systems Group

http://www.web-view.com/pub/psg/

Persoft, Inc.

http://town.hall.org/sponsors/persoft.html

Personal Database Applications

http://www.mindspring.com/~pda/

Personal Library Software, Inc.

http://www.pls.com/

Perspective Visuals, Inc.

http://haven.ios.com/~dinosaur/

Peters-de Laet, Inc.

http://www.pdel.com/

PG Datanet

http://www.datanet.ab.ca/

Phantom of the Attic, Oakland

http://www.ibp.com/pitt/phantom/

Phase Three Logic, Inc.

http://www.aue.com/capfast.html

Pheonix Software Solutions, Inc.

http://www.tcpxray.com/tcpxray/

Phoenix Systems Internet Publishing

http://www.biddeford.com/phoenix/

Photo Comp Graphic Communication

http://a1.com/graphics/

Photodex Corporation

http://www.photodex.com/

Pickering Anomalies and IOTA Asteroid Occultation Section

http://www.anomalies.com/

Pie in the Sky Software

http://www.catalog.com/psky/

Pierian Spring Educational Software

http://www.europa.com/pierian/

Pilot Systems, Inc.

http://www.gmcclel.bossnt.com/pilot/

Pinnacle Post

http://www.halcyon.com/pinnacle/welcome.html

Pinnacle Software

http://WWW.CAM.ORG/~pinnacl/

Pittston Gazette, The

http://www.microserve.net/microserve/pitgaz/index.html

Pixel Generation, inc.

http://www.pixgen.com/

Pixel Pecx

http://www.gayweb.com/206/pixelpec.html

Plaintree Systems

http://www.nstn.ca/plaintree/index.html

Planet Communications

http://www.tc.net/planet/

Planet Earth Communications

http://www.earthcom.net/

Plant Software, Inc., The

http://www.theplant.com/

Play Incorporated

http://www.play.com/

Players Club International

http://branch.com/players/players.html

Playmen Italian Magazine

http://www.playmen.it

PObox EMail Service

http://www.pobox.org.sg/

Point & Click Software, Inc.

http://www.point-and-click.com/pcsi/

Poisoned Pen

http://www.primenet.com/~rosey/poison_pen/poisonpen.html

Polonia Bookstore

http://www.wtinet.com/wti/polonia.htm

PolyEster Records and Books

http://www.glasswings.com.au/PolyEster/index.html

PolyGram Records, Inc.

http://www.polygram.com/polygram/Music.html

Poor Person Productions

http://www.zynet.co.uk/farmer/poor/

Pop Gun Records

http://www.camtech.com.au/popgun/

Pop Rocket, Inc.

http://www.poprocket.com/

Porter Novelli

http://www.porternovelli.com/

Portland Independant Music Project (PIMP)

http://www.iuma.com/PIMP/

Positiva Records

http://www.musicbase.co.uk/music/positiva/

Positive Support Review, Inc.

http://www.psrinc.com/metrics1.htm

PostModern Computing

http://www.pomoco.com/

Power Computing Corporation

http://www.powercc.com/

Powercom and One Com

http://www.powercom.com/

Powernet

http://www.power.net/

PowerNet: An Idea Whose Time Has Come

http://www.pwrnet.com/gd/pnet.htm

PowerVar Canada

http://fox.nstn.ca/~powervar/

Praegitzer Industries Web Server

http://www.pii.com/

PRC, Inc.

http://www.prc.com/

Precision Graphics of Texas

http://mfginfo.com/service/precision/precision.htm

Precision Software

http://www.charm.net/~ibc/ibc2/precisn.html

Preferred net.Shopper

http://www.preferred.com/shop/index.html

PREP Software

http://www.prepsoft.com/prep/

Press Association

http://www.cais.com/djackson/tpa.html

Prestonwood Travel

http://www.wn.com/ptravel/

Prima Travel Centre

http://www.explore.com/prima.html

Prime Time Freeware

http://www.cfcl.com/ptf/

Primetime

http://www.ibos.com/pub/ibos/prime/

Printer Works

http://www.printerworks.com/index.html

Printers

http://www.starnetinc.com/magtech/home.html

PrintMail America

http://www.stpt.com/printmail

PRISM Communications

http://www.tiac.net/users/cody/index.html

Pristine Communications

http://www.pristine.com.tw/

Private Eye

http://www.intervid.co.uk/intervid/eye/gateway.html

Pro-Net Internet Services

http://pronews.pro-net.co.uk/prohome.html

Probe Technology, Inc.

http://www.probe.net/

Process Analysts, Inc.

http://www.pai-colo.com/pai/

Proconsul

http://www.erinet.com/bkottman/Proconsul/

Prode

http://www.prode.milano.it/prode.html

Productivity Point International / Technology Point, Inc.

http://www.techpoint.com/training.html

Programmer's Warehouse

http://www.programmer.com/

Progressive Media Arts

http://www.well.com/user/khampton/PMA.htm

Promedia Services Corp

http://www.promedia.net/

Propulsion Records

http://www.w2.com/docs2/b/propulsion.html

**Pros Entertainment
Services, Inc., The**

http://pages.prodigy.com/PA/sparky/weddings.html

ProSoft Design

http://www.escape.com/~prosoft/pagedsgn.htm

ProSoft International, Inc.

http://www.webcom.com/~prosoft/

Providence Business News

http://www.pbn.com/

PSC Systems

http://www.psclan.com/

PSI-Squared, Ltd.

http://www.inovatec.com/psi

Pulsonic Technology, Ltd.

http://www.pulsonic.com/ptc_home.html

**Punto Soft International
cd-rom Italy**

http://www.eclipse.it/puntosoft/

Putnam Berkley Online

http://www.mca.com/putnam/

Pyromedia

http://infoweb.magi.com/~pyro

Pyxis DBS

http://interlog.com/~pyxis/

Q Group, The

http://www.dfw.net/~tqg/

Q-Zar

http://www.q-zar.com/

Qantas Airways

http://www.anzac.com/qantas/qantas.htm

Qbik Software

http://nz.com/NZ/Commerce/creative-cgi/special/qbik/
qbik.htm

Quadbase

http://www.quadbase.com/quadbase.htm

Quadrat Communications

http://www.interlog.com/~quadrat/

Quagmire

http://www.iuma.com/Quagmire/

**Quality America,
Incorporated**

http://www.theriver.com/qa-inc/

Quality HiTec Services

http://www.qhs.com/

**Quality Software
Management**

http://www.utopia.com/companies/qsm/home.html

Quantex Microsystems Inc.

http://www.qtx.com/

Quantum Research Corporation

http://www.qrc.com/

Quark, Inc.

http://www.quark.com/

Quay Information

http://www.quay.co.uk/

Que Computers

http://loonlink.com/que/

Quest Software, Inc.

http://quests.com/

QuickMedia

http://www.quickmedia.com

Quicktime VR Service

http://www.kwanza.com/~embleton/service.html

Quiltery, The

http://mmink.com/mmink/dossiers/quilt/quilt.html

QwikShop

http://205.139.129.111/q/qwikshop/default.htm

R C Systems, Inc.

http://ifu.ifu.net/html/tech/rcs/rcs.html

R. A. Vess Enterprises

http://www.infi.net/~ravess/index.html

r.u.there?

http://www.personalnet.com/

RABA Technologies, Inc.

http://www.raba.com/

Ractek Company

http://www.digiweb.com/rose/ractek/

Radical Rhythms

http://localhost.ruhr.de/~radical/

RadixNet Information Services

http://www.radix.net/

Rage Records

http://www.w2.com/rage.html

Rainy Day Records

http://www.hidwater.com/RDR/rdrhome.html

Ramworks

http://www.ramworks.com/ramworks/

Random Access, Inc.

http://www.randomc.com/

Raptor Systems, Inc

http://www.raptor.com/

Rashid Sales Co.

http://virtumall.com/Rashid/home.html

Ratvis Travel

http://iceweb.ismennt.is/r/ratvis/

Ravenet Systems, Inc.

http://www.ravenet.com/

Raxco, Inc.

http://www.raxco.com/

Raymond Interactive Theatre, Ltd.

http://www.rit.com/

RCA Victor

http://www.rcavictor.com/

Re:Design, Inc.

http://www.interport.net/~rmeckler/

ReadersNdex

http://www.readersndex.com/

Real Change Homeless Newspaper

http://www.speakeasy.org/realchange/

Reality Interactive

http://www.purple.co.uk/purplet/reality/

Reality Society Records

http://www.iuma.com/Reality_Society/

RealTime Consulting, Inc.

http://www.doit.com/realtime/

Rebelo and Miholer Advertising

http://www.maui.net/~randm/rm.html

Reckless Design Limited

http://www.arlington.com/~reckless/reckless.html

Red Phraug Modern Medium

http://www.teleport.com/~noise/

RedLeaf Software

http://www.cam.org/~dsavic/

Reed Interactive

http://www.ozemail.com.au/~reed/index.html

Regency Court of Canada, Inc.

http://www.regencycourt.com/voyage/

Reggio Citta degli Studi

http://www.rcs.re.it/

Relational Information Systems, Inc.

http://wl.iglou.com/ris/

Reliable Software Technologies Corporation

http://www.access.digex.net/~rst/

Remedy Corporation

http://www.remedy.com/

Remote Telnet Shell Accounts

http://www.eskimo.com/~ajensen/shell.html

Renaissance Technologies

http://www.rentech.com/

Render-Cam Images

http://www.crl.com/~rci/rci.htm

Renee Recker Web Site Design (N.Y.C.)

http://www.interport.net/~rexalot/

Research Dynamics

http://www.txdirect.net/resdyn/

Reservoir Records

http://monsterbit.com/reservoir/reservoir.html

Resolution Business Press

http://www.halcyon.com/ResPress/

Restless Records

http://www.restless.com/

Retix Web

http://www.retix.com/

Revelation Records

http://www.w2.com/revelation.html

Revolution Books

http://virtumall.com/RevBooks/

ReZrVoir

http://www.commerce.com/ReZrVoir/RZV_top.html

Rhinestone Jewelry Word Pins

http://www.rhinestone.com/rhinestone

Ribaum Graphics

http://sc.net/organizations/ribaum/index.html

Richards Group

http://www.x-ads.com/

RichNet

http://www.richnet.net/

Rimini Network

http://infotel.shiny.it/

Rinascita

http://www.rinascita.it/

RingMaster

http://www.accessone.com/ringmaster/

RMC Internet Services

http://www.rmci.net/

Rnet

http://www.edb.com/rnet/index.html

Roadrunner Computer Systems

http://www.roadrunner.com/

Robert McNeel & Associates

http://www.mcneel.com/

Robins Sharpe Associates

http://interlog.com/~rsadvert/

Robinson Video Transfer

http://www.quiknet.com/~rvt/

Rockadillo Records

http://www.sjoki.uta.fi/~latvis/levyyht/rockad.html

Rocket Rentals

http://www.aimnet.com/~blastoff/ROCKET_Rentals.html

Rockwell Collins Printed Circuits

http://www.rockwell.com/rockwell/bus_units/cca/cpc/

Rodale Press

http://shopping2000.com/shopping2000/rodale_pre/
rodale_pre.html

Rogers Communications, Inc.

http://www.rogers.com/

Rollins Information Technology Services

http://www.direct.ca/hss/rollins/

Round Lake Publishing

http://www.starbyte.com/roundlake.html

Royalty Records

http://www.w2.com/royalty.html

RPA

http://www.rpa.com/

Rubber Stamp Queen

http://www.dol.com/queen/

Running Man Computer Services

http://rampages.onramp.net/~fezziksa/

RVIN Development

http://www.ecenter.com/rvin/main.html

S&S International PLC

http://www.sands.com

S.P.C. Microcomputer

http://www.primenet.com/~spc/

Saarbruekcer Zeitung

http://www.sz-sb.de/

Safari Media™

http://www.safari-media.com/

SafeSite

http://www.maagnum.com/safesite.html

Sage Solutions, Inc.

http://www.sagesoln.com/

Saint Mary's Press

http://wwwsmp.smumn.edu/

Sam Boyd's California

http://www.vegas.com/hotels/california/

Sample the Dog

http://www.teleport.com/~sample/

San Francisco Canyon Company

http://www.sfcanyon.com/

San Francisco Free Press

http://www.ccnet.com/SF_Free_Press/welcome.html

Sanctuary Woods Multimedia

http://www.sanctuary.com/

Santa Fe Fine Art

http://www.sffa.com/

SAP AG

http://www.sap-ag.de/

Sapphire Press

http://www.digimark.net/UNCAT/

SaskTel

http://www.sasknet.sk.ca/

Satori Software

http://www.satorisw.com/satori/

Saturday Market

http://www.efn.org/~smarket/

SBC Advertising

http://www.smartpages.com/sbc/index.html

SBI Computer Distribution

http://www.the-wire.com/SBI/

Scala Computer Television AS (Norway)

http://scala-gw.anima.no/

Scandinavian Softline Technology

http://www.softline.fi/

Scatliff And Associates

http://www.mbnet.mb.ca/~scatliff/

SCEPTRE

http://www.gus.com/emp/sceptre/sceptre.html

Schofield Computer Organization

http://fox.nstn.ca/~rschofie/index.html

SCHWA Online

http://kzsu.stanford.edu/uwi/schwa/schwa.html

Science Express, Inc.

http://www.sci-exp.com/

Scratching Post, The

http://www.garlic.com/~ribarbe/sp.html

SCSI Peripherals / WHOLESALE

http://cybermart.com/scuzzy/index.html

Sea Change Corporation

http://www.seawest.seachange.com/

Sealworks, Inc.

http://www.libertynet.org/~swi/

Sears HealthCare

http://www.shopping2000.com/shopping2000/sears-healthcare/

SEATOP Reisen

http://www.reise.de/

Second Nature Software, Inc.

http://www.secondnature.com/

Secret Staircase Bookshop

http://www.secretstaircasebooks.com/

Secure Computing Corporation

http://www.sctc.com/

Security Engineering Services, Inc.

http://www.blackmagic.com/ses/ses.html

SEIKO EPSON

http://www.epson.co.jp/

SelfGrow, Ltd.

http://www.internet-eireann.ie/SelfGrow/default.htm

SenseMedia Online

http://sensemedia.net/

Septagon Records

http://www.netrunner.net/~septagon/Records/

Sequent Computer Systems, Inc.

http://www.sequent.com/public/index.html

Serif, Inc.

http://www.serif.com/

Servasure Systems, Inc.

http://web.ixl.net:8000/Servasure/

Sesha Press Records

http://www.crl.com/www/users/rg/rgeimer/seshaHome.html

Shades Of Light Studios

http://www.ernestallen.com/shadesoflight/

Shadow Island Games

http://www.pbm.com/

Shana Corporation

http://www.shana.com/

Shelter films

http://www.ohone.com/

Shen's Books and Supplies

http://www.shens.com/

Shewey Enterprises, Inc.

http://www.slip.net/~shewey/

Shock Software

http://www.shock.co.uk/

Shooting Brick Productions, Inc.

http://www.europa.com/~brickley/index

Shore Line Records

http://www.geopages.com/Hollywood/1393/

Shuttle Systems International

http://www.worldlink.ca/~shuttle/

Sidea

http://www.sidea.com/

Siemens Nixdorf Informations

http://www.sni.de/public/its/offers/its-13.htm

Sietec Document Management and Archives

http://www.sietec.de/arc/arc.en

Sigma Computer Training

http://www.sigma.unb.ca/sigma/sigma.htm

SIGS Publications

http://www.sigs.com/publications/sigspubs.html

SiliconSoft

http://he.tdl.com/~silicons/

Silver Girl Records

http://www.tumyeto.com/tydu/music/labels/silver/
silver.htm

Simbirsk Telecom

http://www.stc.simbirsk.su/

SimPhonics, Inc.

http://www.simphonics.com/

Simply Computing

http://aws2.cybernet.ca/egate/simply/simply.html

Simucad

http://www.simucad.com/

Sin-Drome Records

http://www.kspace.com/KM/music.sys/SinDrome/pages/
home.html

Sinbad Travel

http://www.spb.su/ryh/sindbad.html

Singapore Telecommunications, Ltd.

http://www.singnet.com.sg/singnet/singtel/singtel.html

Sirius Business Accounting

http://www.siriusacct.com/sirius/

Sistemas de Tecnología Avanzada

http://www.sta.sistecol.com/

SITE Computer Services, Inc.

http://www.ansa.com/~site/home.html

SkinCare Program

http://shani.co.il/~skincare/

Skylonda Group

http://www.skylonda.com/skyhome.html

Slant, The

http://www.rahul.net/tyler/slant.html

Slumberland Records

http://www.denizen.com/trout/slumberland/

Small Media And Large

http://smallmedia.com/

Smart Books, Inc.

http://www.carmelnet.com/SBI/

SmartWorks

http://www.smartworks.com/catalog/

Smithmicro

http://www.smithmicro.com/

Smoke N' Mirrors, Inc.

http://www.snm.com/

SNC International

http://www.sncint.com/sncint/home.html

So Cal Graphics

http://turnpike.net/emporium/S/socal/index.html

SOB Entertainment

http://www.iuma.com/SOB/

Soft-One ClassAct Multimedia

http://www.itsnet.com/classact/index.html

Softbank Corporation

http://www.softbank.co.jp/

Softfarm

http://www.softfarm.com/

SoftPlan Systems

http://www.softplan.com/websoft

SoftSell Business Systems, Inc.

http://www.softsell.com/

SoftSmith Systems, Inc.

http://www.inforamp.net/~softsmit/index.htm

Software Connection Online

http://www.softconn.co.za/

Software Consulting Services

http://nscs.fast.net/

Software Dynamics Consulting

http://www.sdcnet.com/

Software Magic, Inc.

http://www.rust.net/~lbloom/

Software of the Month Club

http://www.cts.com/browse/somc/theclub.html

Software Products International

http://www.cts.com/~spi/

Software Solutions, Inc.

http://www.gmcclel.bossnt.com/ssi/

Software Tailors

http://www.traveller.com/~rew/tailors.html

Software Tools for Artists

http://webcom.com/~stfa/

Softway Pty. Limited

http://www.softway.com.au/

Sojourn Systems

http://www.sojourn.com/

Solid Oak Software, Inc.

http://www.rain.org/~solidoak/

Solution

http://www.solution.de

SONARt

http://www.cam.org/~dim/F/catSO.html

Sonda, S.A.

http://www.sonda.cl/

Sonoma Interconnect

http://www.sonic.net/

Sony Electronic Publishing

http://www.sepc.sony.com/SEPC/index.html

SooNet Corporation

http://www.soonet.ca/

Sound & Vision Media

http://www.svmedia.com/svmedia/

Sound Web Development Yellow Pages

http://www.mediawhse.com/yellow1.html

Source, Inc.

http://www.unicomp.net/sourcetele/

South Carolina Point

http://www.cris.com/~scpoint/

South Hills Datacomm

http://www.shillsdata.com/

Southam, Inc.

http://www.southam.com/

SouthWare Innovations, Inc.

http://www.excelco.com/swinfo.html

SpaceCom Systems, Inc.

http://www.spacecom.com/

SPAN Information Technology, Inc.

http://www.spanit.com/

SPARTA, Inc.

http://www.huntsville.sparta.com/

Special Form Software

http://www.specialform.com/sfs/welcome.html

Specialized Business Solutions

http://www.some.com/sbs/

Specs™ Manufacturing Instructions

http://www.sonic.net/~richw/zip.html

Spectra.Net Communications, Inc.

http://www.spectra.net/

Spectral Research Technologies

http://www.tenn.com/srt/srt.html

Spectrum Trading

http://www.spectrum-t.com/

Speech Systems, Inc.

http://www.speechsys.com/

SpeedSim, Inc.

http://www.speedsim.com/speedsim/

SpiderWeb Creations

http://www.goodnet.com/~rob/web_creations.html

Spinfree Web Design

http://http.bsd.uchicago.edu/~d-lakier/spinfree/

Spire Technologies

http://www.spiretech.com/

Sporting Life Travel

http://www.edensys.com/edensys/sportlife/index.html

Sports Handicapper

http://www.gate.net/~rutech/

Sports Syndicate

http://www.charm.net/~sports/

Sprague Magnetics

http://www.earthlink.net/~sprague-magnetics/

Sprint Drums

http://www.sprint.com/drums/

Sprite Interactive

http://www.cityscape.co.uk/users/di50/

SpyderByte Communications, Inc.

http://www.spyder.net/

Squealer Music

http://www.mal.com/~squealer/

SRA International, Inc.

http://www.sra.com/

SST, Inc.

http://www.webcom.com/~sstinc/

St. Petersburg Press, The

http://www.spb.su/sppress/

Stafford Home and Commercial Fitness

http://www.montana.com/Stafford/Stafford_Fitness.html

Stancom Computing

http://www.iinet.com.au/~cstanley/

Standard Records

http://www.mindspring.com/~ism/Standard.html

Star Electronics

http://www.homeless.com/homepages/bryano@gcomm.com.html

Star-Byte Shopping Mall

http://www.starbyte.com/mall.html

Stardate Internet

http://awinc.com/partners/bc/stardate/

Stardust Resort & Casino

http://www.vegas.com/hotels/stardust/

Starks Multimedia Design

http://www.interport.net/~starks/

Starlight Networks

http://www.starlight.com/

StarMan Group, Multimedia Productions

http://www.indirect.com/www/gstarman/

Starvector Software

http://www.wolfe.net/~svector/sv.htm

Stat Tech

http://www.stattech.com.au/

Station Graphics, Inc.

http://www.pic.net/~station/

Stephens Design

http://www.opendoor.com/StephensDesign/

Steps In Time Bookstore and Coffee House

http://www.ibp.com/pit/steps-in-time/

Steven M. Christensen and Associates

http://christensen.cybernetics.net/Christensen.html

Stolk Microsystems

http://www.eden.com/~sms/sms.html

Stone Bridge Press

http://www.stonebridge.com/~sbp/

Stonehand, Inc.

http://www.stonehand.com/

StonyBrook Software

http://www.sbrook.com/

Storage Systems Solutions

http://www.ell.com/

Straight Line Medium, Inc.

http://www.infi.net/~slm/

Strategic Networks Consulting, Inc.

http://www.snci.com/

Strategics

http://www.ozemail.com.au/~strategi/

Strawberry Tree, Inc.

http://www.strawberrytree.com/

Structured Network Systems

http://www.structured.net/

STS

http://www.alaska.net/~lafferty/sts.html

Stubborn Records

http://www.phantom.com/~giant/hype2/stubborn/
stubborn.html

Subia

http://www.subia.com/subia/

Submarine Cables of the World

http://www.teleport.com/~simoriah/scow/sub.htm

Subtle Software

http://world.std.com/~subtle/index.html

Sumeria Product List

http://www.service.com/D3/sumeria/sumeria.html

Summit Publishing

http://www.callamer.com/~araissi/summit/

Summit Software Services

http://www.teleport.com/~gregman/summit.shtml

Sundance

http://cybermart.com/sundance/

SunExpress

http://www.sun.com/sunexpress/

Sunnyside Computing, Inc.

http://sunnyside.com/

Sunrise Door Software

http://www.oknet.com/sunrise.html

Sunvil Holidays

http://www.its.net/its/si/sunvil.htm

Superbyte, Inc.

http://www.ibag.com/superbyte/

Superlative Software Solutions

http://www.cat.syr.edu/3Si/

SuperLink.NET

http://www.superlink.net/

Supernova Records

http://www.netrail.net/~jordys/

SURE BET

http://www.tiac.net/users/phepp/index.html

Surfdog Records

http://www.professionals.com/~surfdog/records.html

SurfWatch Software

http://www.surfwatch.com/

Svenska Dagladet

http://www.svd.se/

SW International Systems Pte, Ltd.

http://www.swi.com.sg/

Swansystems Oy

http://www.inet.tele.fi/classified/swan.html

Sybex, Inc.

http://www.sybex.com/

Sydney Morning Herald

http://www.smh.com.au/

Sylvest Management Systems

http://www.sylvest.com/

SymCon Software

http://www.interlog.com/~symcon/

Symplex ISDN Routers with Ethernet Interfaces

http://www.iea.com/~symplex/

Synapse Communications, Inc.

http://www.synapse.com/

Synaptic Communications, Inc.

http://www.netbistro.com/synaptic/

Synergetic Resource Corporation

http://www.synernet-indy.com/src/

Synergy Peephole

http://www.eirenet.net/cork/synergy/

Syntax

http://www.syntax.com/

Syracuse Online

http://dataserver.syr.edu:8080/HTTPB/syronline.html

SysTeam Technology Support Division

http://www.systeam.traveller.com/

System Resources Corporation

http://www.srcorp.com/

Systemcorp

http://www.systemcorp.com/index.html

Systems Alliance, Inc.

http://www.access.digex.net/~golshan/alliance.html

Systems Partners, Inc.

http://www.syspart.com/

Systems Solutions

http://www.syspac.com/

T & T Software WWW Server

http://ttsw.com/

T3plus

http://www.t3plus.com/

Taang! Records

http://www.wpi.edu/~joev/taang.html

TAC Systems

http://www.tacsys.com/

Tadpole Technology

http://www.tadpole.com/

TAF Enterprises

http://emall.com/taf/taf.html

Tages-Anzeiger

http://www.thenet.ch/tages-anzeiger/

Talink

http://www.talink.com/

Tampa One Productions

http://CyberAdvantage.com/Video/Video.html

Tanisys Technology

http://www.tanisys.com/

Tanty Records

http://www.easynet.co.uk/goodvibe/tanty.htm

Targeted Communication Management

http://www.iconode.ca/aim/

Tascomm Engineering

http://www.tascomm.fi/

Taxprep Information Systems

http://www.taxprep.com/

TCP3270 for Windows

http://www.3270.McGill.CA/

TD Imports

http://www.nucleus.com/~ccgs/tdi.html

Team America

http://www.vir.com/JAM/team.html

Team Evil

http://www.pt.hk-r.se/~pt94rfe/TeamEvil/TeamEvil.html

team smartyPANTS!

http://www.eden.com/~smarty/

TEC Solutions

http://www.tecs.com/tecs

Tech 2000 Pty, Ltd.

http://www.ozemail.com.au/~tech2000/

Tech Bookstore

http://www.bnt.com/~techbook/

TECHCO

http://www.primenet.com/~techco/

Techlock Distributing

http://www.erinet.com/kenny/

Technetix Unix/Internet Tools

http://teknetix.com/UNIX.html

TechnoGraphy & Storage Computer in Japan

http://www.storage.com/japan.html

Technology Associates of Colorado

http://usa.net/tac/

Technology Futures, Inc.

http://www.tfi.com/

TechStream Communications, Inc.

http://www.techstream.net/

TechWorks

http://www.techwrks.com/

Tecnation Digital World

http://www.tecnation.com/

TeenBeat Records

http://www.iuma.com/TeenBeat/

Teknekron Software Systems

http://www.tss.com/

TeKnowlogy Education Centers

http://www.teknowlogy.com/teknowlogy/

tela computer consulting + design

http://www.tela.bc.ca/tela/

Tele-Communications, Inc. (TCI)

http://www.tcinc.com/

Telebasics Automatisering & Telecommunicatie

http://www.euronet.nl/users/telebas

Telecom Eireann

http://www.broadcom.ie/telecom/dupjmc/teprofile.html

Telecommunications Management & Marketing Research CentreCENTRE.

http://www.lights.com/tmres/

Telecommunications Technology Corp.

http://soho.ios.com/~teltech/

Telelogic

http://www.telelogic.se/

Telepath Internet Connection

http://www.telepath.com/

TeleService Resources, Inc.

http://www.amrcorp.com/amr_mgmt/teleserv/resser.htm

Telluride Times-Journal

http://www.adone.com/telluride/

Telos Online

http://www.telos.ca/

TelTECH Computer Consulting

http://bb.iu.net/teltech/

Temple Records

http://www.rootsworld.com/temple/

TEN

http://www.stv.com/stv/

TENET Computer Group, Inc.

http://www.tenet.com/

Terra Nova Data Solutions

http://www.teleport.com/~tnds

TerraPort Online, Inc.

http://www.terraport.net/

Tetrad Computer Applications

http://www.tetrad.com/

TFSnet Online Information Service

http://www.fileshop.com/

TGV, Inc Home Page

http://www.tgv.com/

ThailandWeb

http://www.webcom.com/~home/th/

Thermal Solutions

http://www.sauna.com/tsi/

Thinque Systems Corporation

http://www.thinque.com/isis/

Thomas Computer Services

http://www.cquest.com/tcs.html

Thomas-Conrad Corporation

http://www.tci.com/

Thoroughbred Horse Racing Information Link

http://www.thril.com/

ThoughtPort Authority, Inc.

http://www.thoughtport.com/

ThreeToad Multimedia

http://www.halcyon.com/tritoad/

Thunderstone Software

http://www.thunderstone.com/

Tickets and Travel, Inc.

http://www.inetdirect.net/tnt

Tiger Mountain Productions

http://www.halcyon.com/mkinder/Tiger.html

Time Machine

http://webmart.org/timelaps/

Times Higher Education Supplement

http://www.timeshigher.newsint.co.uk/

Times Mirror Higher Education Group

http://www.tmhe.com

Timmons, Bonnie

http://www.goworldnet.com/btimmon.htm

TLG Electronics, Inc.

http://www.infinet.com/~tlg/

TNT Online

http://www.tntonline.com/top.htm

Tom Davis+Company

http://www.tiac.net/users/tdavisco/

Too Pure Records

http://www.maires.co.uk/nw2n/pure/pure.html

Top Of Mind Help Desk for Windows

http://www.planet.net/molloy/

Toronto Image Works

http://www.magic.ca/tiw/

ToSoft

http://www.teleport.com/~tosoft/

Total Connectivity Providers

http://www.tcp.co.uk/

Total Point of Sale Solution, The

http://www.netaxs.com/people/bsc/index.html

TouchNET GmbH i. Gr.

http://www.touch.net/

TouchWindow

http://www.touchwindow.com/

Tower Concepts, Inc.

http://www.tower.com/

Traffic Software

http://www.traffic.is/

Trans World Laser Cartridge Recycling

http://www.westdat.com/~bburnett/wdcbp/twt/twt.html

Transatlantic Management

http://euphoria.org/home/labels/transmgt/transmgt.html

Transmission Communications

http://www.brisnet.org.au/transcom/com11.htm

Travel & Entertainment Network

http://www.ten-io.com/index.html

Travel Boutique

http://hisurf.aloha.com/travel/hawaii.html

Travel Experts, Inc.

http://www.prairienet.org/business/travex/homepage.html

Travel Home

http://www.kern.com/travelhome.html

Travel Network

http://www.widdl.com/travnet/index.html

Travel Professionals on the WWW

http://www.slip.net/~jwithers/tawww.html

Travel Source

http://www.travelsource.com/

Travel Systems International, Inc.

http://www.travel-inc.com/Travel/

Travel.Net

http://www.nashville.com/member/travnet.html

Travelcraft, Inc.

http://market.net/travel/tc/index.html

TravelNet Beau Travel

http://www.mv.com/biz/beautravel/

Travis Computing

http://rampages.onramp.net/~reynolds/travis.html

Trax Softworks, Inc.

http://www.webcom.com/~traxsoft/

TRC Toshokan Ryutu Center Co., Ltd.

http://www.trc.co.jp/index.htm

Tri-Cities Connection

http://www.tricon.net/

Tridel.Net

http://www.tridel.com.ph/

Triffet Design Group

http://www.primenet.com/~martman/TDG.html

Trinity Data Systems

http://www.trinity.com/

Trinity Software

http://www.hfk.com/webpages/trinity.html

Trip 'n Spin Recordings Multiverse

http://tripNspin.com/TNS/

Tron BV

http://www.publishnet.nl/tron/

Tropical Penguin, A

http://underground.net/Newmusicians/mmttpt.html

Troubador Systems

http://www.troubador.com/

TSA Systems

http://www.tsa-sys.com/tsa/

TTi Technologies, Inc.

http://www.hypermart.com/tti/default.htm

Tucker Information Systems

http://www.tyrell.net/~tucker/

TuffGong Graphics & Web Design

http://www.rmii.com/~tuffgong/

Tunnel Under

http://membrane.com/tuntitle.html

Turbosales

http://www.turbosales.com/~turbos/info/index.html

TurnKey Video & New Media

http://www.teleport.com/~turnkey/

Twelve Hats Multimedia

http://monster.fiber.net/twelvehats/

Twenty Twenty

http://netsurf.net/2020/

Two Guys Named Hank

http://www.twohanks.com

Tyrell Online Services

http://www.tyrell.net/

U'Mista Cultural Centre

http://www.swifty.com/umista/

U-NET

http://www.u-net.com/

U.S. Micro

http://www.usmicro.com/

Ubi Soft

http://www.ubisoft.com/

UDesign, Incorporated

http://gs1.com/info/udfamily.html

UK Telecom Information Source

http://jumper.mcc.ac.uk/~afs/telecom/

Ultra Technology

http://www.dnai.com/~jfox/

UltraData Credit Union Systems

http://www.ultradata.com/

UNARIUS Academy of Science

http://www.cts.com/~unarius/

Unforgiven Productions

http://www.xmission.com/~unfo/

UNIBOL

http://www.unibol.com/

Unicomp, Inc.

http://www.fortran.com/fortran/unicomp.html

UniDial

http://www.unidial.com/

UniForum Professional Training Series

http://www.uniforum.org/news/html/events/training/front.html

Uniplex Internet Data Service

http://www.uniplex.co.uk/

UniPress W3 Services Division

http://www.unipress.com/w3/

Unisoft System

http://unisoft-system.com/net/

United Computer Exchange Corp. (UCE)

http://www.uce.com/

United International Pictures

http://www.uip.com/

United States Federal Register

http://www.citation.com/

Universal Design

http://www.digifax.com/info

Universal Group Of Companies

http://www.universalgroup.co.uk/

Universal Networks, Inc.

http://www.uninet.com/

Untangle Incorporated

http://www.io.org/~untangle/unthome.html

Up Front Multimedia

http://north.pacificnet.net/~upfront/

Updata Electronic Catalog

http://www.updata.com/

Uptime Computer Solutions, Inc.

http://www.uptime1.com/

UR*OnRamp

http://www.onramp.tuscaloosa.al.us/

US Miracle Communications, Inc.

http://www.miracle.net/

Used Computers, Etc

http://www.xmission.com/~gastown/goldpages/used1.htm

Utopia Technology Partners, Inc.

http://www.utosoft.com/~dennis/index.htm

UV&S

http://www.southwind.net/IMS/uv%2bs/catalog1/

VA Research, Inc.

http://www.varesearch.com/

Validity Corporation

http://www.primenet.com/~valcorp/

ValleyNet

http://www.valley.net/

Value Net Internetwork Services, Inc.

http://www.value.net/

ValuJeT Airlines

http://www.cucruising.com/cu/valujet.html

Van Dyke Technologies

http://www.vandyke.com/vandyke/

Vantageware

http://www.vantageware.com/

Variety Travel Services, Inc.

http://www.net-advisor.com/variety/

Vaughn Communications, Inc.

http://www.primenet.com/~vaughn/

Vector Internet Services

http://www.visi.com/

VectorNet

http://www.vector.net/

Vegas Com

http://www.vegas.com/home.html

Verb Audio

http://www.mindspring.com/~brydaguy/verb.html

VeriSign, Inc.

http://www.verisign.com/

Veritas Software

http://www.veritas.com/

VersaFax

http://www.cosi.com/

Vfive Creative Imaging

http://serv2.fwi.com/~dev/vfive/

ViaCrypt

http://www.viacrypt.com/

Vicon Computers

http://www.interactive.net/~vicon/

Vidar Systems Corporation

http://www.access.digex.net/~vidar/

Video City

http://www.lightspeed.net/~vcity/vcity.htm

Video Publishing House

http://www.vphi.com/

Videoconferencing Systems, Inc.

http://www.mindspring.com/~vsi/vsi.html

Videoflicks Video Movie Store

http://www.videoflicks.com/

Viewpoint Software Solutions

http://home.eznet.net/~viewpt/

ViewSonic Corporation

http://www.viewsonic.com/

Village Pulse

http://www.rootsworld.com/rw/villagepulse/outpost.html

ViperNet

http://www.viper.net/

Virgin Atlantic Airways

http://www.fly.virgin.com/atlantic/

Virginia Internet Services

http://www.vais.net

Virtual Artists

http://www.va.com.au/va/

Virtual Communications

http://www.slip.net/~wieneke/

Virtual Entertainment

http://www.cts.com/~vrman/

Virtual Media

http://www.iaw.on.ca/~virtualm/

Virtual Publishing Company

http://www.accessone.com/~edmitch

Virtual Vegas

http://www.virtualvegas.com

Virtus Corporation

http://www.virtus.com/

Visigenic

http://odbc.visigenic.com/

Vision Achiever

http://os2.iafrica.com/marksman/va.htm

Vision Interactive Multimedia

http://www.calypso.com/vim/index.html

Vision XXI

http://www.hic.net/hicpersonal/d/vxxi2.html

Visionary Designs

http://www.visdesigns.com/

VisionMedia of NY, Inc.

http://www.visionmedia.visionnet.com/

VISIT Computer Telephony Integration

http://www.nortel.com/english/visit/

Vistech Communications/ Internet Services.

http://www.vistech.net/

Visual Information Development, Inc.

http://erehwon.caltech.edu/vidi/vidi-homepage.html

Visual Numerics, Inc.

http://www.vni.com/

Visual SCCS

http://mirror.wwa.com/mirror/busdir/issl/issl.htm

Vive Synergies, Inc.

http://www.vive.com/

vivid studios

http://www.vivid.com/

Vlaamse Uitgeversmaatschappij

http://www.vum.be/vum/

Voice Recognition Systems

http://iglou.com/vrsky/

Vox Pop

http://www.planet.it/voxpop.html

Voyage Records

http://www.vegas.com/vegas/voyage/

VSI

http://www.openstep.com/

VYSOR Integration Inc.

http://www.synapse.net/~vysor/welcome.htm

W. W. Norton & Company, Inc.

http://www.wwnorton.com/

Wa Nui Records

http://planet-hawaii.com/wanui/

WagerNet

http://www.vegas.com/wagernet/

Wahlstrom & Company

http://www.wahlstrom.com/

Walker Interactive Systems

http://www.walker.com/

Wall Street Software

http://www.fastlane.net/homepages/wallst/wallst.html

Walter Shelby Group Web Services

http://www.shelby.com/pub/wsg/html/web/home.html

Ward Consulting, Inc.

http://www.ward.com/

Warner Aspect

http://pathfinder.com/twep/Aspect/Aspect.html

Warner Bros. Records

http://www.wbr.com/

Warrior Records

http://www.iuma.com/Warrior/

Watcom

http://www.watcom.com/

Water Wheel Systems

http://www.waterw.com/

Waveform Records

http://iuma.southern.com/beyond/waveform/

Waytec Electronics

http://www.inmind.com/people/waytec/

We Design, Inc.

http://www.we.com/info/we.html

Web One

http://www.thinque.com

Web Page Design Professionals

http://www.teleport.com/~wpdp/

Web Professionals, Inc.

http://www.professionals.com/

Web Weavers Publishing

http://www.keytech.com/~weavers/index.shtml

WebBase

http://www.expertelligence.com/webbase/

Weber Software and Consulting

http://www.electriciti.com/~wscs/index.html

WebFlow Communications Group

http://fox.nstn.ca/~webflow/

WebMart Virtual Mall And Web Development Services

http://www.webmart.com/icc/webmart.html

WebPub Communications

http://www.io.com/~webpub/

WebSpace

http://www.vnet.net/webspace/

WebTechs

http://www.medium.com/WebTechs/

WEBuilders Consulting

http://www.webuilders.com/

Weightman Group

http://www.weightman.com/

Weitz, Paul

http://www.tiac.net/users/pweitz/

Wellsweep Press

http://www.poptel.org.uk/password/wellswee.html

Westerly Publications

http://www.northcoast.com/unlimited/product_directory/westerly/westerly.html

Western International Systems Education

http://imagineer.com/MARKETPLACE/WISE

Westmoreland Online Incorporated

http://www.westol.com

WGBH Film & Video Resource Center

http://www.wgbh.org/Pages/FVResourceCenter/
ResourceCenterHome.html

WH Networks

http://www.whnet.com/wolfgang/

Whale Song Web Services

http://www.whalesong.com/

White Dolphin Books

http://www.northcoast.com/unlimited/product_directory/
white_dolphin/white_dolphin.html

Whitey's Web Works & Internet Services

http://www.rmii.com/~whitey/

Whole Shebang, The

http://www.shebang.com/

WholeARTS Directory of Musical Entertainment

http://www.wholarts.com/mdir/

Wide World Tours

http://www.val.net/TravelCafe/TheTraveler.html

Wigley

http://www.ozemail.com.au/~bwigley/

Wildwest Travel, Inc.

http://www.webcom.com/~wildwest/

Willow Glen Graphics

http://wgg.com/

Willow Peripherals

http://willow.com/peripherals/

Wilshire Book Company

http://www.mpowers.com/wilshirebooks/home.html

Wimsey Information Services

http://www.wimsey.com/

Wind River Systems

http://www.wrs.com/

Windham Hill Records

http://www.windham.com/

Windward Business Manager

http://awinc.com/windward/

Windy Hills Professional Laboratories

http://perry.gulfnet.com/advertisers/drug_testing/
drug1.htm

Winfield Communication, Inc.

http://www.winc.com/

Wingra Technologies

http://www.wingra.com/

Winkler McManus

http://www.winklermcmanus.com/

Winsor Computing

http://www1.usa1.com/~dwinsor

Wisconsin Health Information Network

http://www.fetch.com/whin/net.html

WiseNet LLC

http://www.wise-net.com/

Wizards of the Coast, Inc.

http://www.wizards.com/

Wolfe Internet Access, L.L.C.

http://www.wolfe.net/

Wollongong Group, The

http://www.twg.com/

WonderNet Digital Communications, Inc.

http://www.wondernet.com/

Woods, Incorporated

http://www.woodsnet.com/

Word Master, Inc.

http://www.wordmaster.com/wm/

Wordlink, Inc.

http://www.wordlink.com/

Words Worth Publishing

http://www.voicenet.com/DVbiz/wwphtml

WorkFlow Designs, Inc.

http://www.wfdesigns.com/~workflow/

Working Assets Long Distance

http://www.cnotes.com/telecom/wald.html

World Information Network

http://www.winnet.net/

World Mall

http://www.webcom.com/~worldmal/

World of Commercial Ballooning

http://www.aero.com/ballooning/commercial/main.htm

World Travel 2000

http://magicnet.net/gtv/wt2000.html

World Wide Business

http://www.wwbiz.ch/telecom/

World Wide Travel Service, Inc.

http://www.wwts.com/world/

World-NET SCT Web Server

http://www.sct.fr/pagehome.html

Worlds, Inc.

http://www.worlds.net/

Worldwide Games

http://www.snswwide.com/games1.html

Wright Publishing Company

http://www.kcilink.com/wpc/

WSNetwork Communication Services

http://www.wsnet.com/

WT Records

http://www.interport.net/~wtrecord/

X Communications Multimedia

http://www.webcom.com/~xcomm/

x86 computers, Inc.

http://www.abwam.com/mbarry/x86/

Xcc Software

http://www.xcc-ka.de/

Xephon

http://www.hiway.co.uk/~xephon/

XLNT Designs, Inc.

http://www.xlnt.com/

Xpand, Inc.

http://www.xpand.com/

XSI MeDIA

http://www.xsimedia.com/

XXL

http://www.xxl.com/

y.a.c.c.

http://www.xmission.com/~vir/

Yggdrasil Computing, Inc.

http://www.yggdrasil.com/

Young & Roehr, Inc.

http://www.teleport.com/~davidwh/

Your Attache, Inc.

http://www.bedrock.com/mall/attache/home.html

Z Media

http://www.tiac.net/users/zwoods

Z-Law Software, Inc.

http://mmink.com/mmink/dossiers/zlaw/zlaw.html

Zboeken

http://www.bookshop.co.uk/@zboeken/

Zero Surge

http://www.targetus.com/zsurge.htm

Zfx, Inc.

http://www.tricon.net/Comm/zfx/zfxhome2.html

Zinc Software, Inc.

http://www.zinc.com/

Zomba/Jive Records

http://www.cyber.nl/bigbro/zomba/

ZooAchtiv

http://www.zooachtiv.com/

Zycad Corporation

http://www.zycad.com/

Appendix C:
Index of Icons

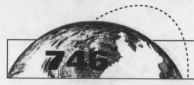

netscape icon

parental guidance icon

search icon

shopping icon

sound icon

video icon

APPENDIX D:

WHAT'S ON THE CD-ROM?

What's on the CD-ROM?

The *New Riders' Official World Wide Web* CD-ROM is designed to make World Wide Web browsing easier than ever with hyperlinks! Using the *New Riders' Official World Wide Web CD-ROM* enables you to link to the Web without having to remember the URLs of the sites you wish to go to.

You can also:

> Use this CD with a Windows, Macintosh, or Unix browser.

> Edit the files to include newly discovered links.

All of the Web sites in the book have been converted to HTML files (the same kind used on the Web). You simply load the file Welcome.htm into your favorite Web browser (for instance, Netscape or Mosaic) and point and click your way onto the World Wide Web.

The files have been organized on the CD-ROM into the following categories:

> Animals
> Architecture
> Art
> Business
> Children
> Computers
> Cooking and Food
> Education
> Entertainment
> Games
> Health
> History and Humanities
> Home Improvement
> Internet/Web Resources
> Media

Music
New Age
Philosophy
Recreation
Religion
Science and Nature
Sports
Travel
Weddings

SYMBOLS

A

. . . .

B

C

. . . .

D

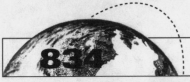

E

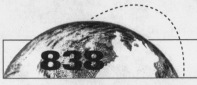

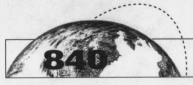

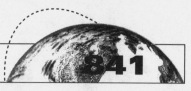

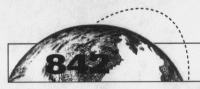

F

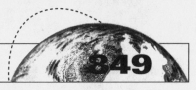

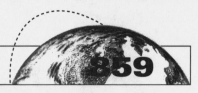

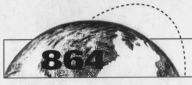

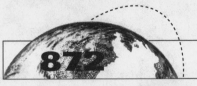

L

M

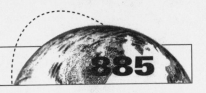

O

. . . .

 Q

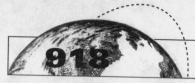

918 ► INDEX

. . . .

V

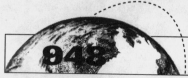

X

Y

Z

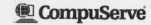

PLUG YOURSELF INTO...

The Macmillan Information SuperLibrary™

Free information and vast computer resources from the world's leading computer book publisher—online!

FIND THE BOOKS THAT ARE RIGHT FOR YOU!

A complete online catalog, plus sample chapters and tables of contents give you an in-depth look at *all* of our books, including hard-to-find titles. It's the best way to find the books you need!

- **STAY INFORMED** with the latest computer industry news through our online newsletter, press releases, and customized Information SuperLibrary Reports.

- **GET FAST ANSWERS** to your questions about MCP books and software.

- **VISIT** our online bookstore for the latest information and editions!

- **COMMUNICATE** with our expert authors through e-mail and conferences.

- **DOWNLOAD SOFTWARE** from the immense MCP library:
    - Source code and files from MCP books
    - The best shareware, freeware, and demos

- **DISCOVER HOT SPOTS** on other parts of the Internet.

- **WIN BOOKS** in ongoing contests and giveaways!

TO PLUG INTO MCP: → **WORLD WIDE WEB: http://www.mcp.com**

GOPHER: gopher.mcp.com

FTP: ftp.mcp.com

REGISTRATION CARD

New Riders' Official World Wide Web Directory

Name _____ Title _____

Company _____ Type of business _____

Address _____

City/State/ZIP _____

Have you used these types of books before? ☐ yes ☐ no

If yes, which ones? _____

_____

How many computer books do you purchase each year? ☐ 1–5 ☐ 6 or more

How did you learn about this book? _____

Where did you purchase this book? _____

Which applications do you currently use? _____

_____

Which computer magazines do you subscribe to? _____

_____

What trade shows do you attend? _____

_____

Comments: _____

_____

_____

Would you like to be placed on our preferred mailing list? ☐ yes ☐ no

☐ **I would like to see my name in print!** You may use my name and quote me in future New Riders products and promotions. My daytime phone number is: _____

New Riders Publishing   201 West 103rd Street ◆ Indianapolis, Indiana 46290 USA

Fax to 317-581-4670   Orders/Customer Service 1-800-653-6156   Source Code NRP95

Fold Here

BUSINESS REPLY MAIL
FIRST-CLASS MAIL PERMIT NO. 9918 INDIANAPOLIS IN
POSTAGE WILL BE PAID BY THE ADDRESSEE

NEW RIDERS PUBLISHING
201 W 103RD ST
INDIANAPOLIS IN 46290-9058